UPDATED VERSION

Instructor's Solutions Manual to accompany

PHYSICS

for Scientists and Engineers

WITH MODERN PHYSICS

THIRD EDITION

Includes complete solutions to all new problems

VOLUME TWO

by

RAYMOND A. SERWAY
James Madison University

STEVE VAN WYK
Chapman College

RALPH V. McGREW
Broome Community College

LOUIS H. CADWELL
Providence College

SAUNDERS GOLDEN SUNBURST SERIES

SAUNDERS COLLEGE PUBLISHING
Harcourt Brace Jovanovich College Publishers
Fort Worth Philadelphia San Diego New York Orlando Austin
San Antonio Toronto Montreal London Sydney Tokyo

Printed in the United States of America.

Serway: Instructor's Solutions Manual for PHYSICS FOR SCIENTISTS AND ENGINEERS, 3/E, UPDATED VERSION

ISBN 0-03-096034-7

345 021 987654321

PREFACE

This instructor's Solutions Manual has been written to accompany the updated third edition of the textbooks **Physics for Scientists and Engineers** and **Physics for Scientists and Engineers with Modern Physics**, both by Raymond A. Serway. The manual includes the following:

(1) Detailed solutions to *all* end-of-chapter problems, with boxed answers.

(2) Answers to even-numbered problems are included at the end of this volume. (Answers to odd-numbered problems are included in the textbooks.)

Because of its large size the manual has been split into two volumes. Volume I contains solutions and answers to problems in Chapter 1 through 22. Volume II contains solutions and answers to problems found in Chapters 23 through 47. As the title of this work implies, this manual was prepared for the convenience of instructors who are teaching this course. Particularly since we have included solutions to *all* of the problems in the text, we strongly urge that instructors exercise precautionary measures to keep their manuals secure. While we recognize that instructors may post solutions to selected problems, we request that the entire solutions manual *not* be made available to students as a courtesy to other instructors who wish to use these problems on exams.

This updated third edition contains about 670 new problems which are identified with an asterisk (*) in front of the solution problem number. In almost all cases, the new problems have replaced an 'old' problem so that the remaining problems' and their numbers, are identical to those in the third edition.

Please note that a Student Study Guide is available, which includes answers to selected end-of-chapter problems, as well as detailed solutions to approximately ten of the odd-numbered problems per chapter. As a convenience to the instructor, these problem numbers are listed at the beginning of this manual and are identified with a bullet ● in front of the solution problem number. The Student Study Guide also contains answers to many of the end-of-chapter questions and other features such as objectives, skills, notes from selected sections, equations and concepts, programmed exercises, and a selection of nineteen computer modules. For additional information about the other ancillary items, please see the Preface of the textbooks.

A great deal of time and effort has been devoted to checking the accuracy of the solutions and preparing this manual. If you should find any errors, omissions, or inconsistencies, despite our efforts, please notify us† and we will attempt to correct them in future printings. We also welcome your comments on the solutions, as well as suggestions for alternate solutions.

Raymond A. Serway
Steve Van Wyk
Ralph McGrew

†Please send you corrections to Prof. Steven Van Wyk, Chapman College, P.O. Box 2285, Bremerton, WA 98310.

ACKNOWLEDGEMENTS

A number of people have made valuable contributions to this enormous project and deserve our sincere thanks and appreciation.

First, we thank John R. Gordon, Lawrence H. Hmurcik, and the late Henry Leap for their fine work on the solutions manual for the second edition of the Serway textbooks. Many of the solutions contained in this manual were taken from this work. We are most grateful to Charles D. Teague for carefully checking solutions to most new problems, and Jeffrey J. Braun for organizing and reviewing the problems as they are presented in the textbooks. Many of the new problems were provided by Ron Canterna, Paul Feldker, Roger Ludin, Richard Reimann, Jill Rugare, Stan Shepard, Som Tyagi, and James Walker. We thank Mary Toscano and Nancy Toscano of M&N TOSCANO, Somerville, Massachusetts and Sue Jarrett and Judy Sarver of Mustard Seed Word Processing, Bremerton, Washington, for their excellent assistance in computer typesetting of this manuscript. Finally, we owe much appreciation to Ellen Newman, Senior Developmental Editor, who coordinated all phases of the project and followed it diligently through its completion.

Serway's Summary of New Problems for PSE Updated Third Edition

Chapter 1

Problems 4, 7, 16, 17, 26, 31, 34, 35, 38, 39, 40, 45, 46, 47, 60, 61, 62, 63

Chapter 2

Problems 9, 12, 14, 18, 20, 24, 32, 35, 36, 40, 41, 44, 46, 64

Chapter 3

Problems 6, 22, 23, 32, 33, 34, 51, 52, 55, 56, 57, 58, 64, 67, 71, 72, 73, 74, 75

Chapter 4

Problems 3, 4, 13, 14, 16, 18, 26, 29, 36, 45, 59, 60, 68, 75, 76, 87

Chapter 5

Problems 16, 17, 19, 22, 27, 29, 35, 36, 47, 49, 51, 56, 61, 62, 63, 64, 68, 72, 76, 77, 82, 89, 90

Chapter 6

Problems 7, 8, 10, 16, 18, 23, 27, 37, 51, 53

Chapter 7

Problems 9, 19, 30, 31, 39, 40, 41, 59, 65, 73, 77, 78, 87, 88, 89

Chapter 8

Problems 15, 21, 30, 32, 36, 49, 50, 54, 62, 63, 68

Chapter 9

Problems 3, 4, 12, 20, 25, 30, 31, 33, 34, 39, 46, 47, 55, 65

Chapter 10

Problems 8, 10, 12, 18, 30, 32, 36, 37, 40, 44, 49, 50, 53

Chapter 11

Problems 5, 8, 14, 16, 19, 26, 28, 43, 47, 53, 55

Chapter 12

Problems 1, 18, 21, 22, 23, 24, 28, 30, 31, 32, 46, 50, 52, 53, 54

Chapter 13

Problems 6, 11, 16, 20, 22, 24, 27, 28, 34, 56, 58, 59, 64

Chapter 14

Problems 5, 6, 7, 9, 10, 14, 18, 19, 27, 28, 30, 32, 34, 46, 47, 56, 59, 60, 62, 68

Chapter 15

Problems 6, 26, 28, 29, 32, 38, 39, 59, 60, 62, 63, 64, 66, 69, 70, 74

Chapter 16

Problems 5, 11, 14, 23, 28, 31, 32, 33, 50, 51, 54

Chapter 17

Problems 25, 28, 30, 31, 35, 38, 40, 46, 52, 54, 58

Chapter 18

Problems 6, 22, 25, 28, 29, 34, 39, 50, 56, 59, 63, 68

Chapter 19

Problems 9, 18, 21, 23, 26, 28, 35, 36, 37, 38, 39, 43, 63

Chapter 20

Problems 5, 10, 12, 16, 17, 22, 23, 26, 27, 32, 48, 51, 53, 54, 57, 59, 60, 61, 63, 65, 70, 71, 82, 83

Chapter 21

Problems 3, 4, 10, 11, 66, 70, 73, 74, 75, 76, 77

Chapter 22

Problems 4, 5, 9, 17, 18, 34, 43, 44, 47, 50, 54, 56, 59, 60, 65, 66

Chapter 23

Problems 2, 6, 11, 12, 13, 14, 21, 46, 58, 62, 65, 66, 70, 74, 77, 78

Chapter 24

Problelms 12, 14, 16, 19, 24, 44, 53, 63, 64

Chapter 25

Problems 8, 24, 26, 45, 46, 64, 70, 71, 74, 75, 76, 77, 87

Chapter 26

Problems 16, 24, 26, 36, 37, 46, 47, 60, 61, 62, 63, 70, 74, 75, 76, 77, 78, 79

Chapter 27

Problems 8, 14, 21, 26, 27, 28, 32, 34, 38, 49, 50, 52, 55, 56, 59, 62, 65, 66, 73

Chapter 28

Problems 6, 9, 11, 12, 13, 22, 23, 28, 29, 30, 33, 36, 38, 41, 56, 57, 70, 71, 72, 75, 87, 88, 89, 90, 91

Chapter 29

Problems 18, 26, 30, 40, 41, 46, 52, 56, 60, 62, 63, 64, 72

Chapter 30

Problems 12, 13, 16, 17, 32, 62, 74, 75, 76, 87, 88, 89

Chapter 31

Problems 44, 54, 56, 58, 60, 61, 67, 69, 71, 72, 73

Chapter 32

Problems 10, 35, 36, 37, 44, 71, 72, 73, 76, 79, 80, 84, 85, 86

Chapter 33

Problems 34, 37, 38, 46, 48, 49, 58, 66, 68, 69, 70, 72, 75, 77, 78, 80, 83, 87

Chapter 34

Problems 8, 11, 12, 14, 17, 20, 26, 27, 28, 30, 51, 52, 59, 60, 61, 62, 63

Chapter 35

Problems 16, 17, 32, 33, 48, 50, 54, 55, 56, 57, 58

Chapter 36

Problems 4, 20, 28, 30, 37, 58, 62, 66, 67, 68, 74, 76, 77, 78

Chapter 37

Problems 4, 6, 8, 10, 28, 35, 38, 39, 40, 41, 43, 44, 46, 48, 52, 54, 58, 62, 68, 70, 71, 72

Chapter 38

Problems 10, 12, 13, 14, 22, 23, 24, 28, 30, 31, 32, 61, 66, 69, 74

Chapter 39

Problems 9, 10, 16, 17, 18, 22, 36, 40, 47, 51, 52

Chapter 40

Problems 8, 24, 28, 32, 40, 46, 58, 65, 67, 68, 69, 70, 72

Chapter 41

Problems 8, 20, 22, 30, 52, 53, 54, 62, 67, 68, 72

Chapter 42

Problems 16, 18, 20, 30, 32, 38, 42, 44, 45, 50, 51, 54

Chapter 43

Problems 4, 6, 7, 31, 32, 34, 36

Chapter 44

Problems 9, 10, 17

Chapter 45

Problems 9, 12, 14, 28, 30, 32, 34, 40, 42, 43, 46, 47, 50, 52, 61, 62, 68, 70, 72, 77, 78, 82, 83, 84

Chapter 46

Problems 6, 7, 17, 23, 32, 33, 34, 37, 38

Chapter 47

Problems 27, 28, 29, 30

SOLUTIONS FROM THE STUDENT STUDY GUIDE

Chapter 23	Chapter 24	Chapter 25	Chapter 26	Chapter 27
23.15	24.13	25.9	26.7	27.5
23.25	24.33	25.17	26.15	27.17
23.27	24.37	25.19	26.23	27.25
23.39	24.39	25.27	26.33	27.31
23.43	24.41	25.51	26.45	27.41
23.45	24.43	25.61	26.57	27.47
23.51	24.47	25.73	26.73	27.51
23.55	24.59	25.79		27.63
23.63		25.81		

Chapter 28	Chapter 29	Chapter 30	Chapter 31	Chapter 32
28.7	29.5	30.11	31.13	32.11
28.17	29.19	30.19	31.19	32.19
28.35	29.27	30.27	31.29	32.33
28.37	29.31	30.37	31.33	32.43
28.43	29.47	30.41	31.41	32.47
28.53	29.53	30.45	31.59	32.57
28.79	29.59	30.51	31.65	32.65
28.81	29.69	30.65		
		30.73		

Chapter 33	Chapter 34	Chapter 35	Chapter 36	Chapter 37
33.15	34.9	35.23	36.7	37.7
33.21	34.15	35.29	36.9	37.19
33.29	34.21	35.31	36.21	37.23
33.33	34.25	35.41	36.33	37.31
33.41	34.31	35.45	36.55	37.45
33.51	34.45	35.47	36.60	37.55
33.61	34.57	35.49	36.65	37.56
33.79		35.53	36.67	37.63
			36.69	37.64

Chapter 38	Chapter 39	Chapter 40	Chapter 41	Chapter 42
38.11	39.3	40.12	41.9	42.7
38.29	39.19	40.13	41.17	42.8
38.55	39.23	40.19	41.21	42.29
38.56	39.33	40.31	41.27	42.31
38.67	39.39	40.35	41.39	42.39
38.68	39.43	40.47	41.57	42.40
38.71	39.53	40.60	41.59	42.41
38.73	39.55	40.61	41.61	42.47
		40.67	41.65	42.52

Chapter 43	Chapter 44	Chapter 45	Chapter 46	Chapter 47
43.9	44.3	45.13	46.11	47.3
43.16	44.7	45.19	46.13	47.10
43.21	44.15	45.31	46.21	47.12
43.22	44.19	45.37	46.25	47.21
43.25	44.25	45.53	46.27	47.23
43.35	44.26	45.57	46.43	47.25
	44.29	45.65	46.44	
		45.73		
		45.75		

TABLE OF CONTENTS

CHAPTER 23

23.1 $F = k\dfrac{q_1 q_2}{r^2} = \dfrac{(8.99 \times 10^9\ \frac{\text{N}\cdot\text{m}^2}{\text{C}^2})(1.6 \times 10^{-19}\ \text{C})^2(6.02 \times 10^{23})^2}{[2(6.37 \times 10^6\ \text{m})]^2} = \boxed{5.14 \times 10^5\ \text{N}}$

***23.2** (a) $N = \left(\dfrac{10\ \text{grams}}{107.87\ \text{grams/mol}}\right)\left(6.02 \times 10^{23}\ \dfrac{\text{atoms}}{\text{mol}}\right)\left(47\ \dfrac{\text{electrons}}{\text{atom}}\right)$

$= \boxed{2.62 \times 10^{24}\ \text{electrons}}$

(b) $10^{-3}\ \text{C} = (\#\ \text{electrons}) \times (1.6 \times 10^{-19}\ \text{C/electron})$

$\#\ \text{electrons added} = 6.25 \times 10^{15}$ or

2.38 electrons for every 10^9 already present

23.3 $F = \dfrac{kq_1q_2}{r^2} = \dfrac{(9 \times 10^9)(1.602 \times 10^{-19})^2}{(3.8 \times 10^{-10})^2}$

$\boxed{F = 1.60 \times 10^{-9}\ \text{N}}$ The protons will repel one another.

23.4 $F = \dfrac{kq_1q_2}{r^2} = \dfrac{(9 \times 10^9)(6.7 \times 10^{-6})(8.4 \times 10^{-6})}{(5.0)^2}$

$\boxed{F = 2.03 \times 10^{-3}\ \text{N}}$ The charges will attract one another.

23.5 $F = \dfrac{kq_1q_2}{r^2}$

$F_1 = \dfrac{(9 \times 10^9)(2.5 \times 10^{-6})(1.3 \times 10^{-6})}{(0.5)^2} = 0.117\ \text{N}$

$F_2 = \dfrac{(9 \times 10^9)(3.2 \times 10^{-6})(2.5 \times 10^{-6})}{(1.5)^2} = 0.032\ \text{N}$

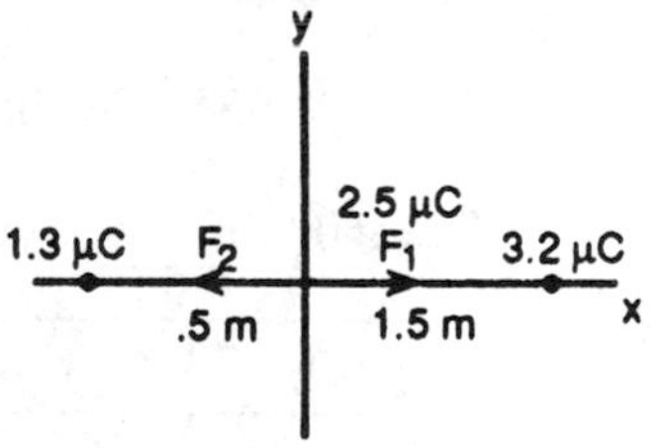

23.5

$F = F_1 - F_2 = 0.117 - 0.032 = \boxed{85.0\ \text{mN}}$ The net force will be in the positive x direction.

***23.6** $F_1 = (-0.0853)\text{ N} = k\dfrac{q_1 q_2}{r_{12}^2}$ $\qquad k = 9 \times 10^9\text{ N}\cdot\text{m}^2/\text{c}^2$, $r_{12} = 1.19\text{ m}$

$$F_2 = (+0.0196)\text{ N} = \frac{k\left(\dfrac{q_1+q_2}{2}\right)^2}{r_{12}^2}$$

From the first equation,

$-1.3421 \times 10^{-11} = q_1 q_2$

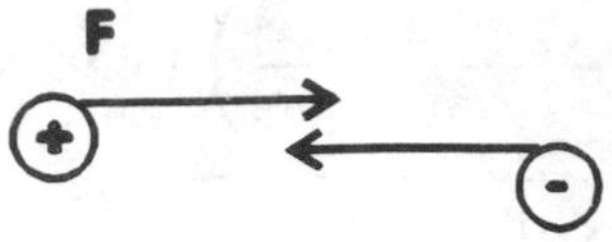

23.6

From the second equation,

$\mid 3.5122 \times 10^{-6} \mid = q_1 + q_2$

Substituting for q_2,

$$-1.3421 \times 10^{-11} = q_1(3.5122 \times 10^{-6} - q_1)$$

$$q_1 = \frac{3.5122 \pm \sqrt{(3.5122)^2 + 4(13.421)}}{2}\ \mu\text{C}$$

$$q_1 = 5.82\ \mu\text{C},\ \text{q}_2 = -2.31\ \mu\text{C}$$

$$\text{or } q_1 = -5.82\ \mu\text{C},\ \text{q}_2 = +2.31\ \mu\text{C}$$

23.7 $F = \dfrac{kq_1q_2}{r^2}$

$$F_1 = \frac{(9 \times 10^9)(7 \times 10^{-6})(2 \times 10^{-6})}{(0.5)^2} = 0.504\text{ N}$$

$$F_2 = \frac{(9 \times 10^9)(7 \times 10^{-6})(4 \times 10^{-6})}{(0.5)^2} = 1.008\text{ N}$$

$F_x = (0.504 + 1.008)\cos 60 = 0.756\text{ N}$

$F_y = (0.504 - 1.008)\sin 60 = -0.436\text{ N}$

$\mathbf{F} = (0.756\text{ N})\boldsymbol{i} - (0.436\text{ N})\boldsymbol{j}$

$\lvert\mathbf{F}\rvert = 0.873$ N at an angle of 330°

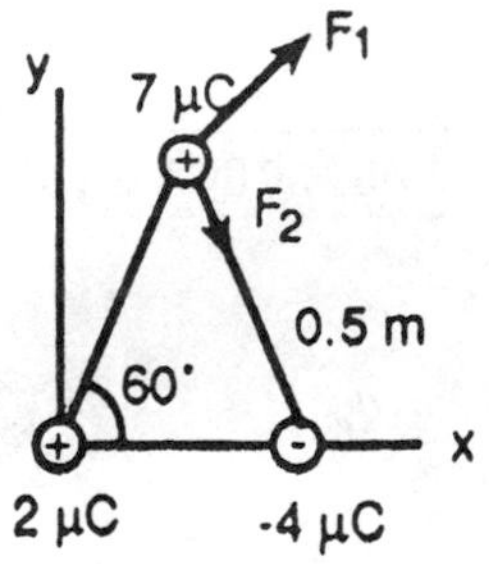

23.7

23.8 $|\mathbf{F}_1| = \dfrac{kq^2}{a^2}$, $|\mathbf{F}_2| = \dfrac{kq^2}{2a^2}$ and $|\mathbf{F}_3| = \dfrac{kq^2}{a^2}$

$$\Sigma F_x = 0 + |F_2|\cos 45° + |F_3| = \frac{(0.707/2 + 1)kq^2}{a^2} \text{ and}$$

$$\Sigma F_y = |F_1| + |F_2|\sin 45° + 0 = \frac{(1 + 0.707/2)kq^2}{a^2}$$

$$\text{Therefore } \mathbf{F} = \boxed{\frac{(1.35)(i + j)kq^2}{a^2}}$$

23.9 $F = \dfrac{kq_1q_2}{r_2}$ $\tan\theta = \dfrac{15}{60}$ $\theta = 14°$

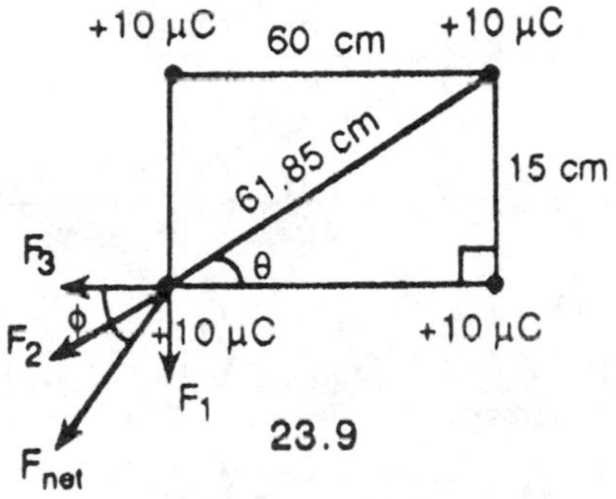

23.9

$$F_1 = \frac{(9 \times 10^9)(10 \times 10^{-6})^2}{(0.15)^2} = 40.0 \text{ N}$$

$$F_3 = \frac{(9 \times 10^9)(10 \times 10^{-6})^2}{(0.6)^2} = 2.50 \text{ N}$$

$$F_2 = \frac{(9 \times 10^9)(10 \times 10^{-6})^2}{(0.6185)^2} = 2.353 \text{ N}$$

$$F_x = -F_3 - F_2\cos 14° = -2.5 - 2.35\cos 14 = -4.78 \text{ N}$$

$$F_y = -F_1 - F_2\sin 14° = -40 - 2.35\sin 14 = -40.57 \text{ N}$$

$$F = \sqrt{F_x^2 + F_y^2} = \sqrt{(-4.78)^2 + (-40.57)^2} = \boxed{40.9 \text{ N}}$$

$$\tan\phi = \frac{F_y}{F_x} = \frac{-40.57}{-4.78} \quad \phi = \boxed{263°}$$

23.10 $F_1 = \frac{q_1}{4\pi\epsilon_0}\left(\frac{q_2(r_1 - r_2)}{|r_1 - r_2|^3} + \frac{q_3(r_1 - r_3)}{|r_1 - r_3|^3} + \frac{q_4(r_1 - r_4)}{|r_2 - r_4|^3}\right)$

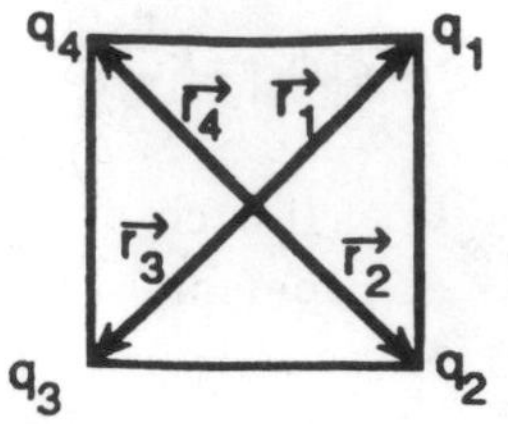

23.10

$$F_2 = \frac{q_2}{4\pi\epsilon_0}\left(\frac{q_1(r_2 - r_1)}{|r_2 - r_1|^3} + \frac{q_3(r_2 - r_3)}{|r_1 - r_3|^3} + \frac{q_4(r_2 - r_4)}{|r_2 - r_4|^3}\right)$$

$$F_3 = \frac{q_3}{4\pi\epsilon_0}\left(\frac{q_1(r_3 - r_1)}{|r_3 - r_1|^3} + \frac{q_2(r_3 - r_2)}{|r_3 - r_2|^3} + \frac{q_4(r_3 - r_4)}{|r_3 - r_4|^3}\right)$$

$$F_4 = \frac{q_4}{4\pi\epsilon_0}\left(\frac{q_1(r_4 - r_1)}{|r_4 - r_1|^3} + \frac{q_2(r_4 - r_2)}{|r_4 - r_2|^3} + \frac{q_3(r_4 - r_3)}{|r_4 - r_3|^3}\right)$$

$$\tau = \Sigma r_i \times F_i$$

$$r_1 \times F_1 = \frac{q_1}{4\pi\epsilon_0}\left(\frac{q_2(r_1 \times r_2)}{|r_1 - r_2|^3} + \frac{q_3(r_1 \times r_3)}{|r_1 - r_3|^3} + \frac{q_4(r_1 \times r_4)}{|r_1 - r_4|^3}\right)$$

$$r_2 \times F_2 = \frac{q_2}{4\pi\epsilon_0}\left(\frac{q_1(r_2 \times r_1)}{|r_2 - r_1|^3} + \frac{q_3(r_2 \times r_3)}{|r_2 - r_3|^3} + \frac{q_4(r_2 \times r_4)}{|r_2 - r_4|^3}\right)$$

$$r_2 \times F_2 = \frac{q_3}{4\pi\epsilon_0}\left(\frac{q_1(r_3 \times r_1)}{|r_3 - r_1|^3} + \frac{q_2(r_3 \times r_2)}{|r_3 - r_2|^3} + \frac{q_4(r_3 \times r_4)}{|r_3 - r_4|^3}\right)$$

$$r_4 \times F_4 = \frac{q_4}{4\pi\epsilon_0}\left(\frac{q_1(r_4 \times r_1)}{|r_4 - r_1|^3} + \frac{q_2(r_4 - r_2)}{|r_4 - r_2|^3} + \frac{q_3(r_4 - r_3)}{|r_4 - r_3|^3}\right)$$

noticing that $r_i \times r_j = -r_j \times r_i$ and that $|r_i - r_j|^3 = |r_j - r_i|^3$

$$\Sigma r_i \times F_i = \tau \equiv 0$$

***23.11** $F = k\frac{q_2}{r^2}$

$$10^4 \text{ N} = \frac{9 \times 10^9 \text{ (N} \cdot \text{m}^2)}{\text{C}^2}\frac{q^2}{1 \text{ m}^2}$$

$$\text{q} = (1.0541 \times 10^{-3} \text{ C})\left(\frac{1 \text{ e}}{1.6 \times 10^{-19} \text{ C}}\right)$$

$$\# \text{ electrons} = 6.5881 \times 10^{15} \text{e's}$$

$$(100 \text{ g})\left(\frac{6.02 \times 10^{23}}{107.87 \text{ g}}\right)\left(47 \frac{\text{electrons}}{\text{atom}}\right) = 2.623 \times 10^{25} \text{ electrons}$$

$$\text{fraction} = \boxed{2.51 \times 10^{-10}}$$

***23.12** $F = k\dfrac{q_1 q_2}{r_{12}^2}$

If each person has a mass of $\approx$ 70 kg and is (almost) composed of water, then each person contains

$$\left(\frac{70,000 \text{ grams}}{18 \text{ grams/mol}}\right)\left(6.02 \times 10^{23}\frac{\text{molecules}}{\text{mol}}\right)\left(10\frac{\text{protons}}{\text{molecule}}\right)$$

$N \cong 2.4 \times 10^{28}$ protons.

With an excess of 1% electrons over protons, each person has a charge

$q = (0.01)(1.6 \times 10^{-19} \text{ C})(2.4 \times 10^{28}) = 3.84 \times 10^{7} \text{ C}$

That would mean a force $F = (9 \times 10^9)\dfrac{(3.84 \times 10^7)^2}{1^2}$ N.

$F = 1.327 \times 10^{25}$ N between the people, almost enough to lift a "weight" equal to that of the Earth,

$Mg = (6 \times 10^{24} \text{ kg})(9.8 \text{ m/s}^2) = 6 \times 10^{25}$ N.

***23.13** $F = k\dfrac{q_1 q_2}{(r_{12})^2} = (9 \times 10^9)\dfrac{(+40)(-40)}{(2000)^2}$

$F = \boxed{-3.6 \times 10^6 \text{ N}}$ (attractive)

***23.14** If we treat the concentrations as point charges,

$$\begin{aligned}
E_+ &= k\frac{q}{r^2} \text{ (downward)} \\
E_- &= k\frac{q}{r^2} \text{ (downward)} \\
E_+ &= (9 \times 10^9)\frac{(40 \text{ C})}{(1000 \text{ m})^2} = 3.6 \times 10^5 \text{ N/C} \downarrow \\
E_- &= (9 \times 10^9)\frac{(40 \text{ C})}{(1000 \text{ m})^2} = 3.6 \times 10^5 \text{ N/C} \downarrow \\
E &= E_+ + E_- = \boxed{7.2 \times 10^5 \text{ N/C}} \text{ downward}
\end{aligned}$$

23.15 (a) For equilibrium $\boldsymbol{F}_g + \boldsymbol{F}_g = 0 \Longrightarrow mg = Eq$ so

$$\boldsymbol{E} = \frac{mg}{q}\boldsymbol{j} = \frac{(9.11 \times 10^{-31})(9.8)}{(-1.6 \times 10^{-19})}\boldsymbol{j} = \boxed{(-5.58 \times 10^{-11}\boldsymbol{j})\ \text{N/C}}$$

(b) $$\boldsymbol{E} = \frac{mg}{q}\boldsymbol{j} = \frac{(1.67 \times 10^{-27})(9.8)}{(1.6 \times 10^{-19})}\boldsymbol{j} = \boxed{(1.02 \times 10^{-7}\boldsymbol{j})\ \text{N/C}}$$

23.16 $E = \frac{F}{q}$; $F = W = mg$

$$610 = \frac{m(9.8)}{24 \times 10^{-6}}$$

$$m = \boxed{1.49 \times 10^{-3}\ \text{kg}}$$

23.17 (a) $$\boldsymbol{E} = \frac{kq}{r^2}\boldsymbol{i} = \frac{(9 \times 10^9)(5.2 \times 10^{-6})}{(3)^2}\boldsymbol{i} = \boxed{(-5200\boldsymbol{i})\ \text{N/C}}$$

(b) $$\boldsymbol{E} = \frac{kq}{r^2}\boldsymbol{j} = \frac{(9 \times 10^9)(5.2 \times 10^{-6})}{(4)^2}\boldsymbol{j} = \boxed{2930\boldsymbol{j}\ \text{N/C}}$$

(c) $$E = \frac{kq}{r^2} = \frac{(9 \times 10^9)(5.2 \times 10^{-6})}{(2.828)^2} = \boxed{5850\ \text{N/C at } 225°}$$

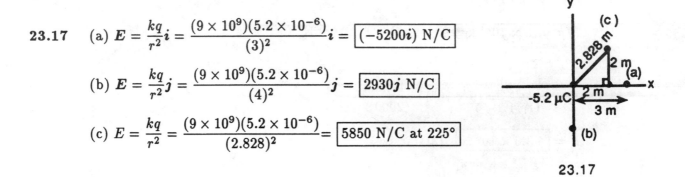

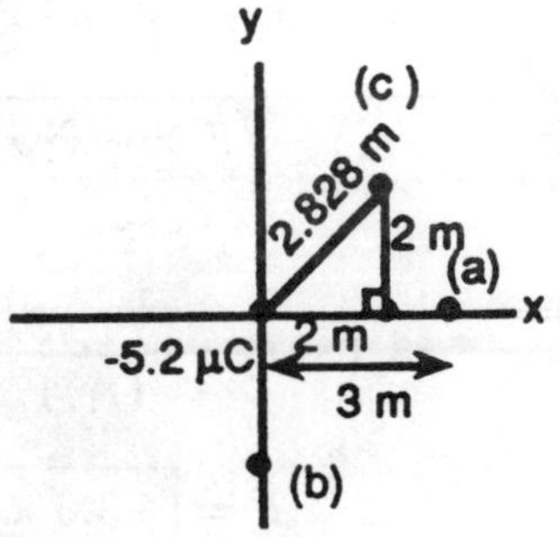

23.17

23.18 $E = \frac{kq}{r^2}$

$$E_1 = \frac{(9 \times 10^9)(4.7 \times 10^{-6})}{(1.5)^2} = 18,800$$

$$E_2 = \frac{(9 \times 10^9)(9.0 \times 10^{-6})}{(1.5)^2} = 36,000$$

$$E = E_1 + E_2 = 18,800 + 36,000 = \boxed{-54,800\boldsymbol{i}\ \text{N/C}}$$

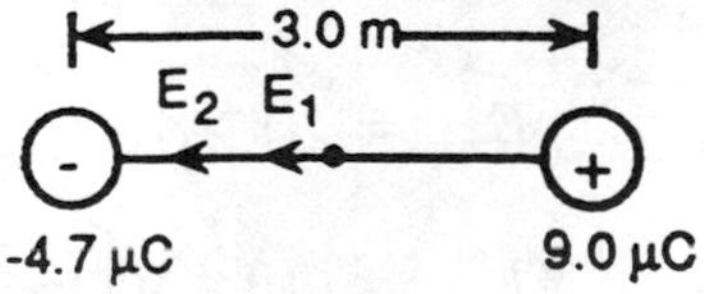

23.18

23.19 (a) $E = \frac{kq}{r^2} = \frac{(9 \times 10^9)(2 \times 10^{-6})}{(1.12)^2} = 14,400 \text{ N/C}$

$E_x = 0$

$E_y = 2(14,400) \sin 26.6° = 1.29 \times 10^4 \text{ N/C}$

$\boxed{\mathbf{E} = 1.29 \times 10^4 \boldsymbol{j} \text{ N/C}}$

(b) $\mathbf{F} = \mathbf{E}q = (1.29 \times 10^4 \boldsymbol{j})(-3 \times 10^{-6})$

$\boxed{\mathbf{F} = -3.87 \times 10^{-2} \boldsymbol{j} \text{ N}}$

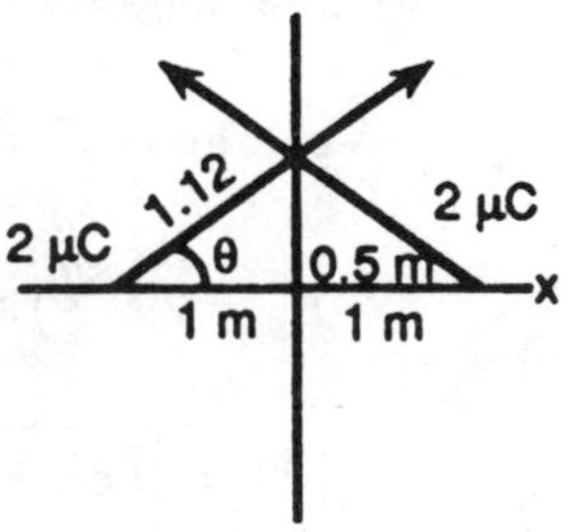

23.19

23.20 Note: $E_1 = E_2 = E_3 = E_4$

$\therefore$ Net $\boxed{E = 0}$

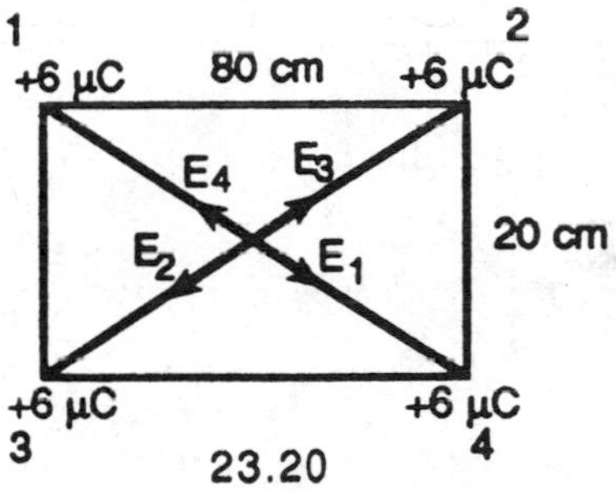

23.20

***23.21** By symmetry, $E_x = 0$

$E_y = 0$

and $\boxed{\mathbf{E} = 0}$

23.22 Note $E_1 = E_2 = E_3$

By symmetry $E_x = 0$

$E_y = 2E_1 \sin 30° - E_2 = 0$

$\therefore$ Net $\boxed{E = 0}$

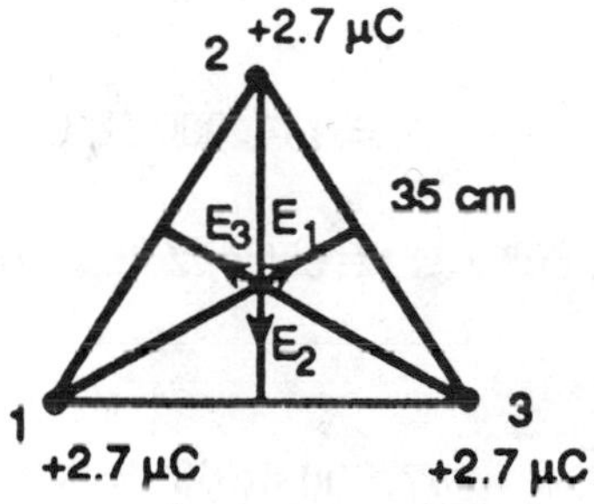

23.22

23.23 (a) At the center of the triangle, $E = 0$ by symmetry

(b) The magnitude of the field contribution due to each charge is $E = \frac{kq}{a^2}$ and by symmetry $E_x = 0$,

$E_y = 2[(\frac{kq}{a^2})\sin 60°] = 1.7\,\frac{kq}{a^2}$,

$|E| = \sqrt{E_x^2 + E_y^2} = 1.73\,\frac{kq}{a^2}$

and $\theta = \tan^{-1}(\frac{E_y}{E_x}) = \tan^{-1}(\infty) = 90°$

relative to the $+x$ direction.

$\mathbf{E} = 1.73\frac{kq}{a^2}j$

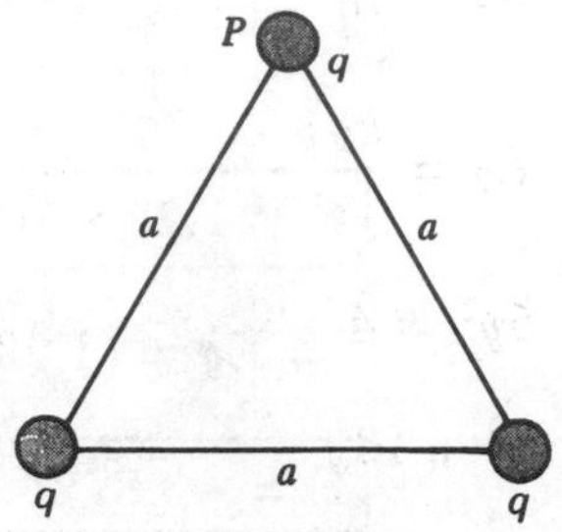

23.23

23.24 $E = \frac{kq}{r^2}$

$$E_1 = \frac{(9\times10^9)(7\times10^{-6})}{(0.5)^2} = 252{,}000\ \text{N/C}$$

$$E_2 = \frac{(9\times10^9)(4\times10^{-6})}{(0.5)^2} = 144{,}000\ \text{N/C}$$

$E_x = E_2 - E_1\cos 60° = 144{,}000 - 252{,}000\cos 60°$

$E_x = 18{,}000$ N/C

$E_y = -E_1\sin 60° = -252{,}000\sin 60° = -218{,}000$ N/C

$\mathbf{E} = [18{,}000\,i - 218{,}000\,j]$ N/C

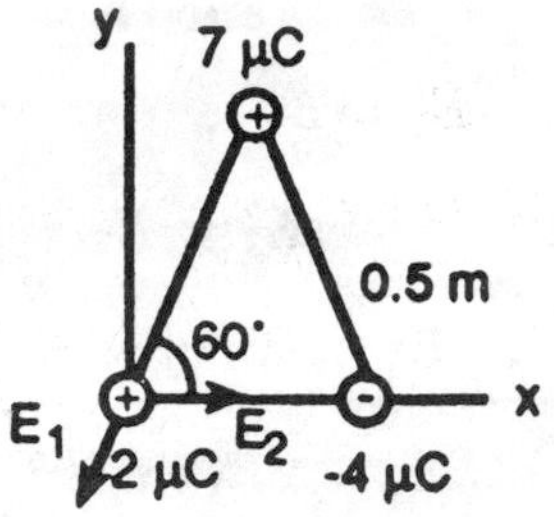

23.24

23.25 (a) $E_x = \frac{-kq}{a^2} + \frac{kq}{(a\sqrt{2})^2}\cos 45° = -0.646\,\frac{kq}{a^2}$

$E_y = -0.646\,\frac{kq}{a^2}$

$E = $ $0.914\,\frac{kq}{a^2}$ at an angle of 225° or $0.646\frac{kq}{a^2}(i+j)$

(b) $F = qE = $ $0.914\,\frac{kq^2}{a^2}$ at an angle of 45°

23.26 $E = \frac{kq}{r^2}$

$E_1 = \frac{k(5\ \mu C)}{(2-y)^2} \qquad E_1 = E_2$

$E_2 = \frac{k(4\ \mu C)}{y^2} \qquad \frac{k(5\ \mu C)}{(2-y)^2} = \frac{k(4\ \mu C)}{y^2}$

$5y^2 = 4(2-y)^2 = 4(4-4y+y^2) = 16 - 16y + 4y^2$

$y^2 + 16y - 16 = 0$

$y = \frac{-16 \pm \sqrt{16^2 - 4(1)(-16)}}{2(1)} = \frac{-16 \pm 17.9}{2} = \boxed{0.944\ \text{m}}$

23.27 $E = \frac{kq}{r^2}$

$E_1 = \frac{k(4.7\ \mu C)}{x^2}$

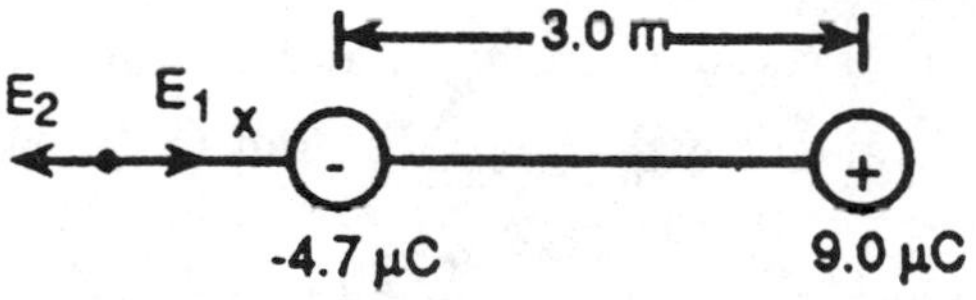

23.27

$E_2 = \frac{k(9\ \mu C)}{(3+x)^2}$

$E_1 = E_2$

$\frac{k(4.7\ \mu C)}{x^2} = \frac{k(9\ \mu C)}{(3+x)^2}$

$4.7(3+x)^2 = 9x^2$

$9 + 6x = x^2 = 1.915x^2$

$0.915x^2 - 6x - 9 = 0$

$x = \frac{6 \pm \sqrt{6^2 - 4(0.915)(-9)}}{2(0.915)}$

$x = \frac{6 \pm 8.30}{1.88} = \boxed{7.82\ \text{m}}$ to the left of the charge distribution.

23.28 $E = \dfrac{k\lambda\ell}{d(\ell+d)} = \dfrac{k(Q/\ell)\ell}{d(\ell+d)} = \dfrac{kQ}{d(\ell+d)}$

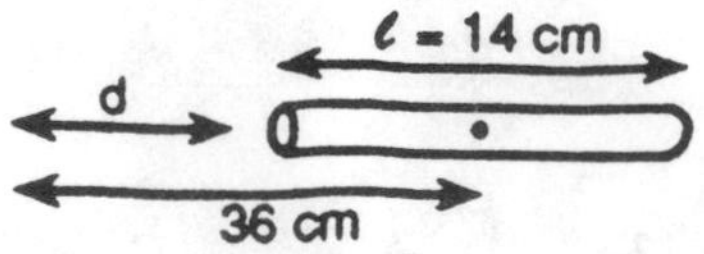

23.28

$$E = \frac{(9\times10^9)(22\times10^{-6})}{(0.29)(0.14+0.29)} = \boxed{1.59\times10^6\ \text{N/C}}$$

The electric field is directed towards the rod.

23.29 $E = \displaystyle\int \frac{kdq}{x^2}$ where $dq = \lambda_0 dx$

$$E = k\lambda_0 \int_{x_0}^{\infty} \frac{dx}{x^2} = k\lambda_0(-\frac{1}{x})\Big|_{x_0}^{\infty} = \boxed{\frac{k\lambda_0}{x_0}}$$

Direction is $-\boldsymbol{i}$ or left for $\lambda_0 > 0$

23.30 A line of charge starts at positive x_0 and to infinity along the x-axis. If the linear charge density is given by $\lambda = \lambda_0 x_0/x$, find the electric field at the origin.

$$|\boldsymbol{E}| = \int \frac{kdq}{x^2} \text{ where } dq = \lambda dx = \frac{\lambda_0 x_0}{x}dx$$

$$|\boldsymbol{E}| = \int_{x_0}^{\infty} k\lambda_0 x_0 \frac{dx}{x^3} = \frac{k\lambda_0 x_0}{2}\frac{1}{x^2}\Big|_{x_0}^{\infty} = \frac{k\lambda_0}{2x_0}$$

$\boldsymbol{E} = \dfrac{k\lambda_0}{2x_0}(-\boldsymbol{i})$ Directed left since the distribution is to the right of the point of interest.

23.31 $E = \dfrac{kxQ}{(x^2+a^2)^{3/2}} = \dfrac{(9\times10^9)(75\times10^{-6})x}{(x^2+0.1^2)^{3/2}} = \dfrac{6.75\times10^5 x}{(x^2+0.01)^{3/2}}$

(a) $x = 0.01$ m $\boldsymbol{E} = \boxed{6.65\times10^6\ \boldsymbol{i}\ \text{N/C}}$

(b) $x = 0.05$ m $\boldsymbol{E} = \boxed{2.41\times10^7\ \boldsymbol{i}\ \text{N/C}}$

(c) $x = 0.3$ m $\boldsymbol{E} = \boxed{6.40\times10^6\ \boldsymbol{i}\ \text{N/C}}$

(d) $x = 1$ m $\boldsymbol{E} = \boxed{6.65\times10^5\ \boldsymbol{i}\ \text{N/C}}$

23.32 $E = \dfrac{Q_z}{4\pi\epsilon_0(z^2+a^2)^{3/2}}$

For a maximum $\dfrac{dE}{dz} = \dfrac{Q}{4\pi\epsilon_0}[\dfrac{1}{(z^2+a^2)^{3/2}} - \dfrac{3z^2}{(z^2+a^2)^{5/2}}] = 0$

$z^2 + a^2 - 3z^2 = 0$

$z = \dfrac{a}{\sqrt{2}}$

Substituting into the expression for E gives

$$E = \frac{Qa}{4\pi\epsilon_0\sqrt{2}(\frac{3}{2}a^2)^{3/2}} = \frac{Q}{4\pi\epsilon_0 3\frac{\sqrt{3}}{2}a^2} = \boxed{\frac{Q}{6\sqrt{3}\pi\epsilon_0 a^2}}$$

23.33 (a) $\rho = \dfrac{Q}{V} = \dfrac{39\times10^{-6}}{\frac{4}{3}\pi(0.04)^3} = \boxed{0.145\ \mathrm{C/m^3}}$

(b) $\sigma = \dfrac{Q}{A} = \dfrac{39\times10^{-6}}{4\pi(0.04)^2} = \boxed{1.94\times10^{-3}\ \mathrm{C/m^2}}$

23.34 $E = 2\pi k\sigma\left(1 - \dfrac{x}{\sqrt{x^2+R^2}}\right)$

$E = 2\pi(9\times10^9)(7.9\times10^{-3})\left(1 - \dfrac{x}{\sqrt{x^2+0.35^2}}\right)$

$E = 4.467\times10^8\left(1 - \dfrac{x}{\sqrt{x^2+0.1225}}\right)$

(a) $x = 0.05$ m $\boxed{E = 3.83\times10^8\ \mathrm{N/C}}$

(b) $x = 0.1$ m $\boxed{E = 3.24\times10^8\ \mathrm{N/C}}$

(c) $x = 0.5$ m $\boxed{E = 8.07\times10^7\ \mathrm{N/C}}$

(d) $x = 2$ m $\boxed{E = 6.69\times10^6\ \mathrm{N/C}}$

23.35 (a)(Eq. 23.17): $E = 2\pi k\sigma(1 - \frac{x}{\sqrt{x^2 + R^2}})$

$$\sigma = \frac{Q}{\pi R^2} = 1.839 \times 10^{-3} \text{ C/m}^2$$

$$E = (1.04 \times 10^8 \text{ N/C})(1 - \frac{0.3 \text{ cm}}{\sqrt{0.3^2 + 3^2} \text{ cm}})$$

$$E = (1.04 \times 10^8 \text{ N/C})(0.9005) = \boxed{9.37 \times 10^7 \text{ N/C}}$$

appx: $E' = 2\pi k\sigma = \boxed{10.4 \times 10^7 \text{ N/C (about 11\% high)}}$

(b) $E = (1.04 \times 10^8 \text{ N/C})(1 - \frac{30 \text{ cm}}{\sqrt{30^2 + 3^2} \text{ cm}})$

$$E = (1.04 \times 10^8 \text{ N/C})(0.00496) = \boxed{5.16 \times 10^5 \text{ N/C}}$$

appx: $E' = k\frac{Q}{r^2} = (9 \times 10^9)\frac{5.2 \times 10^{-6}}{(0.30)^2}\ \boxed{5.20 \times 10^5 \text{ N/C (about 0.8\% high)}}$

23.36 $E_x = 2\pi k\sigma[1 - \frac{x}{\sqrt{x^2 + R^2}}]$

divide numerator and denominator of the right term by x :

$$E_x = 2\pi k\sigma[1 - \frac{1}{\sqrt{1 + R^2/x^2}}]$$

For large x, $R^2/x^2 << 1$, $\sqrt{1 + \frac{R^2}{x^2}} \approx 1 + \frac{R^2}{2x^2}$

so $E_x = 2\pi k\sigma(1 - \frac{1}{[1 + R^2/(2x^2)]})$

$$E_x = 2\pi k\sigma\frac{(1 + R^2/(2x^2) - 1)}{[1 + R^2/(2x^2)]}$$

substitute $\sigma = Q/\pi R^2$ into the equation

$$E_x = \frac{kQ(1/x^2)}{[1 + R^2/(2x^2)]}$$

thus $E_x = kQ(x^2 + \frac{R^2}{2})$; but for $x >> R$, $\frac{1}{x^2 + R^2/2} \approx \frac{1}{x^2}$

therefore $E_x \approx \frac{kQ}{x^2}$ for a disk at large distances.

23.37 **RING**

$$E = \frac{kxQ}{(x^2 + a^2)^{3/2}}$$

$$E = \frac{(9 \times 10^9)(0.04\ \text{m})(25 \times 10^{-6}\ \text{C})}{(0.04^2 + 0.03)^{3/2}} = \boxed{7.20 \times 10^7\ \text{N/C}}$$

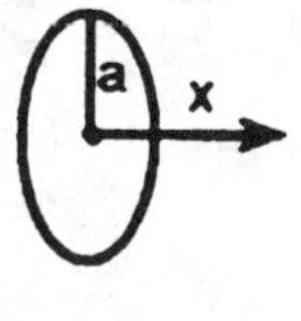

23.37

DISK

$$E = 2\pi k\sigma\left(1 - \frac{x}{\sqrt{x^2 + R^2}}\right)$$

$$\sigma = \frac{q}{A} = \frac{q}{\pi r^2} = \frac{25 \times 10^{-6}}{\pi(0.03)^2} = 8.84 \times 10^{-3}$$

$$E = 2\pi(9 \times 10^9)(8.84 \times 10^{-3})\left(1 - \frac{0.04}{\sqrt{0.04^2 + 0.03^2}}\right) = \boxed{10.0 \times 10^7\ \text{N/C}}$$

23.38 $mq = qE = q(\frac{\sigma}{2\epsilon_0}) = q\frac{Q/A}{2\epsilon_0}$

$$Q = \frac{2\epsilon_0 mgA}{q} = \frac{2(8.85 \times 10^{-12})(0.01)(9.8)(0.2 \times 0.3)}{(-0.7 \times 10^{-6})}$$

$$\frac{Q}{A} = \frac{1.49 \times 10^{-7}\ \text{C}}{(0.2)(0.3)} = \boxed{-2.48\ \mu\text{C/m}^2}$$

Note: "8 mm" merely guarantees that it is "close".

23.39 Due to symmetry $E_y = \int dE_y = 0$, and $E_x = \int dE \sin\theta = k\int \frac{dq \sin\theta}{r^2}$

where $dq = \lambda dx = \lambda r d\theta$, so that,

$$E_x = 2\frac{k\lambda}{r}\int_{\pi/2}^{\pi} \sin\theta d\theta = 2\frac{k\lambda}{r}(-\cos\theta)\Big|_{\pi/2}^{\pi} = \frac{2k\lambda}{r}$$

where $\lambda = q/L$ and $r = L/\pi$. Therefore

$$E_x = \frac{2kq\pi}{L^2} = \frac{2(9 \times 10^9\ \text{N}\cdot\text{m}^2/\text{C}^2)(7.5 \times 10^{-6}\ \text{C})\pi}{(0.14\ \text{m})^2}$$

$E = E_x = 2.16 \times 10^7$ N/C. And since the rod has a negative charge

$\mathbf{E} = \boxed{(-2.16 \times 10^7 \mathbf{i})\ \text{N/C}}$

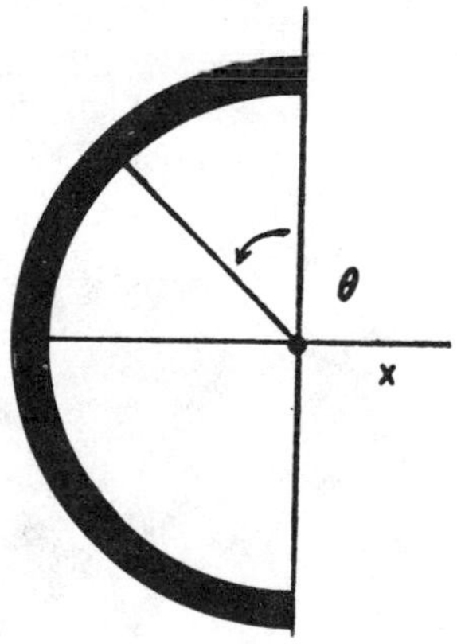

23.39

23.40

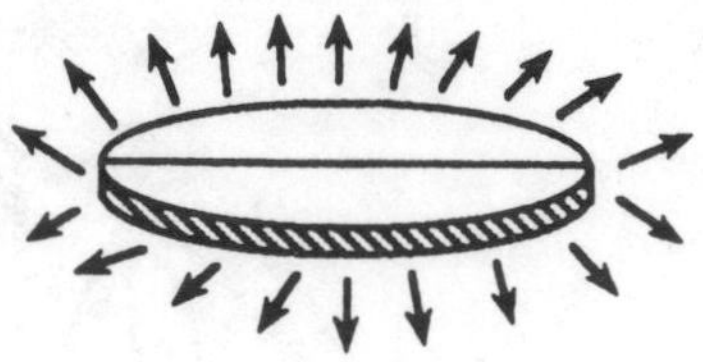

23.40

23.41

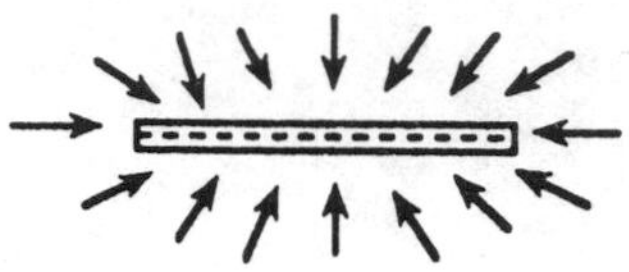

23.41

23.42

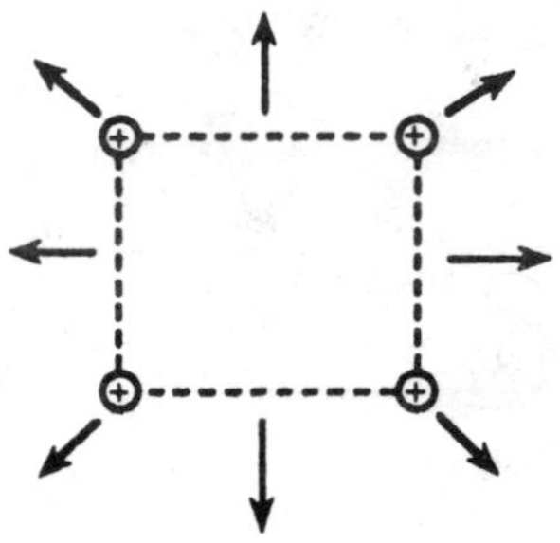

23.42

23.43 (a) $\frac{q_1}{q_2} = \frac{6}{18} = \boxed{-\frac{1}{3}}$

(b) $\boxed{q_1 \text{ is negative, } q_2 \text{ is positive}}$

23.44 $F = qE = ma$

$$a = \frac{qE}{m}$$

$$v = v_0 + at$$

$$v = \frac{qEt}{m}$$

electron: $$v_e = \frac{(1.602 \times 10^{-19})(520)(48 \times 10^{-9})}{9.11 \times 10^{-31}} = \boxed{4.39 \times 10^6 \text{ m/s}}$$

proton: $$v_p = \frac{(1.602 \times 10^{-19})(520)(48 \times 10^{-9})}{1.67 \times 10^{-27}}$$

$\boxed{v_p = 2.39 \times 10^3 \text{ m/s}}$ same direction as the field

23.45 (a) $$a = \frac{qE}{m} = \frac{(1.602 \times 10^{-19})(640)}{(1.67 \times 10^{-27})} = \boxed{6.14 \times 10^{10} \text{ m/s}^2}$$

(b) $v = v_0 + at$

$$1.2 \times 10^6 = (6.14 \times 10^{-10})\, t$$

$$\boxed{t = 1.95 \times 10^{-5} \text{ s}}$$

(c) $$x - x_0 = \frac{1}{2}(v_0 + v)t$$

$$x = \frac{1}{2}(1.2 \times 10^6)(1.95 \times 10^{-5}) = \boxed{11.7 \text{ m}}$$

(d) $$K = \frac{1}{2}mv^2 = \frac{1}{2}(1.67 \times 10^{-27})(1.2 \times 10^6)^2 = \boxed{1.20 \times 10^{-15} \text{ J}}$$

***23.46**

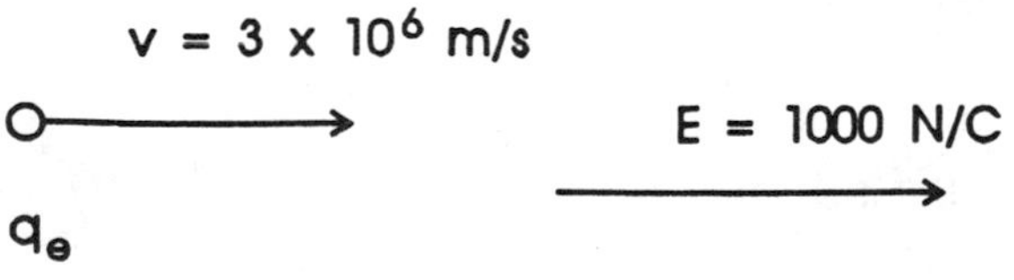

$$(KE)_e = \frac{1}{2}m_e v^2 = Fx = q_e E x$$

$$x = \frac{\frac{1}{2}m_e v^2}{q_e E} = \frac{\frac{1}{2}(9.1 \times 10^{-31} \text{ kg})(3 \times 10^6 \text{ m/s})^2}{(1.6 \times 10^{-19} \text{ C})(10^3 \text{ N/C})}$$

$$x = 0.0256 \text{ m} = \boxed{2.56 \text{ cm}}$$

23.47 First method: Use Newton's laws

$$K = \frac{1}{2}mv^2$$

$$1.6 \times 10^{-17} = \frac{1}{2}(9.11 \times 10^{-31})v^2$$

$$v = 5.93 \times 10^6 \text{ m/s}$$

$$v_0 = v_0^2 + 2a(x - x_0)$$

$$0 = (5.93 \times 10^6)^2 + 2a(-1)$$

$$a = -1.76 \times 10^{14} \text{ m/s}^2 = \frac{eE}{m}$$

$$1.76 \times 10^{14} = \frac{1.602 \times 10^{-19}\ E}{9.11 \times 10^{-31}}$$

$\boxed{E = 1000\ \text{N/C}}$ direction of **E** is parallel to **v**.

Second method: Use energy concepts:

$$W = \Delta K$$

$$Fd = K_i$$

$$eEd = K$$

$$E = \frac{K}{ed} = \frac{1.6 \times 10^{-17}}{(1.6 \times 10^{-19})(0.1)} = 10^3 \text{ N/C}$$

23.48 (a) $a = \dfrac{qE}{m} = \dfrac{(1.602 \times 10^{-19})(4.1 \times 10^3)}{(9.11 \times 10^{-31})}$

$$\boxed{\boldsymbol{a} = -7.21 \times 10^{14}\ \boldsymbol{i}\ \text{m/s}^2}$$

(b) $v = v_0 + at$

$$0 = 8.6 \times 10^5 + (-7.21 \times 10^{14})t$$

$$\boxed{t = 1.19 \times 10^{-9}\ \text{s}}$$

(c) $x - x_0 = \dfrac{1}{2}(v_0 + v)t$

$$x = \frac{1}{2}(8.6 \times 10^5 + 0)(1.19 \times 10^{-9})$$

$$x = 5.12 \times 10^{-4} \text{ m} = \boxed{0.512 \text{ mm}}$$

23.49 (a) $a = \frac{qE}{m} = \frac{(1.602 \times 10^{-19})(6 \times 10^5)}{(1.67 \times 10^{-27})} = 5.76 \times 10^{13}$ m/s $= \boxed{(-5.76 \times 10^{13} \text{ m/s}^2)\boldsymbol{i}}$

(b) $v = v_0 + 2a(x - x_0)$

$$0 = v_0^2 + 2(-5.76 \times 10^{13})(0.07)$$

$$\mathbf{v}_0 = \boxed{(2.84 \times 10^6 \text{ m/s})\boldsymbol{i}}$$

(c) $v = v_0 + at$

$$0 = 2.84 \times 10^6 + (-5.76 \times 10^{13})t$$

$$\boxed{t = 4.93 \times 10^{-8} \text{ s}}$$

23.50 $a = \frac{qE}{m}$

$$x - x_0 = v_0 t + \frac{1}{2}at^2$$

$$x = \frac{1}{2}(\frac{qE}{m})t^2$$

proton $x = \frac{(1.602 \times 10^{-19})(370)(1 \times 10^{-6})^2}{2(1.67 \times 10^{-27})} = 0.02$ m

electron $x = \frac{(1.602 \times 10^{-19})(37)(1 \times 10^{-6})^2}{2(9.11 \times 10^{-31})} = 32.53$ m

distance between them $= \boxed{32.51 \text{ m}}$

23.51 (a) $t = \frac{x}{v} = \frac{0.05}{4.5 \times 10^5} = \boxed{1.11 \times 10^{-7} \text{ s}}$

(b) $a = \frac{qE}{m} = \frac{(1.602 \times 10^{-19})(9.6 \times 10^3)}{(1.67 \times 10^{-27})} = 9.21 \times 10^{11} \text{ m/s}^2$

$$x - x_0 = v_0 t + \frac{1}{2}at^2$$

$$x = \frac{1}{2}(9.21 \times 10^{11})(1.11 \times 10^{-7})^2 = \boxed{5.67 \times 10^{-3} \text{ m}}$$

(c) $v_x = \boxed{4.5 \times 10^5 \text{ m/s}}$

$$v_y = v_0 + at = (9.21 \times 10^{11})(1.11 \times 10^{-7}) = \boxed{1.02 \times 10^5 \text{ m/s}}$$

23.52 $a = \dfrac{qE}{m} = \dfrac{(1.602 \times 10^{-19})(390)}{(9.11 \times 10^{-31})} = 6.86 \times 10^{13}\ \text{m/s}^2$

(a) $t = \dfrac{2v_0 \sin\theta}{a}$ from projectile motion equations

$$t = \frac{2(8.2 \times 10^5)\sin 30°}{16.86 \times 10^{13}} = \boxed{1.2 \times 10^{-8}\ \text{s}}$$

(b) $h = \dfrac{v_0^2 \sin^2\theta}{2a} = \dfrac{(8.2 \times 10^5)^2 \sin^2 30°}{2(6.86 \times 10^{13})} = \boxed{1.23\ \text{mm}}$

(c) $R = \dfrac{v_0^2 \sin^2\theta}{2a} = \dfrac{(8.2 \times 10^5)^2 \sin^2 60°}{2(6.86 \times 10^{13})} = \boxed{4.24\ \text{mm}}$

23.53 $v_0 = 9.55 \times 10^3\ \text{m/s}$

(a) $a = \dfrac{eE}{m} = \dfrac{(1.602 \times 10^{-19})(720)}{(1.67 \times 10^{-27})} = 6.91 \times 10^{10}\ \text{m/s}^2$

$$R = 1.27 \times 10^{-3}\ \text{m}$$

$$R = \frac{v_0^2 \sin 2\theta}{a}$$

$$1.27 \times 10^{-3} = \frac{(9.55 \times 10^3)^2 \sin 2\theta}{6.91 \times 10^{10}}$$

$$\sin 2\theta = 0.962$$

$$\theta = \boxed{37.1°}$$

$$90 - \theta = \boxed{52.9°}$$

(b) $t = \dfrac{R}{v_{0x}} = \dfrac{R}{v_0 \cos\theta}$

$$37.1° : t = \boxed{1.67 \times 10^{-7}\ \text{s}}$$

$$52.9° : t = \boxed{2.21 \times 10^{-7}\ \text{s}}$$

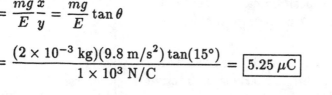

23.54 Equal torques $\Longrightarrow mgx = qEy$

$$q = \frac{mg}{E}\frac{x}{y} = \frac{mg}{E}\tan\theta$$

$$q = \frac{(2\times10^{-3}\text{ kg})(9.8\text{ m/s}^2)\tan(15°)}{1\times10^3\text{ N/C}} = \boxed{5.25\ \mu\text{C}}$$

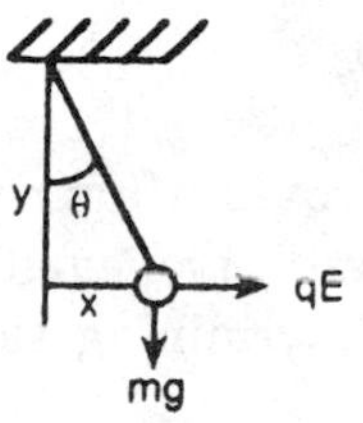

23.54

23.55 (a) From the sketch (in text) we can sum force components to find $\Sigma F_x = E_x q - T\sin\theta = 0$, and $\Sigma F_y = E_y q + T\cos\theta - mg = 0$
Combining these two equations we get

$$q = \frac{mg}{E_x\cot\theta + E_y} = \frac{(0.001)(9.8)}{(3\cot 37° + 5)10^5} = \boxed{1.09\times10^{-8}\text{ C}}$$

(b) From the two equations for ΣF_x and ΣF_y we also find

$$T = \frac{E_x q}{\sin 37°} = \boxed{5.43\times10^{-3}\text{ N}}$$

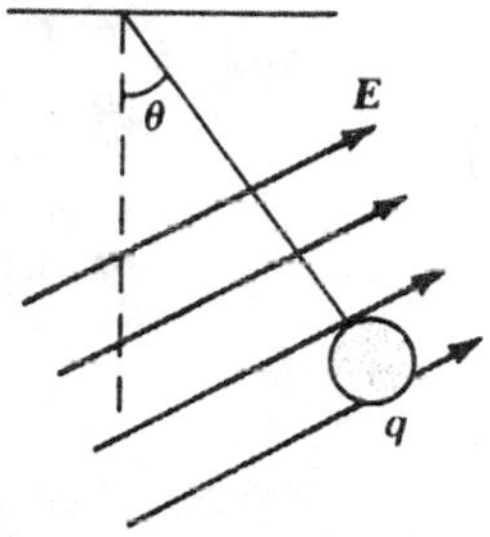

23.55

23.56 For each sphere we require $\Sigma F_x = Eq - F_e - T\sin\theta = 0$ and $\Sigma F_y = T\cos\theta - mg = 0$ where F_e is the electrostatic force between the charges given by $F_e = kq^2[2(\ell\sin\theta)]^2$, and ℓ is the length of the cord. Solving these two equations we find

$$E = \frac{kq}{4\ell^2\sin^2\theta} + (\frac{mg}{q})\tan\theta = \boxed{4.42\times10^5\ \text{N/C}}$$

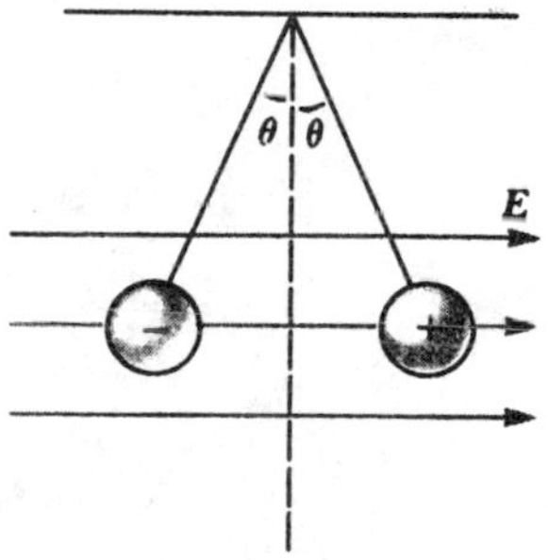

23.56

23.57 (a) From the $2Q$ charge we have $F_e - T_2\sin\theta_2 = 0$ and $mg - T_2\cos\theta_2 = 0$.

Combining these we find $\dfrac{F_e}{mg} = \dfrac{T_2\sin\theta_2}{T_2\cos\theta_2} = \tan\theta_2$.

From the Q charge we have $F_e - T_1\sin\theta_1 = 0$ and $mg - T_1\cos\theta_1 = 0$.

Combining these we find $\dfrac{F_e}{mg} = \dfrac{T_1\sin\theta_1}{T_1\cos\theta_1} = \tan\theta_1$. Combining these two results we find $\boxed{\theta_2 = \theta_1}$

(b) $F_e = \dfrac{k2QQ}{r^2} = \dfrac{2kQ^2}{r^2}$ if we assume θ is small than $h \approx \ell$ and

$\tan\theta \approx \dfrac{(r/2)}{\ell}$. Substitute expressions for F_e and $\tan\theta$ into either equation found in part (a) and solve for r.

$\dfrac{F_e}{mg} = \tan\theta$ then $\dfrac{2kQ^2}{r^2}(\dfrac{1}{mg}) \approx \dfrac{r}{2\ell}$ and solving for r we find $r = [\dfrac{4kQ^2\ell}{mg}]^{1/3}$.

***23.58** At an equilibrium position, the net force on the charge Q is zero. The equilibrium position can be located by first determining the angle θ corresponding to equilibrium.

In terms of the lengths s, $\frac{1}{2}a\sqrt{3}$, and r, shown in Figure 23.58, the charge at the origin exerts an attractive force $k_eQq/(s+\frac{1}{2}a\sqrt{3})^2$. The other two charges exert equal repulsive forces of magnitude k_eQq/r^2. The horizontal components of the two repulsive forces add, balancing the attractive force,

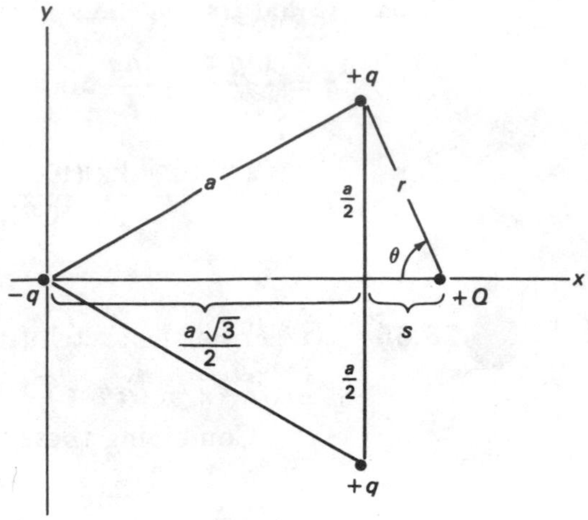

23.58

$$F_{\text{net}} = k_eQq\left\{\frac{2\cos\theta}{r^2} - \frac{1}{(s+\frac{1}{2}a\sqrt{3})^2}\right\} = 0$$

From Figure 23.58,

$$r = \frac{\frac{1}{2}a}{\sin\theta} \qquad s = \frac{1}{2}a\cot\theta$$

The equilibrium condition is expressed in terms of θ by

$$F_{\text{net}} = \left(\frac{4}{a^2}\right)k_eQq\left\{2\cos\theta\sin^2\theta - \frac{1}{(\sqrt{3}+\cot\theta)^2}\right\} = 0$$

This gives an equation for the equilibrium value of θ,

$$2\cos\theta\sin^2\theta(\sqrt{3}+\cot\theta)^2 = 1$$

One method for solving for θ is to tabulate the left side. To three significant figures the value of θ corresponding to equilibrium is 81.7°. The distance from the origin to the equilibrium position is

$$x = \tfrac{1}{2}a(\sqrt{3}+\cot 81.7°)$$

$$x = \boxed{0.939a}$$

θ	$2\cos\theta\sin^2\theta(\sqrt{3}+\cot\theta)^2$	
60°	4	
70°	2.654	
80°	1.226	
90°	0	between θ = 80° and 90°
81°	1.091	
81.5°	1.024	
81.7°	0.997	

23.59 15 cm = d cos 30°

$d = 0.1732\text{ m};\quad \theta = \sin^{-1}(\frac{17.32}{50}) = 20.27°$

$\frac{F_q}{mg} = \tan\theta = 0.36793;\quad F_q = \frac{2kq^2}{(0.3)^2}\cos 30°$

$\frac{\sqrt{3}q^2}{4\pi\epsilon_0(0.3)^2} = 0.36793(9.81\text{ m/s}^2)(0.002\text{ kg})$

$q = \sqrt{4.167\times 10^{-14}\text{ C}^2} = \boxed{0.204\ \mu\text{C}}$

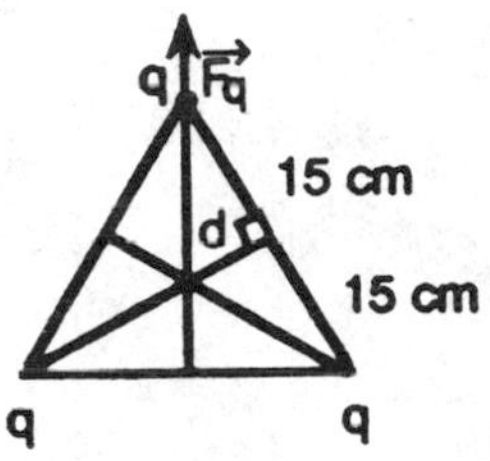

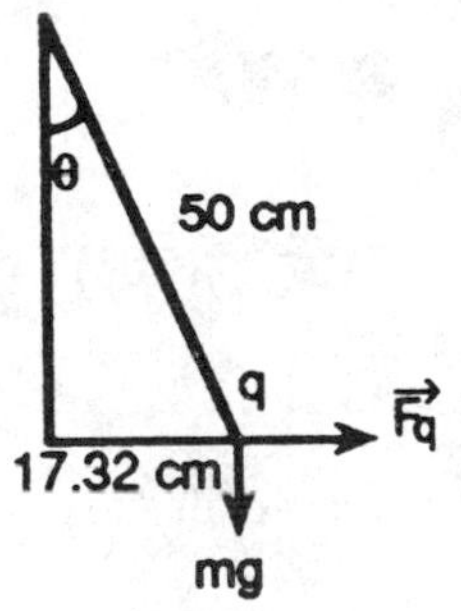

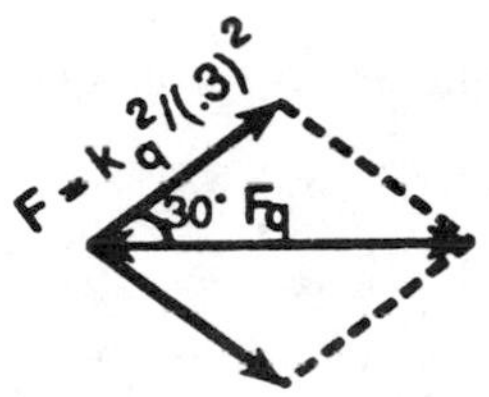

23.59

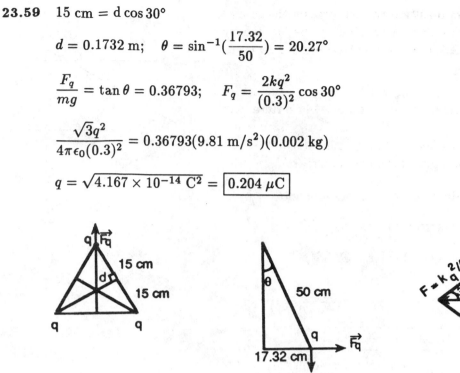

23.60 (a) For the mass m we have $F_e - T_1\sin\theta_1 = 0$ and $mg - T_1\cos\theta_1 = 0$. Combining these we find $\frac{F_e}{mg} = \frac{T_1\sin\theta}{T_1\cos\theta_1} = \tan\theta_1$. For the mass $2m$ we have $F_e - T_2\sin\theta_2 = 0$ and $2mg - T_2\cos\theta_2 = 0$. Combining these we find $\theta_1 = \tan^{-1}(2\tan\theta_2) \approx 2\theta_2$.

(b) $F_e = \frac{kQQ}{r^2} = \frac{kQ^2}{r^2}$ and $r_1 + r_2 = r$.

If we assume θ_1 and θ_2 are small then $\tan\theta_1 \approx \frac{r_1}{\ell}$ and $\tan\theta_2 \approx \frac{r_2}{\ell}$. Substitute expressions for $F_e, \tan\theta_1$ and $\tan\theta_2$ into two equations found in part (a) then solve for r. $\frac{F_e}{mg} = \tan\theta_1$ then $\frac{kQ^2}{mg}r^2 \approx \frac{r_1}{\ell}$ and solving for r_1 we find $r_1 \approx \frac{kQ^2\ell}{mg\,r^2}$. Also $\frac{F_e}{2mg} = \tan\theta_2$ then $r_2 \approx \frac{kQ^2\ell}{2mg\,r^2}$ and solving for r_2 we find $r_2 \approx \frac{kQ^2\ell}{2mg\,r^2}$. And now

$r = r_1 + r_2 \approx \frac{3kQ^2\ell}{2mg\,r^2}$ thus $r^3 \approx \frac{3kQ^2\ell}{2mg}$ and $r = [\frac{3kQ^2\ell}{2mg}]^{1/3}$

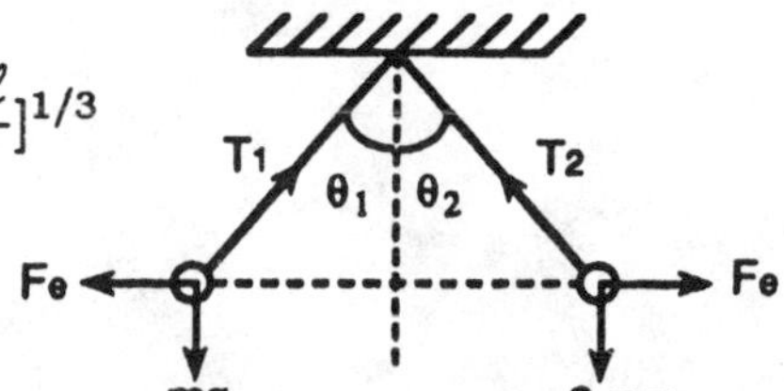

23.60

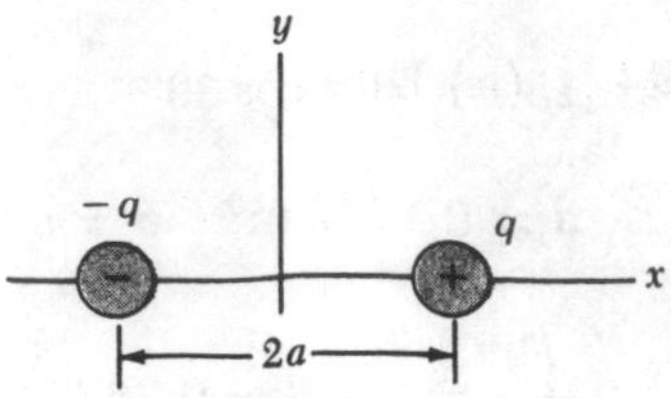

23.61

23.61 The electric field at any point x is

$$E = kq\{\frac{1}{(x-a)^2} - \frac{1}{[x-(-a)]^2}\}i = \frac{kq(4ax)}{(x^2-a^2)^2}i.$$

When $x >> a$, $E = \frac{(4a)(kq)}{x^4}\ i = [\frac{2kp}{x^3}]i$ where

$p = 2qa$.

***23.62** A water molecule of electric dipole moment

$P_E = 2qa = 6.24 \times 10^{-30}$ C · m

is placed in an electric field E = 10^4 N/C.

$$\text{(a)}\ T_{max} = \mathbf{p} \times \mathbf{E} = (6.24 \times 10^{-30})(10^4) = \boxed{6.24 \times 10^{-26}\ \text{N}\cdot\text{m}}$$

$$\text{(b)}\ U = -\mathbf{p}\cdot\mathbf{E}$$

$$U_{min} = -(6.24 \times 10^{-30})(10^4) = \boxed{-6.24 \times 10^{-26}\ \text{J}}$$

$$U_{max} = +(6.24 \times 10^{-30})(10^4) = \boxed{+6.24 \times 10^{-26}\ \text{J}}$$

23.63 (a) Due to symmetry the field contribution from each negative charge is equal and opposite to each other. Therefore their contribution to the net field is zero. The field contribution of the $+q$ charge is $E = \frac{kq}{r^2} = \frac{kq}{(3a^2/4)} = \frac{4kq}{3a^2}$ in the negative y-direction, i.e., $\mathbf{E} = \frac{4kq}{3a^2}(-\jmath)$.

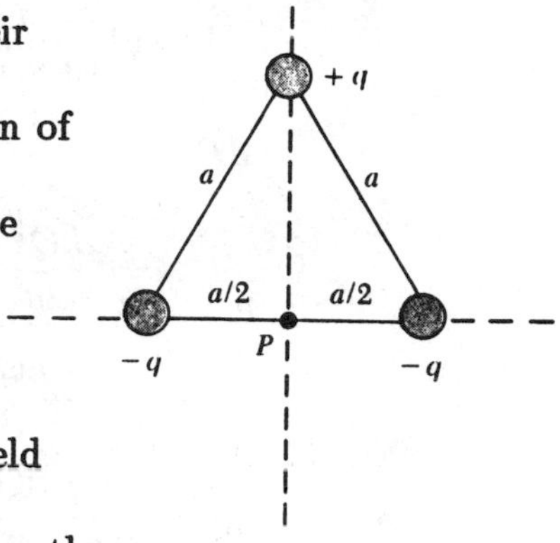

23.63

(b) If $F_e = 0$ then E at P must equal zero. In order for the field to cancel at P the $-4q$ charge must be above $+q$ charge on the y-axis. Then

$$E = 0 = -\frac{kq}{1^2} + \frac{k(4q)}{(1+y)^2}$$
$$0 = -1 + \frac{4}{(1+y)^2}$$
$$0 = y^2 + 2y - 3$$

$y = -3$ or $y =$ so only the positive answer is acceptable.

Therefore the $(-4q)$ charge must be placed one meter above the $+q$ charge or 2 meters above point P along the $+y$-axis

23.64 Find E at $P_1 + P_2$ and use superposition principle.

(a) $E_{P_1} = [\frac{kR}{(R^2+R^2)^{3/2}}](\lambda 2\pi R) + [\frac{kR}{(R^2+R^2)^{3/2}}](\lambda 2\pi R) = \frac{\pi\lambda k}{R\sqrt{2}}$

directed along the axis toward the negative ring

(b) $E_{P_2} = [\frac{3kR}{(3R^2+R^2)^{3/2}}](\lambda 2\pi R) - [\frac{kR}{(R^2)^{3/2}}](\lambda 2\pi R)$

$= (\frac{\pi\lambda k}{R})(-0.517)$ directed along axis toward the rings.

***23.65** Following Example 23.8,

$$E = \frac{kQ}{d(2a+d)} \qquad \text{(Eq. 23.15)}$$

$$dF = \frac{kQQ}{2a}\frac{dx}{d(d+2a)}$$

$$F = \frac{kQ^2}{2a}\int_{x=b-2a}^{b}\frac{dx}{x(x+2a)} = \frac{kQ^2}{2a}\left(-\frac{1}{2a}\ln\frac{2a+x}{x}\right)_{b-2a}^{b}$$

$$= \frac{+kQ^2}{4a^2}\left(-\ln\frac{2a+b}{b}+\ln\frac{b}{b-2a}\right) = \frac{kQ^2}{4a^2}\ln\frac{b^2}{(b-2a)(b+2a)}$$

$$F = \left(\frac{kQ^2}{4a^2}\right)\ln\left(\frac{b^2}{b^2-4a^2}\right)$$

***23.66**

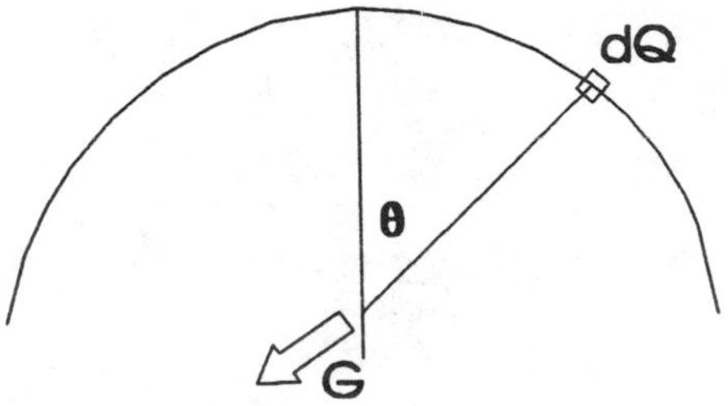

$$Q = \int \lambda dl = 12\ \mu\text{C}$$

$$= \int_{-90}^{90}\lambda_0\cos\theta R d\theta = \lambda_0 R\sin\theta\,|_{-90}^{90} = \lambda_0 R[1-(-1)] = 2\lambda_0 R$$

$$(2\lambda_0)(0.6)\ \text{m} = 12\ \mu\text{C}$$

$$\lambda_0 = 10\ \mu\text{C/m}$$

$$dF_y = \frac{1}{4\pi\epsilon_0}\frac{(3\ \mu\text{C})\lambda\text{dl}}{\text{R}^2}\cos\theta$$

$$= \frac{1}{4\pi\epsilon_0}\frac{3\mu\text{C}\lambda_0\cos^2\theta\text{Rd}\theta}{\text{R}^2}$$

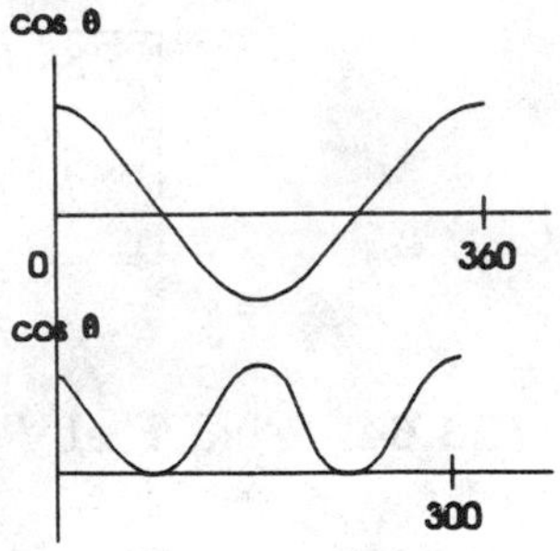

23.66

$$F_y = \int_{-90}^{90} 9\times10^9\ \frac{\text{N}\cdot\text{m}^2}{\text{C}^2}\frac{(3\times10^{-6}\ \text{C})(10\times10^{-6}\ \text{C/m})}{(0.6\ \text{m})}\cos^2\theta d\theta$$

$$= \frac{9(30)}{(0.6)}(10^{-3}\ \text{N})\int_{-\pi/2}^{\pi/2}\left(\frac{1}{2}+\frac{1}{2}\cos 2\theta\right)\text{d}\theta$$

$$= (0.45\ \text{N})\left(\frac{1}{2}\pi+\frac{1}{4}\sin 2\theta\,|_{-\pi/2}^{\pi/2}\right)$$

$$F = \boxed{0.707\ \text{N}}\ \text{Downward}$$

23.67
$$a = \frac{F}{m} = \frac{eE}{m}$$
$$= \frac{(1.6 \times 10^{-19}\text{ C})(3 \times 10^{6}\text{ N/C})}{9.11 \times 10^{-31}\text{ kg}} = 5.27 \times 10^{17}\text{ m/s}^2$$
$$v^2 = v_0^2 + 2a(x - x_0)$$
$$d = \frac{v^2}{2a} = \frac{(3 \times 10^7\text{ m/s})^2}{2(5.27 \times 10^{17}\text{ m/s}^2)}(3 \times 10^7\text{ m/s})^2 = \boxed{0.854\text{ mm}}$$

23.68 Each element of the rod dx produces a field at the origin,

$dE = \frac{k\lambda dx}{x^2}$. Therefore

$$E = k\int_d^{\ell+d} \frac{\lambda dx}{x^2} = \frac{k\lambda_0}{d}\int_d^{\ell+d} \frac{(x-d)dx}{x^2}$$

$$\boxed{E = \frac{k\lambda_0}{d}[ln(1+\frac{\ell}{d}) - \frac{\ell}{\ell+d}](-i)}$$

23.69 (a) The electric field at point P due to each element of length dx, is $dE = \frac{kdq}{(x^2+y^2)}$ and is directed along the line joining the element of length to point P. By symmetry,

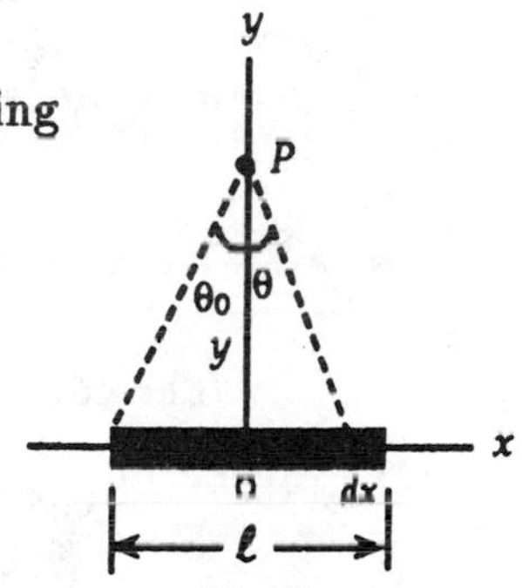

23.69

$E_x = \int dE_x = 0$ and since $dq = \lambda dx$

$E = E_y = \int dE_y = \int dE\cos\theta$ where

$$\cos\theta = \frac{y}{(x^2+y^2)^{1/2}}$$

Therefore $E = 2k\lambda y \int_0^{\ell/2} \frac{dx}{(x^2+y^2)^{3/2}} = \frac{2k\lambda\sin\theta_0}{y}$

(b) For a bar of infinite length, $\theta \longrightarrow 90°$ and

$$E_y = \frac{2k\lambda}{y}$$

***23.70**

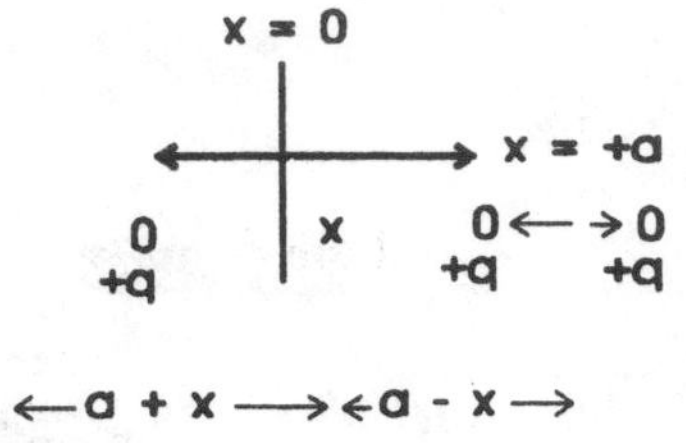

23.70

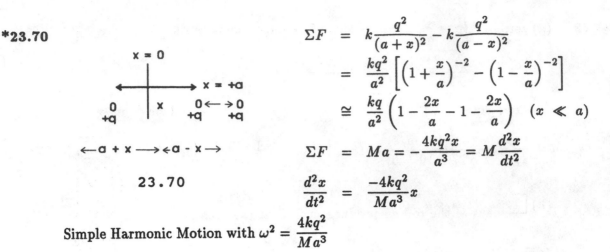

$$\Sigma F = k\frac{q^2}{(a+x)^2} - k\frac{q^2}{(a-x)^2}$$
$$= \frac{kq^2}{a^2}\left[\left(1+\frac{x}{a}\right)^{-2} - \left(1-\frac{x}{a}\right)^{-2}\right]$$
$$\cong \frac{kq}{a^2}\left(1-\frac{2x}{a}-1-\frac{2x}{a}\right) \quad (x \ll a)$$
$$\Sigma F = Ma = -\frac{4kq^2x}{a^3} = M\frac{d^2x}{dt^2}$$
$$\frac{d^2x}{dt^2} = \frac{-4kq^2}{Ma^3}x$$

Simple Harmonic Motion with $\omega^2 = \dfrac{4kq^2}{Ma^3}$

23.71 (a) There are 7 terms which contribute:

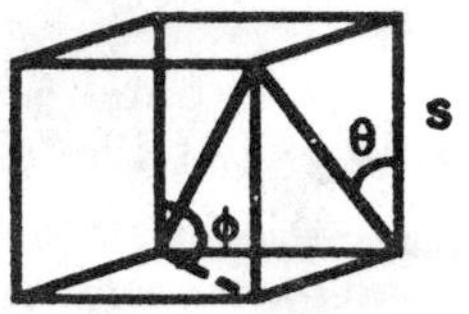

23.71

3 are s away (along sides)

3 are $\sqrt{2}s$ away (face diagonals) and $\sin\theta = \dfrac{1}{\sqrt{2}} = \cos\theta$

1 is $\sqrt{3}s$ away (body diagonal) and $\sin\theta = \dfrac{1}{\sqrt{3}}$

The component in each direction is the same by symmetry.

$$\boldsymbol{F} = \frac{kq^2}{s^2}\left[1+\frac{2}{2\sqrt{2}}+\frac{1}{3\sqrt{3}}\right](\boldsymbol{i}+\boldsymbol{j}+\boldsymbol{k}) = \boxed{\frac{kq^2}{s^2}(1.90)(\boldsymbol{i}+\boldsymbol{j}+\boldsymbol{k})}$$

(b) $F = \sqrt{F_x^2+F_4^2+F_z^2} = \boxed{3.29\dfrac{kq^2}{s^2}, \text{ away from the origin}}$

23.72 (a) zero contribution from the same face due to symmetry,

opposite face contributes $4(\frac{kq}{r^2}\sin\theta)$

where $r = \sqrt{(\frac{s}{2})^2 + (\frac{s}{2})^2 + s^2} = \sqrt{1.5}\,s = 1.22\,s$ and $\sin\phi = s/r$

$$E = 5\frac{kqs}{r^3} = \frac{4}{(1.22)^3}\frac{kq}{s^2} = \boxed{2.18\,\frac{kq}{s^2}}$$

(b) **The direction is in the k direction**

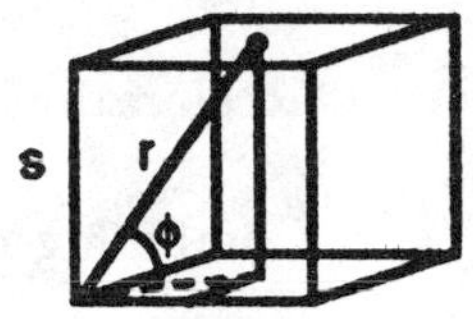

23.72a

23.73 By symmetry $\Sigma E_x = 0$. Using the distances as labeled in

Figure 23.38 of the text,

$$\Sigma E_y = k\{[\frac{q}{(a^2+y^2)}]\sin\theta + [\frac{q}{(a^2+y^2)}]\,sin\theta - \frac{2q}{y^2}\}$$

But $\sin\theta = \frac{y}{\sqrt{(a^2+y^2)}}$, so $E = \Sigma E_y = 2kq[\frac{y}{(a^2+y^2)^{3/2}} - \frac{1}{y^2}]$.

Expand $(a^2+y^2)^{-3/2}$ as $(a^2+y^2)^{-3/2} = y^{-3} - (3/2)a^2y^{-5} + \ldots$

Therefore for $a << y$ we can ignore terms in powers higher than 2,

and we have $E = 2kq[\frac{1}{y^2} - (\frac{3}{2})\frac{a^2}{y^4} - \frac{1}{y^2}]$ or $E = [-\frac{k3qa^2}{y^4}]\jmath$

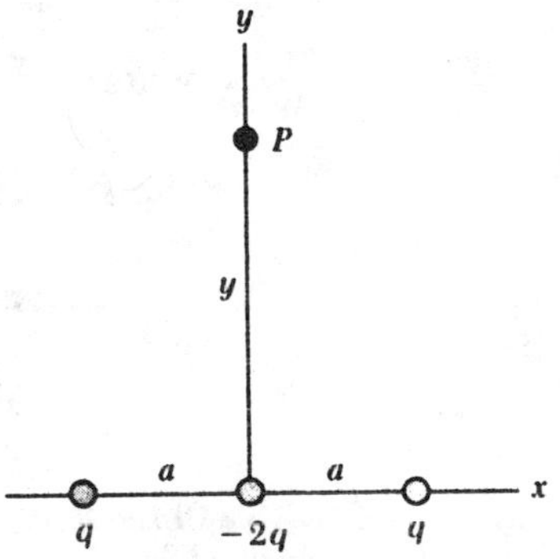

23.73

23.74 The electrostatic forces exerted on the two charges result in a net torque $\tau = -2Fa\sin\theta = 2Eqa\sin\theta$. For small θ, $\sin\theta \approx \theta$ and using $p = 2qa$, we have $\tau = Ep\theta$. The torque produces an angular acceleration given by $\tau = I\alpha = \frac{Id^2\theta}{dt^2}$.

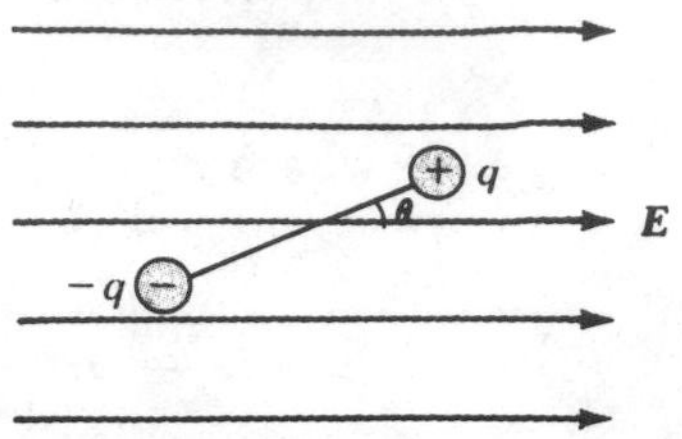

23.74

Combining these two expressions for torque we have $\frac{d^2\theta}{dt^2} + (\frac{Ep}{I})\theta = 0$. This equation can be written in the form $\frac{d^2\theta}{dt^2} = -\omega^2\theta$

where $\omega^2 = \frac{Ep}{I}$. This is the same form as Eq. 13.15 and the frequency of oscillation is found by comparison with Eq. 13.17, or $f = \frac{1}{2\pi}\sqrt{\frac{pE}{I}}$

23.75 The field on the axis of the ring is calculated in Example 23.8, $E = E_x = \frac{kxQ}{(x^2+a^2)^{3/2}}$. The force experienced by a charge q placed along the axis of the ring is $F = -kQq[\frac{x}{(x^2+a^2)^{3/2}}]$

and when $x << a$, this becomes $F = -(\frac{kQq}{a^3})x$. This expression for the force is in the form of Hooke's law with an effective spring constant of $K = \frac{kQq}{a^3}$ and since $\omega = 2\pi f = \sqrt{\frac{k}{m}}$,

we have $f = \frac{1}{2\pi}\sqrt{\frac{kQe}{ma^3}}$

***23.76** (a) $N = \eta\,\mathrm{m}\cdot\mathrm{m/s} = \mathrm{kg}\cdot\mathrm{m/s^2}$

$$\eta = \underline{\mathrm{kg/m}\cdot\mathrm{s}}$$

(b) At terminal velocity,

$$6\pi\eta r v_T = m_O g - m_{\text{air}} g$$

$$v_T = \frac{(m_O - m_A)g}{6\pi\eta r} = \frac{\frac{4}{3}\pi r^3(\rho_O - \rho_A)g}{6\pi\eta r}$$

$$v_T = \frac{2r^2 g}{9\eta}(\rho_O - \rho_A)$$

23.77 (a) $V = \sum_i \frac{kq_i}{r_i} = \frac{kq}{r}$

$$V = \frac{(9\times10^9)(1.6\times10^{-9})}{2} = \boxed{7.20\ \text{V}}$$

(b) $V = \frac{(9\times10^9)(8\times10^{-10})}{1.5} + \frac{(9\times10^9)(8\times10^{-10})}{2.5} = 4.8 + 2.88 = \boxed{7.68\ \text{V}}$

(c) $V = (9\times10^9)(\frac{16}{4}\times10^{-10})(\frac{1}{1.25} + \frac{1}{1.75} + \frac{1}{2.25} + \frac{1}{2.75}) = \boxed{7.85\ \text{V}}$

(d) $V = (9\times10^9)(\frac{16\times10^{-10}}{N})\sum_{I=1}^{N}(\frac{1}{1+\frac{2}{2N}+\frac{2}{N}(I-1)})$

Utilize the following program:

```
K = 9E9
Q = 16E − 10
N = 256
J = 0
DO 20  I = 1, 256
L = 1/(1 + 2/(2 × N) + (2/N) × (I − 1))
J = J + L
V = K × (Q/N) × J
PRINT "V =" ; V; "VOLTS"
END
```

This may be compared to the *exact* answer

$$V = k\frac{Q}{\ell}\ln(\frac{\ell + d}{d})$$

$$V = (9\times10^9)(\frac{16\times10^{-10}}{2})\ln 3 = \boxed{7.91\ \text{V}}$$

23.78 $Q = 1.6 \times 10^{-9}$ C

$a = 1$ m

$x = 3$ m

(a) $E = \dfrac{kQ}{x^2} = \dfrac{(9 \times 10^9)(1.6 \times 10^{-9})}{3^2} = 1.6$ N/C

(b) $E = \sum_i \dfrac{kQ_i \cos\theta}{r_i^2} = \dfrac{2k(Q/2)}{(3^2 + 1^2)} \dfrac{3}{\sqrt{3^2 + 1^2}}$

$$E = \frac{kQ}{x^2} = \frac{(9 \times 10^9)(1.6 \times 10^{-9})(3)}{(10)^{3/2}} = 1.366 \text{ N/C}$$

(c) $E = \dfrac{4k(Q/4)3}{(3^2 + 1^2)^{3/2}} = 1.366$ N/C

(d) A similar result occurs for $N = 64$ parts around the ring,

since the exact result is

$$E = \frac{kx}{(x^2 + a^2)^{3/2}} Q = 1.366 \text{ N/C}$$

CHAPTER 24

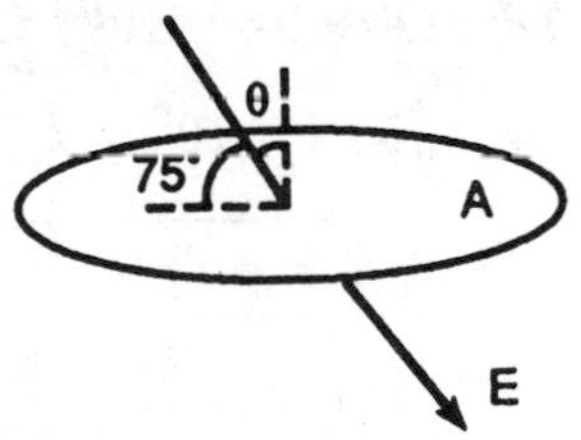

24.1

24.1 (a) $\phi = EA\cos\theta$

$$\phi = (6.2 \times 10^5)(3.2)\cos 0^\circ = \boxed{1.98 \times 10^6\ \mathrm{N \cdot m^2/C}}$$

(b) $\phi = EA\cos\theta$

$$\phi = (6.2 \times 10^5)(3.2)\cos 90^\circ = \boxed{0}$$

(c) $\phi = EA\cos\theta$

$$\phi = (6.2 \times 10^5)(3.2)\cos 15^\circ = \boxed{1.92 \times 10^6\ \mathrm{N \cdot m^2/C}}$$

24.2 (a) $\phi = EA\cos\theta$

$$\phi = (3.5 \times 10^3)(0.35 \times 0.70)\cos 0^\circ = \boxed{858\ \mathrm{N \cdot m^2/C}}$$

(b) $\theta = 90^\circ$ $\boxed{\phi = 0}$

(c) $\phi = (3.5 \times 10^3)(0.35 \times 0.70)\cos 40^\circ = \boxed{657\ \mathrm{N \cdot m^2/C}}$

24.3 (a) $\phi = \boldsymbol{E} \cdot \boldsymbol{A} = (a\boldsymbol{i} + b\boldsymbol{j}) \cdot A\boldsymbol{i} = \boxed{aA}$

(b) $\phi = (a\boldsymbol{i} + b\boldsymbol{j}) \cdot A\boldsymbol{j} = \boxed{bA}$

(c) $\phi = (a\boldsymbol{i} + b\boldsymbol{j}) \cdot A\boldsymbol{k} = \boxed{0}$

24.4 (a) $A = 300\ \mathrm{cm}^2\left(\frac{\mathrm{m}}{100\ \mathrm{cm}}\right)^2 = 0.003\mathrm{m}^2$

$$\phi_{A'} = EA'\cos\theta$$

$$\phi_{A'} = (7.8 \times 10^4)(0.03)\cos 180^\circ = \boxed{-2340\ \mathrm{N \cdot m^2/C}}$$

(b) $\phi_A = EA\cos\theta = (7.8 \times 10^4)(A)\cos 60^\circ$

$$\cos 60^\circ = \frac{10\ \mathrm{cm}}{w} \Longrightarrow w = 20\ \mathrm{cm}$$

$$A = (20\ \mathrm{cm})(30\ \mathrm{cm}) = 0.06\ \mathrm{m}^2$$

$$\phi_A = (7.8 \times 10^4)(0.06)\cos 60^\circ = \boxed{+2340\ \mathrm{N \cdot m^2/C}}$$

(c) The bottom and the two triangular sides all lie *parallel* to $\boldsymbol{E}$, so $\phi = 0$ for each of these. Thus

$$\phi = -2340 + 2340 + 0 + 0 + 0 = \boxed{0}$$

24.5 $\phi = EA\cos\theta \qquad A = \pi r^2 = \pi(0.2)^2$

$5 \cdot 2 \times 10^5 = E(0.126)\cos 0° \qquad A = 0.126\ \text{m}^2$

$\boxed{E = 4.14 \times 10^6\ \text{N/C}}$

24.6 $\Phi = \int \mathbf{E} \cdot d\mathbf{A} = \int E_z dA = \int_0^w cxdxh = ch \int_0^w xdx = \boxed{\dfrac{chw^2}{2}}$

24.7 $\Phi = \int \mathbf{E} \cdot d\mathbf{A} = \int E_z dA \quad \text{where } y = \dfrac{h}{w}x$

$$= \int_0^w (bx)(ydx) = \int_0^w (bx)\left(\frac{h}{w}x\right)dx$$

$$= \frac{bh}{w}\int_0^w x^2 dx = \frac{bh}{w}\frac{1}{3}w^3$$

$\boxed{\Phi = \dfrac{bhw^2}{3}}$

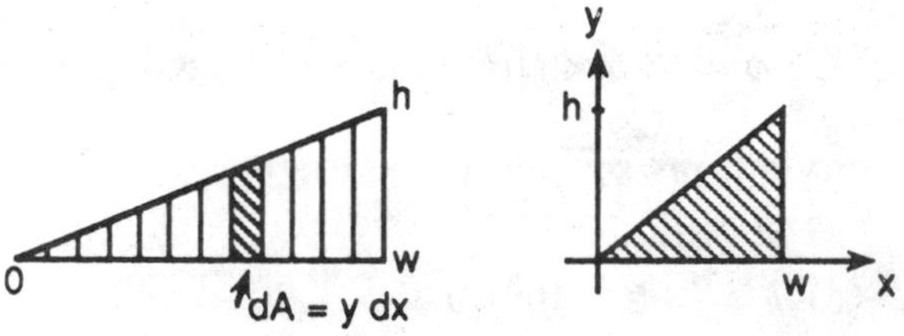

24.7

24.8 The flux entering the closed surface equals the flux exiting the surface. The flux entering the bottom area of cone is $\phi = \int \mathbf{E} \cdot d\mathbf{A} = E\pi R^2$. This is the same as the flux that exists the conical sides.

24.9 $\phi = EA\cos\theta$ thru the base; $\quad \phi = (52)(36)\cos 180° = \boxed{+1.87\ \text{kN} \cdot \text{m}^2/\text{C}}$

Note the same number of electric field lines go through the base as go through the pyramid's surface not counting the base. $\boxed{\phi = +1.87\ \text{kN}{\cdot}\text{m}^2/\text{C}}$

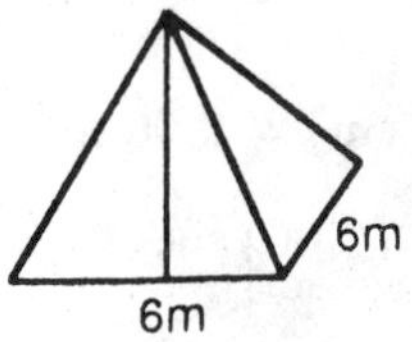

24.9

24.10 $\phi_c = \dfrac{q_{in}}{\epsilon_0}$

thru S_1 $\quad \phi_1 = \dfrac{-2Q + Q}{\epsilon_0} = \boxed{-\dfrac{Q}{\epsilon_0}}$

thru S_2 $\quad \phi_2 = \dfrac{+Q - Q}{\epsilon_0} = \boxed{0}$

thru S_3 $\quad \phi_3 = \dfrac{-2Q + Q - Q}{\epsilon_0} = \boxed{\dfrac{-2Q}{\epsilon_0}}$

thru S_4 $\quad \phi_4 = \boxed{0}$

24.11 $\phi = \dfrac{q}{\epsilon_0} = \dfrac{+5 \times 10^{-6}}{8.85 \times 10^{-12}} = \boxed{5.65 \times 10^5 \text{ N} \cdot \text{m}^2/\text{C}}$

***24.12** Use Gauss' Law to determine the charge on the Earth.

$$E(4\pi R_{\text{Earth}}^2) = Q/\epsilon_0$$

With $R_{\text{Earth}} = 6.4 \times 10^6$ m, and E = −100 N/C,

$$Q_{\text{Earth}} = \boxed{-4.6 \times 10^5 \text{ C}}$$

24.13 (a) $\phi_c = \dfrac{q_{in}}{\epsilon_0} = \dfrac{12 \times 10^{-6}}{8.85 \times 10^{-12}} = \boxed{1.36 \times 10^6 \text{ N} \cdot \text{m}^2/\text{C}}$

(b) $\phi_c = \dfrac{1}{2}(1.36 \times 10^6 \text{ N} \cdot \text{m}^2/\text{C}) = \boxed{6.78 \times 10^5 \text{ N} \cdot \text{m}^2/\text{C}}$

(c) No, the same amount of field lines will penetrate each surface, no matter how the radius changes.

***24.14** If the area of one face of the cube is A,

$$E \cdot 6A = \frac{Q}{\epsilon_0}$$

Through one face,

$$\Phi_E = E \cdot A = \frac{Q}{6\epsilon_0} = \frac{12 \times 10^{-6}}{6(8.85 \times 10^{-12})} = \boxed{2.26 \times 10^5 \text{ N} \cdot \text{m}^2/\text{C}}$$

24.15 $\phi_c = \dfrac{q_{in}}{\epsilon_0} = \dfrac{(+5 - 9 + 27 - 84)(1 \times 10^{-6})}{8.85 \times 10^{-12}} = \boxed{-6.89 \times 10^6 \text{ N} \cdot \text{m}^2/\text{C}}$

Since the net electric flux is negative, more lines enter than leave the surface.

***24.16** From Gauss' Law,

$$\Phi_E = E \cdot A = \frac{Q}{\epsilon_0} = \frac{0.0462 \times 10^{-6}}{8.85 \times 10^{-12}} = \boxed{5.22 \times 10^3 \text{ N} \cdot \text{m}^2/\text{C}}$$

24.17 $\phi = \dfrac{q}{\epsilon_0}$

$4.8 \times 10^7 = \dfrac{q}{8.85 \times 10^{-12}}$ where $q = 4.25 \times 10^{-4}\text{C}$

$Q + 2Q + 4Q + 8Q + 16Q = q$

$31Q = q$

$Q = \dfrac{4.248 \times 10^{-4}}{31} = 1.37 \times 10^{-5}\text{C} = \boxed{13.7\ \mu\text{C}}$

$\boxed{\text{NO}}$

24.18 (a) $E = \dfrac{kQ}{r^2}$

$8.9 \times 10^2 = \dfrac{(9 \times 10^9)Q}{(0.75)^2}$

$\boxed{Q = -5.56 \times 10^{-8}\text{ C}}$

(b) Negative charge has spherically symmetric charge distribution.

***24.19**
$$\phi_E = E \cdot A = \frac{kQ}{R^2}\pi r^2$$
$$= \frac{(9 \times 10^9 \text{ N} \cdot \text{m/C}^2)(10^{-5} \text{ C})}{(0.1 \text{ m}^2)}\pi(10^{-3} \text{ m})^2$$
$$\phi_E = \boxed{28.3 \text{ N}\cdot\text{m}^2/\text{C}}$$

24.20 (a) $\phi_c = \frac{q_{in}}{\epsilon_0} = \frac{1.70 \times 10^{-6}}{8.85 \times 10^{-12}} = 1.92 \times 10^7 \text{ N} \cdot \text{m}^2/\text{C}$

$$\phi = \frac{1}{6}\phi_c = \boxed{3.2 \times 10^6 \text{ N} \cdot \text{m}^2/\text{C}}$$

(b) $\phi_c = \boxed{1.92 \times 10^7 \text{ N} \cdot \text{m}^2/\text{C}}$

(c) The answer to (a) would change because the flux through each face of the cube would not be equal with an unsymmetrical charge distribution. The sides of the cube nearer the charge would have more flux and the ones farther away would have less. The answer to (b) would remain the same, since the overall flux would remain the same.

24.21 (a) $\phi_c - \frac{q_{in}}{\epsilon_0}$

$$8.6 \times 10^4 = \frac{q}{8.85 \times 10^{-12}}$$

$$\boxed{q = 7.61 \times 10^{-7} \text{ C}}$$

(b) Since the net flux is positive, the net charge must be positive. It can have any distribution.

(c) The net charge would have the same magnitude but be negative

24.22 (a)

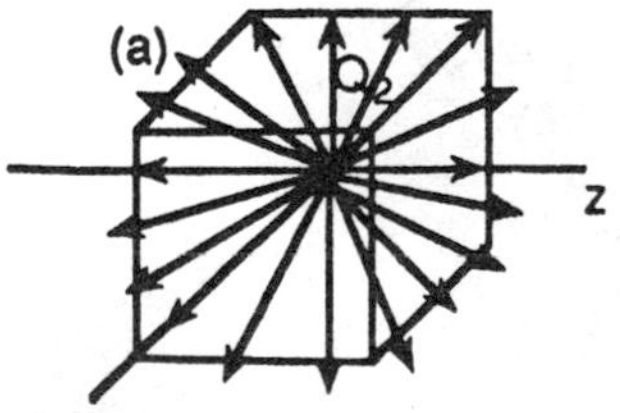

24.22

(b) $\phi_c = \frac{q_{in}}{\epsilon_0} = \boxed{0}$

(c) $\phi_c = \frac{4 \times 10^{-6}}{8.85 \times 10^{-12}} = \boxed{4.52 \times 10^5 \text{ N} \cdot \text{m}^2/\text{C}}$

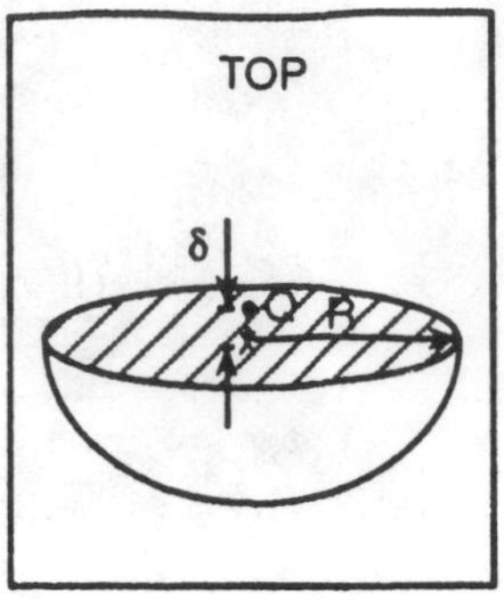

24.23

24.23 (a) $\boxed{\dfrac{+Q}{2\epsilon_0}}$ Simply consider half of a closed sphere.

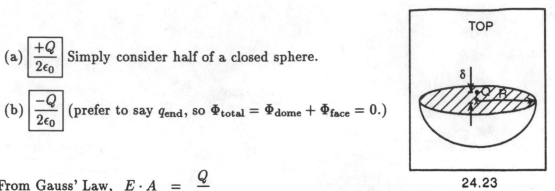

(b) $\boxed{\dfrac{-Q}{2\epsilon_0}}$ (prefer to say q_{end}, so $\Phi_{\text{total}} = \Phi_{\text{dome}} + \Phi_{\text{face}} = 0$.)

***24.24** From Gauss' Law,

$$E \cdot A = \frac{Q}{\epsilon_0}$$

$$\sigma = \frac{Q}{A} = \epsilon_0 E = (8.85 \times 10^{-12})(130)$$

$$= \boxed{1.15 \times 10^{-9}\ \text{C/m}^2}$$

24.25 (a) $\boxed{E = 0}$

(b) $E = \dfrac{kQ}{r^2} = \dfrac{(9 \times 10^9)(32 \times 10^{-6})}{(0.20)^2} = \boxed{7.2 \times 10^6\ \text{N/C}}$

24.26 (a) $E = \boxed{0}$

(b) $E = \dfrac{kQ}{r^2} = \dfrac{(9 \times 10^9)(7 \times 10^{-6})}{(0.125)^2} = \boxed{4.03 \times 10^6\ \text{N/C}}$

(c) $E = \dfrac{kQ}{r^2} = \dfrac{(9 \times 10^9)(7 \times 10^{-6})}{(0.3)^2} = \boxed{7 \times 10^5\ \text{N/C}}$

24.27 (a) $\rho = \dfrac{Q}{\frac{4}{3}\pi a^3} = \dfrac{5.7 \times 10^{-6}}{\frac{4}{3}\pi (0.04)^3} = 2.13 \times 10^{-2}\ \text{C/m}^2$

$$q_{\text{in}} = \rho\left(\frac{4}{3}\pi r^3\right) = (2.13 \times 10^{-2})\left(\frac{4}{3}\pi\right)(0.02)^3$$

$$q_{\text{in}} = 7.14 \times 10^{-7}\ \text{C} = \boxed{0.713\ \mu\text{C}}$$

(b) $q_{\text{in}} = \boxed{5.7\ \mu\text{C}}$

24.28 (a) $\phi = \dfrac{q_{\text{in}}}{\epsilon_0} = \dfrac{\rho(\frac{4}{3}\pi r^3)}{\epsilon_0}$

$$\phi = \frac{(6 \times 10^{-3})(\frac{4}{3}\pi)(5 \times 10^{-3})^3}{8.85 \times 10^{-12}} = \boxed{355 \text{ N} \cdot \text{m}^2/\text{C}}$$

(b) $\phi = \dfrac{q_{\text{in}}}{\epsilon_0} = \rho\dfrac{(\frac{4}{3}\pi a^3)}{\epsilon_0} = \dfrac{(6 \times 10^{-3})(\frac{4}{3}\pi)(10 \times 10^{-3})^3}{8.85 \times 10^{-12}} = \boxed{2.84 \text{ kN} \cdot \text{m}^2/\text{C}}$

(c) $\phi = \boxed{2.84 \text{ kN} \cdot \text{m}^2/\text{C}}$

24.29 (a) $E = \dfrac{kQr}{a^3} = \boxed{0}$

(b) $E = \dfrac{kQr}{a^3} = \dfrac{(9 \times 10^9)(26 \times 10^{-6})(0.10)}{(0.40)^3} = \boxed{3.66 \times 10^5 \text{ N/C}}$

(c) $E = \dfrac{kQ}{r^2} = \dfrac{(9 \times 10^9)(26 \times 10^{-6})}{(0.4)^2} = \boxed{1.46 \times 10^6 \text{ N/C}}$

(d) $E = \dfrac{kQ}{r^2} = \dfrac{(9 \times 10^9)(26 \times 10^{-6})}{(0.6)^2} = \boxed{6.5 \times 10^5 \text{ N/C}}$

The direction for each electric field is radially outward.

24.30 $E = \dfrac{kQr}{a^3}$

$$8.6 \times 10^4 \text{ N/C} = \frac{(9 \times 10^9)Q(0.05)}{(0.1)^3}$$

$$Q = 1.91 \times 10^{-7} \text{ C}$$

$$E = \frac{kQ}{r^2} = \frac{(9 \times 10^9)(1.91 \times 10^{-7})}{(0.15)^2}$$

$$\mathbf{E} = \boxed{(7.64 \times 10^4 \hat{\mathbf{r}}) \text{ N/C}}$$

24.31 $\oint \mathbf{E} \cdot d\mathbf{A} = \frac{Q_{in}}{\epsilon_0} = \frac{1}{\epsilon_0} \int_0^1 \frac{a}{r} 4\pi r^2 dr$

$$E 4\pi r^2 = \frac{4\pi a}{\epsilon_0} \int_0^r r dr = \frac{4\pi a}{\epsilon_0} \frac{r^2}{2}$$

$\boxed{E = \frac{a}{2\epsilon_0}}$ = constant magnitude.

(Direction is radially outward from center for positive a;

radially inward for negative a.)

24.32 (a) $E = \frac{2k\lambda}{r} = \frac{2(9 \times 10^9)(90 \times 10^{-6})}{0.1} = \boxed{1.62 \times 10^7 \text{ N/C}}$

(b) $E = \frac{2k\lambda}{r} = \frac{2(9 \times 10^9)(90 \times 10^{-6})}{0.2} = \boxed{8.1 \times 10^6 \text{ N/C}}$

(c) $E = \frac{2k\lambda}{r} = \frac{2(9 \times 10^9)(90 \times 10^{-6})}{1} = \boxed{1.62 \times 10^6 \text{ N/C}}$

Note the electric field in each case is directed toward the filament.

24.33 (a) $E = \frac{2k\lambda}{r} = \frac{2(9 \times 10^9)(\frac{2\times10^{-6}}{7})}{0.1} = \boxed{5.14 \times 10^4 \text{ N/C}}$

(b) $\phi = EA\cos\theta = (5.14 \times 1064)2\pi(0.1)(0.02) = \boxed{646 \text{ N} \cdot \text{m}^2/\text{C}}$

24.34 (a) $E = \frac{2k\lambda}{r}$

$$3.6 \times 10^4 = \frac{2(9 \times 10^9)(\frac{Q}{2.4})}{(0.19)}$$

$\boxed{Q = +9.12 \times 10^{-7} \text{ C}}$

(b) $\boxed{E = 0}$

24.35 $\oint \mathbf{E} \cdot d\mathbf{A} = \frac{Q_{in}}{\epsilon_0} = \frac{\int \rho dv}{\epsilon_0} = \frac{\rho}{\epsilon_0} \ell \pi r^2$

$$E 2\pi r \ell = \frac{\rho}{\epsilon_0} \ell \pi r^2$$

$$\boxed{\mathbf{E} = \frac{\rho}{2\epsilon_0} r\hat{r}}$$

24.36 (a) $\sigma = (8.6 \times 10^{-6}\ \mathrm{C/cm^2})\left(\frac{100\ \mathrm{cm}}{\mathrm{m}}\right)^2 = 8.6 \times 10^{-2}\ \mathrm{C/m^2}$

$$E = \frac{\sigma}{2\epsilon_0} = \frac{8.6 \times 10^{-2}}{2(8.85 \times 10^{-12})} = \boxed{4.86 \times 10^9\ \mathrm{N/C}}$$

(b) The field is essentially uniform as long as the distance from the center of the wall to the field point is much less than the dimensions of the wall.

24.37 $E = \frac{\sigma}{2\epsilon_0} = \frac{9.0 \times 10^{-6}}{2(8.85 \times 10^{-12})} = \boxed{5.08 \times 10^5\ \mathrm{N/C}}$

24.38 (a) $E = \frac{kQ}{r^2} = \frac{(9 \times 10^9)(6.4 \times 10^{-6})}{(0.15)^2} = \boxed{2.56 \times 10^6\ \mathrm{N/C}}$

Note the electric field points radially inward.

(b) $\boxed{E = 0}$

24.39 $\oint E dA = E(2\pi r \ell) = \frac{q}{\epsilon_0} \qquad E = \frac{q/\ell}{2\pi\epsilon_0 r} = \frac{\lambda}{2\pi\epsilon_0 r}$

(a) $r = 3$ cm $\boxed{E = 0}$ inside the conductor

(b) $r = 10$ cm $\quad \mathrm{E} = \frac{30 \times 10^{-9}}{2\pi(8.85 \times 10^{-12})(0.1)} = \boxed{5400\ \mathrm{N/C}}$

(c) $r = 100$ cm $\quad \mathrm{E} = \frac{30 \times 10^{-9}}{2(8.85 \times 10^{-12})(1)} = \boxed{540\ \mathrm{N/C}}$

24.40 (a) $E = \frac{\sigma}{2\epsilon_0}$ $\sigma = 2(8 \times 10^4)(8.85 \times 10^{-12})$

$\boxed{\sigma = 1.42 \times 10^{-6}\ \text{C/m}^2}$

(b) $\sigma = \frac{Q}{A}$ $Q = \sigma A = (1.42 \times 10^{-6})\left(\frac{1}{4}\right)$ C

$Q = 3.55 \times 10^{-7}\ \text{C} = \boxed{0.355\ \mu\text{C}}$

24.41 (a) $\sigma_T = \frac{1}{2}\frac{q}{A} = \frac{1}{2}\frac{(4 \times 10^{-8}\text{C})}{(0.5\ \text{m})^2} = \boxed{8 \times 10^{-8}\ \text{C/m}^2}$

(b) $E = \frac{\sigma}{\epsilon_0} = \frac{8 \times 10^{-8}\ \text{C/m}^2}{8.85 \times 10^{-12}\ \text{C}^2/\text{N} \cdot \text{m}^2} = \boxed{9.04 \times 10^3\ \text{N/C}}$

(c) $E = \boxed{9.04 \times 10^3\ \text{N/C}}$

24.42 A very large, thin, flat plate of aluminum of area A has a total charge Q uniformly distributes over its surfaces. If the same charge is spread uniformly over the *upper* surface of an otherwise identical glass plate, compare the electric fields just above the center of the upper surface of each plate.

24.43 (a) $E = \frac{kQ}{r^2} = \boxed{0}$ inside since all the charge is on the surface of the sphere.

(b) $E = \frac{kQ}{r^2} = \frac{8.99 \times 10^9 \text{N} \cdot \text{m}^2/\text{C}(40 \times 10^{-9}\text{C})}{(0.17\ \text{m})^2} = \boxed{12.4\ \text{kN/C}}$

(c) $E = \frac{kQ}{r^2} = \frac{8.99 \times 10^9 \text{N} \cdot \text{m}^2/\text{C}(40 \times 10^{-9}\text{C})}{(0.75\ \text{m})^2} = \boxed{639\ \text{N/C}}$

(d) No change.

***24.44** Use Gauss' Law to evaluate the electric field in each region

$\mathbf{E} = 0$ inside the sphere

$\mathbf{E} = \frac{1}{4\pi\epsilon_0}\frac{Q}{r^2}$ between sphere and shell

$\mathbf{E} = 0$ inside shell

$\mathbf{E} = \frac{1}{4\pi\epsilon_0}\frac{2Q}{r^2}$ outside shell

Charge $-Q$ is on the outer surface of the sphere. Charge $+Q$ is on the inner surface of the shell, and $+2Q$ is on the outer surface of the shell.

24.45 (a) $\boxed{E = 0}$

(b) $E = \dfrac{kQ}{r^2} = \dfrac{(9 \times 10^9)(8 \times 10^{-6})}{(0.03)^2} = \boxed{8 \times 10^7 \text{ N/C}}$

(c) $\boxed{E = 0}$

(d) $E = \dfrac{kQ}{r^2} = \dfrac{(9 \times 10^9)(4 \times 10^{-6})}{(0.07)^2} = \boxed{7.35 \times 10^6 \text{ N/C}}$

24.46 (a) $\boxed{q_{\text{in}} = 0}$

(b) $\boxed{q_{\text{in}} = 8.00\ \mu\text{C}}$

(c) $\boxed{q_{\text{in}} = 0}$ since $E = 0$

(d) $\boxed{q_{\text{in}} = 4.00 \mu\text{C}}$

24.47 (a) Inside surface; since E inside the conducting shell is zero, the total charge inside the gaussian surface must be zero.

$0 = \lambda \ell + q_{\text{in}} \Longrightarrow \dfrac{q_{\text{in}}}{\ell} = \boxed{-\lambda}$

so the inside charge/length $= -\lambda$ Outside surface: The total charge will be $2\lambda\ell$ plus the induced charge or $Q = 2\lambda\ell + \lambda\ell = 3\lambda\ell$

so the outside charge/length $= \boxed{3\lambda}$

(b) $E = \dfrac{2k(3\lambda)}{r} = \boxed{\dfrac{6k\lambda}{r}}$

24.48 $E = \dfrac{\sigma}{\epsilon_0}$

(a) $5.6 \times 10^4 = \dfrac{\sigma}{8.85 \times 10^{-12}}$

$\sigma = 4.96 \times 10^{-7} \text{ C/m}^2 = \boxed{0.496\ \mu\text{C/m}^2}$

(b) $2.8 \times 10^4 = \dfrac{\sigma}{8.85 \times 10^{-12}}$

$\sigma = 2.48 \times 10^{-7} \text{ C/m}^2 = \boxed{0.248\ \mu\text{C/m}^2}$

***24.53** (a) at center $E_+ = 0$ so e^- feels no force at r,

$$\frac{+e}{\frac{4}{3}\pi R^3}\frac{\frac{4}{3}\pi r^3}{\epsilon_0} = 4\pi r^2 E \text{ outward}$$

$$E = \frac{er}{4\pi\epsilon_0 R^3} \text{ outward}$$

$$\boxed{F = \frac{-e^2 r}{4\pi\epsilon_0 R^3} \text{ inward}}$$

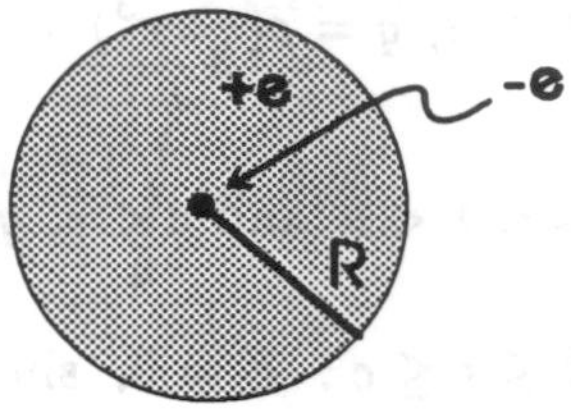

24.53

(b) $F = kr$ inward with $k = \dfrac{r^2}{4\pi\epsilon_0 R^2}$

(c) $F = ma$ $\quad \dfrac{ke^2}{mR^3}r = a$

$$\omega^2 = \frac{ke^2}{mR^3}$$

$$f = \frac{\omega}{2\pi} \qquad \boxed{f = \frac{1}{2\pi}\sqrt{\frac{ke^2}{mR^3}}}$$

$$2.47 \times 10^{15} = \frac{1}{2\pi}\sqrt{\frac{(9 \times 10^9 \text{ N}\cdot\text{m}^2)(1.6 \times 10^{-19} \text{ C})^2}{(9 \times 10^9 \text{ N}\cdot\text{m}^2/\text{C}^2)(9.11 \times 10^{-31} \text{ kg})\text{R}^3}}$$

$$1.0501 \times 10^{-30} = R^3$$

(d) $R = \boxed{1.02 \times 10^{-10} \text{ m}}$

24.54 $dV = 4\pi r^2 dr \quad dq = \rho dV = (Cr)(4\pi r^2 dr) = 4\pi C r^3 dr$

(a) $r < b$

$$Q = \int dq = 4\pi C \int_0^r r^3 dr = \frac{4\pi\, Cr^4}{4} = \boxed{\pi\, Cr^4}$$

(b) $r > b$

$$Q = \int dq = 4\pi\, C \int_0^b r^3 dr = 4\pi\, C\frac{b^4}{4} = \boxed{\pi\, Cb^4}$$

24.55 $\oint \mathbf{E} \cdot d\mathbf{A} = E(4\pi r^2) = \frac{q}{\epsilon_0}$

(a) For $r > R$; $q = \int_0^R Ar^2(4\pi r^2)dr = 4\pi\frac{AR^5}{5}$ and $E = \frac{AR^5}{5\epsilon_0 r^2}$

(b) For $r < R$; $q = \int_0^r Ar^2(4\pi r^2)dr = \frac{4\pi Ar^5}{5}$ and $E = \frac{Ar^3}{5\epsilon_0}$

24.56 In this case the charge density is *not uniform* and Gauss' law is written as: $\oint \mathbf{E} \cdot d\mathbf{A} = \frac{1}{\epsilon_0}\int \rho dV$. We use a gaussian surface which is a cylinder of radius r, length ℓ, and is coaxial with the charge distribution.

(a) When $r < R$ this becomes $E(2\pi r\ell) = \frac{1}{\epsilon_0}\int_0^r (a - \frac{r}{b})dV$ The element of volume is a cylindrical shell of radius r, length ℓ and thickness dr so that $dV = 2\pi r\ell dr$

$$E(2\pi r\ell) = (\frac{2\pi\ell\rho_0 r^2}{\epsilon_0})[\frac{a}{2} - \frac{r}{3b}]$$

Therefore inside the cylinder $E = \boxed{\frac{\rho_0 r}{2\epsilon_0}(a - \frac{2r}{3b})}$

(b) When $r > R$, Gauss' law becomes

$$E(2\pi r\ell) = \frac{\rho_0}{\epsilon_0}\int_0^R (a - \frac{r}{b})(2\pi r\ell dr)$$

$E = \boxed{\frac{\rho_0 R^2}{2\epsilon_0 r}(a - \frac{2R}{3b})}$ outside the cylinder

24.57 (a) $g = \dfrac{GM}{r^2}$ (points inward)

$$\Phi_g = \oint \mathbf{g} \cdot dA = \oint (-\frac{GM}{r^2}\,\hat{r}) \cdot (dA\,\hat{r}) = -GM \oint \frac{dA}{r^2} \cos 0$$

for a spherical surface of radius r, r is constant and

$$\Phi_g = -\frac{GM}{r^2} \oint dA = -\frac{GM}{r^2} \cdot 4\pi r^2 = -4\pi GM.$$

But the mass enclosed by the sphere is $M_{end} = M$, so $\oint \mathbf{g} \cdot d\mathbf{A} = -4\pi G M_{encl}$

$$-4\pi r^2 g = -4\pi G\rho \cdot \frac{4}{3}\pi r^3 : \; g = G \cdot \frac{4}{3}\pi \rho r = G \cdot \frac{4}{3}\pi \frac{M_E r}{\frac{4}{3}\pi R_E^3} = \boxed{\frac{GM_E}{R_E^3} r}$$

24.58 Consider the field due to a single sheet and let E_+ and E_- represent the fields due to the positive and negative sheets. The field at any distance from each sheet has a magnitude given by Eq. 24.10. $|E_+| = |E_-| = \sigma/2\epsilon_0$.

(a) To the left of the positive sheets E_+ is directed toward the left and E_- toward the right and the net field over this region is $\boxed{E = 0}$

(b) In the region between the sheets E_+ and E_- are both directed towards the right and the net field $\boxed{E = \dfrac{\sigma}{\epsilon_0} \text{ toward the right}}$

(c) To the right of the negative sheet E_+ and E_- are again oppositely directed and $\boxed{E = 0}$

For each sheet alone: $|\mathbf{E}_1| = |\mathbf{E}_2| = \dfrac{\sigma}{2\epsilon_0}$

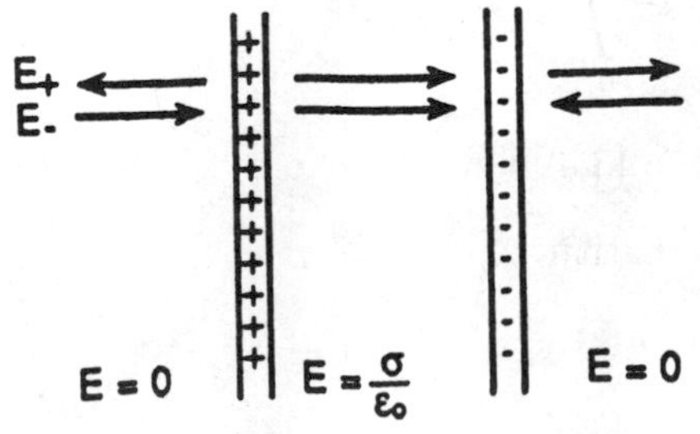

24.58

24.59 The magnitude of the field due to each sheet given by Eq. 24.10 is $E = \sigma/2\epsilon_0$ and directed perpendicular to the sheet.

(a) In region to the left of the pair of sheets both field are directed toward the left and the net field is $E = \boxed{\frac{\sigma}{\epsilon_0} \text{ to the left}}$

(b) In the region between the sheets the fields due to the individual sheets are oppositely directed and the net field $\boxed{E = 0}$

(c) In the region to the right of the pair of sheets both fields are directed toward the right and the net field is $E = \boxed{\frac{\sigma}{\epsilon_0} \text{ to the right}}$

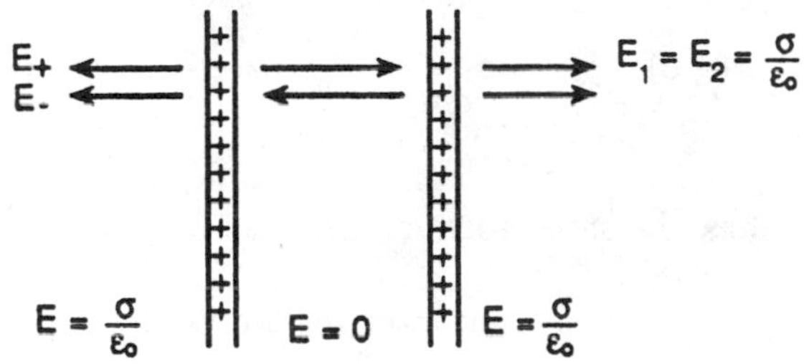

24.59

24.60 The electric field throughout the region is directed along x, therefore **E** will be perpendicular to dA over the four faces of the surface which are parallel to the yz plane; and E will be parallel to dA over the two faces which are perpendicular to the yz plane. Therefore

$$\phi = \int_a^{a+c} E_x dA_x = E_x A \,|_a^{a+c} = (3 + 2x^2)ab \,|_a^{a+c}$$

$$\phi = [3 + 2(a+c)^2]ab - [3 + 2a^2]ab = 2abc(2a + c)$$

Substituting the given values for a, b, and c

we find $\phi = \boxed{0.269 \text{ N} \cdot \text{m}^2/\text{C}}$

$Q = \epsilon_0 \phi = \boxed{2.38 \times 10^{-12} \text{ C}}$

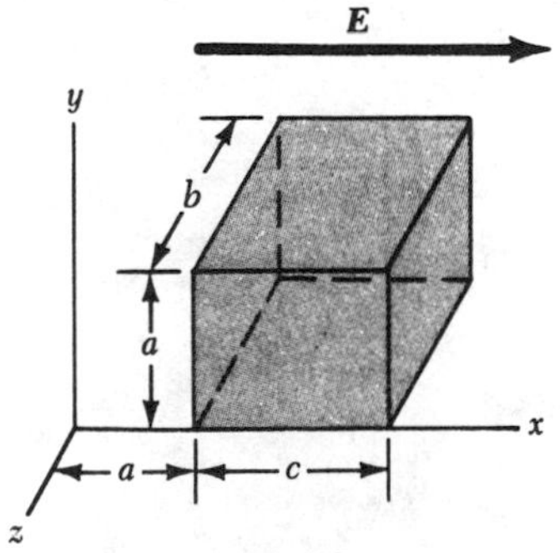

24.60

24.61 (a) Refer to Figure 24.31 of the text. Consider a cylindrical shaped gaussian surface perpendicular to the y-axis with one end cap in the yz plane and the other end cap containing the point x.

Use Gauss' law: $\int \mathbf{E} \cdot d\mathbf{A} = \frac{q}{\epsilon_0}$.

By symmetry the electric field is zero along the $y-$axis and $\mathbf{E}$ is perpendicular to $d\mathbf{A}$ over the wall of the gaussian cylinder. Therefore the only contribution to the integral is over the end cap containing the point x :

$\int \mathbf{E} \cdot d\mathbf{A} = \frac{q}{\epsilon_0}$ or $EA = \frac{Ax\rho}{\epsilon_0}$ so

that at a distance x from the mid line of the slab, $E = \frac{\rho x}{\epsilon_0}$

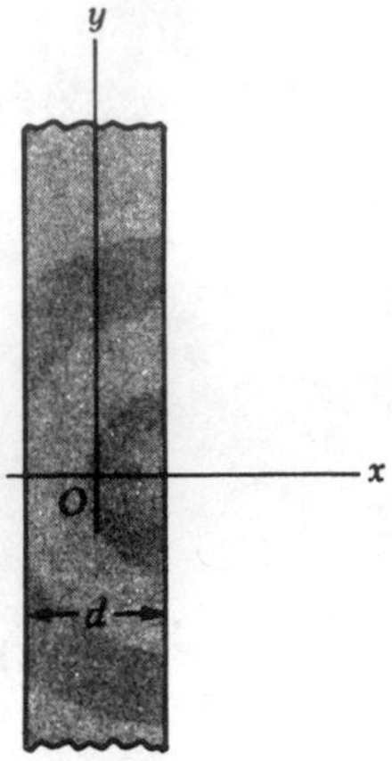

24.61

(b) $a = \frac{F}{m} = \frac{Eq}{m} = \frac{\rho x(-e)}{\epsilon_0 m} = (-\frac{\rho e}{m\epsilon_0})x$

Notice that this has the same form as Eq. 13.12 $a = -(\frac{k}{m})x$ which is the condition which characterizes simple harmonic motion. Also from Eq. 13.17; $f = \frac{1}{2\pi}\sqrt{\frac{k}{m}}$

In this case $k = \frac{\rho e}{\epsilon_0}$. Therefore the electron will

oscillate with a frequency $f = \frac{1}{2\pi}(\frac{\rho e}{m\epsilon_0})$

24.62 (a) For $x > \frac{d}{2}$ $\quad dq = \rho dV = \rho A\, dx = C\, Ax^2\, dx$

$$\int \mathbf{E} \cdot d\mathbf{A} = \frac{1}{\epsilon_0} \int dq$$

$$2EA = \frac{CA}{\epsilon_0} \int_{-d/2}^{d/2} x^2 dx$$

$$2EA = \frac{1}{3}\left(\frac{CA}{\epsilon_0}\right)\left(\frac{d^3}{8} + \frac{d^3}{8}\right)$$

$$E = \frac{Cd^3}{24\epsilon_0}$$

$$\boxed{\mathbf{E} = \frac{Cd^3}{24\epsilon_0}\mathbf{i} \quad \text{for } x > \frac{d}{2}; \quad \mathbf{E} = -\frac{Cd^3}{24\epsilon_0}\mathbf{i} \quad \text{for } x < -\frac{d}{2}}$$

(b) For $-\frac{d}{2} < x < \frac{d}{2}$

$$\int \mathbf{E} \cdot d\mathbf{A} = \frac{1}{\epsilon_0} \int dq = \frac{CA}{\epsilon_0} \int_0^x x^2 dx = \frac{CAx^3}{3\epsilon_0}$$

$$\boxed{\mathbf{E} = \frac{Cx^3}{3\epsilon_0}\mathbf{i} \quad \text{for } x > 0; \quad \mathbf{E} = -\frac{Cx^3}{3\epsilon_0}\mathbf{i} \quad \text{for } x < 0}$$

***24.63** $\frac{4}{3}\frac{\pi r^3 \rho}{\epsilon_0} = 4\pi r^2 E_+$

$$\mathbf{E}_+ = \frac{\rho r}{3\epsilon_0}\mathbf{r} = \frac{\rho \mathbf{r}}{3\epsilon_0}$$

$$\frac{4}{3}\frac{\pi r_1^3 \rho}{\epsilon_0} = 4\pi r_1^2 E_-$$

$$\mathbf{E}_- = \frac{\rho r_1}{3\epsilon_0}(-\mathbf{r}_1) = \frac{-\rho}{3\epsilon_0}\mathbf{r}_1$$

$$\mathbf{r} = \mathbf{a} + \mathbf{r}_1 \qquad \mathbf{E}_- = \frac{-\rho(\mathbf{r} - \mathbf{a})}{3\epsilon_0}$$

$$\mathbf{E} = \mathbf{E}_+ + \mathbf{E}_- = \frac{\rho \mathbf{r}}{3\epsilon_0} - \frac{\rho \mathbf{r}}{3\epsilon_0} + \frac{\rho \mathbf{a}}{3\epsilon_0}$$

$$\mathbf{E} = \frac{\rho a}{3\epsilon_0}\mathbf{j}$$

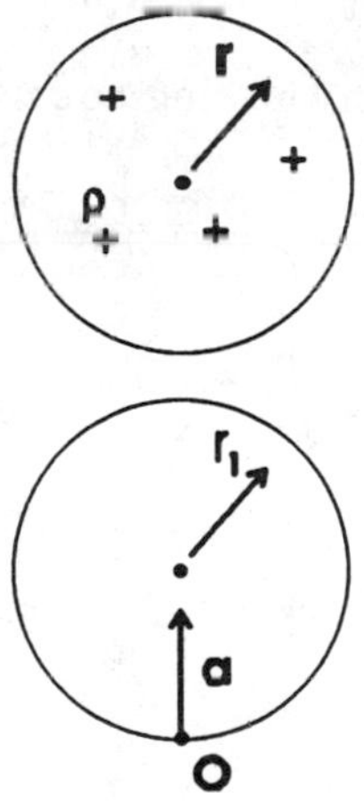

24.63

***24.64** The total flux through a surface enclosing the charge Q is Q/ϵ_0. The flux through the ring is

$$\Phi_{\text{ring}} = \int \mathbf{E} \cdot d\mathbf{A}$$

where the integation covers the area of the ring. We must evaluate this integral and set it equal to $\frac{1}{4}Q/\epsilon_0$ to find how b and R are related.
In Figure 24.64, take $d\mathbf{A}$ to be the area of an annular ring of radius s and widths ds. The flux through $d\mathbf{A}$ is

$$\mathbf{E} \cdot d\mathbf{A} = E\, dA \cos\theta = E(2\pi s ds) \cos\theta$$

The magnitude of the electric field has the same value at all points within the annual ring,

$$E = \frac{1}{4\pi\epsilon_0}\frac{Q}{r^2} = \frac{1}{4\pi\epsilon_0}\frac{Q}{s^2 + b^2}$$

and

$$\cos\theta = \frac{b}{r} = \frac{b}{(s^2 + b^2)^{1/2}}$$

Integrate from $s = 0$ to $s = R$ to get the flux through the entire ring

$$\begin{aligned} \Phi_{\text{ring}} &= \frac{Qb}{2\epsilon_0}\int_0^R \frac{s\, ds}{(s^2 + b^2)^{3/2}} \\ &= \frac{Qb}{2\epsilon_0}\left[-(s^2 + b^2)^{1/2}\right]\Big|_0^R \\ &= \frac{Q}{2\epsilon_0}\left[1 - \frac{b}{(R^2 + b^2)^{1/2}}\right] \end{aligned}$$

The flux through the ring equals $Q/4\epsilon_0$ provided

$$\frac{b}{(R^2 + b^2)^{1/2}} = \frac{1}{2}$$

This is satisfied if $R = \sqrt{3}\, b$.

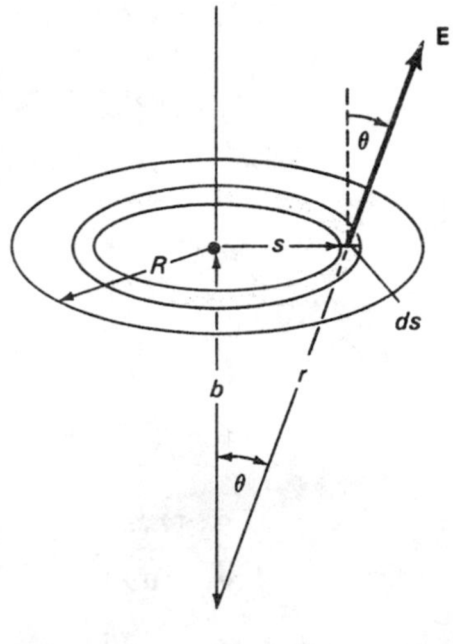

24.64

CHAPTER 25

25.1 Since the arc is along an equipotential surface

$W = -\Delta U = -(V_B - V_A)q_0 = (0)q_0 = 0$

25.2 $\Delta U = q\Delta V$

$$\Delta U = (12 \times 10^{-6})(65) = (7.8 \times 10^{-4}\ \text{J})\left(\frac{1\ \text{eV}}{1.602 \times 10^{-19}\ \text{J}}\right) = \boxed{4.88 \times 10^{15}\ \text{eV}}$$

25.3 (a) $\frac{1}{2}mv^2 = qV$

$$\frac{1}{2}(1.67 \times 10^{-27})v^2 = (1.602 \times 10^{-19})(120)$$

$$\boxed{v = 1.52 \times 10^5\ \text{m/s}}$$

(b) $\frac{1}{2}mv^2 = qV$

$$\frac{1}{2}(9.11 \times 10^{-31})v^2 = (1.602 \times 10^{-19})(120)$$

$$\boxed{v = 6.49 \times 10^6\ \text{m/s}}$$

25.4 $v = 0.4(3 \times 10^8\ \text{m/s}) = 1.2 \times 10^8\ \text{m/s}$

$$\frac{1}{2}mv^2 = q\Delta V$$

$$\frac{1}{2}(9.11 \times 10^{-31})(1.2 \times 10^8)^2 = (1.602 \times 10^{-19})\Delta V$$

$$\boxed{\Delta V = 4.09 \times 10^4\ \text{V}}$$

25.5 (a) $U = qV$

$$U = (1.602 \times 10^{-19})(2.7 \times 10^3) = \boxed{4.33 \times 10^{-16}\ \text{J}}$$

(b) $U = \frac{1}{2}mv^2$

$$4.33 \times 10^{-16} = \frac{1}{2}(2)(1.67 \times 10^{-27})v^2$$

$$\boxed{v = 5.09 \times 10^5\ \text{m/s}}$$

25.6 $\Delta K = 0 - \frac{1}{2}mv_0^2 = qV$

$-\frac{1}{2}(9.11 \times 10^{-31})(4.2 \times 10^5)^2 = 1.602 \times 10^{-19}$ V

$\boxed{V = -0.502 \text{ V}}$

25.7 $\Delta U = q\Delta V$

$7.37 \times 10^{-17} = q(115)$

$\boxed{q = 6.41 \times 10^{-19} \text{ C}}$

***25.8** (a) $K = (14 \text{ MeV})(1.6 \times 10^{-13} \text{ J/MeV}) = \boxed{2.24 \times 10^{-12} \text{ J}}$

(b) $K = \boxed{14 \text{ MeV}}$

(c) $\frac{1}{2}mv^2 = 2.24 \times 10^{-12}$ J

$$v = \sqrt{\frac{2(2.24 \times 10^{-12} \text{ J})}{1.67 \times 10^{-27} \text{ kg}}} = \boxed{5.18 \times 10^7 \text{ m/s}}$$

25.9 $v = 0.3(3 \times 10^8 \text{ m/s}) = 9 \times 10^7$ m/s

$\Delta U = \frac{1}{2}mv^2 = \frac{1}{2}(9.11 \times 10^{-31})(9 \times 10^7)^2 = 3.69 \times 10^{-15}$ J

$3.69 \times 10^{-15} = \frac{1}{2}(1.67 \times 10^{-27})v^2$

$\boxed{v = 2.10 \times 10^6 \text{ m/s}}$

25.10 $\Delta U = q\Delta V = (-4.7 \times 10^{-6})(-180) = \boxed{8.46 \times 10^{-4} \text{ J}}$

25.11 $\Delta U = q\Delta V = (1.602 \times 10^{-19})(6.022 \times 10^{23})(14) = \boxed{1.35 \times 10^6 \text{ J}}$

25.12 $V = Ed$

$20 = E(0.3 \times 10^{-3})$

$\boxed{E = 6.67 \times 10^4 \text{ V/m}}$

25.13 $\Delta V = Ed = (2.4 \times 10^4)(0.018) = \boxed{4.32 \times 10^3 \text{ V}}$

$\Delta U = q\Delta V = (1.602 \times 10^{-19}\text{C})(4.32 \times 10^2 \text{ V}) = \boxed{6.92 \times 10^{-17} \text{ J}}$

25.14 (a) $V = Ed = (5.9 \times 10^3 \text{ V/m})(0.01 \text{ m}) = \boxed{59.0 \text{ V}}$

(b) $\frac{1}{2} mv^2 = qV$

$\frac{1}{2}(9.11 \times 10^{-31})v^2 = 1.602 \times 10^{-19}(59)$

$\boxed{v = 4.56 \times 10^6 \text{ m/s}}$

25.15 $\Delta U = \frac{1}{2}\text{ m}(v_f^2 - v_0^2) = \frac{1}{2}(9.11 \times 10^{-31})([1.4 \times 10^5]^2 - [3.7 \times 10^6]^2) = 6.23 \times 10^{-18} \text{ J}$

$\Delta U = q\Delta V \qquad 6.23 \times 10^{-18} = 1.602 \times 10^{-19}\, \Delta V$

$\boxed{\Delta V = +38.9 \text{ V}}$

25.16 (a) $\Delta U = -qEd = -(1.602 \times 10^{-19})(480)(0.052) = \boxed{-4.00 \times 10^{-18} \text{ J}}$

Note that it *loses* electric potential energy.

(b) It *gains* a kinetic energy of $\boxed{4.00 \times 10^{-18} \text{ J}}$

25.17 $\Delta U = qEd$

$5 \times 10^{-18} = (1.602 \times 10^{-19})E(0.02)$

$\boxed{E = 1.56 \times 10^3 \text{ N/C}}$

25.18 $V_B - V_A = -\int_A^B \mathbf{E} \cdot d\mathbf{s} = -\int_A^C \mathbf{E} \cdot d\mathbf{s} - \int_C^B \mathbf{E} \cdot d\mathbf{s}$

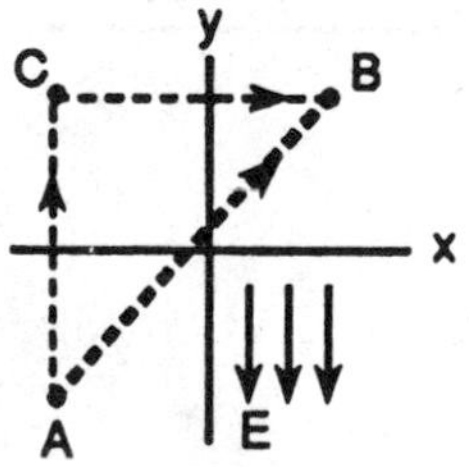

25.18 and 25.19

$V_E - V_A = (-E \cos 180°) \int_{-0.3}^{0.5} dy - (E \cos 90°) \int_{-0.2}^{0.4} dx$

$V_E - V_A = (325)(0.8) = \boxed{260 \text{ V}}$

25.19 $\Delta V = Ed = (325\text{ V/m})(0.8\text{ m}) = \boxed{260\text{ V}}$

B is at the higher potential.

25.20 (a) $V = -E_x \Delta x$

$$V = -(250\text{ V/m})(0.20\text{ m}) = \boxed{-50.0\text{ V}}$$

(b) $\Delta U = qV = (12 \times 10^{-6})(-50) = \boxed{-6.00 \times 10^{-4}\text{ J}}$

25.21 $V = \dfrac{kQ}{r}$

$$3.6 \times 10^4 = \frac{(9 \times 10^9)(8 \times 10^{-6})}{r}$$

$$\boxed{r = 2.00\text{ m}}$$

25.22 $V = \dfrac{kQ}{r}$

$$r = \frac{kQ}{V} = \frac{9 \times 10^9\text{ N}\cdot\text{m}^2/\text{C}^2(8 \times 10^{-9}\text{C})}{\text{V}} = \frac{72}{V}$$

For $V = 100$ V, 50 V, 25 V, $\boxed{r = 0.720\text{ m}, 1.44\text{ m and } 2.88\text{ m}}$

The spacing is inversely proportional to the change in V.

25.23 $V = Er$

$$400 = (150)r$$

$$\boxed{r = 2.67\text{ m}}$$

$$\boxed{q = 1.19 \times 10^{-7}\text{ C}}$$

***25.24** (a) Since the charges are equal and placed symmetrically, $\boxed{F = 0}$

(b) Since $F = qE = 0$, $\boxed{E = 0}$

(c) $V = 2k\frac{q}{r} = 2\left(9 \times 10^9 \frac{\text{N}\cdot\text{m}^2}{\text{C}^2}\right)\left(\frac{2 \times 10^{-6}\text{ C}}{0.8\text{ m}}\right)$

$V = 4.5 \times 10^4\text{ V} = \boxed{45\text{ kV}}$

25.25 $V = \frac{kq}{r}$

$$V = 9 \times 10^9\left(\frac{+2.8 \times 10^{-6}}{1.65} + \frac{-4.6 \times 10^{-6}}{0.4}\right)$$

$$\boxed{V = -8.82 \times 10^4\text{ V}}$$

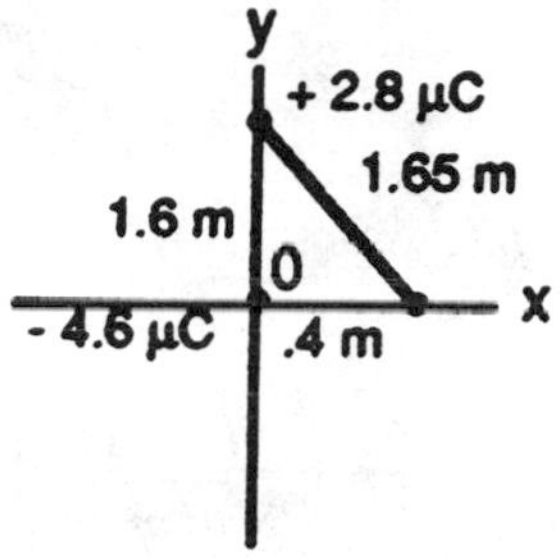

25.25

***25.26** (a)

$$E_x = \frac{kq_1}{x^2} + \frac{kq_2}{(x+2)^2} = 0$$

$$E_x = k\left(\frac{+q}{x^2} - \frac{2q}{(x+2)^2}\right) = 0$$

$$2qx^2 = q(x+2)^2$$

$$x^2 - 4x - 4 = 0$$

$$E = 0 \text{ when } x = \frac{-4 \pm \sqrt{16+16}}{2} = \boxed{-4.83\text{ m}}$$

(b)

$$U = \frac{kq_1}{x} + \frac{kq_2}{(2-x)} = 0$$

$$U = k\left(\frac{+q}{x} - \frac{2q}{2-x}\right) = 0$$

$$2qx = q(2-x) \quad \text{For } 0 \le x \le 2$$

$$U = 0 \text{ when } x = \boxed{0.667\text{ m}}$$

$$\text{and } \frac{q}{|x|} = \frac{-2q}{|2-x|}$$

$$x = \boxed{-2\text{ m}} \quad \text{for } x < 0$$

25.27 $V = \sum_i k\frac{q_i}{r_i}$

$$V = (9 \times 10^9)(7 \times 10^{-6})\left[\frac{-1}{0.01} - \frac{1}{0.01} + \frac{1}{0.0387}\right]$$

$$\boxed{V = 1.10 \times 10^7 \text{ V}}$$

[6ex]

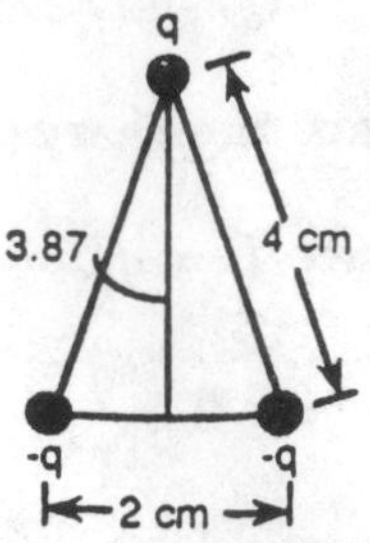

25.27

25.28 $V = \sum_i k\frac{q_i}{r_i}$

$$V = k\left(\frac{q_1 - q_2}{a} + \frac{q_1 - q_2}{\sqrt{a^2 + b^2}}\right)$$

$$V = (9 \times 10^9)\left(\frac{5\mu\text{C} - 10\mu\text{C}}{0.04} + \frac{5\mu C - 10\mu\text{C}}{0.64}\right)$$

$$V = (9 \times 10^9)(-5 \times 10^{-6})(\frac{1}{0.4} + \frac{1}{0.64}) = \boxed{-1.83 \times 10^5 \text{ V}}$$

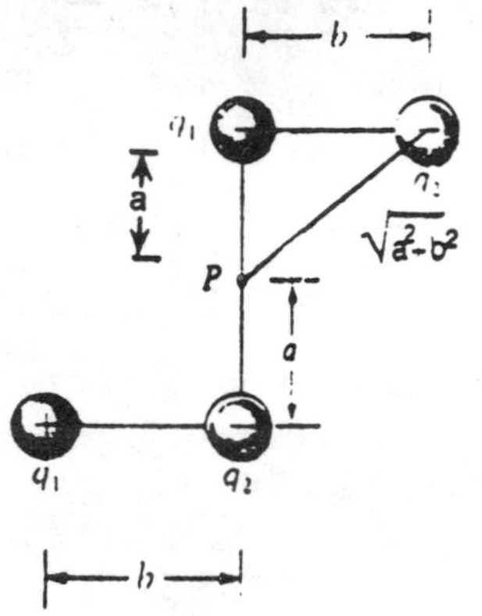

25.28

25.29 (a) $U = \frac{qQ}{4\pi\epsilon_0 r} = \frac{(5 \times 10^{-9}\text{C})(-3 \times 10^{-9}\text{C})(8.99 \times 10^9 \ \frac{\text{V·m}}{\text{C}})}{(0.35 \text{ m})} = \boxed{-3.86 \times 10^{-7} \text{ J}}$

The minus sign means it takes 3.86×10^{-7} J to separate the two charges.

[4ex]

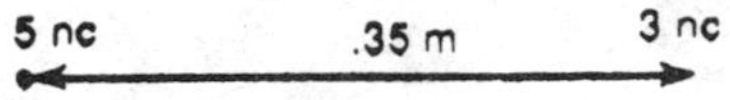

25.29

(b) $$V = \frac{Q_1}{4\pi\epsilon_0 r_1} + \frac{Q_2}{4\pi\epsilon_0 r_2}$$
$$= \frac{(5 \text{ nC})(8.99 \times 10^9 \ \frac{\text{V·m}}{\text{C}})}{0.175 \text{ m}} + \frac{(-3 \text{ nC})(8.99 \times 10^9 \ \frac{\text{V·m}}{\text{C}})}{0.175 \text{ m}} = \boxed{103 \text{ V}}$$

25.30 $U = \frac{kq_1q_2}{r} = \frac{(9 \times 10^9)(-9 \times 10^{-6})(-1 \times 10^{-6})}{(0.7)} = \boxed{0.116 \text{ J}}$

25.31 (a) $U = \frac{kq_1q_2}{r} = \frac{-(9\times10^9)(1.602\times10^{-19})^2}{0.0529\times10^{-9}} = -4.37\times10^{-18}\text{ J} = \boxed{-27.3\text{ eV}}$

(b) $U = \frac{kq_1q_2}{r} = \frac{-(9\times10^9)(1.602\times10^{-19})^2}{2^2(0.0529\times10^{-9})} = \boxed{-6.81\text{ eV}}$

(c) $U = \frac{kq_1q_2}{r} = \frac{-ke^2}{\infty} = \boxed{0}$

25.32 $U = \sum \frac{kq_iq_j}{r_{ij}}$

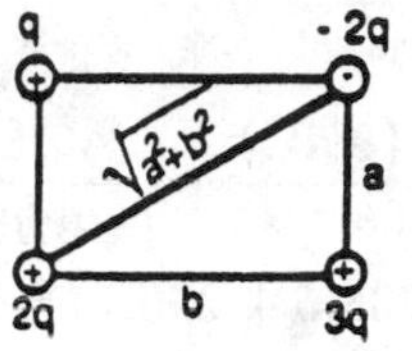

25.32

$$U = k\left[\frac{q(-2q)}{b} + \frac{(-2q)(3q)}{a} + \frac{(2q)(3q)}{b} + \frac{q(2q)}{a} + \frac{q(3q)}{\sqrt{a^2+b^2}} + \frac{2q(-2q)}{\sqrt{a^2+b^2}}\right]$$

$$U = kq^2\left[\frac{-2}{0.4} - \frac{6}{0.2} + \frac{6}{0.4} + \frac{2}{0.2} + \frac{3}{0.447} - \frac{4}{0.447}\right]$$

$$U = (9\times10^9)(6\times10^{-6})^2\left[\frac{4}{0.4} - \frac{4}{0.2} - \frac{1}{0.447}\right] = \boxed{-3.96\text{ J}}$$

25.33
$$\begin{aligned} U &= U_1 + U_2 + U_3 + U_4 \\ &= 0 + U_{12} + (U_{13} + U_{23}) + (U_{14} + U_{24} + U_{34}) \\ &= 0 + \frac{kq^2}{s} + \frac{kq^2}{s}(\frac{1}{\sqrt{2}} + 1) + \frac{kq^2}{s}(1 + \frac{1}{\sqrt{2}} + 1) \\ &= \frac{kq^2}{s}[4 + \frac{2}{\sqrt{2}}] = \boxed{5.41\ \frac{kq^2}{s}} \end{aligned}$$

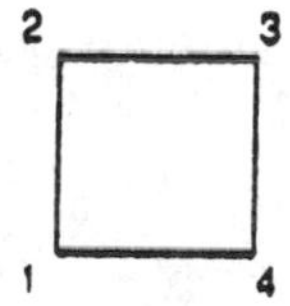

25.33

An alternate solution is to recognize that there are 4 side pairs and 2 face diagonal pairs to get the $4 + \frac{2}{\sqrt{2}}$.

25.34 $U = \frac{kq_1q_2}{r} = (9\times10^9)(5\times10^{-6})^2(\frac{2}{0.4} + \frac{2}{0.3} + \frac{2}{0.5})$

$U = \boxed{3.53\text{ J}}$

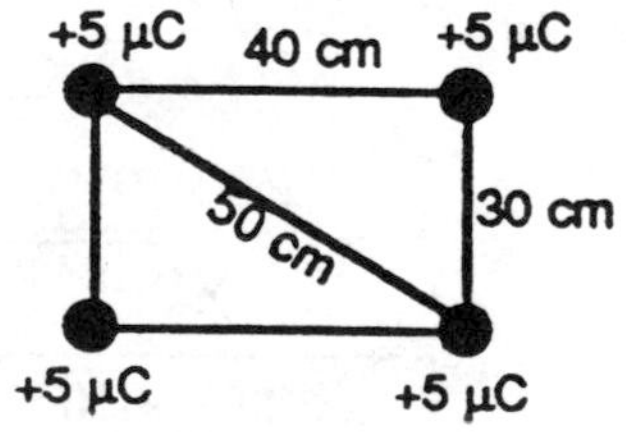

25.34

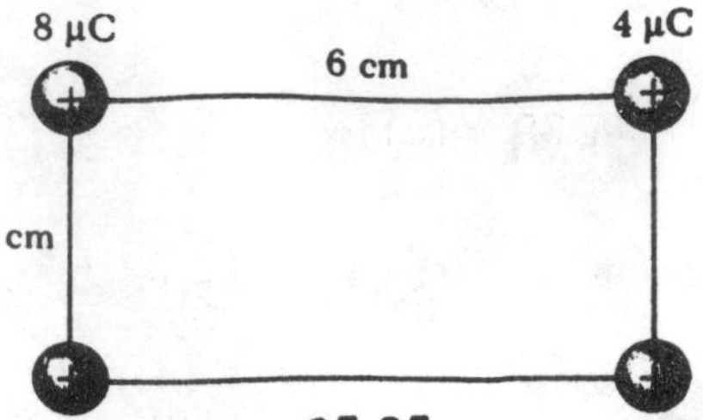

25.35

25.35 Find ΔU by taking the first 4 μC to charge to infinty.

$$\Delta U_1 = \frac{kq_2q_1}{r_{21}} + \frac{kq_2q_3}{r_{23}} + \frac{kq_2q_4}{r_{24}} - 0$$
$$= (8.99 \times 10^9)\left[\frac{(4\,\mu C)(8\,\mu C)}{0.06} + \frac{(4\,\mu C)(4\,\mu C)}{(\sqrt{0.45}) \times 10^{-2}} + \frac{(4\,\mu C)(2\,\mu C)}{0.03}\right]$$
$$= (8.99 \times 10^9)(533 + 238.5 + 266.7) \times 10^{-12} = 9.333 \text{ J}$$

Now take the second charge to infinity.

$$\Delta V_2 = \frac{kq_3q_1}{r_{31}} + \frac{q_3q_4}{r_{34}} = (8.99 \times 10^9)\left[\frac{(4\,\mu C)(8\,\mu C)}{0.03} + \frac{(4\,\mu C)(2\,\mu C)}{0.06}\right]$$
$$= (8.99 \times 10^9)(1066.7 + 133.3)(10^{-12}) = 10.788 \text{ J}$$

$$\Delta U = \Delta U_1 + \Delta U_2 = \boxed{20.1 \text{ J}}$$

25.36 A cube has 12 sides and 6 faces. Consequently, there are 12 side pairs separated by 5, $2 \times 6 = 12$ face diagonal pairs separated by $\sqrt{2}s$, and 4 interior diagonal pairs separated by $\sqrt{3}s$.

$$U = \frac{kq^2}{s}[12 + \frac{12}{\sqrt{2}} + \frac{4}{\sqrt{3}}] = \boxed{22.8\,\frac{kq^2}{s}}$$

25.37 $\Delta V = V_{2R} - V_0 = \dfrac{kQ}{\sqrt{R^2 + (2R)^2}} - \dfrac{kQ}{R} = \dfrac{kQ}{R}[\dfrac{1}{\sqrt{5}} - 1] = -0.533\dfrac{kQ}{R}$

25.38 (a) $V = \dfrac{kQ}{\sqrt{x^2 + a^2}}$

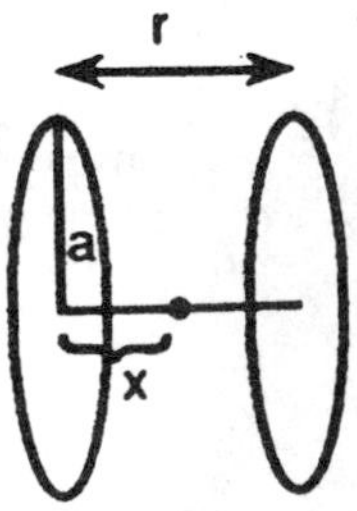

25.38

$$V = \frac{2(9 \times 10^9)(5 \times 10^{-6})}{\sqrt{0.15^2 + 0.30^2}}$$

$$\boxed{V = 2.68 \times 10^5 \text{ V}}$$

(b) $\boxed{V = 0}$

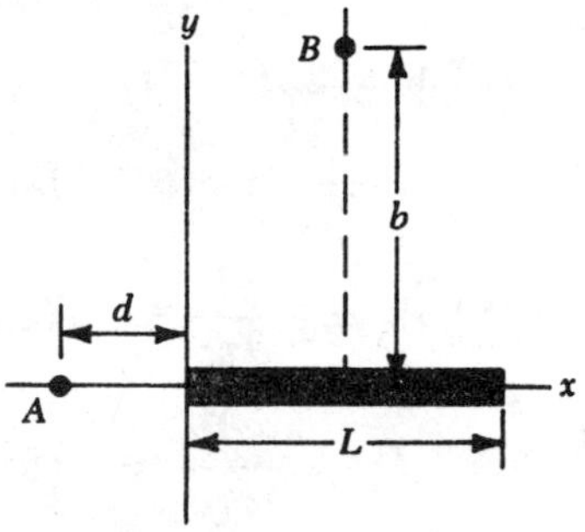

25.39 and 25.40

25.39 (a) $[\alpha] = [\frac{\lambda}{x}] = \frac{\mathrm{C}}{\mathrm{m}} \cdot (\frac{1}{\mathrm{m}}) = \frac{\mathrm{C}}{\mathrm{m}^2}$

(b) $V = k\int \frac{dq}{r} = k\int \frac{\lambda dx}{r}$

$$= k\alpha \int_0^L \frac{x dx}{(d+x)} = \boxed{k\alpha[L - d\,\ell n(1 + \frac{L}{d})]}$$

25.40 $V = \int \frac{kdq}{r} = k\int \frac{\alpha x dx}{\sqrt{b^2 + (\frac{L}{2} - x)^2}}$

Let $z = \frac{L}{2} - x$

Then $x = \frac{L}{2} - z$

$dx = -dz$

$$V = k\alpha \int \frac{(\frac{L}{2} - z)(-dz)}{\sqrt{b^2 + z^2}} = -kd\frac{L}{2}\int \frac{dz}{\sqrt{b^2+z^2}} + k\alpha \int \frac{zdz}{\sqrt{b^2+z^2}}$$

$$= -\frac{k\alpha L}{2}\,\ell n(z + \sqrt{z^2 + b^2}) + k\alpha\sqrt{z^2 + b^2}$$

$$= -\frac{k\alpha L}{2}\ell n\left[(\frac{L}{2} - x) + \sqrt{(\frac{L}{2} - x)^2 + b^2}\right]\Bigg|_0^L + k\alpha\sqrt{(\frac{L}{2} - x)^2 + b^2}\Bigg|_0^L$$

$$= -\frac{k\alpha L}{2}\ell n\left[\frac{\frac{L}{2} - L + \sqrt{(\frac{L}{2})^2 + b^2}}{\frac{L}{2} + \sqrt{(\frac{L}{2}) + b^2}}\right] + k\alpha\left[\sqrt{(\frac{L}{2} - L)^2 + b^2} - \sqrt{(\frac{L}{2})^2 + b^2}\right]$$

$$= \boxed{-\frac{k\alpha L}{2}\ell n\left[\frac{\sqrt{\frac{L^2}{4} + b^2} - \frac{L}{2}}{\sqrt{\frac{L^2}{4} + b^2} + \frac{L}{2}}\right]}$$

25.41 $dV = \frac{kdq}{\sqrt{r^2 + x^2}}$ where $dq = \sigma dA = \sigma 2\pi r dr$

$$V = 2\pi\sigma k\int_a^b \frac{rdr}{\sqrt{r^2 + x^2}} = \boxed{2\pi k\sigma[\sqrt{x^2 + b^2} - \sqrt{x^2 + a^2}]}$$

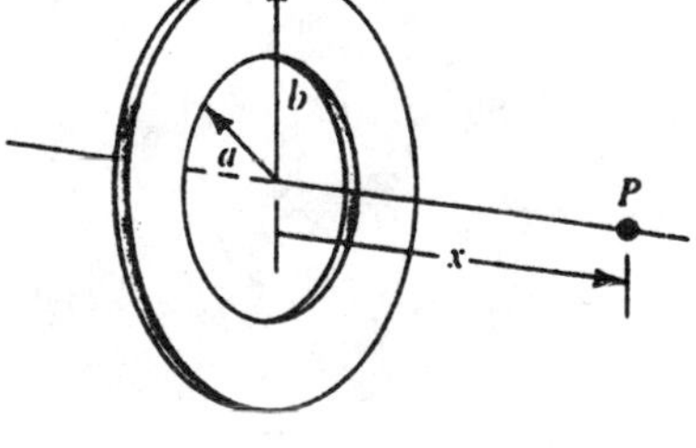

25.41

25.42 (a) $V = 3x^2y - 4xz - 5y^2$

$$V = 3(1)^2(0) - 4(1)2 - 5(0)^2 = \boxed{-8.00\ \text{V}}$$

(b) $$E_x = \frac{-\partial V}{\partial x} = -(6xy - 4z) = -(6(1)(0) - 4(2)) = \boxed{+8.00\ \text{V/m}}$$

$$E_y = \frac{-\partial V}{\partial y} = -(3x^2 - 10y) = -(3(1)^2 - 10(0)) = \boxed{-3.00\ \text{V/m}}$$

$$E_z = -\frac{\partial V}{\partial z} = -(-4x) = +4(1) = \boxed{+\ 4.00\ \text{V/m}}$$

25.43 $V = 5x - 3x^2y + 2yz^2$ Evaluate E at $(1, 0 - 2)$

$$E_x = -\frac{\partial V}{\partial x} = -5 + 6xy = -5 + 6(1)(0) = -5$$

$$E_y = -\frac{\partial V}{\partial y} = +3x^2 - 2z^2 = 3(1)^2 - 2(-2)^2 = -5$$

$$E_z = -\frac{\partial V}{\partial z} = -4yz = -4(0)(-2) = 0$$

$$E = \sqrt{E_x^2 + E_y^2 + E_z^2} = \sqrt{-5^2 + (-5)^2 + 0^2} = \boxed{7.08\ \text{N/C}}$$

25.44 $V = 4xz - 5y + 3z^2$

$$E_x = -\frac{\partial V}{\partial x} = -4z = -4(3) = -12\ \text{V/m}$$

$$E_y = -\frac{\partial V}{\partial y} = -(-5) = +5\ \text{V/m}$$

$$E_z = -\frac{\partial V}{\partial z} = -(4x + 6z) = -(4(2) + 6(3)) = -26\ \text{V/m}$$

$$E = \sqrt{E_x^2 + E_y^2 + E_z^2} = \sqrt{(-12)^2 + 5^2 + (-26)^2} = \boxed{29.1\ \text{V/m}}$$

***25.45** $V = 10 - 7x$

(a) $x(m) \;=\; 0 \quad 3 \quad 6$

$V \;=\; \underline{10\text{ V}} \quad \underline{-11\text{ V}} \quad \underline{-32\text{ V}}$

(b) $E = -\dfrac{dV}{dx} = \underline{7\text{ N/C}}\ \textit{along}\ +x.$

***25.46** $V = 12x^2 - 10x + 62$

(a) $E = -\dfrac{dV}{dx} = 24x - 10$

at $x = 2$ m, $\text{E} = \boxed{38\text{ V/m}}$

(b) $E = 0$ when $24x = 10$

$x = \boxed{0.417\text{ m}}$

25.47 (a) For $r < R$ $\quad V = \dfrac{kQ}{R}$

$E_r = -\dfrac{dV}{dr} = \boxed{0}$

(b) For $r \geq R$ $\quad V = \dfrac{kQ}{r}$

$E_r = -\dfrac{dV}{dr} = -(-\dfrac{kQ}{r^2}) = \boxed{\dfrac{kQ}{r^2}}$

25.48 $V = \dfrac{kQ}{2R}(3 - \dfrac{r^2}{R^2})$ for $r < R$; $\quad V = \dfrac{kQ}{r}$ for $r > R$

(a) $E_r = -\dfrac{dV}{dr} = -\dfrac{kQ}{2R^3}(-2r) = \boxed{\dfrac{kQr}{R^3}\text{ radially outward for } r < R}$

(b) $E_r = -\dfrac{dV}{dr} = -kQ(-\dfrac{1}{r^2}) = \boxed{\dfrac{kQ}{r^2}\text{ radially outward for } r > R}$

25.49 (a) $V = \dfrac{kq2d}{x^2[1 - (\frac{d}{x})^2]} = \dfrac{9 \times 10^9(3 \times 10^{-6})2(2 \times 10^{-3})}{(6 \times 10^{-3})^2[1 - 1/9]} = \boxed{3.38\text{ MV}}$

(b) $V \cong \dfrac{kq2d}{x^2} = \boxed{3.00\text{ MV}}$ so there is -11% difference.

25.50 (a) $E_x = \frac{\partial V}{\partial x} = -\frac{d}{dx}\left(\frac{kq2a}{x^2 - a^2}\right) = -2kqa\frac{d}{dx}(x^2 - a^2)^{-1} = kq2a(x^2 - a^2)^{-2}(2x)$

$$E = \frac{4kqax}{(x^2 - a^2)^2}\mathbf{i}$$

(b) $E = \frac{4(9 \times 10^9 \text{ N}\cdot\text{m}^2/\text{C}^2)(3 \times 10^{-6}\text{ C})(3)(2 \times 10^{-3}\text{ m})^2}{[(6 \times 10^{-3}\text{ m})^2 - (2 \times 10^{-3}\text{ m})^2]^2}\mathbf{i} = \boxed{1.27 \times 10^9\mathbf{i}\text{ N/C}}$

25.51 $V = \frac{kq}{r}$

$$7.5 \times 10^3 = \frac{(9 \times 10^9)q}{(0.3)}$$

$$q = \frac{2.5 \times 10^{-7}\text{ C}}{1.602 \times 10^{-19}\text{ C/e}} = \boxed{1.56 \times 10^{12}\text{ electrons}}$$

25.52 $V = \frac{kq}{r}$

$$1300 = \frac{(9 \times 10^9)q}{0.5}$$

$$\sigma = \frac{q}{4\pi r^2} = \frac{7.22 \times 10^{-8}}{4\pi(0.25)^2} = \boxed{9.20 \times 10^{-8}\text{ C/m}^2}$$

25.53 (a) $E = 0$; $V = \frac{kq}{R} = \frac{(9 \times 10^9)(26 \times 10^{-6})}{0.14} = \boxed{1.67\text{ MV}}$

(b) $E = \frac{kq}{r^2} = \frac{(9 \times 10^9)(26 \times 10^{-6})}{(0.2)^2} = \boxed{5.85\text{ MV/m}}$

$$V = \frac{kq}{r} = \frac{(9 \times 10^9)(26 \times 10^{-6})}{(0.2)} = \boxed{1.17\text{ MV}}$$

(c) $E = \frac{kq}{R^2} = \frac{(9 \times 10^9)(26 \times 10^{-6})}{(0.14)^2} = \boxed{11.9\text{ MV/m}}$

$$V = \frac{kq}{R} = \boxed{1.67\text{ MV}}$$

25.54 $E = \dfrac{kq}{r^2}$

$$890\ \text{N/C} = \frac{(9 \times 10^9\ \text{N}\cdot\text{m}^2/\text{C}^2)q_2}{(0.47\ \text{m})^2}$$

$$q_2 = 2.18 \times 10^{-8}\ \text{C}$$

$$V = \frac{kq_1}{r_1} = \frac{kq_2}{r_2}$$

$$\frac{q_1}{q_2} = \frac{r_1}{r_2}$$

$$\frac{q_1}{2.18 \times 10^{-8}\ \text{C}} = \frac{0.94}{0.47}$$

$$\boxed{q_1 = 4.37 \times 10^{-8}\ \text{C}}$$

25.55 $q_1 + q_2 = 20\ \mu\text{C} \qquad q_1 = 20\ \mu\text{C} - q_2$

$$\frac{q_1}{q_2} = \frac{r_1}{r_2}$$

$$\frac{20\ \mu\text{C} - q_2}{q_2} = \frac{4\ \text{cm}}{6\ \text{cm}}$$

$$6(20\ \mu\text{C} - q_2) = 4q_2; \qquad q_2 = 12\ \mu\text{C}$$

$$q_1 = 20\ \mu\text{C} - 12\ \mu\text{C} = 8\ \mu\text{C}$$

(a) $E_1 = \dfrac{kq_1}{r_1^2} = \dfrac{(9 \times 10^9)(8 \times 10^6)}{(0.4)^2} = \boxed{4.5 \times 10^7\ \text{V/m}}$

$E_2 = \dfrac{kq_2}{r_2^2} = \dfrac{(9 \times 10^9)(12 \times 10^6)}{(0.6)^2} = \boxed{3 \times 10^7\ \text{V/m}}$

(b) $V_1 = V_2 = \dfrac{kq}{r} = \boxed{1.80\ \text{MV}}$

25.56 (a) $A = (38.0\ \text{cm}^2)(\dfrac{1\ \text{m}}{100\ \text{cm}})^2 = 3.8 \times 10^{-3}\ \text{m}^2$

$\bar{\sigma} = \dfrac{q}{A} = \dfrac{43 \times 10^{-9}}{3.8 \times 10^{-3}} = \boxed{11.3\ \mu\text{C/m}^2}$

(b) $E_{\text{in}} = \boxed{0}$

(c) $\bar{E}_{\text{out}} = \dfrac{\bar{\sigma}}{\epsilon_0} = \dfrac{11.3 \times 10^{-6}\ \text{C/m}^2}{\epsilon_0} = \boxed{1.28 \times 10^6\ \text{V/m}}$

25.57 (a) $E_{\max} = 3 \times 10^6 \text{ V/m} = \dfrac{kQ}{r^2} = \dfrac{kQ}{r}\dfrac{1}{r} = V_{\max}\dfrac{1}{r}$

$$V_{\max} = E_{\max}r = 3 \times 10^6(0.15) = \boxed{450 \text{ kV}}$$

(b) $\dfrac{kQ_{\max}}{r^2} = E_{\max} \quad \{\text{or } \dfrac{kQ_{\max}}{r} = V_{\max}\}$

$$Q_{\max} = \frac{E_{\max}r^2}{k} = 3 \times 10^6(0.15)^2 = \boxed{7.50\ \mu\text{ C}}$$

25.58 (a) $E_{\max} = \dfrac{kq_{\max}}{r^2} \qquad 3 \times 10^6 = \dfrac{9 \times 10^9 q}{(0.2)^2}$

$$\boxed{q = 13.3\ \mu\text{C}}$$

(b) $V = \dfrac{kq}{r} = \dfrac{(9 \times 10^9)(13.3 \times 0^{-6})}{0.2} = \boxed{600{,}000 \text{ V}}$

25.59 $V = Ed = (3 \times 10^6 \text{ V/m})(0.1 \text{ m}) = 3 \times 10^5 \text{ V}$

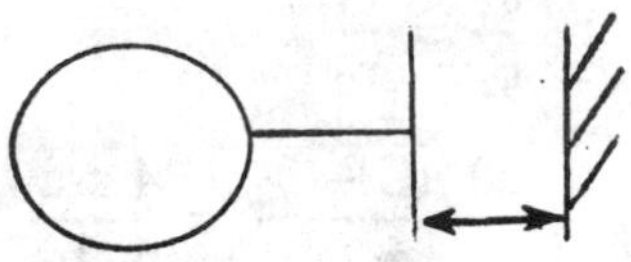

25.59

What charge is needed to get this voltage?

$$V = \frac{kQ}{r} = (9 \times 10^9 \text{ N}\cdot\text{m}^2/\text{C}^2)\frac{\text{Q}}{(0.15 \text{ m})} = 3 \times 10^5 \text{ V}$$

$$\boxed{Q = 5.00\ \mu\text{C}}$$

25.60 Energy $= 12 \text{ MeV} = (12 \times 10^6 \text{ eV})(1.6 \times 10^{-19} \text{ J/eV}) = 1.92 \times 10^{-12} \text{ J}$

$$I = \frac{\text{Charge}}{\Delta \text{t}} = 100\ \mu A = \frac{(1.6 \times 10^{-19}\text{C})}{\Delta \text{t}}; \quad \Delta t = 1.6 \times 10^{-15} \text{ s}$$

$$\text{Power} = \frac{\text{Energy}}{\Delta \text{t}} = \frac{(1.92 \times 10^{-12} \text{ J})}{1.6 \times 10^{-15} \text{ s}} = \boxed{1200 \text{ W}}$$

25.61 (a) $E = \dfrac{Q}{4\pi\epsilon_0 r^2}$

$$V = \frac{Q}{4\pi\epsilon_0 r}$$

$$\frac{|V|}{|E|} = r$$

$$r = \frac{3000 \text{ V}}{500 \text{ V/m}} = \boxed{6.00 \text{ m}}$$

(b) $V = -3000 \text{ V} = \dfrac{Q}{4\pi\epsilon_0(6 \text{ m})}$

$$Q = \frac{-3000 \text{ V}}{(8.99 \times 10^9 \text{ V} \cdot \text{m/C})}(6 \text{ m}) = \boxed{-2.00\ \mu\text{C}}$$

25.62 From Eq. 25.13

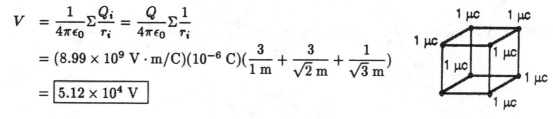

$$V = \frac{1}{4\pi\epsilon_0}\Sigma\frac{Q_i}{r_i} = \frac{Q}{4\pi\epsilon_0}\Sigma\frac{1}{r_i}$$

$$= (8.99 \times 10^9 \text{ V} \cdot \text{m/C})(10^{-6} \text{ C})(\frac{3}{1 \text{ m}} + \frac{3}{\sqrt{2} \text{ m}} + \frac{1}{\sqrt{3} \text{ m}})$$

$$= \boxed{5.12 \times 10^4 \text{ V}}$$

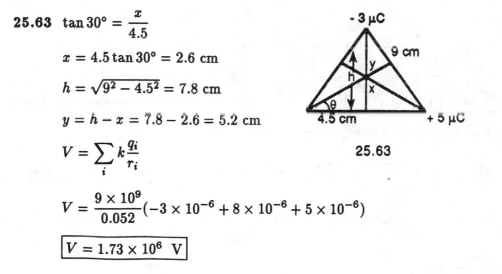

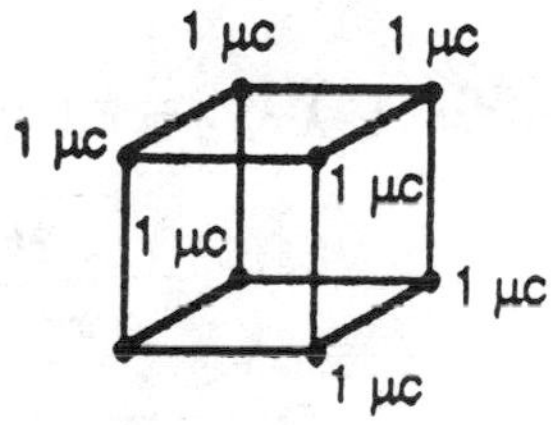

25.62

25.63 $\tan 30° = \dfrac{x}{4.5}$

$x = 4.5 \tan 30° = 2.6$ cm

$h = \sqrt{9^2 - 4.5^2} = 7.8$ cm

$y = h - x = 7.8 - 2.6 = 5.2$ cm

$$V = \sum_i k\frac{q_i}{r_i}$$

$$V = \frac{9 \times 10^9}{0.052}(-3 \times 10^{-6} + 8 \times 10^{-6} + 5 \times 10^{-6})$$

$$\boxed{V = 1.73 \times 10^6 \text{ V}}$$

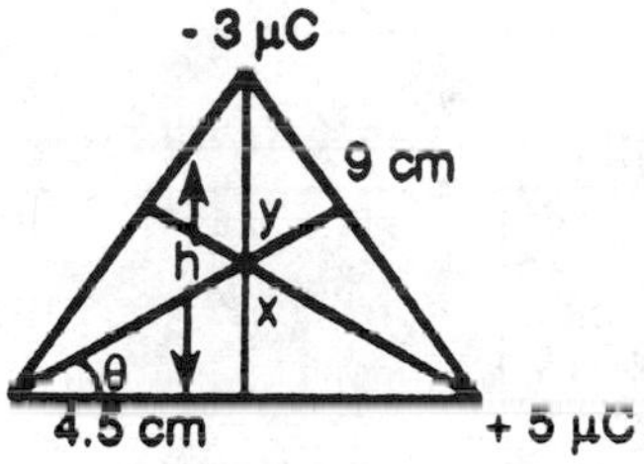

25.63

***25.64** (a) $k\frac{q}{R} = 200\ V$ and $k\ \frac{q}{(R+0.1)} = 150\ V$

This yields two simultaneous equations

$kq = 200\ R$ and $kq = 150(R + 0.1)$

$R = \boxed{0.30\ \text{m}}$

(b) $(9 \times 10^9)\frac{q}{0.3} = 200$

$q = 6.67 \times 10^{-9}\ \text{C} = \boxed{6.67\ \text{nC}}$

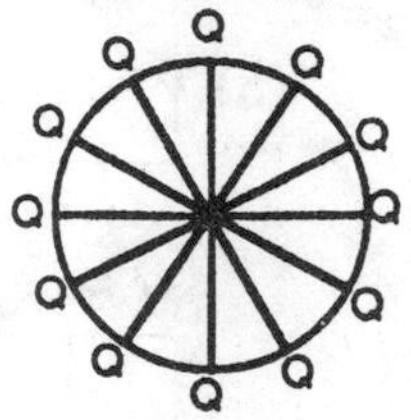

25.65

25.65 (a) $$V = \frac{1}{4\pi\epsilon_0}\Sigma\frac{Q_i}{r_i} = \frac{Q}{4\pi\epsilon_0}\Sigma\frac{1}{r_i} = \frac{12Q}{4\pi\epsilon_0 R}$$

$$= \frac{(8.99 \times 10^9\ \text{V}\cdot\text{m/C})(12)(2 \times 10^{-6})}{1.2\ \text{m}} = \boxed{180\ \text{kV}}$$

(b) $$V = \frac{Q}{4\pi\epsilon_0}\Sigma\frac{1}{r_i} = \frac{12\ Q}{4\pi\epsilon_0\sqrt{2}\ R} = \boxed{1.27 \times 10^5\ \text{V}}$$

25.66 (a) $$V = kq\left(\frac{1}{x+d} - \frac{2}{x} + \frac{1}{x-d}\right) = kq\left[\frac{x(x-d) - 2(x+d)(x-d) + x(x+d)}{x(x+d)(x-d)}\right]$$

$$= \boxed{\frac{2kqd^2}{x^3 - xd^2}}$$

(b) $$\boxed{V = \frac{2kqd^2}{x^3} \quad \text{for} \quad \frac{d}{x} << 1}$$

25.67 (a) $$V = \frac{kq2d^2}{x^3[1 - \frac{d^2}{x^2}]} = \frac{3 \times 10^6\ d}{x[1 - (\frac{d}{x})^2]} = \frac{1 \times 10^6}{0.889}$$

$$= \boxed{1.12\ \text{MV}}$$

(b) 1.00 MV so there is 11.1% difference.

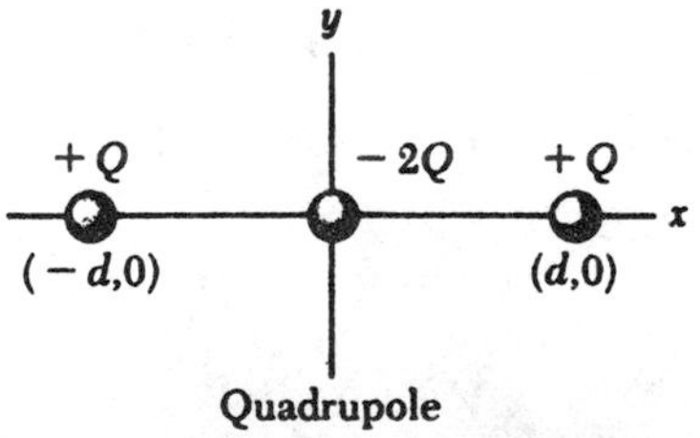

25.66, 25.67, and 25.75

25.68 (a) $$E_x = -\frac{dV}{dx} = -\frac{d}{dx}\left(\frac{2kQd^2}{x^3 - xd^2}\right) = \frac{(2kQd^2)(3x^2 - d^2)}{(x^3 - xd^2)^2}$$

(b) $$E_x = \frac{2(8.99 \times 10^9\ \text{N}\cdot\text{m}^2/\text{C}^2)(3 \times 10^{-6}\ \text{C})(2 \times 10^{-3}\ \text{m})^2[3(6 \times 10^{-3}\ \text{m})^2 - (2 \times 10^{-3}\ \text{m})^2]}{[(6 \times 10^{-3}\ \text{m})^3 - (6 \times 10^{-3}\ \text{m})(2 \times 10^{-3}\ \text{m})^2]^2}$$

$$= \boxed{609 \times 10^6\ \text{N/C}}$$

25.69 (a) $V(x) = V(-x) = \dfrac{2kQ}{\sqrt{a^2 + x^2)}}, \quad \dfrac{V}{kQ/a} = \dfrac{2a}{\sqrt{a^2 + x^2}}$

$\frac{x}{a}$	$\frac{V}{kQ/a}$
0	2
± 1	1.4
± 2	0.89
± 3	0.63

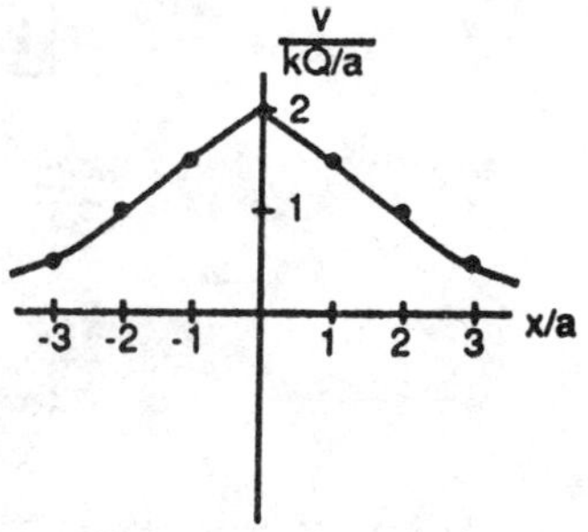

25.69 a

(b) $V(y) = V(-y) = kQ/a[(a/|a - y|) - (a/|a + y|)]$

$\frac{y}{a}$	$\frac{V}{kQ/a}$
0	0
1	∞
2	$\frac{1}{2}$
3	$\frac{1}{4}$
4	$\frac{2}{15}$
$\frac{1}{2}$	$\frac{4}{3}$

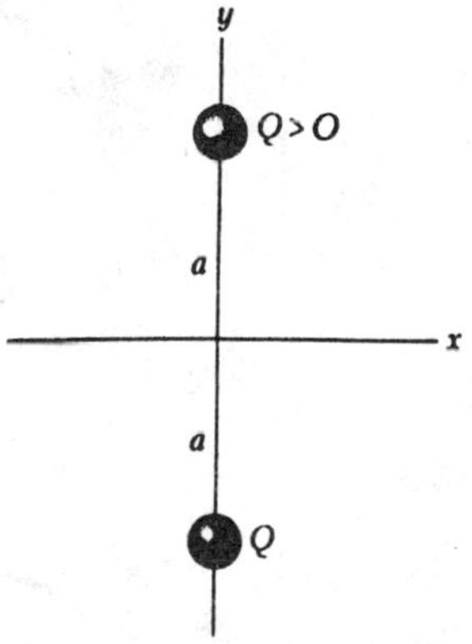

25.69

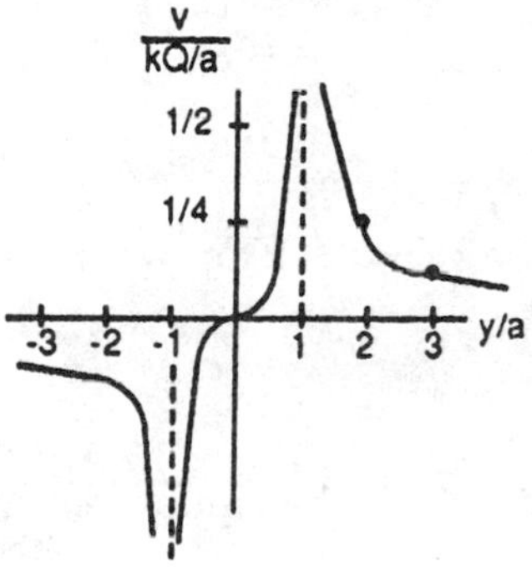

b

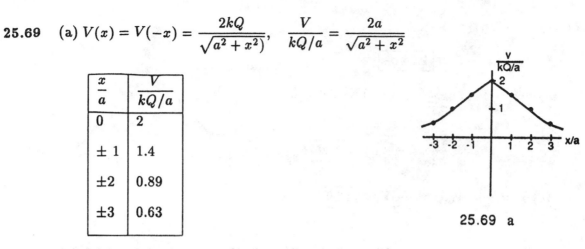

***25.70** $U = qV = k\dfrac{q_1 q_2}{r_{12}}$

$$= (9 \times 10^9)\frac{(38)(54)(1.6 \times 10^{-19})^2}{(5.5 + 6.2) \times 10^{-15}}$$

$$= 4.04 \times 10^{-11}\ \text{J}$$

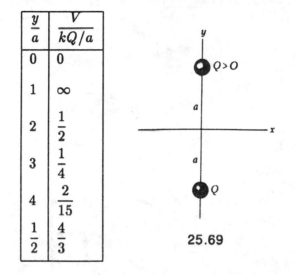

$$U = \boxed{253\ \text{MeV}}$$

***25.71** $r_{\text{new}} = \sqrt[3]{2}r_{\text{old}}$

(a) $\sigma_{\text{new}} = \dfrac{2\sigma_0}{\sqrt[3]{4}} = \boxed{1.26\ \sigma_0}$

(b) $E_0 = \dfrac{kq_0}{r_0^2}$

$E_{\text{new}} = \dfrac{kq_n}{r_n^2} = \dfrac{2}{\sqrt[3]{4}}E_0 = \boxed{1.26\ E_0}$

(c) $V = \dfrac{kq}{r}$ $\quad V_{\text{new}} = \dfrac{2}{\sqrt[3]{2}}V_0 = \boxed{1.59\ V_0}$

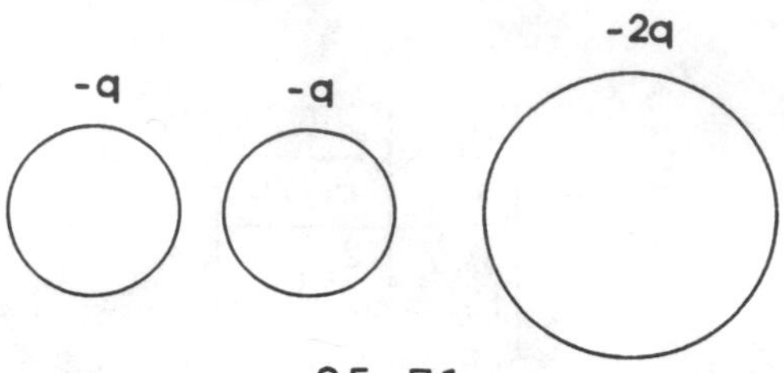

25.71

25.72 $P = IV = (500 \times 10^{-6}\ \text{A})(1.5 \times 10^4\ \text{V}) = \boxed{7.50\ \text{W}}$

25.73 $W = \displaystyle\int_0^Q V\,dq$ where $V = \dfrac{kq}{r}$; $\boxed{W = \dfrac{kQ^2}{2R}}$

***25.74** Find the equipotential surface where

$$V = \frac{kq}{r_1} - \frac{2kq}{r_2} = 0$$

From the diagram, a sphere of radius **r** centered at $\left(-\frac{4}{3}R, 0, 0\right)$ will have r_1 and r_2 such that $r_2 \stackrel{?}{=} 2r_1$.

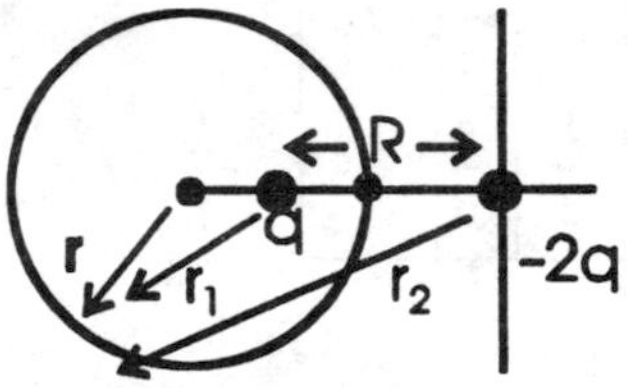

25.74

$$\left|-\frac{4R}{3}\mathbf{i} + \frac{2R}{3}\mathbf{r}\right| \stackrel{?}{=} 2\left|-\frac{R}{3}\mathbf{i} + \frac{2R}{3}\mathbf{r}\right|$$

$$\frac{16R^2}{9} - \frac{16R^2}{9}\mathbf{i}\cdot\mathbf{r} + \frac{4\ R^2}{9} \stackrel{?}{=} 4\left(\frac{R^2}{9} - \frac{4R^2}{9}\mathbf{i}\cdot\mathbf{r} + \frac{4R^2}{9}\right)$$

Therefore, a sphere of radius $\frac{2}{3}R$ centered at $\left(-\frac{4}{3}R, 0, 0\right)$ is an equipotential surface with $V = 0$.

***25.75** $V_2 - V_1 = -\displaystyle\int_{r_1}^{r_2} \mathbf{E}\cdot d\mathbf{r} = -\int_{r_1}^{r_2} \frac{\lambda}{2\pi\epsilon_0 r}dr$

$V_2 - V_1 = \dfrac{-\lambda}{2\pi\epsilon_0}\ln\left(\dfrac{r_2}{r_1}\right)$

***25.76** (a) From Gauss' Law,

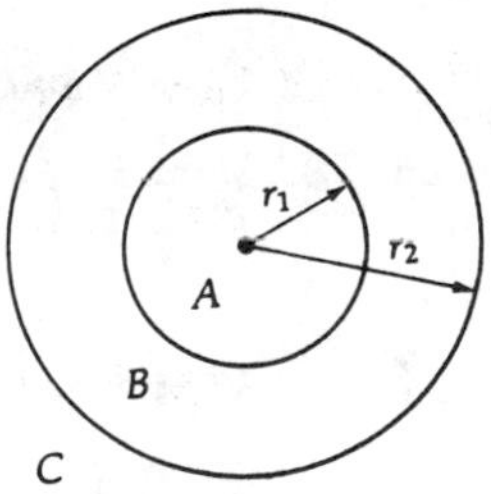

$E_A = 0.$ (no charge within)

$$E_B = k\,\frac{q_A}{r^2} = (9\times10^9)\frac{(10^{-8})}{r^2} = \left(\frac{90}{r^2}\,\mathbf{r}\right)\ \mathrm{N/C}$$

$$\mathrm{E_C} = \mathrm{k}\,\frac{(\mathrm{q_A}+\mathrm{q_B})}{\mathrm{r}^2} = (9\times10^9)\frac{(-5\times10^{-9})}{\mathrm{r}^2} = \left(-\frac{45}{\mathrm{r}^2}\,\mathbf{r}\right)\ \mathrm{N/C}$$

(b) $$V_C = k\,\frac{(q_A+q_B)}{r^2} = (9\times10^9)\frac{(-5\times10^{-9})}{r} = \left(-\frac{45}{r}\right)\ \mathrm{V}$$

25.76

$$\therefore\ \text{At } r_2,\ V = -\frac{45}{0.3} = -150\ \mathrm{V}.$$

$$\text{Inside } r_2,\ V_B = -150\ \mathrm{V} + \int_{\mathrm{r_2}}^{\mathrm{r}} \frac{90}{\mathrm{r}^2}\,\mathrm{dr}$$

$$V_B = -150 + 90\left(\frac{1}{r} - \frac{1}{0.3}\right) = \left(-450 + \frac{90}{r}\right)\ \mathrm{V}$$

$$\therefore\ \text{At } r_1,\ V = -450 + \frac{90}{0.15} = +150\ \mathrm{V}$$

$$V_A = +150\ \mathrm{V}$$

***25.77** The force acting on the point charge is $F = EQ$, and the work done on the particle is

$$W = \int_{x=0}^{\infty} F(x)dx = \frac{1}{2}mv^2$$

From Eq. 25.19, $E_x = \dfrac{kQx}{(x^2+a^2)^{3/2}}$

$$W = Q\int_{x=0}^{\infty} \frac{kQx\,dx}{(x^2+a^2)^{3/2}} = \frac{kQ^2}{2}\int_{x=0}^{\infty}\frac{2x\,dx}{(x^2+a^2)^{3/2}}$$

$$W = +\frac{kQ^2}{a} = \frac{1}{2}mv^2$$

$$\therefore\ v = \left(\frac{2kQ^2}{mR}\right)^{1/2}$$ where $R = a$ is the radius of the ring.

25.78 $V = k\int_a^{a+L}\frac{\lambda dx}{\sqrt{x^2+b^2}} = k\lambda \ell n[x+\sqrt{(x^2+b^2)}]|_a^{a+L}$

$$V = k\lambda \ell n[\frac{a+L+\sqrt{(a+L)^2+b^2}}{a+\sqrt{a^2+b^2}}]$$

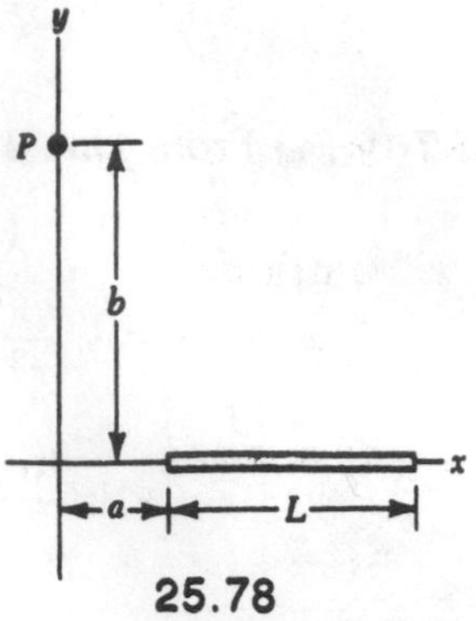

25.78

25.79 $E_y = \frac{\partial V}{\partial y} = \frac{\partial}{\partial y}[\frac{kQ}{\ell}\ell n(\frac{\ell+\sqrt{\ell^2+y^2}}{y})]$

$$\boxed{E_y = \frac{kQ}{\ell y}[1-\frac{y^2}{\ell^2+y^2+\ell\sqrt{\ell^2+y^2}}]}$$

25.80 (a) $\boxed{E_A > E_B \text{ since } E = \frac{\Delta V}{\Delta s}}$

(b) $E_B = \frac{\Delta V}{\Delta s} = \frac{(6-2)\text{ V}}{2\text{ cm}} = \boxed{200\text{ N/C}}$

(c) See Figure 25.80

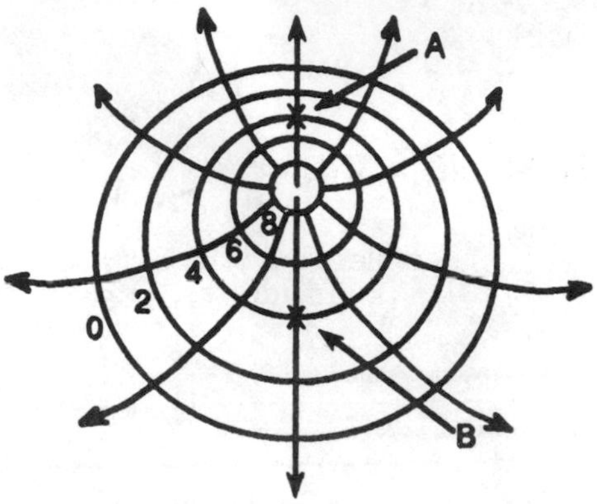

25.80

25.81 (a) $E_r = -\frac{\partial V}{\partial r} = \boxed{\frac{2kp\cos\theta}{r^3}}$

In spherical coordinates, the θ component of the gradient is $\frac{1}{r}(\frac{\partial}{\partial\theta})$, therefore

$$E_\theta = -\frac{1}{r}(\frac{\partial V}{\partial \theta}) = \boxed{\frac{kp\sin\theta}{r^3}}$$

For $r >> a$, $E_r(0°) = \frac{2kp}{r^3}$ and $E_\theta(90°) = \frac{kp}{r^3}$

These results are reasonable for $r >> a$.

However for $r \to 0$, $E(0) \to \infty$.

(b) $V = \frac{kpy}{(x^2+y^2)^{3/2}}$: $\boxed{E_x = \frac{3kpxy}{(x^2+y^2)^{5/2}}}$

$$E_y = -\frac{\partial V}{\partial y} = \boxed{\frac{kp(2y^2-x^2)}{(x^2+y^2)^{5/2}}}$$

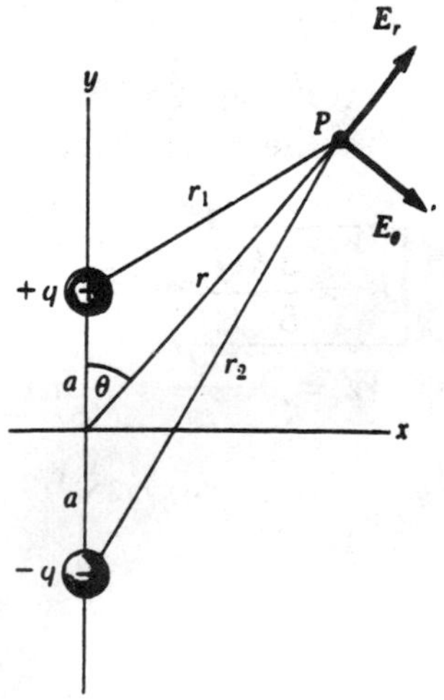

25.81

25.82 For an element of area which is a ring of radius r and width dr, $dV = \dfrac{k\,dq}{\sqrt{r^2 + x^2}}$

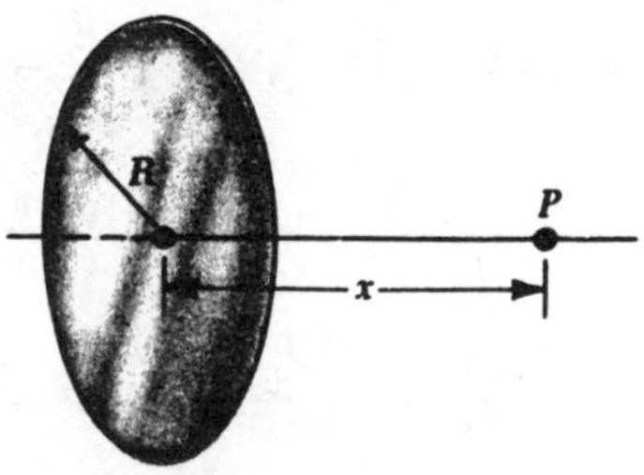

25.82

$$dq = \sigma dA = Cr(2\pi r dr) \text{ and } V = C(2\pi k)\int_0^R \frac{r^2 dr}{\sqrt{r^2 + x^2}}$$

$$V = C(2\pi k)\left\{\frac{R}{2}\sqrt{R^2 + x^2} + \frac{x^2}{2}\ell n\left(\frac{x}{R + \sqrt{R^2 + x^2}}\right)\right\}$$

25.83 $dU = V dq$ where the potential $V = \dfrac{kq}{r}$.

The element of charge in a shell is $dq = \rho$ (volume element)

or $dq = \rho(4\pi r^2 dr)$ and the charge q in a sphere of radius r is,

$$q = 4\pi\rho\int_0^r r^2 dr = \rho\left(\frac{4\pi r^3}{3}\right).$$

Substituting this into the expression for dU we have

$$dU = \left(\frac{kq}{r}\right)dq = k\rho\left(\frac{4\pi r^3}{3}\right)\left(\frac{1}{r}\right)\rho(4\pi r^2 dr) = k\left(\frac{16\pi^2}{3}\right)\rho^2 r^4 dr$$

$$U = \int dU = k\left(\frac{16\pi^2}{3}\right)\rho^2\int_0^R r^4 dr = k\left(\frac{16\pi^2}{15}\right)\rho^2 R^5$$

But the *total* charge, $Q = \rho\frac{4}{3}\pi R^3$, therefore

$$\boxed{U = \frac{3}{5}\frac{kQ^2}{R}}$$

25.84 (a) $V_B - V_A = -\int_A^B \mathbf{E}\cdot d\mathbf{s}$ and the field a distance r from a uniformly charged line (where $r >>$ radius of charged line) is

$$E = \frac{\lambda}{2\pi\epsilon_0 r} = \frac{2k\lambda}{r}.$$

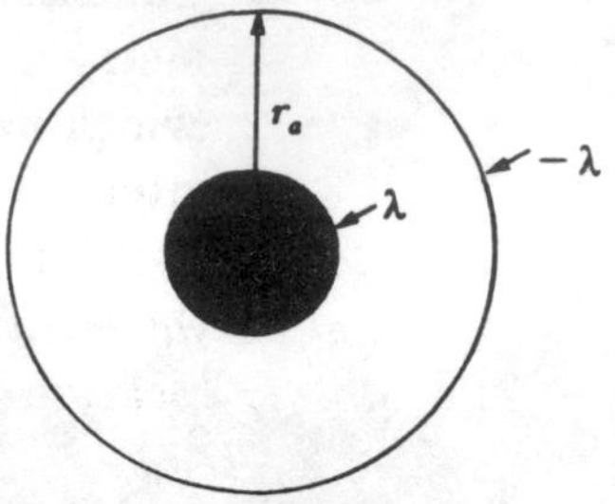

25.84

In this case the field between the central wire and the coaxial cylinder is directed perpendicular to the line of charge so that

$$V_B - V_A = -\int_{r_a}^{r_b} \frac{2k\lambda}{r}\, dr$$

$$V_B - V_A = 2k\lambda \ell n\left(\frac{r_a}{r_b}\right) \text{ or } \boxed{\Delta V = 2k\lambda \ell n\left(\frac{r_a}{r_b}\right)}$$

(b) From part(a) the potential at a distance r from the anode is $V = 2k\lambda\ell n(\frac{r_a}{r})$. The field at r is given by

$$E = -\frac{\partial V}{\partial r} = -2k\lambda\frac{r}{r_a}\left(-\frac{r_a}{r^2}\right) = 2k\lambda\left(\frac{1}{r}\right),$$

but from part (a)

$$2k\lambda = \frac{V}{\ell n(r_a/r_b)}. \quad \text{Therefore } E = \frac{V}{r\ell n(r_a/r_b)}.$$

25.85 Problem similiar to Ch 23.79 (see that solution).

25.86 Problem similiar to Ch 23.80 (see that solution).

***25.87** Electrostatic equilibrium positions are points where the electric field is zero. Symmetry suggests that the equilibrium positions lie on lines that pass through the charges and that bisect the opposite side. As Figuire 25.87 shows, these three lines intersect at the point $(2\text{ m})/\sqrt{3} = 1.155$ m from each vertex. This intersection is one position where the elctric field is zero. But, there are three other positions where the electric field is zero—one along each of the three lines. We can figure out their location by applying the condition

$$E_x = -\frac{\partial V}{\partial x} = 0$$

The potential at a point P on the x-axis is given by

$$V = \frac{q}{4\pi\epsilon_0}\left\{\frac{2}{R} + \frac{1}{\sqrt{3}-x}\right\}$$

where r and x are expressed in meters and are related by

$$r^2 = 1 + x^2$$

Setting

$$\frac{\partial V}{\partial x} = \frac{q}{4\pi\epsilon_0}\left\{\left(\frac{-2}{r^2}\right)\frac{\partial r}{\partial x} + \frac{1}{(\sqrt{3}-x)^2}\right\} = 0$$

and using $\partial r/\partial x = x/r$ gives the equation that locates equilibrium positions on the x-axis

$$\frac{2x}{r^3} = \frac{1}{(\sqrt{3}-x)^2}$$

This can be rewritten as

$$f(x) = 2x(\sqrt{3}-x)^2 - (1+x^2)^{3/2} = 0$$

The equation is satisfied by two values of x corresponding to positions inside the triangle. To five-significant-figure accuracy, the solutions are

$$x = 0.57735\text{ m} \quad \text{and} \quad x = 0.24859\text{ m}$$

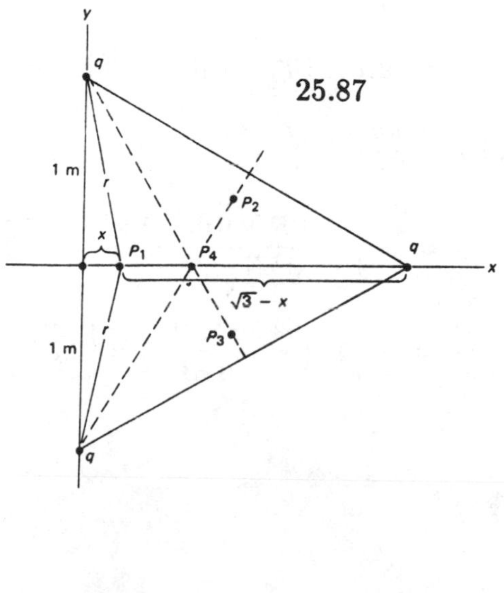

25.87

CHAPTER 26

26.1 $C = \frac{Q}{V}$

$$4 \times 10^{-9}\text{ F} = \frac{53 \times 10^{-6}\text{ C}}{\text{V}}$$

$$\boxed{V = 1.33 \times 10^4\text{ V}}$$

26.2 $C(\text{F}) = \frac{q(\text{C})}{[V(\text{J/C})]}; \quad \text{F} = \frac{\text{C}^2}{\text{J}} = \frac{\text{C}^2}{\text{N} \cdot \text{m}}$

26.3 $C = \frac{Q}{V} = \frac{73 \times 10^{-12}\text{ C}}{52\text{ V}} = \boxed{1.40\text{ pF}}$

26.4 $C = \frac{Q}{V} = \frac{1.6 \times 10^{12}\text{ electrons}(1.602 \times 10^{-19}\text{ C/electron})}{14\text{ V}} = 1.83 \times 10^{-8}\text{ F} = \boxed{18.3\text{ nF}}$

26.5 $C = \frac{Q}{V}$

$$19 \times 10^{-6}\text{ F} = \frac{Q}{36\text{ V}}$$

$$Q = 6.84 \times 10^{-4}\text{ C} = \boxed{684\ \mu\text{C}}$$

26.6 (a) $C = \frac{q}{V} \quad V = \frac{kq}{r}$

$$C = \frac{q}{kq/r} = \frac{r}{k}$$

$$r = (9.1 \times 10^{-11}\text{ F})(9 \times 10\text{ N} \cdot \text{m}^2/\text{C}^2) = \boxed{0.819\text{ m}}$$

(b) $V = \frac{kq}{r}$

$$q = \frac{(2.8 \times 10^4\text{ V})(0.819\text{ V})}{9 \times 10^9\text{ N} \cdot \text{m}^2/\text{C}^2} = \boxed{2.55 \times 10^{-6}\text{ C}}$$

$$\sigma = \frac{q}{4\pi r^2} = \frac{2.55 \times 10^{-6}}{4\pi(0.817)^2} = \boxed{3.02 \times 10^{-7}\text{ C/m}^2}$$

26.7 $E = \frac{kq}{r^2}$

$$q = \frac{(4.9\times10^4\ \mathrm{N/C})(0.21\ \mathrm{m})^2}{9\times10^9\ \mathrm{N\cdot m^2/C^2}} = 0.24\ \mu\mathrm{C}$$

(a) $\sigma = \frac{q}{A} = \frac{0.24\times10^{-6}}{4\pi(0.12)^2} = \boxed{1.33\ \mu\mathrm{C/m^2}}$

(b) $C = 4\pi\epsilon_0 r = 4\pi(8.85\times10^{-12})(0.012) = \boxed{13.3\ \mathrm{pF}}$

26.8 (a) $\frac{Q_1}{Q_2} = \frac{R_1}{R_2}$

$Q_1 + Q_2 = (1 + \frac{R_1}{R_2})Q_2 = 3.5Q_2 = 7\ \mu C$

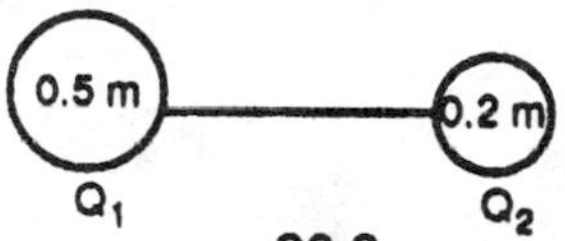

26.8

$\boxed{Q_2 = 2\ \mu C}$ $\boxed{Q_1 = 5\ \mu C}$

$$V_1 = V_2 = \frac{Q_1}{C_1} = \frac{Q_2}{C_2} = \frac{5\ \mu C}{(8.99\times10^9\ \frac{\mathrm{m}}{\mathrm{F}})^{-1}(0.5\ \mathrm{m})} = 9.0\times10^4\ \mathrm{V}$$

Thus the total potential is $\boxed{90\ \mathrm{kV}}$

26.9 (a) If induction effects are negligible, the charges on the two spheres are distributed uniformly, although with different charge densities. According to Eq. 30–9, the common potential V of the spheres can be expressed as

$$V = \frac{Q_1}{4\pi\epsilon_0 R_1} = \frac{Q_2}{4\pi\epsilon_0 R_2}$$

Thus, with $Q = Q_1 + Q_2$, We have

$$Q = 4\pi\epsilon_0(R_1 + R_2)V$$

and, hence, $C = \frac{Q_1 + Q_2}{V} = \boxed{4\pi\epsilon_0(R_1 + R_2)}$

(b) The charge ratio is $\boxed{\frac{Q_1}{Q_2} = \frac{R_1}{R_2}}$

Notice that the charge *density* is in the inverse ratio to the charge itself; that is,

$$\frac{\sigma_1}{\sigma_2} = \frac{Q_1/4\pi R_1^2}{Q_2/4\pi R_2^2} = \frac{R_2}{R_1}$$

26.10 $C = \frac{\epsilon_0 A}{d}$

$$A = \frac{(1\text{ F})(1 \times 10^{-3}\text{ m})}{8.85 \times 10^{-12}\text{ C}^2/\text{N}\cdot\text{m}^2}\left(\frac{1\text{ mi}}{1.609 \times 10^3\text{ m}}\right)^2 = \boxed{43.6\text{ mi}^2}$$

26.11 $C = \frac{\epsilon_0 A}{d}$

$$d = \frac{\epsilon_0 A}{\text{C}} = \frac{(8.85 \times 10^{-12}\text{ C}^2/\text{N}\cdot\text{m}^2)(0.12\text{ m})^2}{7 \times 10^{-12}\text{ F}} = \boxed{1.52 \times 10^{-3}\text{ m}}$$

26.12 $C = \frac{\epsilon_0 A}{d}$

$$A = \frac{(9 \times 10^{-12}\text{F})(0.2 \times 10^{-3}\text{ m})}{8.85 \times 10^{-12}\text{ C}^2/\text{N}\cdot\text{m}^2} = \boxed{2.03 \times 10^{-4}\text{ m}^2}$$

26.13 $Q = \frac{\epsilon_0 A}{s} V$

$$\frac{Q}{A} = \sigma = \frac{\epsilon_0 V}{s}$$

$$s = \frac{\epsilon_0 V}{\sigma} = \frac{(8.8452 \times 10^{-12}\frac{\text{C}^2}{\text{N}\cdot\text{m}^2})(150\text{ V})}{30 \times 10^{-9} \times 10^4\text{ C/m}^2} = \boxed{4.42\ \mu\text{m}}$$

26.14 $F_e = mg \tan\theta$

$$E = \frac{F_e}{q} = \frac{mg}{q}\tan\theta = \frac{(3.5 \times 10^{-4}\text{ kg})(9.81\text{ m/s}^2)}{3 \times 10^{-8}\text{ C}}\tan 15° = 3.1 \times 10^4\text{ N/C}$$

$$V = Es = (3.1 \times 10^4\text{ N/C})(0.04\text{ m}) = \boxed{1240\text{ V}}$$

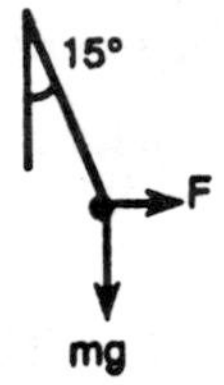

26.14

26.15 (a) $V = Ed$

$$E = \frac{20 \text{ N}}{1.8 \times 10^{-3} \text{ m}} = \boxed{1.11 \times 10^{4} \text{ V/m}}$$

(b) $E = \dfrac{\sigma}{\epsilon_0}$

$$\sigma = (1.11 \times 10^{4} \text{ N/C})(8.85 \times 10^{-12} \text{ C}^2/\text{N} \cdot \text{m}^2) = \boxed{9.83 \times 10^{-8} \text{ C/m}^2}$$

(c) $C = \dfrac{\epsilon_0 A}{d} = \dfrac{(8.85 \times 10^{-12})(7.6 \text{ cm}^2)(1 \text{ m}/100 \text{ cm})^2}{1.8 \times 10^{-3}} = \boxed{3.74 \times 10^{-12} \text{ F}}$

(d) $V = \dfrac{Q}{C}$ $\quad Q = (20)(3.74 \times 10^{-12}) = \boxed{74.7 \text{ pC}}$

***26.16** $C = \dfrac{\kappa \epsilon_0 A}{d} = 60 \times 10^{-15} \text{ F}$

$$d = \frac{\kappa \epsilon_0 A}{C} = \frac{(1)(8.85 \times 10^{-12})(21 \times 10^{-12})}{60 \times 10^{-15}}$$

$$d = 3.1 \times 10^{-9} \text{ m} = \boxed{3.1 \text{ nm}}$$

26.17 The potential difference between the plates is

$$V = Ed = (3 \times 10^{6} \text{ V/m})(3 \times 10^{-3} \text{ m}) = 9 \times 10^{3} \text{ V}$$

The capacitance value is

$$C = \frac{Q}{V} = \frac{1 \times 10^{-6} \text{C}}{9 \times 10^{3} \text{ V}} = 1.11 \times 10^{-10} \text{ F} = 111 \text{ pF}$$

$A = \pi R^2 = \dfrac{Cd}{\epsilon_0}$, so that

$$R = \sqrt{\frac{Cd}{\pi \epsilon_0}} = \sqrt{\frac{(1.11 \times 10^{-10} \text{ F})(3 \times 10^{-3} \text{ m})}{\pi (8.85 \times 10^{-12} \text{ F/m})}} = \boxed{0.109 \text{ m}}$$

26.18 $C = \dfrac{\epsilon_0 A}{d} = \dfrac{(8.85 \times 10^{-12} \text{ C}^2/\text{N} \cdot \text{m}^2)(7 \text{ cm}^2)(1 \text{ m}/100 \text{ cm})^2}{0.8 \times 10^{-3} \text{ m}} = \boxed{7.74 \text{ pF}}$

26.19 $Q = \epsilon_0 A \frac{\Delta V}{\Delta s} = \frac{(8.854 \times 10^{-12} \frac{C^2}{N \cdot m^2})(10^{-2}\ m^2)(200\ V)}{0.005\ m} = \boxed{3.54\ nC}$

26.20 Using Eq. 26.4, $C = \frac{l}{2k \ln(b/a)}$ where a and b are inner and outer radii.

$$a = be^{(-l/2kC)} = (0.015\ m)e^{-[0.06/(2k \times 10^{-12}\ F)]} = \boxed{1.07 \times 10^{-2}\ m}$$

26.21 (a) $C = \frac{l}{2k \ln(\frac{b}{a})} = \frac{50}{2(9 \times 10^9) \ln(\frac{7.27}{2.58})} = \boxed{2.68\ nF}$

(b) Method 1:

$$V = 2kr \ln(\frac{b}{a})$$

$$\lambda = \frac{q}{\ell} = \frac{8.1 \times 10^{-6}\ C}{50\ m} = 1.62 \times 10^{-7}\ C/m$$

$$V = 2(9 \times 10^9)(1.62 \times 10^{-7}) \ln(\frac{7.27}{2.58}) = \boxed{3.02\ kV}$$

Method 2:

$$V = \frac{Q}{C} = \frac{8.1 \times 10^{-6}}{2.68 \times 10^{-9}} = \boxed{3.02\ kV}$$

26.22 $C = \frac{l}{2k \ln(\frac{b}{a})}$ where $a_2 = \frac{a_1}{2}$

$$\frac{b}{a_2} = \frac{b}{a_1/2} = \frac{2b}{a_1}$$

$$2kC = \frac{l_1}{\ln(\frac{b}{a_1})} = \frac{l_2}{\ln(\frac{b}{a_2})}$$

$$\frac{l_2}{l_1} = \frac{\ln(\frac{b}{a_2})}{\ln(\frac{b}{a_1})} = \frac{\ln(2\frac{b}{a_1})}{\ln(\frac{b}{a_1})} = \frac{\ln 2 + \ln(\frac{b}{a_1})}{\ln(\frac{b}{a_1})} = 1 + \frac{\ln 2}{\ln(4)} = \boxed{1.50}$$

26.23 (a) $C = \frac{ab}{k(b-a)} = \frac{(7)(0.14)}{(9 \times 10^9)(0.14 - 0.07)} = \boxed{15.6\ \text{pF}}$

(b) $C = \frac{Q}{V} \quad V = \frac{Q}{C} = \frac{4 \times 10^{-6}\ \text{C}}{15.6 \times 10^{-12}\ \text{F}} = \boxed{256\ \text{kV}}$

***26.24** $C = 4\pi\epsilon_0 R = \frac{6.37 \times 10^6}{9 \times 10^9} = \boxed{7.08\ \mu F}$

26.25 $Q = \frac{Vab}{k(b-a)} = \frac{(1000\ \text{V})(0.10\ \text{m})(0.12\ \text{m})}{(9 \times 10^9\ \text{N} \cdot \text{m}^2/\text{C})(0.12\ \text{m} - 0.10\ \text{m})} = \boxed{66.7 \times 10^{-9}\ \text{C}}$

***26.26**

$$E_{\text{max}} = 3 \times 10^6\ \text{V/m}$$

$$V = E_{\text{max}} r = (3 \times 10^6\ \text{V/m})(0.05\ \text{m}) = \boxed{150\ \text{kV}}$$

26.27 $C = C_1 + C_2 = \boxed{18.0\ \text{F}}$

26.28 $\text{C} = \frac{\text{C}_1\text{C}_2}{\text{C}_1 + \text{C}_2} = \frac{2(16)}{2+16} = \boxed{1.78\ \mu\text{F}}$

26.40 $C_p = 8 + 1 = 9\ \mu\text{F}$

$$C_s = \left(\frac{1}{9} + \frac{1}{2}\right)^{-1} = 1.64\ \mu\text{F}$$

$$C_p = 4 + 1.64 = 5.64\ \mu\text{F}$$

$$C_s = \left(\frac{1}{2} + \frac{1}{5.64}\right)^{-1} = 1.48\ \mu\text{F}$$

$$C_p = 1.48 + 3 + 3 = \boxed{7.48\ \mu\text{F}}$$

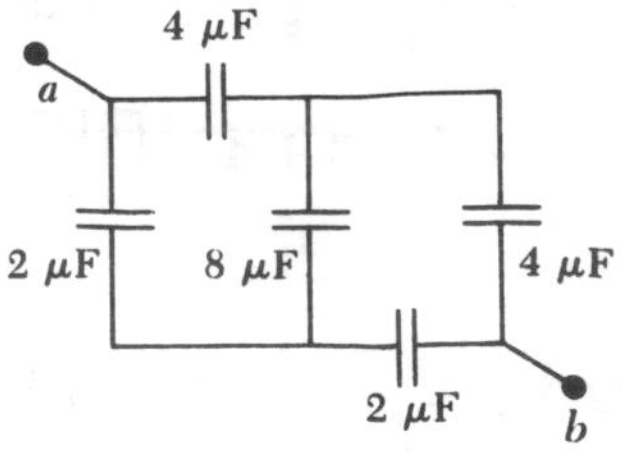

26.40

26.41 $C_s = \left(\frac{1}{5} + \frac{1}{7}\right)^{-1} = 2.92\ \mu\text{F}$

$$C_p = 2.92 + 4 + 6 = \boxed{12.9\ \mu\text{F}}$$

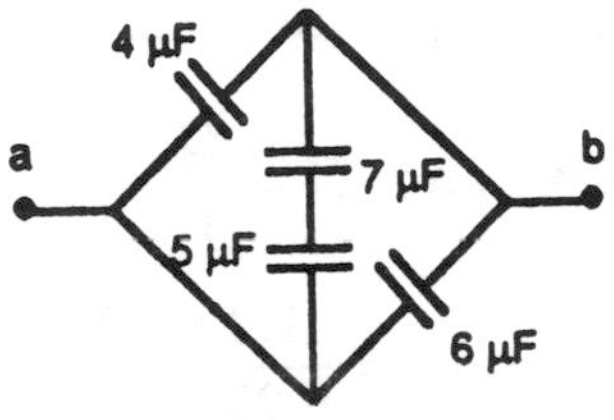

26.41

26.42

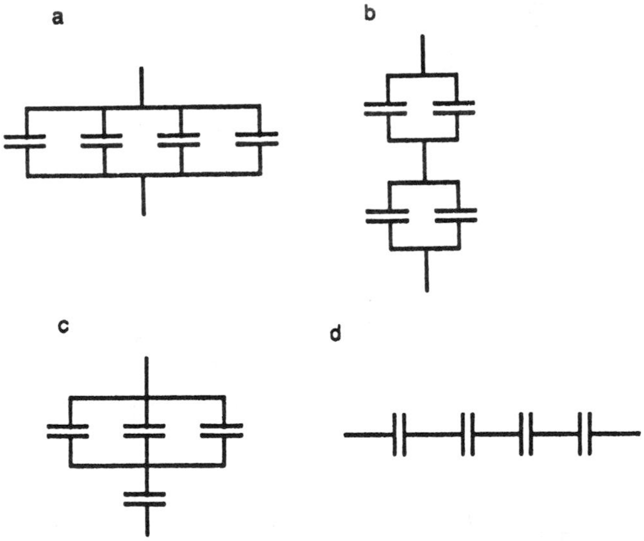

26.42

26.43 The system may be considered to be two capacitors in series

$$C_1 = \frac{\epsilon_0 A}{t_1}$$

$$C_2 = \frac{\epsilon_0 A}{t_2}$$

$$\frac{1}{C} = \frac{1}{C_1} + \frac{1}{C_2} = \frac{t_1 + t_2}{\epsilon_0 A}$$

$$\boxed{C = \frac{\epsilon_0 A}{t_1 + t_2} = \frac{\epsilon_0 A}{s - d}}$$

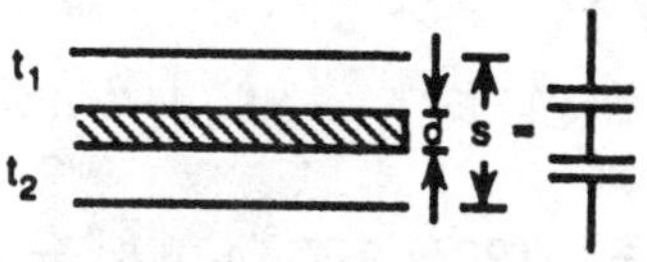

26.43

26.44 $C_{eq} = 5.96\ \mu\text{F}$ (From problem 31)

$$U = \frac{1}{2}CV^2 = \frac{1}{2}(5.96 \times 10^{-6}\ \text{F})(15\ \text{V})^2 = \boxed{6.71 \times 10^{-4}\ \text{J}}$$

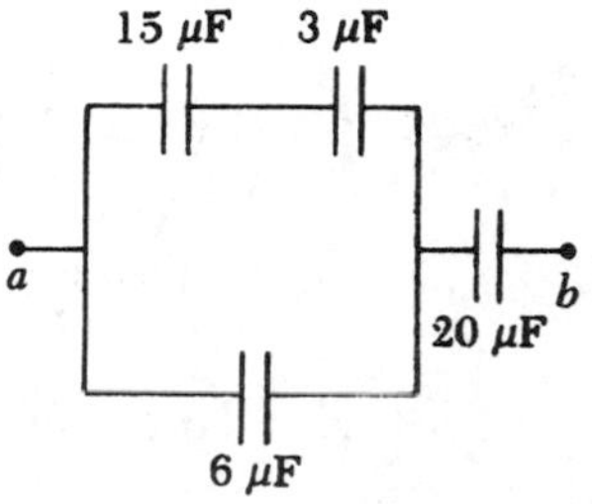

26.44

26.45 $U = \frac{1}{2}CV^2$

$$U = \frac{1}{2}(18 \times 10^{-6})(100)^2 = \boxed{90.0\ \text{mJ}}$$

***26.46** $U = \frac{1}{2}CV^2 = \frac{1}{2}\frac{Q^2}{C}$

If U is quadrupled, both Q and V are doubled.

***26.47** $U = \frac{1}{2}CV^2 = \frac{1}{2}\frac{Q^2}{C} = 1.3 \times 10^{-4}\ \text{J}$

(a) $Q = \sqrt{2UC} = \sqrt{2(1.3 \times 10^{-4})(12 \times 10^{-6})}$

$Q = 55.9 \times 10^{-6}\ \text{C} = \boxed{55.9\ \mu\ \text{C}}$

(b) $V = \frac{Q}{C} = \frac{55.9 \times 10^{-6}\ \text{C}}{12 \times 10^{-6}\ \text{F}} = \boxed{4.65\ \text{V}}$

26.48 $U = \frac{1}{2}CV^2$

(a) $C_p = C_1 + C_2 = 25\ \mu\text{F} + 5\ \mu\text{F} = 30\ \mu\text{F}$

$$U = \frac{1}{2}(30 \times 10^{-6})(100)^2 = \boxed{0.15\ \text{J}}$$

(b) $C_s = (\frac{1}{C_1} + \frac{1}{C_2})^{-1} = (\frac{1}{25\ \mu\text{F}} + \frac{1}{5\ \mu\text{F}})^{-1} = 4.167\ \mu\text{F}$

$$U = \frac{1}{2}CV^2$$

$$V = \sqrt{\frac{2U}{C}} = \sqrt{\frac{(0.15)(2)}{4.167 \times 10^{-6}}} = \boxed{268\ \text{V}}$$

26.49 $A = (5\ \text{cm}^2)(\frac{1\ \text{m}}{100\ \text{cm}})^2 = 5 \times 10^{-4}\ \text{m}^2$

$$C = \frac{k\epsilon_0 A}{d} = \frac{(1)(8.85 \times 10^{-12})(5 \times 10^{-4})}{d} = 16\ p\text{F}$$

$$d = 2.764 \times 10^{-4}\ \text{m}$$

$$U = \frac{1}{2}CV^2 = \frac{1}{2}(16 \times 10^{-12})(10)^2 = \boxed{8 \times 10^{-10}\ \text{J}}$$

$$U_e = \frac{U}{Ad} = \frac{8 \times 10^{-10}\ \text{J}}{(5 \times 10^{-4}\ \text{m}^2)(2.764 \times 10^{-4}\ \text{m})} = \boxed{5.79 \times 10^{-3}\ \text{J/m}^3}$$

26.50 $U = \frac{\epsilon_0 E^2}{2}$; $\quad E = \sqrt{\frac{2U}{\epsilon_0}} = \sqrt{\frac{(2)(2.1 \times 10^{-9})\ \text{J/m}^3}{8.85 \times 10^{-12}\ \text{C}^2/\text{N} \cdot \text{m}^2}} = \boxed{21.8\ \text{V/m}}$

26.51 $W = U = \int F\, dx$, and $\int_0^x F\, dx = \frac{Q^2}{2C} = \frac{Q^2 x}{2\epsilon_0 A}$; $\quad F = \frac{Q^2}{2\epsilon_0 A}$

26.52 1 J = 10^7 ergs

$$u = \frac{U}{V} = \frac{1}{2}\epsilon_0 E^2$$

$$\frac{1 \times 10^{-7}}{V} = \frac{1}{2}(8.85 \times 10^{-12})(3000)^2$$

$$V = (2.51 \times 10^{-3}\ \text{m}^3)\left(\frac{1000\ \text{liter}}{\text{m}^3}\right) = \boxed{2.51\ \text{liters}}$$

26.53 $U = \dfrac{CV^2}{2}$ where $C = \dfrac{R}{k}$ and $V = \dfrac{kQ}{R}$

$$U = \frac{(\frac{R}{k})(\frac{kQ}{R})^2}{2} = \frac{kQ^2}{2R}$$

26.54 The electric field strength within the capacitor is

$$E(r) = \frac{Q}{4\pi\epsilon_0}\frac{1}{r^2}$$

Then, the energy stored in a spherical shell between r and $r + dr$ is

$$dU = u\ d(\text{volume}) = u(4\pi r^2 dr)$$

$dU = \dfrac{Q^2}{8\pi\epsilon_0}\dfrac{dr}{r^2}$ from which we obtain

$$U = \frac{Q^2}{8\pi\epsilon_0}\int_{R_1}^{R_2}\frac{dr}{r^2} = \frac{Q^2}{8\pi\epsilon_0}\frac{(R_2 - R_1)}{R_1 R_2}$$

Now, $C = \dfrac{4\pi\epsilon_0 R_1 R_2}{R_2 - R_1}$ for a spherical capacitor therefore,

$U = \dfrac{1}{2}\dfrac{Q^2}{C}$ which is the desired result.

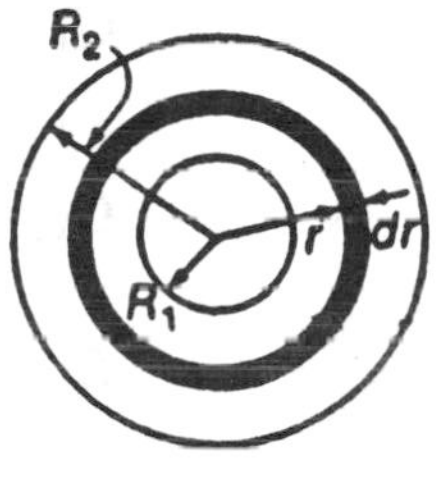

26.54

26.55 (a) $C = \dfrac{\kappa\epsilon_0 A}{d} = \dfrac{(2.1)(8.85 \times 10^{-12})(175\ \text{cm}^2)(\frac{1\ \text{m}}{100\ \text{cm}})^2}{0.04 \times 10^{-3}\ \text{m}} = \boxed{8.13\ \text{nF}}$

(b) $V = Ed = (60 \times 10^6)(0.04 \times 10^{-3}) = \boxed{2.40\ \text{kV}}$

26.65 Inserting the dielectric creates two new capacitances in series

$$C_1 = \frac{\kappa\epsilon_0 A}{d/4} = 4\kappa\frac{\epsilon_0 A}{d}; \quad \text{and} \quad C_2 = \frac{\epsilon_0 A}{3d/4} = \frac{4}{3}\cdot\frac{\epsilon_0 A}{d}$$

$$\frac{1}{C_s} = \frac{1}{C_1} + \frac{1}{C_2} = \frac{1}{4\kappa C_0} + \frac{1}{\frac{4}{3}C_0} = (\frac{1}{4\kappa} + \frac{3}{4})\frac{1}{C_0}$$

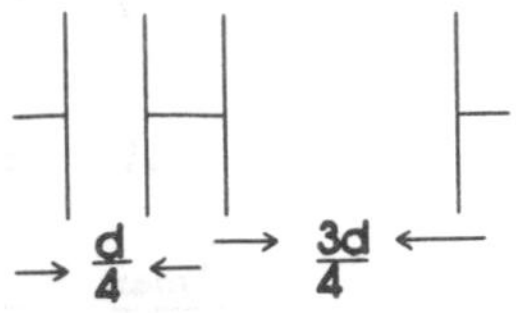

26.65

$$C_s = C_0(\frac{1}{4\kappa} + \frac{3}{4})^{-1}$$

$$C_s = (340 \text{ pF})(1.223) = \boxed{416 \text{ pF}}$$

26.66 (a) $C = \kappa C_0 = \frac{\kappa\epsilon_0 A}{d} = \frac{(173)(8.85 \times 10^{-12})(10^{-4} \text{ m}^2)}{0.10 \times 10^{-3} \text{ m}} = \boxed{1.53 \times 10^{-9} \text{ F}}$

(b) The battery delivers the free charge Q :

$$Q = CV = (1.53 \times 10^{-9} \text{ F})(12 \text{ V}) = \boxed{18.4 \text{ nC}}$$

(c) The surface density of free charge is

$$\sigma = \frac{Q}{A} = \frac{18.4 \times 10^{-9} \text{ C}}{1 \times 10^{-4} \text{ m}^2} = \boxed{1.84 \times 10^{-4} \text{ C/m}^2}$$

The surface density of polarization charge is,

$$\sigma_p = \sigma(1 - \frac{1}{\kappa}) = \sigma(1 - \frac{1}{173}) = \boxed{1.83 \times 10^{-4} \text{ C/m}^2}$$

(d) We have $E = E_0/\kappa$ and $E_0 = V/d$; hence,

$$E = \frac{V}{kd} = \frac{12 \text{ V}}{(173)(10^{-4} \text{ m})} = \boxed{694 \text{ V/m}}$$

26.67 In series: $\frac{1}{C_1} + \frac{1}{C_2} = \frac{1}{C_2/4} \qquad \frac{C_1 + C_2}{C_1 C_2} = \frac{4}{C_2}$

$C_1 + C_2 = 4C; \quad C_2 = 3C_1$

In parallel: $C_1 + C_2 = 4\ \mu F; \quad C_1 + 3C_1 = 4\ \mu F$ therefore $C_1 = \boxed{1.00\ \mu\text{F}}$

$C_2 = 3C_1 = \boxed{3.00\ \mu\text{F}}$

26.68 (a) $C = [\frac{1}{3} + \frac{1}{6}]^{-1} + [\frac{1}{2} + \frac{1}{4}]^{-1} = \boxed{3.33\ \mu\text{F}}$

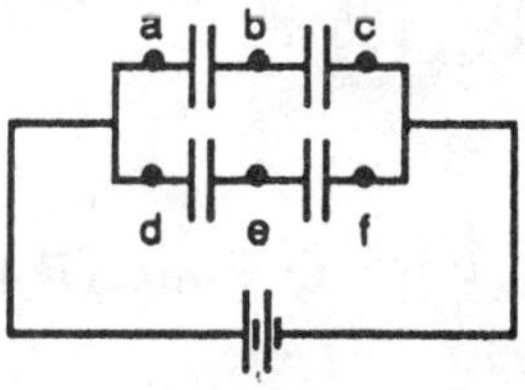

26.68

(b) $V_3 = \frac{Q_3}{C_3} = \frac{180\ \mu\text{C}}{3\ \mu\text{F}} = \boxed{60\ \text{V}}$

$V_6 = \frac{Q_6}{C_6} = \frac{180\ \mu\text{C}}{6\ \mu\text{F}} = \boxed{30\ \text{V}}$

$V_2 = \frac{Q_2}{C_2} = \frac{120\ \mu\text{C}}{2\ \mu\text{F}} = \boxed{60\ \text{V}}$

$V_4 = \frac{Q_4}{C_4} = \frac{120\ \mu\text{C}}{4\ \mu\text{F}} = \boxed{30\ \text{V}}$

(c) $Q_{ac} = C_{ac}V_{ac} = (2\ \mu\text{F})(90\ \text{V}) = \boxed{180\ \mu\text{C}}$; Therefore $Q_3 = Q_6 = \boxed{180\ \mu\text{C}}$

$Q_{df} = C_{df}V_{df} = (\frac{8}{6}\ \mu\text{F})(90\ \text{V}) = \boxed{120\ \mu\text{C}}$;

(d) $U_T = \frac{1}{2}C_{eq}V^2 = \frac{1}{2}(3.3 \times 10^{-6}\ \text{F})(90\ \text{V})^2 = \boxed{1.34 \times 10^{-2}\ \text{J}}$

26.69 $C = \frac{Q}{V} = \frac{Q}{80\ \text{V}} = \frac{[Q + (9.0 \times 10^{-5}\ \text{C})]}{110\ \text{V}}$

$$Q = \frac{9.0 \times 10^{-5}\ \text{C}}{(110\ \text{V})[(1/80\ \text{V}) - (1/110\ \text{V})]} = 24 \times 10^{-5}\ \text{C}$$

$$C = \frac{Q}{V} = \frac{24 \times 10^{-5}\ \text{C}}{80\ \text{V}} = \boxed{3.00\ \mu\text{F}}$$

***26.70** $C_0 = \frac{\epsilon_0 A}{d}$

$$C = \frac{1}{\frac{1}{\left(\frac{\epsilon_0 A}{(1-f)d}\right)} + \frac{1}{\left(\frac{\kappa\epsilon_0 A}{fd}\right)}}$$

$$C = \frac{1}{\frac{(1-f)d}{\epsilon_0 A} + \frac{fd}{\kappa\epsilon_0 A}}$$

$$C = \frac{\kappa\epsilon_0 A}{\kappa(1-f)d + fd}$$

$$= \frac{\kappa\epsilon_0 A}{\kappa d - \kappa f d + fd}$$

$$= \boxed{\frac{\kappa}{\kappa + f - \kappa k f}\, C_0}$$

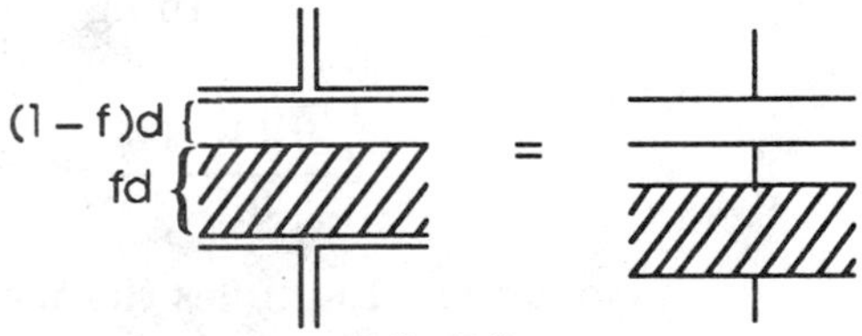

26.70

check : $f \to 0$ $C = \frac{k}{k}\, C_0 = C_0$

$f \to 1$ $C = \frac{k}{k + 1 - k}\, C_0 = kC_0$

26.71 $C_0 = \frac{Q_1}{V_0}; \quad \kappa C_0 = \frac{Q_2}{V_0}$

$$\kappa = \frac{Q_2}{Q_3} = \frac{350\ \mu\text{C}}{150\ \mu\text{C}} = \boxed{2.33}$$

26.72 $U = \frac{1}{2}CV^2; \quad Q = mc\Delta T + mL$

$$\frac{1}{2}CV^2 = m(c\Delta T + L_f)$$

$$\frac{1}{2}(52 \times 10^{-6}\text{ F})V^2 = (6 \times 10^{-6}\text{ kg})[(\frac{1.28\text{ J}}{\text{kg}^\circ \cdot \text{C}})(327.3 - 20)^\circ\text{C} + 24.5 \times 10^4\text{ J/g}]$$

$$V = \sqrt{\frac{2(0.383\text{ J})}{52 \times 10^{-6}\text{ F}}} = \boxed{121\text{ V}}$$

26.73 (a) $C_s = (\frac{1}{8} + \frac{1}{10} + \frac{1}{14})^{-1} = 3.37\ \mu\text{F}$

$$U = \frac{1}{2}(3.37 \times 10^{-6})(12)^2 = \boxed{0.243\text{ mJ}}$$

(b) $C_p = 8 + 10 + 14 = 32\ \mu\text{F}$

$$U = \frac{1}{2}CV^2 = \frac{1}{2}(32 \times 10^{-6})(12)^2 = \boxed{2.30\text{ mJ}}$$

***26.74** gasoline: $\left(\frac{126,000\text{ Btu}}{1\text{ gal}}\right)\left(\frac{1.054 \times 10^3\text{ J}}{1\text{ Btu}}\right)\left(\frac{1\text{ gal}}{3.786 \times 10^{-3}\text{ m}^3}\right)\left(\frac{1\text{ m}^3}{670\text{ kg}}\right)$

$= 5.24 \times 10^7$ J/kg

battery: $\frac{(12\text{ V})\,(100\ \frac{\text{C}}{\text{s}})\,(3600\text{ s})}{16\text{ kg}} = 2.70 \times 10^5\text{ J/kg}$

capacitor: $\frac{\frac{1}{2}(0.1)(144)}{0.1} = 72\text{ J/kg}$

gasoline has 194 times the specific energy content of the battery, 727,000 times that of the capacitor. One could do still better with hydrogen.

***26.75**
$$\begin{aligned} Q = C(100\text{ V}) &= (C + 10\ \mu\text{F})30\text{ V} \\ 100C &= 30C + 300\ \mu\text{F} \\ C &= \frac{300}{70}\ \mu\text{F} = \boxed{4.29\ \mu\text{F}} \end{aligned}$$

***26.76** $V_{\text{max}} = 10^3$ V, each cap is 6 pF,

$$C_{eq} = \frac{1}{\frac{1}{6\ p\text{F}} \times 5} = \frac{6\ p\text{F}}{5} = 1.2\ p\text{F}$$

$\boxed{\text{put five 6 } p\text{F capacitors in series}}$

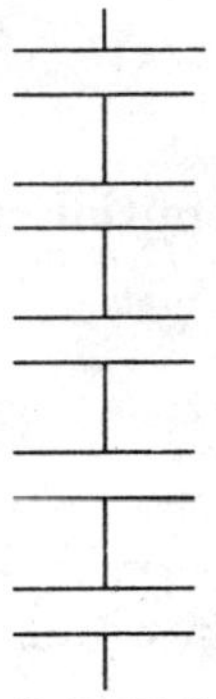

26.76

***26.77**
$$V_2 = \frac{Q}{C_2}$$
$$V_3 = \frac{Q}{C_3}$$

$$\begin{aligned} V_{\text{max}} = V_1 + V_2 = \frac{Q}{2\ \mu\text{F}} + \frac{Q}{3\ \mu\text{F}} &= 800\text{ V} \\ Q\left(\frac{1}{2} + \frac{1}{3}\right) &= 800 \times 10^{-6}\text{ C} \end{aligned}$$

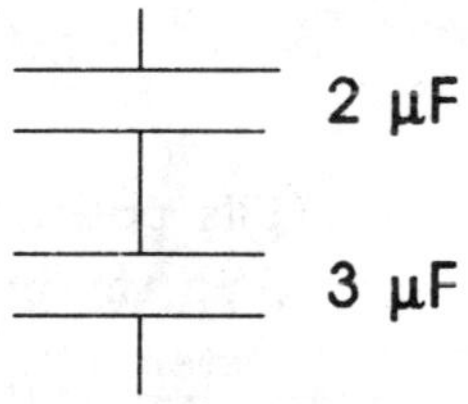

26.77

$$Q = 960\ \mu\text{C}$$
$$\frac{Q}{C_2} = V_2 = 480\text{ V} \quad \frac{Q}{C_3} = V_3 = 320\text{ V}$$
$$\boxed{480\text{ V}} = V_{\text{max}}$$

***26.78** (a) We use Equation (26.12) to find the potential energy. As we will see, the potential V changes as the dielectric is withdrawn. The initial and final energies are

$$U_i = \frac{1}{2}\left(\frac{Q^2}{C_i}\right) \quad \text{and} \quad U_f = \frac{1}{2}\left(\frac{Q^2}{C_f}\right)$$

But the initial capacitance (with the dielectric) is $C_i = \kappa C_f$. Therefore:

$$U_f = \frac{1}{2}\kappa\left(\frac{Q^2}{C_i}\right)$$

Since the work done by the external force in removing the dielectric equals the change in potential energy, we have

$$W = U_f - U_i = \frac{1}{2}\kappa\left(\frac{Q^2}{C_i}\right) - \frac{1}{2}\left(\frac{Q^2}{C_i}\right) = \frac{1}{2}\left(\frac{Q^2}{C_i}\right)(\kappa - 1)$$

To express this relation in terms of the potential V_i, we substitute $Q = C_iV_i$, and evaluate:

$$W = \frac{1}{2}(C_iV_i^2)(\kappa - 1) = \frac{1}{2}(2 \times 10^{-9}\ \text{F})(100\ \text{V})^2(5 - 1) = \boxed{4.00 \times 10^{-5}\ \text{J}}$$

The positive result confirms that the final energy of the capacitor is greater than the initial energy. The extra energy comes from the work done *on* the system by the external force that pulled out the dielectric.

(b) The final potential difference across the capacitor is given by

$$V_f = \frac{q}{C_f}$$

Substituting $C_f = C_i/\kappa$ and $Q = C_iV_i$ gives

$$V_f = \kappa V_i = (5)(100\ \text{V}) = \boxed{500\ \text{V}}$$

Even though the capacitor is isolated and its charge remains constant, the potential difference across the plates does increase in this case.

***26.79** $\kappa = 3$, $E_{max} = 2 \times 10^8$ V/m $= V_{max}d$

$$\text{For } C = \frac{\kappa\epsilon_0 A}{d} = 0.25 \times 10^{-6} \text{ F},$$

$$A = \frac{Cd}{\kappa\epsilon_0} = \frac{CE_{max}}{\kappa\epsilon_0 V_{max}}$$

$$A = \frac{(0.25 \times 10^{-6})(2 \times 10^8)}{3(8.85 \times 10^{-12})(4000)} = \boxed{0.188 \text{ m}^2}$$

26.80 (a) $C_1 = \frac{\kappa_1\epsilon_0 A/2}{d}$; $C_2 = \frac{\kappa_2\epsilon_0 A/2}{d/2}$; $C_3 = \frac{\kappa_3\epsilon_0 A/2}{d/2}$

$$(\frac{1}{C_2} + \frac{1}{C_3})^{-1} = \frac{C_2C_3}{C_2 + C_3} = \frac{\epsilon_0 A}{d}(\frac{\kappa_2\kappa_3}{\kappa_2 + \kappa_3})$$

$$C = C_1(\frac{1}{C_2} + \frac{1}{C_3})^{-1} = \boxed{\frac{\epsilon_0 A}{d}(\frac{\kappa_1}{2} + \frac{\kappa_2\kappa_3}{\kappa_2 + \kappa_3})}$$

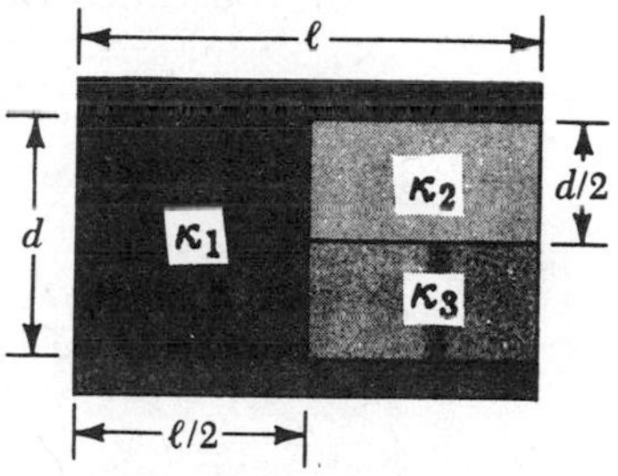

26.80

(b) Using the given values we find:

$$C_{total} = 1.76 \times 10^{-12} \text{ F} = \boxed{1.76 \text{ pF}}$$

26.81 When $V_{db} = 0$, $V_{bc} = V_{dc}$ and $\frac{Q_2}{C_2} = \frac{Q_3}{C_3}$

Also $V_{ba} = V_{da}$ or $\frac{Q_1}{C_1} = \frac{Q_4}{C_4}$. From these equations we have

$$C_2 = (\frac{C_3}{C_4})(\frac{Q_2}{Q_1})(\frac{Q_4}{Q_3})C_1$$

However from the properties of capacitors in series, we have

$Q_1 = Q_2$ and $Q_3 = Q_4$. Therefore

$$C_2 = (\frac{C_3}{C_4})C_1 = \frac{9}{12}(4\ \mu\text{F}) = \boxed{3.00\ \mu\text{F}}$$

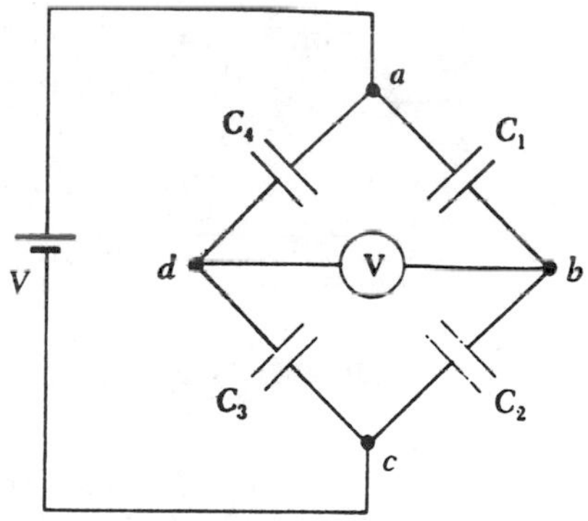

26.81

26.82 Let C = the capacitance of an individual capacitor, and C_p and C_s represent the equivalent capacitance of the group in parallel and series.

While being charged in parallel, $Q = C_p V_{chg} = (5 \times 10^{-3}\ F)(800\ V) = 4$ C.

While being discharged in series

$$V_{\text{disch}} = \frac{Q}{C_s} = \frac{Q}{C/10} = \frac{4\ C}{5 \times 10^{-5}\ \text{F}} = \boxed{8 \times 10^4\ V}$$

or 100 times the original voltage.

Note that for N capacitors, $V_{\text{disch}} = N^2 V_{chg}$

26.83 (a) $C_0 = \dfrac{\epsilon_0 A}{d} = \dfrac{Q_0}{V_0}$. When the dielectric is inserted at constant voltage, $C = \kappa C_0 = \dfrac{Q}{V_0}$; $\quad U_0 = \dfrac{C_0 V_0^2}{2}$

$$U = \frac{CV_0^2}{2} = \frac{\kappa C_0 V_0^2}{2} \text{ and } \frac{U}{U_0} = \kappa$$

Negative work is done by the external force in introducing the dielectric. A force is exerted on the dielectric (see Problem 47) due to the interaction of the induced charges on the dielectric with the *non uniform* electric field at the ends of the plates.

(b) $Q_0 = C_0 V_0$ and $Q = CV_0 = \kappa C_0 V_0$ so Q *increases* by a factor κ.

26.84 (a) $V = Ed$; $\quad d = \dfrac{V}{E} = \dfrac{6000\ \text{V}}{14 \times 10^6\ \text{V/m}} = 4.28 \times 10^{-4}$ m

$$C = \frac{\kappa \epsilon_0 A}{d}; \quad A = \frac{Cd}{\kappa \epsilon_0}$$

$$A = \frac{(2 \times 10^{-7}\ \text{F})(4.28 \times 10^{-4}\ \text{m})}{(5.6)(\epsilon_0)} = \boxed{1.73\ \text{m}^2}$$

(b) $U = \dfrac{CV^2}{2} = \dfrac{(2 \times 10^{-7}\ \text{F})(6000\ \text{V})^2}{2} = \boxed{3.60\ \text{J}}$

26.85 (a) $C = \frac{\epsilon_0}{d}[(l-x)(l+x)l + \kappa l x] = \frac{\epsilon_0}{d}[l^2 + lx(\kappa - 1)]$

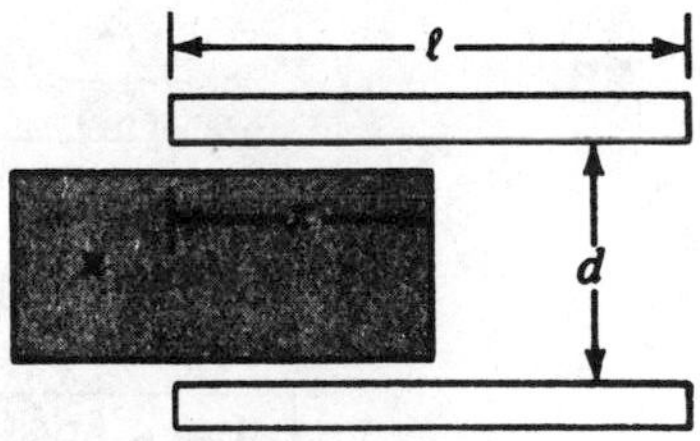

26.85

(b) $U = \frac{1}{2}CV^2 = \frac{1}{2}(\frac{\epsilon_0 V^2}{d})[l^2 + lx(\kappa - 1)]$

(c) $|\mathbf{F}| = |-\frac{dU}{dx}| = \frac{\epsilon_0 V^2}{2d} l(\kappa - 1)$, *to the right*

(d) $F = \frac{1}{2}(2000)^2[(8.85 \times 10^{-12}) + (2 \times 10^{-3})](0.05)(4.5 - 1)$

$= \boxed{1.55 \times 10^{-3}\ \text{N}}$

26.86 Initially (capacitors charged in parallel),

$q_1 = C_1 V = (6\ \mu\text{F})(250\ \text{V}) = 1500\ \mu\text{C};\quad q_2 = C_2 V = (2\ \mu\text{F})(250\ \text{C}) = 500\ \mu\text{C}$

After reconnection (positive plate to negative plate)

$q'_{\text{total}} = q_1 - q_2 = 1000\ \mu\text{C}$ and

$V' = \frac{q'_{\text{total}}}{C_{\text{total}}} = \frac{1000\ \mu\text{C}}{8\ \mu\text{F}} = 125$ V. Therefore,

$q'_1 = C_1 V' = (6\ \mu\text{F})(125\ \text{V}) = \boxed{750\ \mu\text{C}}$

$q'_2 = C_2 V' = (2\ \mu\text{F})(125\ \text{V}) = \boxed{250\ \mu\text{C}}$

26.87 The configuration of N stacked plates is the equivalent of $(N - 1)$ capacitors connected in parallel. Since all capacitors will have the same dielectric, separation and area of overlap, C for each will be the same: $C = \frac{\kappa \epsilon_0 A}{d}$. Parallel capacitors add directly and since the number of capacitors is $(N - 1)$, then

$C_{\text{eq}} = C(N-1) = \frac{\kappa \epsilon_0 A}{d}(N - 1)$

26.88 (a) $F = \frac{Q^2}{2\epsilon_0 A}$ $\quad W = mg$

$$mg = \frac{Q^2}{2\epsilon_0 A} \qquad (25 \times 10^{-6})(9.8) = \frac{Q^2}{2(8.85 \times 10^{-12})(0.1)^2}$$

$$\boxed{Q = 6.59 \times 10^{-9}\ \text{C}}$$

(b) $E = \frac{\sigma}{\epsilon_0} = \frac{Q}{\epsilon_0 A} = \frac{6.59 \times 10^{-9}}{8.85 \times 10^{-12}(0.1)^2} = \boxed{7.44 \times 10^4\ \text{V/m}}$

(c) $V = Ed \qquad 375 = 7.44 \times 10^4 d \qquad \boxed{d = 5.04\ \text{mm}}$

(d) $C = \frac{\epsilon_0 A}{d} = \frac{(8.85 \times 10^{-12})(0.1)^2}{5.04 \times 10^{-3}} = \boxed{17.6\ \text{pF}}$

or

$$V = \frac{Q}{C} \qquad 375 = \frac{6.59 \times 10^{-9}}{C} \qquad C = \boxed{17.6\ \text{pF}}$$

26.89 E_{max} occurs at the inner conductor's surface.

$E_{max} = \frac{2k\lambda}{a}$ from Eq 24.9

$\Delta V = 2k\lambda \ln(\frac{b}{a})$ from Example 26.2

$$E_{max} = \frac{\Delta V}{a \ln(b/a)}$$

$$\Delta V_{max} = E_{max} a \ln(\frac{b}{a}) = (18 \times 10^6\ \text{V/m})(0.8 \times 10^{-3}\ \text{m}) \ln(\frac{3}{0.8}) = \boxed{19.0\ \text{kV}}$$

26.90 $E = \frac{2k\lambda}{a}; \quad \Delta V = 2k\lambda \ln(\frac{b}{a})$

$$\Delta V_{max} = E_{max} a \ln(\frac{b}{a})$$

$$\frac{dV_{max}}{da} = E_{max}[\ln(\frac{b}{a}) + a(\frac{1}{b/a})(-\frac{b}{a^2})] \equiv 0$$

$$\ln(\frac{b}{a}) = 1$$

$$\frac{b}{a} = e^1$$

$$\boxed{a = \frac{b}{e}}$$

26.91 Assume a potential difference across a and b, and notice that the voltage across the 8 μF capacitor must be zero by symmetry. Then the equivalent capacitance can be determined from the following circuit:

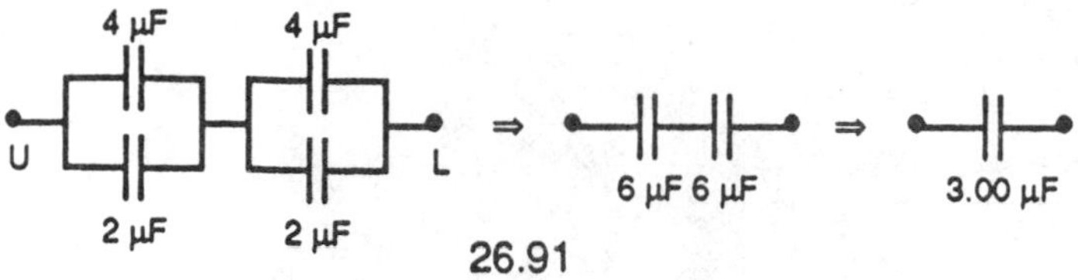

26.91

26.92 By symmetry, the potential difference across $3C$ is zero, so the circuit reduces to

$$C_{eq} = \frac{(2C)(4C)}{2C + 4C} = \frac{8}{6}C = \boxed{\frac{4}{3}C}$$

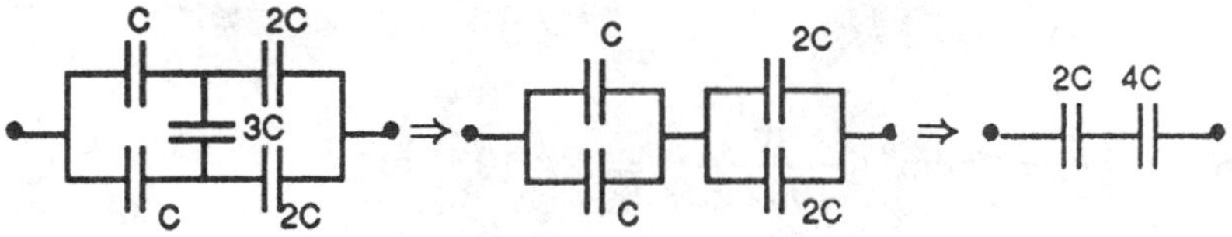

26.92

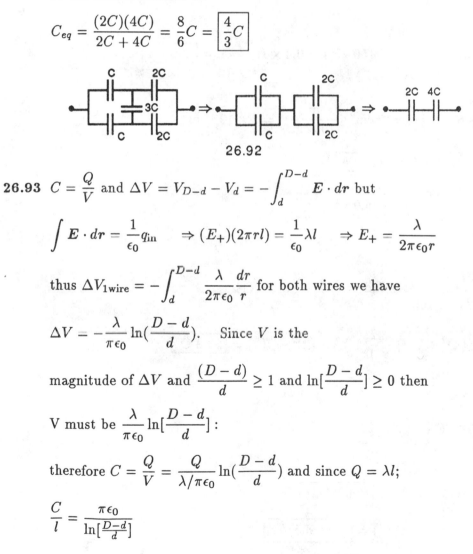

26.93 $C = \frac{Q}{V}$ and $\Delta V = V_{D-d} - V_d = -\int_d^{D-d} \mathbf{E} \cdot d\mathbf{r}$ but

$$\int \mathbf{E} \cdot d\mathbf{r} = \frac{1}{\epsilon_0} q_{\text{in}} \quad \Rightarrow (E_+)(2\pi r l) = \frac{1}{\epsilon_0}\lambda l \quad \Rightarrow E_+ = \frac{\lambda}{2\pi\epsilon_0 r}$$

thus $\Delta V_{1\text{wire}} = -\int_d^{D-d} \frac{\lambda}{2\pi\epsilon_0} \frac{dr}{r}$ for both wires we have

$\Delta V = -\frac{\lambda}{\pi\epsilon_0} \ln(\frac{D-d}{d})$. Since V is the

magnitude of ΔV and $\frac{(D-d)}{d} \geq 1$ and $\ln[\frac{D-d}{d}] \geq 0$ then

V must be $\frac{\lambda}{\pi\epsilon_0} \ln[\frac{D-d}{d}]$:

therefore $C = \frac{Q}{V} = \frac{Q}{\lambda/\pi\epsilon_0} \ln(\frac{D-d}{d})$ and since $Q = \lambda l$;

$$\frac{C}{l} = \frac{\pi\epsilon_0}{\ln[\frac{D-d}{d}]}$$

CHAPTER 27

27.1 $I = \frac{dQ}{dt} = \frac{3 \times 10^{12}(1.602 \times 10^{-19})}{1} = 4.81 \times 10^{-7} = \boxed{0.481\ \mu\text{A}}$

27.2 $I = \frac{ne}{t} \qquad q = ne$

$$30 \times 10^{-6} = \frac{n(1.602 \times 10^{19})}{40.0}$$

$$\boxed{n = 7.49 \times 10^{15} \text{ electrons}}$$

27.3 $I = \frac{dq}{dt} = \frac{q\omega}{2\pi} = (8 \times 10^{-9}\ \text{C})(50\ \text{s}^{-1}) = 0.4 \times 10^{-6}\ \ \text{A} = \boxed{400\ \text{nA}}$

27.4 $q = 4t^3 + 5t + 6; \qquad A = (2\ \text{cm}^2)(\frac{\text{m}}{100\ \text{cm}})^2 = 2 \times 10^{-4}\ \text{m}^2$

(a) $I = \frac{dq}{dt} = 12t^2 + 5 = \boxed{17.0\ \ \text{A}}$

(b) $J = \frac{I}{A} = \frac{17}{2 \times 10^{-4}} = \boxed{85.0\ \text{kA/m}^2}$

27.5 $q = \int I dt = \int_2^4 (2t^2 - 3t + 7)dt = \frac{2}{3}t^3 - \frac{3}{2}t^2 + 7t \,\Big|_2^4$

$$q = \frac{2}{3}(4)^3 - \frac{3}{2}(4)^2 + 7(4) - \frac{2}{3}(2^3) + \frac{3}{2}(2)^2 - 7(2) = \boxed{33.3\ \text{C}}$$

27.6 $Q(t) = \int_0^t I dt = I_0\tau(1 - e^{-t/\tau})$

(a) $Q(\tau) = I_0\tau(1 - e^{-1}) = \boxed{(0.632)I_0\tau}$

(b) $Q(10\tau) = I_0\tau(1 - e^{-10}) = \boxed{(0.99995)I_0\tau}$

(c) $Q(\infty) = I_0\tau(1 - e^{-\infty}) = \boxed{I_0\tau}$

27.7 $n = 19.3 \times 10^3 \dfrac{\text{kg}}{\text{m}^3} \dfrac{6.022 \times 10^{26}\text{ atoms}}{167\text{ kg}} \dfrac{1\ e}{\text{atom}} = \boxed{5.90 \times 10^{28}\text{ e/m}^3}$

***27.8** We first calculate n, the number of current-carrying electrons per unit volume in copper. Assuming one free conduction electron per atom, $n = N_{\text{A}}\rho/M$, where N_{A} is Avogadro's number and ρ and M are the density and the atomic weight of copper, respectively.

$$n = \left(1\ \frac{\text{electron}}{\text{atom}}\right) \frac{N_{\text{A}}\rho}{M}$$

$$n = \left(1\ \frac{\text{electron}}{\text{atom}}\right)\left(6.02 \times 10^{23}\ \frac{\text{atoms}}{\text{mol}}\right)\left(\frac{1}{63.54\ \frac{\text{g}}{\text{mol}}}\right)\left(8.92\ \frac{\text{g}}{\text{cm}^3}\right)\underbrace{\left(\frac{10^6\text{ cm}^3}{1\text{ m}^3}\right)}_{\text{Conversion ratio}}$$

$$n = 8.45 \times 10^{28}\ \frac{\text{electrons}}{\text{m}^3}$$

From Equation 27.5, we obtain, for the drift speed v_{d},

$$v_{\text{d}} = \frac{1}{nqA} = \frac{1\text{ A}}{\left(8.45 \times 10^{28}\ \frac{\text{electrons}}{\text{m}^3}\right)\left(1.602 \times 10^{-19}\ \frac{\text{C}}{\text{electron}}\right)(10^{-6}\text{ m}^2)}$$

$$v_{\text{d}} = \boxed{7.39 \times 10^{-5}\text{ m/s}}$$

This is less than 0.1 millimeter per second. At this speed, it takes an electron 3.76 hours to travel just one meter!

27.9 (a) $I = JA = (2000\text{ A/cm}^2)\ (5\text{ cm})(15\text{ cm}) = \boxed{150\text{ kA}}$

(b) $q = It = (1.5 \times 10^5\text{ C/s})(3600\text{ s}) = \boxed{540\ \text{MC}}$

27.10 (a) $J = \dfrac{I}{A} = \dfrac{5\text{ A}}{\pi(0.004\text{ m})^2} = \boxed{9.95 \times 10^4\text{ A/m}^2}$

(b) $J_2 = \dfrac{1}{4}J_1 \quad ; \quad \dfrac{I}{A_2} = \dfrac{1}{4}\dfrac{I}{A_1}$

$$A_1 = \frac{1}{4}A_2$$

$$\pi(0.004)^2 = \frac{1}{4}\pi r_2^2$$

$$r_2 = 2(0.004) = 0.008\text{ m} = \boxed{0.800\text{ cm}}$$

27.11 $J = \dfrac{I}{A} = \dfrac{10\ \mu\text{A}}{2\pi(6 \times 10^{-3}\ \text{m})(20\ \text{m})} = \boxed{1.33 \times 10^{-5}\ \text{A/m}^2}$

27.12 $J = \sigma E$

$$\frac{3A}{\pi(0.012)^2\ \text{m}^2} = \sigma(120\ \text{N/C})$$

$$\sigma = 55.3(\Omega \cdot \text{m})^{-1} \qquad \rho = \frac{1}{\sigma} = \boxed{0.0181\ \Omega \cdot \text{m}}$$

27.13 $J = \sigma E = 6.289 \times 10^7(\Omega \cdot \text{m})^{-1}(2.1 \times 10^3\ \text{N/C}) = \boxed{1.32 \times 10^{11}\ \text{A/m}^2}$

***27.14** The distance between opposite faces of the cube is $\ell = \sqrt[3]{\dfrac{90\ \text{g}}{10.5\ \text{g/cm}^3}} = 2.046\ \text{cm}$

(a) $R = \dfrac{\rho\ell}{\text{A}} = \dfrac{\rho\ell}{\ell^2} = \dfrac{\rho}{\ell} = \dfrac{1.59 \times 10^{-8}\ \Omega\ \text{m}}{2.046 \times 10^{-2}\ \text{m}} = \boxed{7.77 \times 10^{-8}\ \Omega}$

(b) $I = \dfrac{V}{R} = \dfrac{10^{-5}\ \text{V}}{7.77 \times 10^{-8}\ \Omega} = 12.87\ \text{A}$

$$I = nqvA \qquad n = \frac{10.5\ \text{g/cm}^3}{107.87\ \text{g/mol}}\left(6.02 \times 10^{23}\ \frac{\text{electrons}}{\text{mol}}\right)$$

$$n = 5.86 \times 10^{28}/\text{m}^3$$

$$v = \frac{I}{nqA} = \frac{12.78\ \text{A}}{(5.86 \times 10^{28})(1.6 \times 10^{-19})(0.0246)^2}$$

$$v = \boxed{3.28 \times 10^{-6}\ \text{m/s}}$$

27.15 $R = \dfrac{\rho\ell}{A} = \dfrac{(1.59 \times 10^{-8}\ \Omega \cdot \text{m})(40\ \text{m})}{0.4 \times 10^{-6}\ \text{m}^2} = \boxed{1.59\ \Omega}$

27.16 $A = \pi r^2 = \pi(0.512 \times 10^{-3}\ \text{m})^2 = 8.24 \times 10^{-7}\ \text{m}^2$

$$R = \frac{\rho\ell}{A} = \frac{(1.7 \times 10^{-8}\ \Omega \cdot \text{m})(15\ \text{m})}{8.24 \times 10^{-7}\ \text{m}^2} = \boxed{0.310\ \Omega}$$

27.17 $A = (0.031\ \text{cm}^2)(\frac{\text{m}}{100\ \text{cm}})^2 = 3.1 \times 10^{-6}\ \text{m}^2$

$$R = \frac{\rho \ell}{A} = 0.24 = \frac{\rho(2.4)}{3.1 \times 10^{-6}}$$

$$\rho = 3.1 \times 10^{-7}\ \Omega \cdot \text{m}$$

$$\sigma = \frac{1}{\rho} = \boxed{3.23 \times 10^6\ (\Omega \cdot \text{m})^{-1}}$$

27.18 $r = 0.001 \times 10^{-2}\ \text{m} \qquad A = \pi r^2 = 3.14 \times 10^{-10}\ \text{m}^2$

$$R = \frac{\rho \ell}{A} = \frac{(5.6 \times 10^{-8})(0.15)}{3.14 \times 10^{-10}} = \boxed{26.7\ \Omega}$$

27.19 $\frac{R}{\ell} = 3.28 \times 10^{-3}\ \Omega/\text{m}$

$$R = \frac{\rho \ell}{A}$$

$$\frac{R}{\ell} = \frac{\rho}{A}$$

$$3.28 \times 10^{-3} = \frac{(1.7 \times 10^{-8})}{A}$$

$$A = 5.18 \times 10^{-6} = \pi r^2$$

$d = \boxed{2.56\ \text{mm}}$ (approx. 10 gauge wire)

$$d = 2r = 2(1.28 \times 10^{-3}\ \text{m})$$

27.20 $R = \frac{\rho \ell}{A} = \frac{(11 \times 10^{-8}\ \Omega \cdot \text{m})(1.5\ \text{m})}{\frac{\pi(10^{-4}\ \text{m})^2}{4}} = \boxed{21.0\ \Omega}$

***27.21** $A_0 \ell_0 = A\ell = \left(\frac{A_0}{1.25}\right)(1.25\ \ell_0)$

Since $R = \frac{\rho \ell}{A}$ and $R_0 = \frac{\rho \ell_0}{A_0}$,

$$R = \frac{\rho(1.25\ \ell_0)}{(A_0/1.25)} = \boxed{1.56\ R_0}$$

27.22 $\frac{(\rho_{Al}\ell)}{\pi(r_{Al})^2} = \frac{(\rho_{Cu}\ell)}{\pi(r_{Cu})^2}$

$$\frac{r_{Al}}{r_{Cu}} = \frac{\rho_{Al}}{\rho_{Cu}} = \frac{2.82 \times 10^{-8}}{1.7 \times 10^{-8}}$$

$$\boxed{\frac{r_{Al}}{r_{Cu}} = 1.29}$$

27.23 (a) Given $M = \rho_d V = \rho_d AL \longrightarrow A = \frac{M}{\rho_d L}$; $\rho_d \equiv$ density; $\rho_r \equiv$ resistivity

and $R = \frac{\rho_r L}{A} = \frac{\rho_r L}{(\frac{M}{\rho_d L})} = \frac{\rho_r \rho_d L^2}{M}$

so $L = \sqrt{\frac{MR}{\rho_r \rho_d}} = \sqrt{\frac{1 \times 10^{-3}(0.5)}{(8.93 \times 10^3)(1.7 \times 10^{-8})}} = \boxed{1.81 \text{ m}}$

(b) $V = \frac{M}{\rho_d}$: $\pi r^2 \ell = \frac{M}{\rho_d}$: $r = \sqrt{\frac{M}{\pi \rho_d L}} = \sqrt{\frac{10^{-3}}{\pi(8930)(1.81)}} = 0.00014 \text{ m} = 0.14 \text{ mm}$

$\boxed{\text{diameter} = 0.28 \text{ mm}}$

27.24 $V = IR$

$110 = 7R$ $\boxed{R = 15.7\ \Omega}$

27.25 $V = IR$; $R = \frac{\rho\ell}{A}$; $A = 0.6 \text{ mm}^2(\frac{\text{m}}{1000 \text{ mm}})^2 = 6 \times 10^{-7}\text{m}^2$

$V = \frac{I\rho\ell}{A}$

$0.9 = \frac{I(5.6 \times 10^{-8})(1.5)}{6 \times 10^{-7}}$

$\boxed{I = 6.43 \text{ A}}$

***27.26** (a) $J = \frac{I}{A} = \frac{8 \times 10^{-6}\ \text{A}}{\pi(1 \times 10^{-3}\ \text{m})^2} = \boxed{2.55\ \text{A/m}^2}$

(b) From $I = nev_d$, we have

$$n = \frac{I}{ev_d} = \frac{2.55\ \text{A/m}^2}{(1.60 \times 10^{-19}\ \text{C})(3 \times 10^8\ \text{m/s})} = \boxed{5.31 \times 10^{10}\ \text{m}^{-3}}$$

(c) From $I = \Delta Q/\Delta t$, we have

$$\Delta t = \frac{\Delta Q}{I} = \frac{N_A e}{I} = \frac{(6.02 \times 10^{23})(1.60 \times 10^{-19}\ \text{C})}{8 \times 10^{-6}\ \text{A}}$$

$$= \boxed{1.20 \times 10^{10}\ \text{s}} \quad \text{(or about 381 years!)}$$

***27.27** (a) Applying Ohm's law, we find the resistance of the rod,

$$R = \frac{V}{I} = \frac{15\ \text{V}}{4 \times 10^{-3}\ \text{A}} = 3750\ \Omega = \boxed{3.75\ \text{k}\Omega}$$

(b) The length of the rod is determined from Equation (27.10): $R = \rho\ell/A$. Solving for ℓ gives

$$\ell = \frac{RA}{\rho}$$

Substituting numerical values for R, A, and the values of ρ given for carbon in Table 27.1, we obtain

$$\ell = \frac{(3.75 \times 10^3\ \Omega)(5 \times 10^{-6}\ \text{m}^2)}{(3.5 \times 10^{-5}\ \Omega \cdot \text{m})} = \boxed{536\ \text{m}}$$

***27.28** $J = \sigma E$

$$\sigma = \frac{J}{E} = \frac{6 \times 10^{-13}\ \text{A/m}^2}{100\ \text{V/m}} = \boxed{6 \times 10^{-15}\ (\Omega \cdot \text{m})^{-1}}$$

27.29 (a) $\rho = \rho_0[1 + \alpha(T - T_0)]$

$$= (2.82 \times 10^{-8}\ \Omega \cdot \text{m})(1 + 3.9 \times 10^{-3}(30°)) = \boxed{3.15 \times 10^{-8}\ \Omega \cdot \text{m}}$$

(b) $J = \dfrac{E}{\rho} = \dfrac{0.2\ \text{V/m}}{3.15 \times 10^{-8}\ \Omega \cdot \text{m}} = \boxed{6.35 \times 10^{6}\ \text{A/m}^2}$

(c) $I = JA = \dfrac{\pi d^2}{4} J = \dfrac{\pi(10^{-4}\ \text{m})^2}{4}(6.35 \times 10^{6}\ \text{A/m}^2) = \boxed{49.9\ \text{mA}}$

(d) $v_d = \dfrac{\text{J}}{\text{ne}}$

$$n = \frac{6.02 \times 10^{23}\ \text{electrons}}{\dfrac{26.98\ \text{g}}{2.70 \times 10^{6}\ \text{g/m}^3}} = 6.02 \times 10^{25}\ \text{electrons/m}^3$$

$$v_d = \frac{(6.35 \times 10^{6}\ \text{A/m}^2)}{(6.02 \times 10^{25}\ \text{electrons/m}^3)(1.6 \times 10^{-19}\ \text{C})} = \boxed{0.659 \times 10^{-3}\ \text{m/s}}$$

(e) $V = E\ell = (0.2\ \text{V/m})(2\ \text{m}) = \boxed{0.400\ \text{V}}$

27.30 $R = R_0[1 + \alpha\Delta T]$

$$\frac{R}{R_0} = 1 + \alpha\Delta T = 1 + (-0.5 \times 10^{-3})(140)$$

$$\frac{R}{R_0} = 0.93;\quad \boxed{7\%\ \text{decrease}}$$

27.31 $R = R_0[1 + \alpha\Delta T]$

$$R - R_0 = R_0\alpha\Delta T$$

$$\frac{R - R_0}{R_0} = \alpha\Delta T = (5 \times 10^{-3})25 = \boxed{0.125}$$

***27.32** Assuming linear change of resistance with temperature, $R = R_0(1 + \alpha\Delta T)$

$$R_{77\,\mathrm{K}} = (1\ \Omega)[1 + (3.92 \times 10^{-3})(-216°\ \mathrm{C})] = \boxed{0.153\ \Omega}$$

27.33 $R = R_o[1 + \alpha\Delta T] = (18.0\ \Omega)[1 + (3.9 \times 10^{-3})(40)] = \boxed{20.8\ \Omega}$

***27.34** For aluminum,

$$\alpha_E = 3.9 \times 10^{-3}/°\mathrm{C} \quad \text{(Table 27.1)}$$
$$\alpha = 24 \times 10^{-6}/°\mathrm{C} \quad \text{(Table 19.2)}$$

$$R = \frac{\rho\ell}{A} = \frac{\rho_0[1 + \alpha_E\Delta T]\ell(1 + \alpha\Delta T)}{A(1 + \alpha\Delta T)^2}$$

$$R = R_0\frac{(1 + \alpha_E\Delta T)}{(1 + \alpha\Delta T)} = (1.234\ \Omega)\frac{(1.39)}{(1.0024)}$$

$$R = \boxed{1.711\ \Omega}$$

27.35 $\rho = \rho_0(1 + \alpha\Delta T)$ or $\Delta T_w = \dfrac{1\alpha/w}{\rho_w/\rho_0 w}$

Require that $\rho_w = 4\rho_{0_{Cu}}$ so that

$$\Delta T_w = \left(\frac{\frac{1}{4.5\times10^{-3}}}{\mathrm{C}^\circ}\right)\left(\frac{4(1.7 \times 10^{-8})}{5.6 \times 10^{-8}} - 1\right) = 47.6°\mathrm{C}$$

Therefore $T_w = 47.6°\mathrm{C} + \mathrm{T}_0 = \boxed{67.6°\mathrm{C}}$

27.36 $\alpha = \dfrac{1}{R_0}(\dfrac{\Delta R}{\Delta T}) = (\dfrac{1}{R_0})\dfrac{2R_0 - R_0}{T - T_0}$

$$\alpha = \frac{1}{T - T_0}$$

so $T = (\dfrac{1}{\alpha}) + T_0$ and $T = (\dfrac{1}{0.4 \times 10^{-3}\ \mathrm{C}^{\circ-1}})$ so $T = \boxed{2520°\mathrm{C}}$

27.37 $R = R_0[1 + \alpha(T - 20°\mathrm{C})]$

$$R_0 = \frac{R}{1 + \alpha(T - 20°\mathrm{C})} = \frac{85\ \Omega}{1 + 3.4 \times 10^{-3}(45 - 20)} = 78.34\ \Omega$$

$$80\ \Omega = (78.34\ \Omega)[1 + (3.4 \times 10^{-3})(T - 20°\mathrm{C})]$$

$$T = \boxed{26.2°\mathrm{C}}$$

***27.38** $P = IV = \frac{V^2}{R} = 500\text{ W}$

$$R = \frac{(110\text{ V})^2}{(500\text{ W})} = 24.2\ \Omega$$

(a) $R = \frac{\rho \ell}{A} \quad \ell = \frac{RA}{\rho} = \frac{(24.2\ \Omega)\pi(2.5\times10^{-4}\text{ m})^2}{1.5\times10^{-6}\ \Omega\cdot\text{m}}$

$$\ell = \boxed{3.17\text{ m}}$$

(b)
$$\begin{aligned} R &= R_0[1+\alpha\Delta T] \\ &= 24.2\ \Omega[1+(0.4\times10^{-3})(1180)] = 35.6\ \Omega \\ P &= \frac{V^2}{R} = \frac{(110)^2}{35.6} = \boxed{340\text{ W}} \end{aligned}$$

27.39 $J = \frac{1}{\rho}E = \frac{1}{2.44\times10^{-8}\ \Omega\cdot\text{m}}(0.74\text{ V/m}) = \boxed{3.03\times10^{7}\text{ A/m}^2}$

27.40 $\rho = \frac{m}{nq^2\tau}$

$$\tau = \frac{m}{\rho n q^2} = \frac{9.11\times10^{-31}}{(1.7\times10^{-8})(8.48\times10^{28})(1.602\times10^{19})^2} = 2.46\times10^{-14}\text{ s}$$

$$v_d = \frac{qE}{m}\tau$$

$$7.84\times10^{-4} = \frac{(1.602\times10^{-19})E(2.46\times10^{-14})}{9.11\times10^{-31}}$$

$$\boxed{E = 0.180\ \text{V/m}}$$

27.41 $\rho = \dfrac{m}{nq^2\tau}$; $\tau = 2.47 \times 10^{-14}$ s (See Example 27.6)

$\ell = v\tau = (8.6 \times 10^5 \text{ m/s})(2.47 \times 10^{-14} \text{ s}) = \boxed{2.12 \times 10^{-8} \text{ m}}$

27.42 (a) n is $\boxed{\text{unaffected}}$

(b) $|\mathbf{J}| = \dfrac{I}{A} \; \alpha \; I$ so it $\boxed{\text{doubles}}$ too

(c) $J = nev_d$ so v_d $\boxed{\text{doubles}}$

(d) $\tau = \dfrac{\text{m}\sigma}{\text{nq}^2}$ is $\boxed{\text{unchanged}}$ as long as σ does not change due to heating.

27.43 $P = IV \quad V = IR$

$P = \dfrac{V^2}{R} \quad I = \dfrac{V}{R}$

$P = \dfrac{(10)^2}{120} = \boxed{0.833 \text{ W}}$

27.44 $P = IV$

$100 \times 10^3 = I(200)$

$\boxed{I = 500 \text{ A}}$

27.45 $\dfrac{\rho}{\rho_0} = \dfrac{V^2/R}{V_0^2/R} = \left(\dfrac{V}{V_0}\right)^2 = \left(\dfrac{140}{120}\right)^2 = 1.361$

$\Delta\% = \dfrac{\rho - \rho_0}{\rho_0} \cdot 100 = \left(\dfrac{\rho}{\rho_0} - 1\right) \cdot 100 = (1.361 - 1)100 = \boxed{36.1\%}$

27.46 $U = (360\ \text{A}\cdot\text{h})(12\ \text{V})(\frac{3600\ \text{s}}{\text{h}}) = \boxed{1.56\times 10^{7}\ \text{J}}$

27.47 $P = \frac{V^2}{R}$

$125 = \frac{V^2}{55}$

$\boxed{V = 82.9\ \text{V}}$

27.48 $P = 0.8(1500\ \text{hp})(0.746\times 10^{3}\ \text{W/hp}) = 895,200\ \text{W}$

$P = IV$

$895,200 = I(2000)$

$\boxed{I = 448\ \text{A}}$

***27.49** (a)

$$\begin{aligned} P &= I^2R \\ 300\ \text{W} &= (1.5\ \text{A})^2R \\ R &= \boxed{133\ \Omega} \end{aligned}$$

(b) $\rho = 10^{-6}\ \Omega\cdot\text{m} \qquad A = \pi(3\times 10^{-4})^2/4$

$$\begin{aligned} R &= \frac{\rho\ell}{A} \\ \ell &= \frac{RA}{\rho} = \frac{(133)(\pi)(3\times 10^{-4})^2}{4\times 10^{-6}} = \boxed{9.42\ \text{m}} \end{aligned}$$

***27.50** (a) $P = I^2R = \frac{V^2}{R} = \frac{(100)^2}{20} = 500\ \text{W}$

$U_{1\ \text{hr}} = \frac{1}{5}(500\ \text{W})(3600\ \text{s}) = \boxed{360\ \text{kJ}}$

(b) $\overline{P} = \frac{\Delta U}{\Delta t} = \frac{(500\ \text{W})\cdot(1\ \text{s})}{5\ \text{s}} = \boxed{100\ \text{W}}$

27.51 $U = P(\Delta t) = \frac{V^2}{R}(\Delta t) = mc(\Delta T)$ where c is the specific heat capacity of water and ΔT is the increase in temperature.

$$R = \frac{V^2 \Delta t}{mc\Delta T} = \frac{(110\text{ V})^2(600\text{ s})}{(1.5\text{ kg})(4184\text{ J/kg})(50°\text{C} - 10°\text{C})} = \boxed{28.9\ \Omega}$$

Note that for water $c = 1$ cal/g $\cdot°$ C or 4184 J/kg $\cdot°$ C

***27.52**

$$P = IV = (2\text{ A})(120\text{ V}) = 240\text{ W}$$

$$\Delta U = (0.5\text{ kg})(4186\text{ J/kg °C})(77\text{ °C}) = 161\text{ kJ}$$

$$t = \frac{\Delta U}{P} = \frac{1.61 \times 10^5\text{ J}}{240\text{ W}} = \boxed{672\text{ s}}$$

27.53 Energy used in a 24 hr day = (0.187 kW)(24 h) = 4.488 kWh

$$\therefore \text{cost} = 4.488\text{ kWh}\left(\frac{\$0.06}{\text{kWh}}\right) = \$0.269 = \boxed{26.9¢}$$

27.54 (a) $V = IR$

$$R = \frac{V}{I} = \frac{110}{8} = \boxed{13.75\ \Omega}$$

(b) $P = I^2R$

$$750 = I^2(13.75)$$

$$I = \boxed{7.39\text{ A}}$$

***27.55** At operating temperature,

(a) $P = IV = (1.53 \text{ A})(120 \text{ V}) = \boxed{184 \text{ W}}$

(b) Use the change in resistance to find the final operating temperature of the toaster.

$$R = R_0(1 + \alpha\Delta T)$$

$$\frac{120}{1.53} = \frac{120}{1.8}[1 + (0.4 \times 10^{-3})\Delta T]$$

$$\Delta T = 441° \text{ C}$$

$$T = 20° \text{ C} + 441° \text{ C} = \boxed{461 \text{ °C}}$$

***27.56** 2 wires $\rightarrow \ell = 100$ m

$$R = \frac{0.108\ \Omega}{300 \text{ m}}(100 \text{ m}) = 0.036\ \Omega$$

(a) $V_{\text{home}} = V_{\text{line}} - IR = 120 - (110)(0.036) = \boxed{116 \text{ V}}$

(b) $P = IV = (110 \text{ A})(116 \text{ V}) = \boxed{12.8 \text{ kW}}$

(c) $P_{\text{wires}} = I^2R = (110 \text{ A})^2(0.036\ \Omega) = \boxed{436 \text{ W}}$

27.57 $R = R_0[1 + \alpha(T - T_0)]$; Thus

$$T = T_0 + \frac{1}{\alpha}[\frac{R}{R_0} - 1] = T_0 + \frac{1}{\alpha}[\frac{I_0}{I} - 1]$$

In this case $I = 0.1\ I_0$, so $T = T_0 + \frac{1}{\alpha}(9) = 20° + \frac{9}{0.0045/°\text{C}}$

$T = \boxed{2020°\text{C}}$

27.58 $R = \frac{V}{I} = \frac{12}{I} = \frac{6}{(I-3)}$ thus $12I - 36 = 6I$ and $I = 6$ A

Therefore $R = \frac{12 \text{ V}}{6 \text{ A}} = \boxed{2.00\ \Omega}$

***27.59** (a) $P = IV$

$$I = \frac{P}{V} = \frac{8000\ \text{W}}{12\ \text{V}} = \boxed{667\ \text{A}}$$

(b) $t = \dfrac{U}{P} = \dfrac{2 \times 10^7 \text{J}}{8000\ \text{W}} = 2500\ \text{s}$

$$d = vt = (20\ \text{m/s})(2500\ \text{s}) = \boxed{50\ \text{km}}$$

27.60 (a) $R = \dfrac{\rho\ell}{A} = \dfrac{(1.7 \times 10^{-8})(0.24)}{(0.08)(0.002)} = \boxed{2.55 \times 10^{-5}\ \Omega}$

(b) $m = (\text{Vol})(\text{Density})$: but $R = \dfrac{\rho\ell}{A}$ and $A = \dfrac{\text{Vol}}{\ell}$. Therefore

$$m = \frac{\rho\ell^2}{R}(\text{Density})$$

$$m = \left[\frac{(1.7 \times 10^{-8}\ \Omega \cdot \text{m})(1.5 \times 10^3\ \text{m})^2}{4.5\ \Omega}\right](8.9 \times 10^3\ \text{kg/m}^3) = \boxed{75.8\ \text{kg}}$$

27.61 $R = \dfrac{\rho\ell_0}{A_0} = \dfrac{\rho\ell}{A}$; $\quad V = A\ell = A_0\ell_0$

$$R_0 = \frac{\rho\ell_0^2}{V} \text{ and } R = \frac{\rho\ell^2}{V}$$

so $R = \dfrac{\rho}{V}[\ell_0 + \Delta\ell]^2$ which yields $R = \rho\ell_0^2 V[1 + \dfrac{2\Delta\ell}{\ell_0} + (\dfrac{\Delta\ell}{\ell_0})^2]$

Letting $\alpha = \dfrac{\Delta\ell}{\Delta\ell_0}$ the tensile strain (see Section 12.4) we have $R = R_0[1 + 2\alpha + \alpha^2]$

***27.62** $I = \dfrac{dq}{dt}$

$$q = \int_{t=0}^{t} I dt = \int_{t=0}^{\infty} (0.0025)e^{-0.833\,t} dt$$

$$q = (2.5 \times 10^{-3}) \frac{e^{-0.833\,t}}{-0.833} \Big|_0^{\infty} = \boxed{3.00 \times 10^{-3}\ \text{C}}$$

27.63 (a) $R = \frac{\rho \ell}{A} = \frac{\rho L}{\pi(r_b^2 - r_a^2)}$

(b) $R = (3.5 \times 10^5\ \Omega \cdot \text{m})\frac{0.04\ \text{m}}{\pi[(0.012\ \text{m})^2 - (0.005\ \text{m})^2]}$

$R = 3.74 \times 10^7\ \Omega = \boxed{37.4\ \text{M}\Omega}$

27.64 (a) $R = \int_{r_a}^{r_b} \frac{\rho dr}{2\pi r L} = \frac{\rho}{2\pi L}\ln(\frac{r_b}{r_a})$

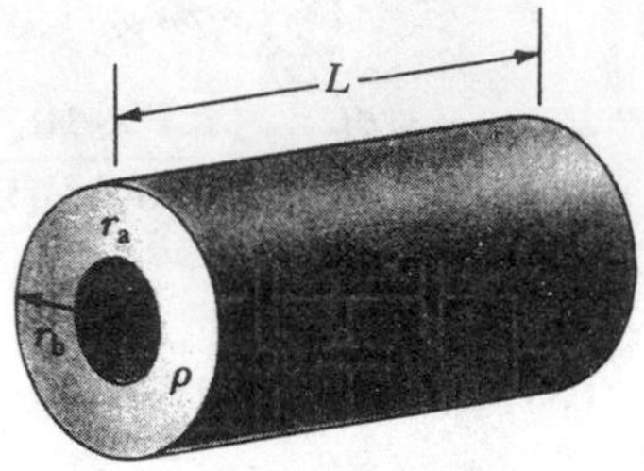

27.63 and 27.64

(b) Using the given values

$$R = \frac{3.5 \times 10^5\ \Omega \cdot \text{m}}{2\pi(0.04\ \text{m})}\ln(\frac{1.2}{0.5})$$

$$= 1.22 \times 10^6\ \Omega = \boxed{1.22\ \text{M}\Omega}$$

***27.65** $\alpha = \frac{1}{\rho}\frac{d\rho}{dT}$

(a) Separating variables,

$$\int_{\rho_0}^{\rho} \frac{d\rho}{\rho} = \int_{T_0}^{T} \alpha dT$$

$$\ln\left(\frac{\rho}{\rho_0}\right) = \alpha(T - T_0)$$

$$\rho = \rho_0 e^{\alpha(T-T_0)}$$

(b) From the series expansion $e^x = 1 + x$,

$$\rho = \rho_0[1 + \alpha(T - T_0)]$$

***27.66** $V = -E \cdot \ell$ or $dV = E \cdot dx$

$V = IR = -E \cdot \ell$

$I = \frac{dq}{dt} = -RE \cdot \ell = -\frac{A}{\rho \ell}E \cdot \ell$

$I = \frac{dq}{dt} = -\frac{A}{\rho}E = -\sigma A\frac{dV}{dx}$

Current flows in the direction of decreasing voltage.

27.67 $R = \int \frac{\rho dx}{A} = \int \frac{\rho dx}{wy}$ where $y = y_1 + \frac{y_2 - y_1}{L}x$

$$R = \frac{\rho}{w}\int_0^L \frac{dx}{y_1 + \frac{y_2 - y_1}{L}x} = \frac{\rho L}{w(y_2 - y_1)}\ln(y_1 + \frac{y_2 + y_1}{L}x)\Big|_0^L$$

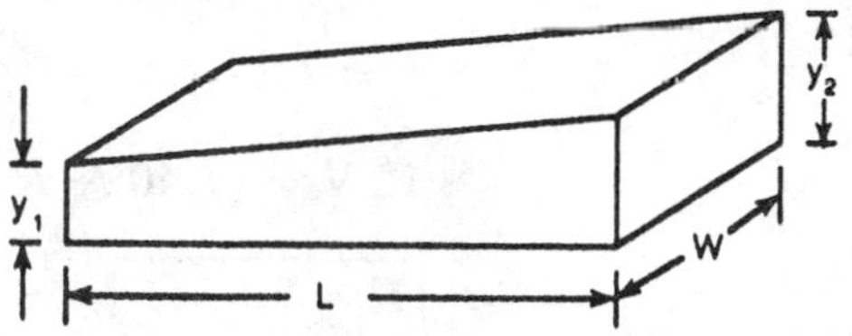

27.67

$$\boxed{R = \frac{\rho L}{w(y_2 - y_1)}\ln(\frac{y_2}{y_1})}$$

27.68 From the geometry of the longitudinal section of the resistor shown in the figure we see that $\frac{(b-r)}{y} = \frac{(b-a)}{h}$ and from this the radius at a distance y from the base is $r = (a-b)\frac{y}{h} + b$ and for the element of volume shown $dR = \frac{\rho dy}{\pi r^2}$ so

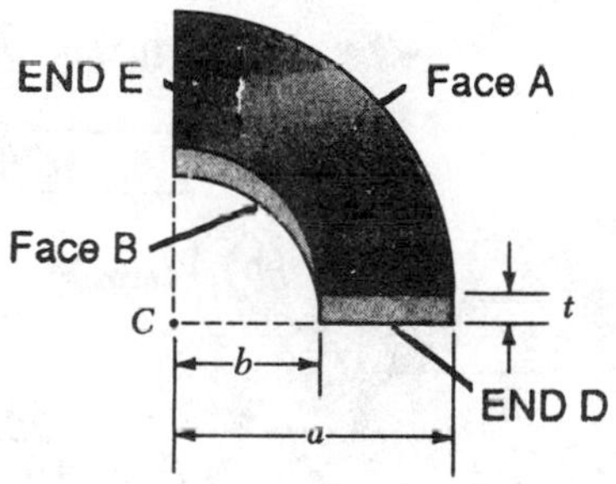

27.68 and 27.69

$$R = \frac{\rho}{\pi}\int_0^h \frac{dy}{[(a-b)(y/h)+b]^2}$$

Using the integral formula $\int \frac{du}{(au+b)^2} = -\frac{1}{a(au+b)}$

$$R = \frac{\rho}{\pi}\frac{h}{ab}$$

***27.69** $\rho = \frac{RA}{\ell} = \frac{V}{I}\frac{A}{\ell}$

(a) $\bar{\rho} = 1.49 \times 10^{-6}\ \Omega\cdot\text{m}$ (Close to tabled value)

(b) $\rho = \frac{RA}{\ell} = 1.70 \times 10^{-6}\ \Omega\cdot\text{m}$

CHAPTER 28

28.1 $\mathcal{E} = IR + Ir$

$12\text{ V} = (1.40\text{ A})R + (1.40\text{ A})(0.9\ \Omega)$

$\boxed{R = 7.67\ \Omega}$

28.2 $P = I^2R$

$P = (1.40\text{ A})^2(0.90\ \Omega) = \boxed{1.76\text{ W}}$

28.3 (a) $V_{\text{term}} = IR$

$10\text{ V} = I(5.6\ \Omega)$

$\boxed{\text{I} = 1.79\text{ A}}$

(b) $V_{\text{term}} = \mathcal{E} - IR$

$10\text{ V} = \mathcal{E} - (1.79\text{A})(0.2\ \Omega)$

$\mathcal{E} = \boxed{10.4\text{ V}}$

28.4 $V = IR$

$15.0\text{ V} = (60.0\text{ A})R$

$\boxed{R = 0.250\ \Omega}$

28.5 $V = I_1R_1 = 2R_1$ and $V = I_2(R_1 + R_2) = (1.6)(R_1 + 3)$

Therefore $2R_1 = 1.6(R_1 + 3)$ or $R_1 = \boxed{12.0\ \Omega}$

***28.6** (a) $V = \mathcal{E} - IR = 1.5\text{ V} - (0.058\text{ A})(0.311\ \Omega)$

$V = \boxed{1.48\text{ V}}$

(b) $\mathcal{E} = I(r + R)$

$$R = \frac{\mathcal{E}}{I} - r = \frac{1.5\text{ V}}{0.058\text{ A}} - 0.311\ \Omega = \boxed{25.6\ \Omega}$$

28.7 (a) $P = \dfrac{V^2}{R}$

$$20\ \text{W} = \frac{(11.6\ \text{V})^2}{R}$$

$$\boxed{R = 6.73\ \Omega}$$

(b) $V = IR$

$$11.6\ \text{V} = I(6.73\ \Omega)$$

$$I = 1.72\ \text{A}$$

$$\mathcal{E} = IR + Ir$$

$$15\ \text{V} = 11.6\ \text{V} + (1.72\ \text{A})r$$

$$\boxed{r = 1.98\ \Omega}$$

28.8 $\mathcal{E} = IR + Ir$

$$I = \frac{\mathcal{E}}{R + r} = \frac{5\ \text{V}}{(18 + 0.45)\ \Omega} = 0.271\ \text{A}$$

$$V = IR = (0.271\ \text{A})(18\ \Omega) = \boxed{4.88\ \text{V}}$$

***28.9** The total resistance is $R = \dfrac{3\ \text{V}}{0.6\ \text{A}} = 5.0\ \Omega$

(a) $R_{\text{lamp}} = R - r_{\text{batteries}} = 5.0\ \Omega - 0.41\ \Omega = \boxed{4.59\ \Omega}$

(b) $\dfrac{P_{\text{batteries}}}{P_{\text{total}}} = \dfrac{(0.408\ \Omega)I^2}{(5\ \Omega)I^2} = 0.0816 = \boxed{8.16\%}$

28.10 (a) $\mathcal{E} = IR + Ir;\quad I = \dfrac{\mathcal{E}}{R + r} = \dfrac{6\ \text{V}}{(5 + 188)\ \Omega} = \boxed{31.1\ \text{mA}}$

(b) $V = IR = (31.1 \times 10^{-3}\text{A})(56\ \Omega) = \boxed{1.74\ \text{V}}$

***28.11** Using 2 Ω, 3 Ω, 4 Ω resistors,

there are 7 series and 10 parallel combinations

Series		Parallel		
2 Ω	5 Ω	1.2 Ω	5.2 Ω	2.22 Ω
3 Ω	6 Ω	1.33 Ω	4.33 Ω	2.0 Ω
4 Ω	7 Ω	1.71 Ω	3.71 Ω	2.1 Ω
	9 Ω	0.923 Ω		

***28.12** If all 3 resistors are placed in parallel,

$$\frac{1}{R} = \frac{1}{500} + \frac{2}{250} = \frac{5}{500}$$

$$R = 100\ \Omega$$

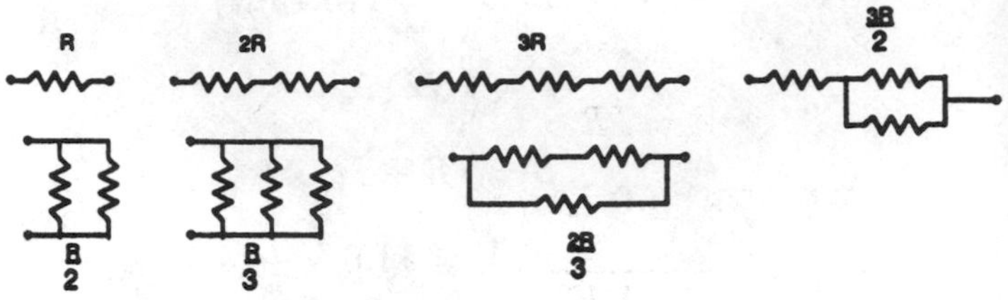

28.12

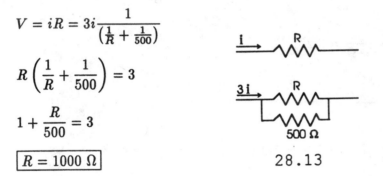

***28.13** The voltage drop is the same across either combination

$$V = iR = 3i\frac{1}{\left(\frac{1}{R} + \frac{1}{500}\right)}$$

$$R\left(\frac{1}{R} + \frac{1}{500}\right) = 3$$

$$1 + \frac{R}{500} = 3$$

$$\boxed{R = 1000\ \Omega}$$

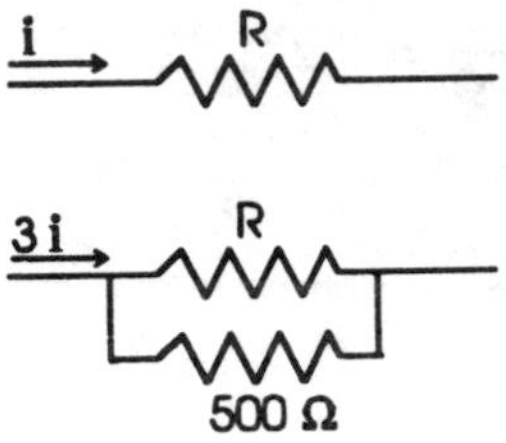

28.13

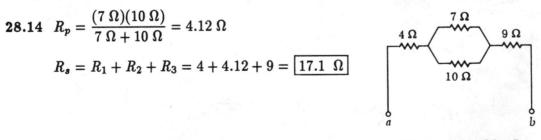

28.14 $R_p = \dfrac{(7\ \Omega)(10\ \Omega)}{7\ \Omega + 10\ \Omega} = 4.12\ \Omega$

$$R_s = R_1 + R_2 + R_3 = 4 + 4.12 + 9 = \boxed{17.1\ \Omega}$$

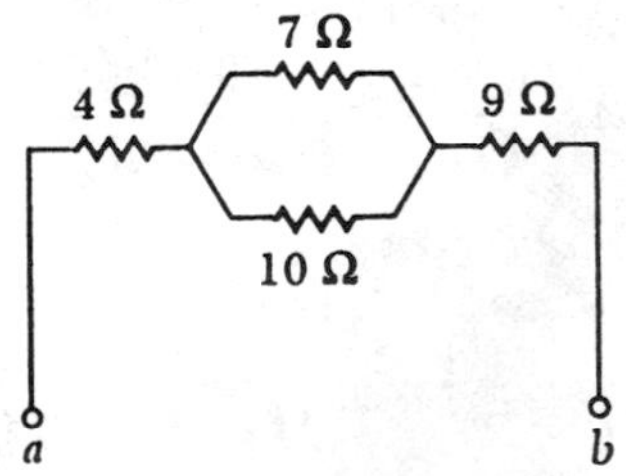

28.14 and 28.15

28.15 $V = IR$

$34 \text{ V} = I(17.1\ \Omega)$

$I = \boxed{1.99 \text{ A}}$ thru 4 Ω, 9 Ω resistors

$V = IR$

$V = (1.99 \text{ A})(4.12\ \Omega)$

$V = 8.20 \text{ V}$

$V = IR$	$V = IR$
$8.20 \text{ V} = I(7\ \Omega)$	$8.20 \text{ V} = I(10\ \Omega)$
$\boxed{\text{I} = 1.17 \text{ A}}$	$\boxed{\text{I} = 0.82 \text{ A}}$
thru 7 Ω resistor	thru 10 Ω resistor

28.16 $R_s = R_1 + R_2$

$R_s = 5.1 + 3.5 = 8.6\ \Omega$

$$R_p = \frac{R_1 R_2}{R_1 + R_2} = \frac{2(8.6)}{2 + 8.6} = 1.62\ \Omega$$

$R_{eq} = (4.1 + 1.62 + 3.8)\ \Omega = \boxed{9.52\ \ \Omega}$

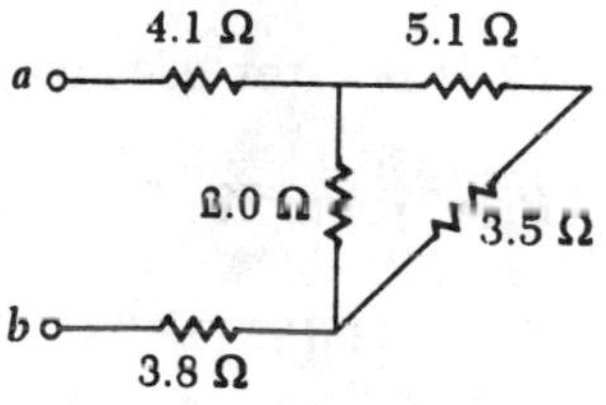

28.16

28.17 $R_{eq} = \left(\frac{1}{R} + \frac{1}{2R} + \frac{1}{3R}\right)^{-1} = \boxed{0.545R}$

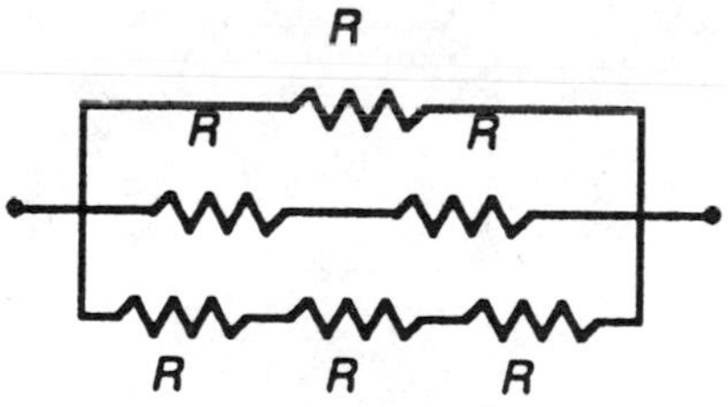

28.17

28.18 (a) $V = IR$

$33 \text{ V} = I_1(11) \quad 33 \text{ V} = I_2(22\ \Omega)$

$I_1 = 3 \text{ A} \quad I_2 = 1.5 \text{ A}$

$P = I^2R \quad P = 1.5^2(22)$

$P_1 = 3^2(11) \quad P_2 = 49.5 \text{ W}$

$P_1 = 99 \text{ W}$ $\boxed{\text{The 11 }\Omega\text{ Resistor uses more power}}$

(b) $P_1 + P_2 = 99 + 49.5 = 148.5 \text{ W}$

$P = IV = (4.5)(33) = 148.5 \text{ W}$

(c) $R_s = R_1 + R_2 = (11 + 22)\ \Omega = 33\ \Omega$

$V = IR \quad P = I^2R$

$33 \text{ V} = I(33\ \Omega) \quad P_1 = I^2(11) = 11 \text{ W}$

$I = 1 \text{ A} \quad P_2 = I^2(22) = \boxed{22 \text{ W}}$

The 22 Ω resistor uses more power.

(d) $P_1 + P_2 = (11 + 22)\ \Omega = 33 \text{ W}$

$P = IV = (1)(33) = 33 \text{ W}$

(e) The parallel configuration.

28.10 $R_p = (\frac{1}{3} + \frac{1}{1})^{-1} = 0.75\ \Omega$

$R_s = 2 + 0.75 + 4 = 6.75\ \Omega$

$V = IR$

$18 = I(6.75)$

$I_{batt} = 2.67\ \text{A}$

$P = I^2R \quad P_2 = (2.67)^2 2 = \boxed{14.3\ \text{W}}$ through $2\ \Omega$

$P_4 = (2.67)^2(4) = \boxed{28.5\ \text{W}}$ through $4\ \Omega$

$V_2 = IR = (2.67)(2) = 5.34\ \text{V}$

$V = (2.67)(4) = 10.67\ \text{V}$

$18 - 16.00 = 2.0\ \text{V}\ (= V_3 = V_1)$

$V = IR \quad 2 = I(3) \quad I_3 = 0.67\ \text{A} \quad P_3 = (0.67)^2(3) = \boxed{1.33\ \text{W}}$ through $3\ \Omega$

$2 = I(1) \quad I_1 = 2\ \text{A} \quad P_1 = (2)^2(1) = \boxed{4.00\ \text{W}}$ through $1\ \Omega$

Total power $= 48.0\ \text{W}$

$P = IV = (2.67)(18) = 48.0\ \text{W}$

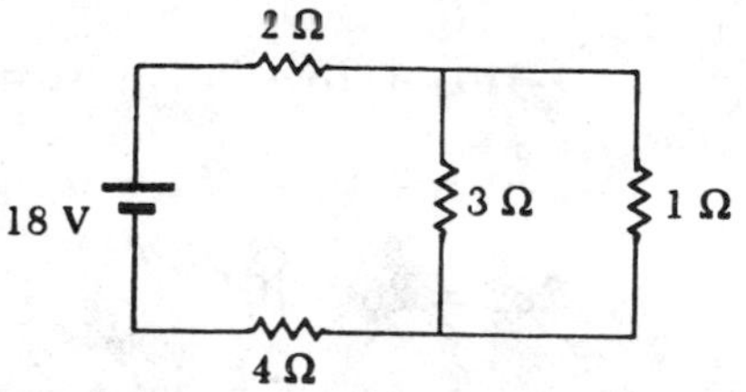

28.19

28.20 For the 2 Ω, 2 Ω, 1 Ω parallel combination

$$R = (\frac{1}{2\ \Omega} + \frac{1}{2\ \Omega} + \frac{1}{2\ \Omega})^{-1} = \frac{1}{2}\ \Omega$$

For the 3 Ω in parallel with the 5 Ω, from equation 32.3

$$R = (\frac{1}{3\ \Omega} + \frac{1}{5\ \Omega})^{-1} = \frac{15}{8}\ \Omega$$

The network becomes

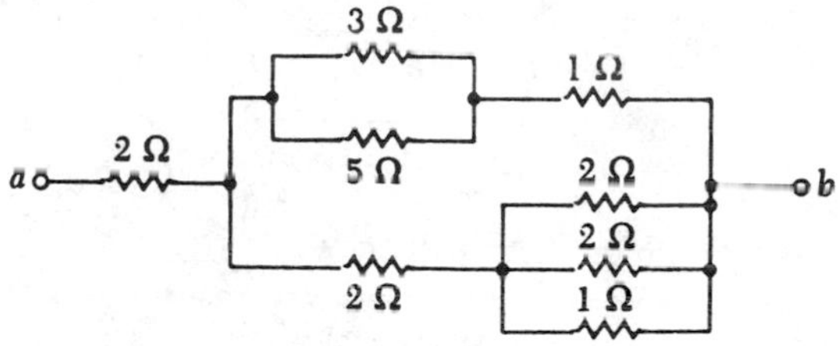

28.20

For the $\frac{15}{8}$ Ω and 2 Ω in series,

$$R = 2\ \Omega + \frac{15}{8}\ \Omega = \frac{16 + 15}{8}\ \Omega = \frac{31}{8}\ \Omega$$

For the 2 Ω and $\frac{1}{2}$ Ω in series,

$$R = 2\ \Omega + \frac{1}{2}\ \Omega = \frac{5}{2}\ \Omega$$

For the total resistance,

$$R = 2\ \Omega + (\frac{8}{31} + \frac{2}{5})^{-1}\ \Omega$$

$$= 2\ \Omega + (\frac{155}{40 + 62})\ \Omega = 2\ \Omega + \frac{155}{102}\ \Omega$$

$$= \frac{359}{102}\ \Omega = \boxed{3.34\ \Omega}$$

28.21 (a) Conservation of voltage loop 1:

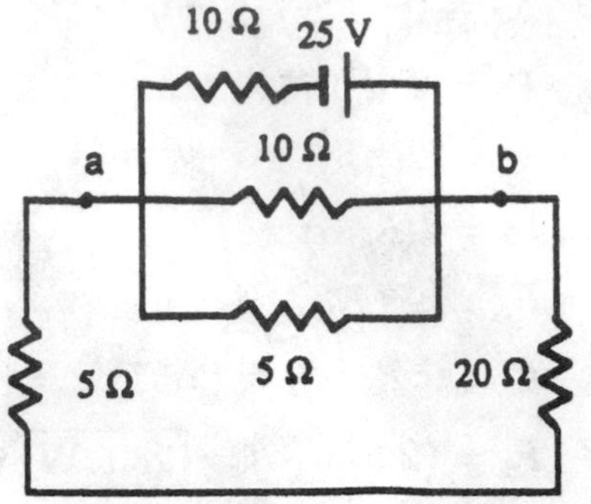

$-10I_1 + 25 - 20I - 5I = 0$

$-10I_1 + 25 - 25I = 0$

$25I = 25 - 10I_1$

$I = 1 - 0.4I_1$ (1)

Conservation of voltage loop 2:

$-10I_1 + 25 - 10I_2 = 0$

$10I_2 = 25 - 10I_1$

$I_2 = 2.5 - I_1$

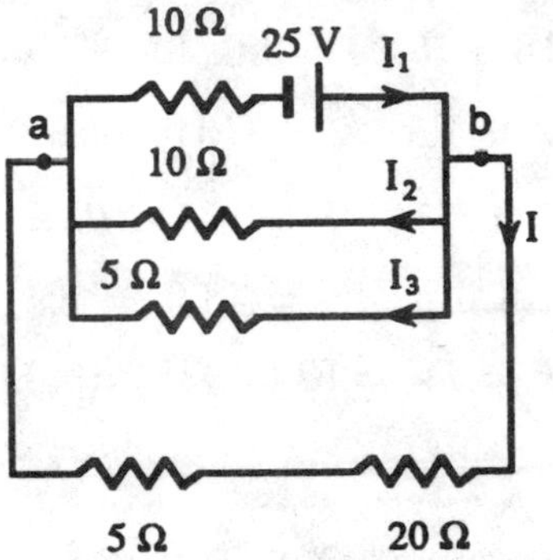

28.21

Conservation of voltage loop 3:

$-10I_1 + 25 - 5I_3 = 0$

$5I_3 = 25 - 10I_1$

$I_3 = 5 - 2I_1$

Conservation of currents:

$I_3 + I_2 + I = I_1$

$(5 - 2I_1) + (2.5 - I_1) + (1 - 0.4I_1) = I_1$

$8.5 - 3.4I_1 = I_1$

$8.5 = 4.4I_1$

$I_1 = 1.93 \text{ A}$

Substitute into equation (1):

$I = 1 - 0.4I_1 = \boxed{0.227 \text{ A}}$

(b) $V = IR$

$V = (0.277)(2.5) = \boxed{5.68 \text{ V}}$

***28.22** The top, center, and bottom junctions are at the same potential so the vertical resistors carry no current and the equivalent resistance will be unchanged if they are removed. Then we have

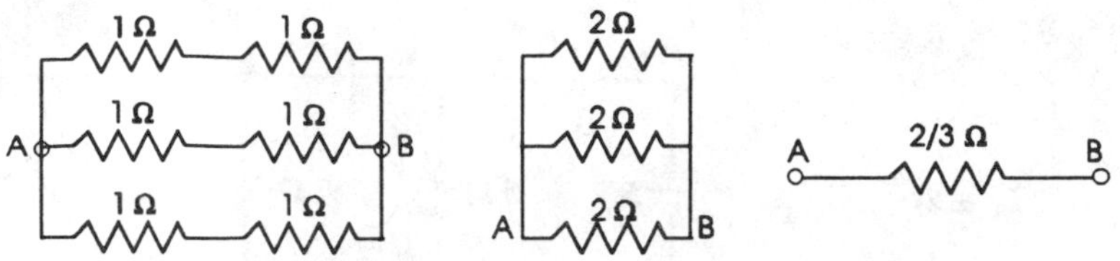

28.22

***28.23** Denoting the two resistors as x and y,

$$x + y = 690, \quad \text{and} \quad \frac{1}{150} = \frac{1}{x} + \frac{1}{y}$$

$$\frac{1}{150} = \frac{1}{x} + \frac{1}{690 - x} = \frac{(690 - x) + x}{x(690 - x)}$$

$$x^2 - 690x + 103,500 = 0$$

$$x = \frac{690 \pm \sqrt{(690)^2 - 414,000}}{2}$$

$$x = \boxed{470\ \Omega} \quad y = \boxed{220\ \Omega}$$

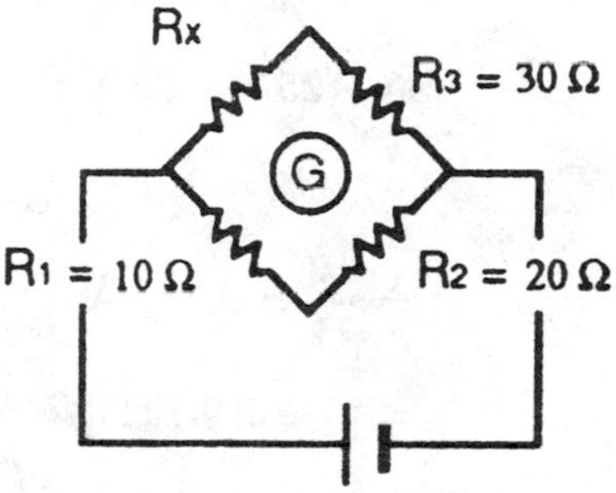

Wheatstone Bridge

28.23

28.24 (a) Since all the current flowing in the circuit must pass through the series 100 Ω resistor.

$$P = RI^2$$

$$P_{max} = RI_{max}^2$$

$$I_{max} = \sqrt{\frac{P_{max}}{R}} = \sqrt{\frac{25\text{ W}}{100\ \Omega}} = \frac{1}{2}\text{ A}$$

$$R_{eq} = 100\ \Omega + \left(\frac{1}{100} + \frac{1}{100}\right)^{-1}\Omega = 150\ \Omega$$

$$V_{max} = R_{eq}I_{max} = \boxed{75.0\text{ V}}$$

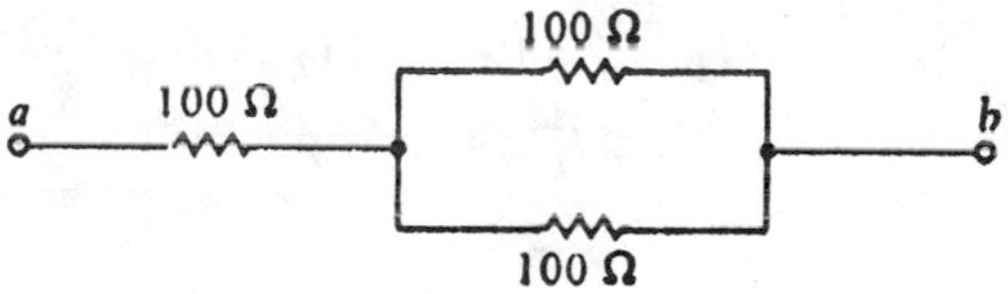

28.24

(b) $P = VI = (75\text{ V})(0.5\text{ A}) = \boxed{37.5\text{ W}}$ total power

$$P_1 = \boxed{25.0\text{ W}} \quad P_2 = P_3 = RI^2 = (100\ \Omega)\left(\frac{1}{4}\text{ A}\right)^2 = \boxed{6.25\text{ W}}$$

28.25 $I_2 = I_1 + I_3$

$5 - 3I_1 - 5I_2 = 0$

$10 - 5I_2 - 7I_3 = 0$

$5 - 3I_1 - 5(I_1 + I_3) = 0$

$10 - 5(I_1 + I_3) - 7I_3 = 0$

$5 - 8I_1 = 5I_3 = 0$

$10 - 5I_1 - 12I_3 = 0$

$60 - 96I_1 - 60I_3 = 0$

$-50 + 25I_1 + 60I_3 = 0$

$10 - 71I_1 = 0$

$I_1 = \frac{10}{71} = 0.141 \text{ A}$

$I_2 = [5 - 3(0.141)]/5 = 0.914 \text{ A}$

$I_3 = I_2 - I_1 = 0.774 \text{ A}$

$V_{ab} = V_b - V_a = 0 - [10 + 3(0.14)] = \boxed{-10.42 \text{ V}}$

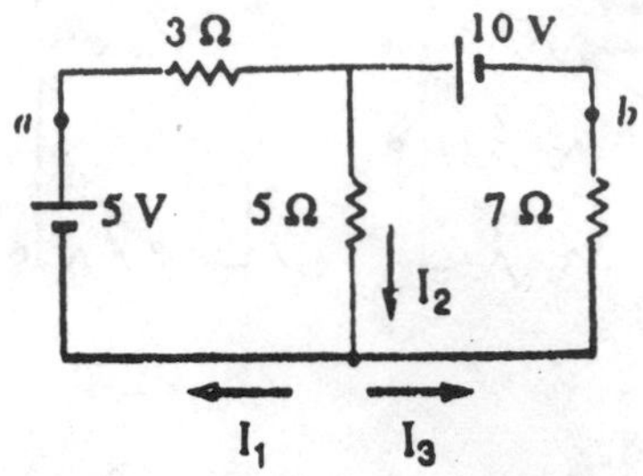

28.25 28.26 and 28.28

28.26 $-7I_3 + 10 - 5I_2 = 0$

$7I_3 = 10 - 5I_2$

$7I_3 = 1.43 - 0.71I_2$

$+5 - 3I_1 - 5I_2 = 0$

$3I_1 = 5 - 5I_2$

$I_1 = 1.67 - 1.67I_2$

$I_2 = I_1 + I_3$

$I_2 = (1.67 - 1.67I_2) + (1.43 - 0.71I_2)$

$I_2 = 3.1 - 2.38I_2$

$3.38I_2 = 3.1$

$I_2 = \boxed{0.915 \text{ A}}$ $I_3 = \boxed{0.774 \text{ A}}$ $I_1 = \boxed{0.141 \text{ A}}$

28.27

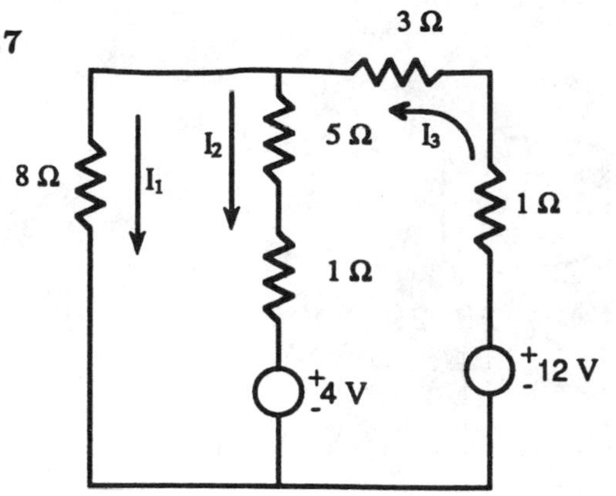

28.27

From Kirchhoff's current rule

$I_3 = I_1 + I_2$

From Kirchhoff's voltage rule applied to the loop containing I_2 and I_3

$12\text{ V} - 4I_3 - 6I_2 - 4\text{ V} = 0$

$8 = 4I_3 + 6I_2$

From Kirchhoff's voltage rule applied to the loop containing I_1 and I_2

$-6I_2 - 4\text{ V} + 8\,I_1 = 0$

$8I_1 = 4 + 6I_2$

Solving the above linear systems

$$\boxed{I_1 = \frac{11}{13}\text{ A},\quad I_2 = \frac{6}{13}\text{ A},\quad I_3 = \frac{17}{13}\text{ A}}$$

***28.28** Using Kirchoff's Law, clockwise around the loop,

$-5\text{ V} - i(2\ \Omega) - i(3\ \Omega) + 15\text{ V} = 0$

$$i = \frac{10\text{ V}}{5\ \Omega} = 2\text{ A}$$

(a) $V_a = \boxed{-5.00\text{ V}}$

(b) $V_b = -5\text{ V} - (2\text{ A})(2\ \Omega) = \boxed{-9.00\text{ V}}$

(c) $V_c = -5\text{ V} - (2\text{ A})(2\ \Omega) - (2\text{ A})(3\ \Omega) = \boxed{-15.0\text{ V}}$

***28.29** Using Kirchoff's Law,

$12\text{ V} - (0.01\ \Omega)i_1 - (0.06\ \Omega)i_3 = 0$

$10\text{ V} - (1\ \Omega)i_2 - (0.06\ \Omega)i_3 = 0$

and $i_1 + i_2 = i_3$

$12 - 0.07i_1 - 0.06i_2 = 0$

$10 - 1.06i_2 - 0.06i_1 = 0$

Solving simultaneously,

$i_1 = 171.671\text{ A}$

$i_2 = -0.283\text{ A}$ in the dead battery

$i_3 =$ $\boxed{171.388\text{ A is the starter}}$

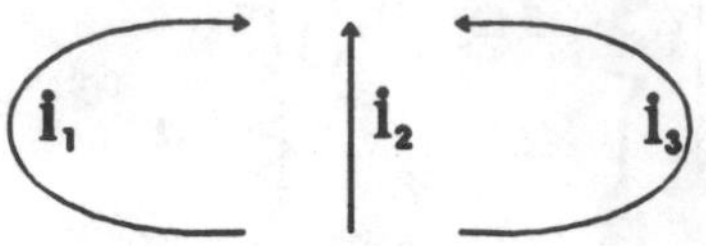

28.29

***28.30** $V_{ab} = i_1(1\ \Omega) + (i_1 - i_2)(1\ \Omega)$

$V_{ab} = i_1(1\ \Omega) + i_2(1\ \Omega) - (i - i_1 + i_2)(5\ \Omega)$

$V_{ab} = (i - i_1)(3\ \Omega) + (i - i_1 + i_2)(5\ \Omega)$

Let $i = 1$ A, $i_1 = x$ and $i_2 = y$

$$\begin{cases} V = 2x - y & y = 2x - V \\ V = -4x + 6y + 5 \\ V = 8 - 8x + 5y \end{cases}$$

$$\begin{cases} 7V = 8x + 5 \\ 6V = 2x + 8 \end{cases}$$

$$V = \frac{27}{17} \qquad R = \frac{V}{i} = \boxed{\frac{27}{17}\ \Omega}$$

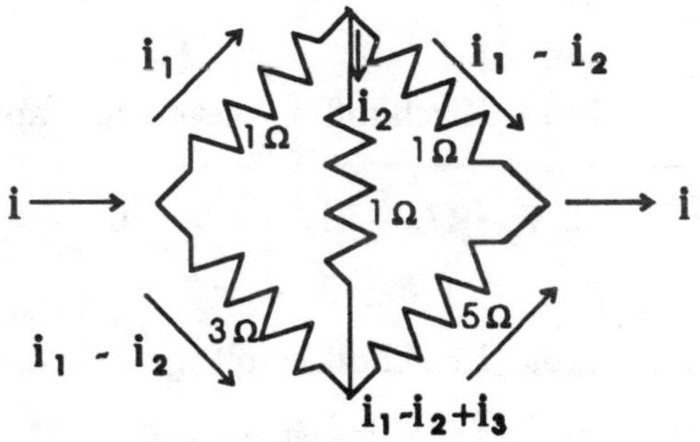

28.30

28.31 $24 - 6I_1 - 3I_3 = 0$

$12 + 24 - 6I_1 - 6I_2 = 0$

$36 - 6I_1 = I_2$

$6 - I_1 = I_2$

$I_1 = I_3 + I_2$

$I_1 = (8 - 2I_1) + (6 - I_1)$

$I_1 = 14 - 3I_1$

$I_1 = 3.50$ A

$\boxed{I_2 = 2.50\text{ A}}$

$\boxed{I_3 = 1.00\text{ A}}$

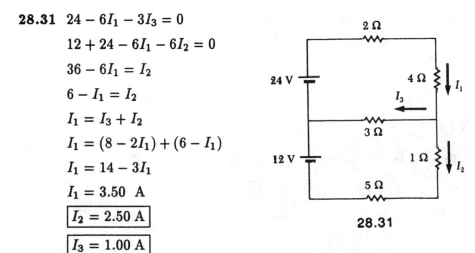

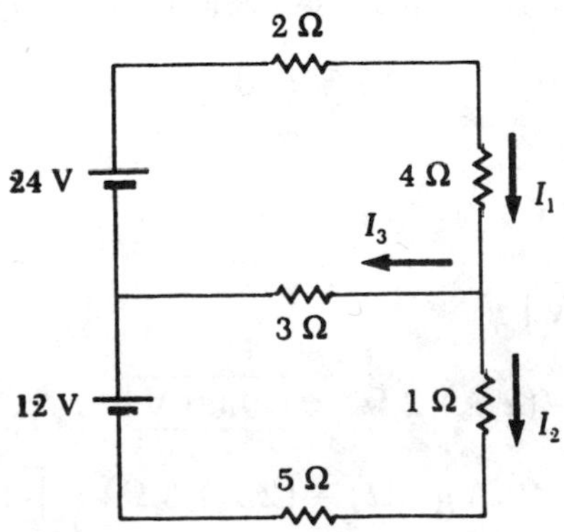

28.31

28.32

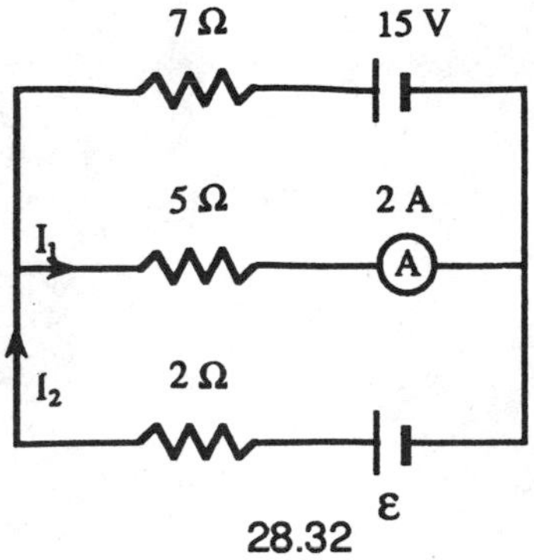

28.32

$+15 - 7I_1 - 2(5) = 0$

$5 = 7I_1$

$\boxed{I_1 = 0.714\text{ A}}$

$I_3 = I_1 + I_2 = 2\text{ A}$

$0.71 + I_2 = 2$

$\boxed{I_2 = 1.29\text{ A}}$

$+\mathcal{E} - 2(1.29) - 5(2) = 0$

$\boxed{\mathcal{E} = 12.6\text{ V}}$

***28.33** [1] $70 - 60 - i_2(3\text{ k}\Omega) - i_1(2\text{ k}\Omega) = 0$

[2] $80 - i_3(4\text{ k}\Omega) - 60 - i_2(3\text{ k}\Omega) = 0$

[3] $i_2 = i_1 + i_3$

(a) Substituting in for i_2 and solving the resulting simultaneous equations yields

$i_1 = 0.385$ mA (through R_1)

$i_3 = 2.692$ mA (through R_3)

$i_2 = 3.08$ mA (through R_2)

(b) $V_{cf} = -60\text{ V} - (3.08\text{ mA})(3\text{ k}\Omega) = -69.2\text{ V}$

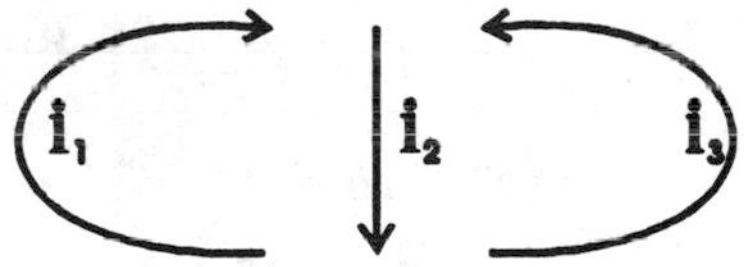

28.33

28.34

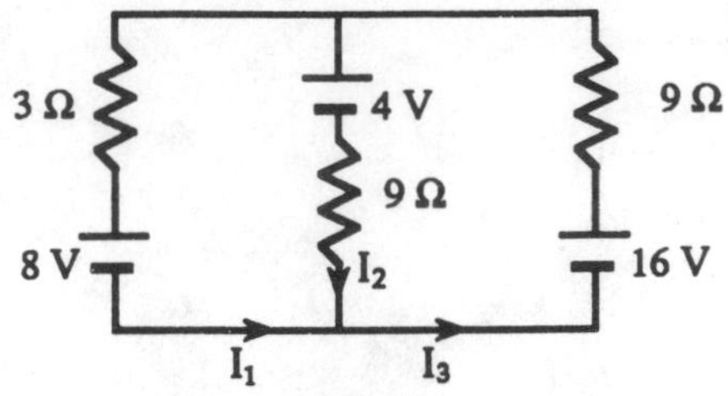

28.34

$$+16 - 9I_3 - 4 - 9I_2 = 0$$

$$12 - 9I_3 = 9I_2$$

$$I_2 = 1.33 - I_3 \qquad (1)$$

$$+16 - 9I_3 - 3I_1 - 8 = 0$$

$$8 - 9I_3 = 3I_1$$

$$I_1 = 2.67 - 3I_3 \qquad (2)$$

$$I_2 + I_1 = I_3 \qquad (3)$$

$$(1.33 - I_3) + (2.67 - 3I_3) = I_3$$

$$4 = 5I_3$$

$\boxed{I_3 = 0.799 \text{ A}}$ $\boxed{I_2 = 0.533 \text{ A}}$ $\boxed{I_1 = 0.266 \text{ A}}$

28.35

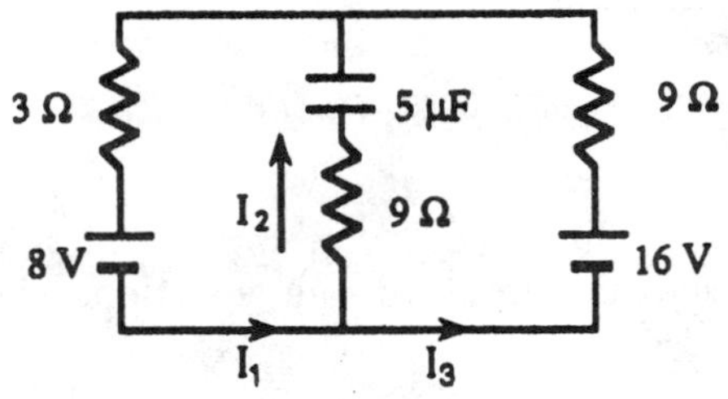

28.35

(a) $+16 - 9I - 3I - 8 = 0$ $\quad I_2 \to 0$ steady state

$8 - 12I = 0 \qquad I = I_1 = I_3$

$12I = 8$

$\boxed{I = 0.67 \text{ A}}$

(b) $+16 - 9(0.67) - \dfrac{Q}{5 \times 10^{-6}} = 0$

$\boxed{Q = 50.0\ \mu\text{C}}$

***28.36**

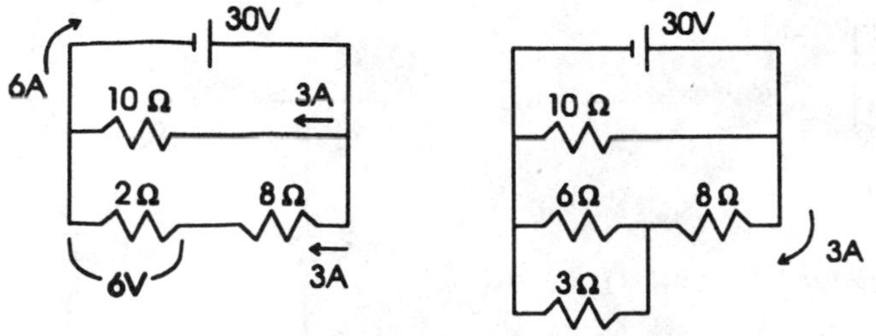

28.36

(a) $\boxed{5.00\ \Omega}$

(b) $\boxed{6.00\ \text{A}}$

(c) $\boxed{1.00\ \text{A}}$

28.37 (a) $I_1 = I_2 + I_3$

Clockwise around the top loop,

$12\ \text{V} - (2\ \Omega)I_3 - (4\ \Omega)I_1 = 0$

Traversing the bottom loop,

$8\ \text{V} - (6\ \Omega)I_2 + (2\ \Omega)I_3 = 0$

$I_1 = 3 - \frac{1}{2}I_3 \quad I_2 = \frac{4}{3} - \frac{1}{3}I_3$ and $\boxed{I_3 = 0.909\ A}$

(b) $V_a - (0.909\ \text{A})(2\ \Omega) = V_b$

$V_a - V_b = \boxed{1.82\ \text{V}}$

***28.38** $i_1 = i_2 + i_3$

$18 - i_1(6) - i_3(12) = 0$

$18 - i_1(6) - i_2(4) + 8 = 0$

$18 - 6i_2 - 18i_3 = 0$

$26 - 10i_2 - 6i_3 = 0$

$i_2 = 2.5\ \text{A}$ (through R_2)

$i_3 = 167\ \text{mA}$ (through R_3)

$i_1 = 2.67\ \text{A}$ (through R_1)

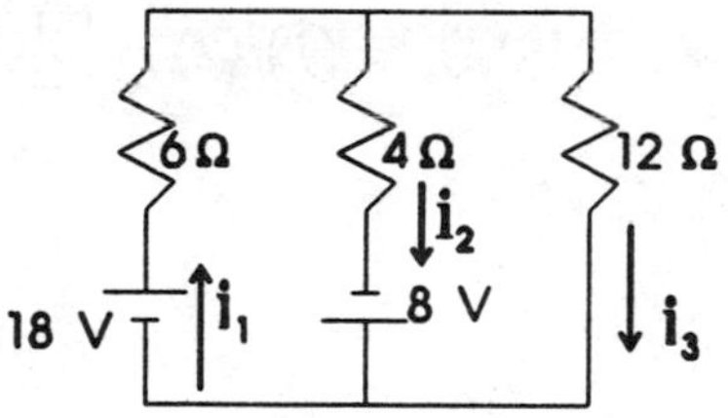

28.38

28.39 $50 - 2I_1 - 2I_2 = 0 \quad (1)$

$20 - 2I_3 - 2I_2 = 0 \quad (2)$

$I_1 = I_2 + I_3 \quad (3)$

Substitute (3) into (1), and solve for I_1, I_2 and I_3

$I_1 = 20\ \text{A}; \quad I_2 = 5\ \text{A}; \quad I_3 = 15\ \text{A}$

$P = I^2 R$

$(2\ \Omega)_1 : P = I_1^2(2\ \Omega) = (20\ \text{A})^2(2\ \Omega) = \boxed{800\ \text{W}}$

$(4\ \Omega) :$ (Half of I_2 goes through each) $P = (\frac{5}{2}\ \text{A})^2(4\ \Omega) = \boxed{25.0\ \text{W}}$

$(2\ \Omega) : P = I_3^2(2\ \Omega) = (15\ \text{A})^2(2\ \Omega) = \boxed{450\ \text{W}}$

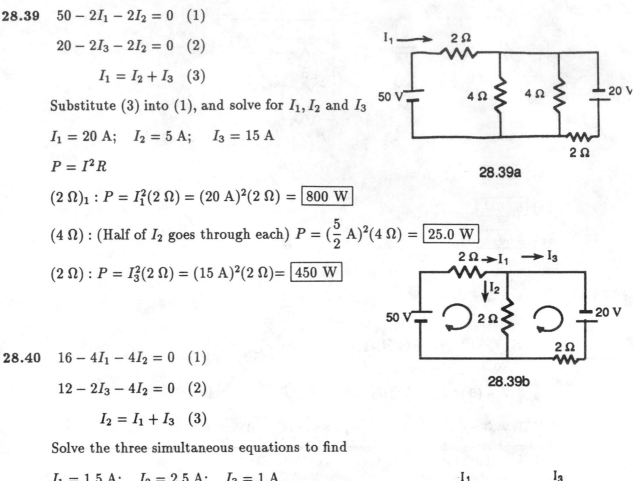

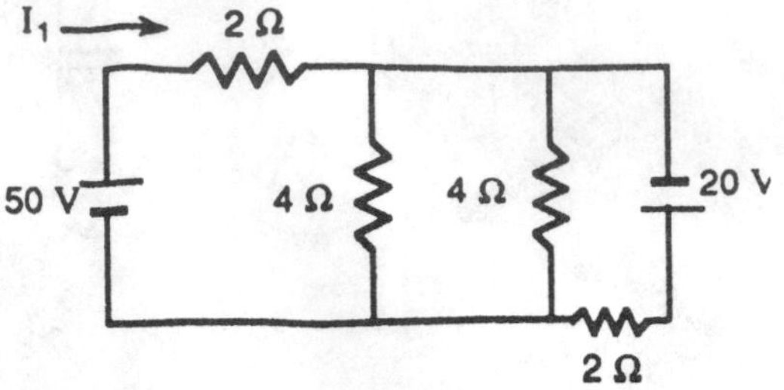

28.39a

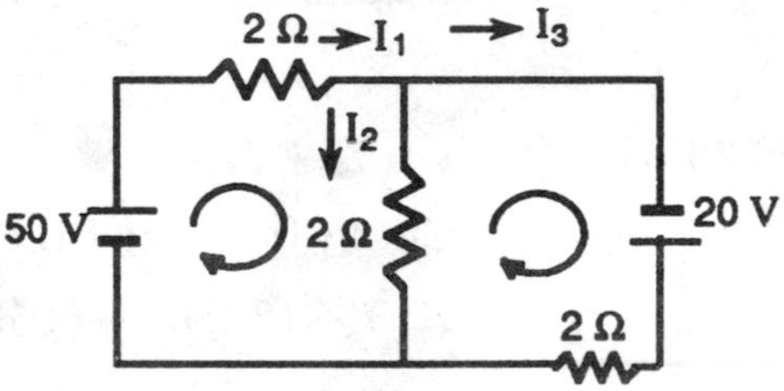

28.39b

28.40 $16 - 4I_1 - 4I_2 = 0 \quad (1)$

$12 - 2I_3 - 4I_2 = 0 \quad (2)$

$I_2 = I_1 + I_3 \quad (3)$

Solve the three simultaneous equations to find

$I_1 = 1.5\ \text{A}; \quad I_2 = 2.5\ \text{A}; \quad I_3 = 1\ \text{A}$

$(4\ \Omega)_1 : \quad P = (I_1)^2(4\ \Omega) = (1.5)^2(4) = \boxed{9.00\ \text{W}}$

$(4\ \Omega)_2 : \quad P = (I_2)^2(4\ \Omega) = (2.5)^2(4) = \boxed{25.0\ \text{W}}$

$(2\ \Omega) : \quad P = (I_3)^2(2\ \Omega) = (1)^2(2) = \boxed{2.00\ \text{W}}$

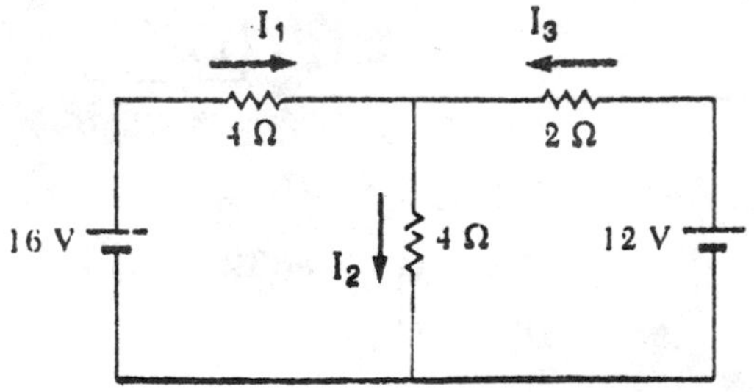

28.40

***28.41** $U = \frac{1}{2}CV^2 \qquad V = QC$

$U = \frac{1}{2}\frac{Q^2}{C}$

If Q is halved, U falls to one-quarter. $\boxed{U_f = 3\ \text{J}}$

28.42

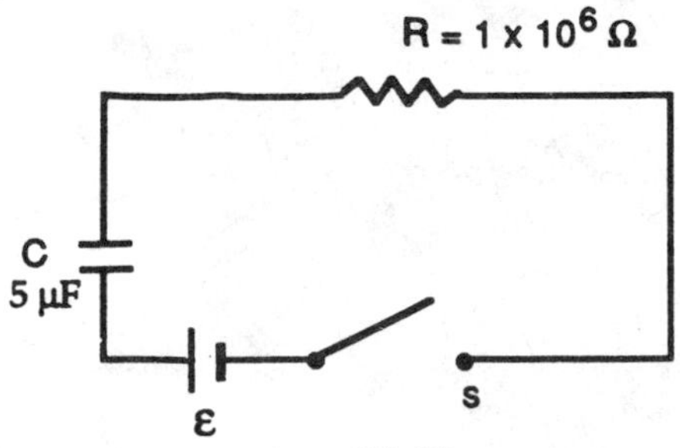

28.42

(a) $RC = (1 \times 10^6\ \Omega)(5 \times 10^{-6}\ \text{F}) = \boxed{5.00\ \text{s}}$

(b) $Q = C\mathcal{E} = (5 \times 10^{-6}\ \text{C})(30\ \text{V}) = \boxed{150\ \mu\text{C}}$

28.43 $I(t) = \dfrac{\mathcal{E}}{R} e^{-t/RC}$

$$I(t) = \frac{30}{1 \times 10^{-6}} \exp\left[\frac{-10}{(1 \times 10^6)(5 \times 10^{-6})}\right]$$

$$\boxed{I(t) = 4.06 \times 10^{-6}\ \text{A}}$$

28.44 $q(t) = C\mathcal{E}[1 - e^{t/RC}]$

$$\frac{q}{C\mathcal{E}} = 1 - e^{-t/RC}$$

$$e^{-t/RC} = 1 - \frac{q}{C\mathcal{E}}$$

$$t = -RC\ \ln(1 - \frac{q}{C\mathcal{E}})$$

where $q_{\text{max}} = q(\infty) = C\mathcal{E} \longrightarrow \dfrac{q_{\text{max}}}{2} = \dfrac{C\mathcal{E}}{2}$

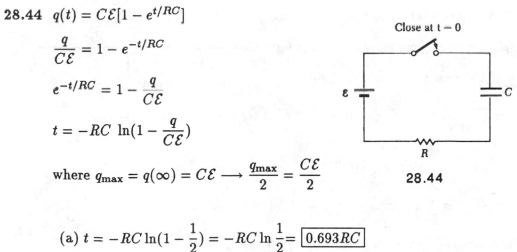

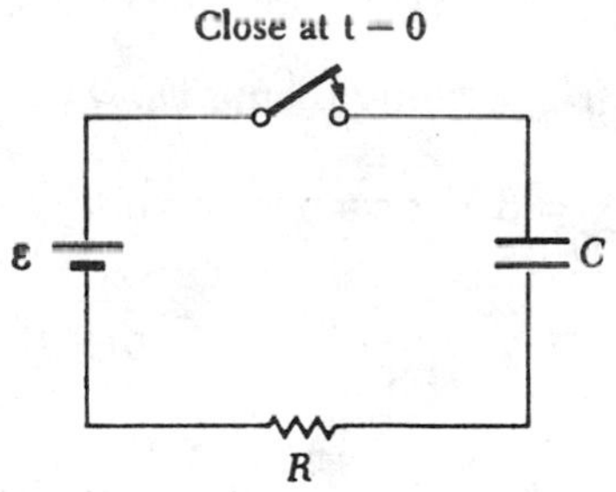

28.44

(a) $t = -RC\ln(1 - \frac{1}{2}) = -RC\ln\frac{1}{2} = \boxed{0.693RC}$

(b) Forever

28.45 (a) $\tau = RC = (4 \times 10^{-6}\ \Omega)(3 \times 10^{-6}\ \text{F}) = \boxed{12.0\ \text{s}}$

(b) $I = \dfrac{\mathcal{E}}{R} e^{-t/RC}$

$$I = \frac{12}{4 \times 10^6} e^{-t/12}$$

$$q = C\mathcal{E}[1 - e^{-t/RC}]$$

$$q = 3 \times 10^{-6}(12)[1 - e^{-t/12})$$

$\boxed{q = 36.0 \times 10^{-6}[1 - e^{-t/12}]\ \text{C}}$ $\boxed{I = 3.00 \times 10^{-6}\ e^{-t/12}\ \text{A}}$

28.46 (a) $\tau = RC = (150 \times 10^6\ \Omega)(750 \times 10^{-12}\ \text{F}) = \boxed{0.113\ \text{s}}$

(b) $I = \dfrac{Q}{RC}\ e^{-t/RC}$

$$I = \frac{6 \times 10^{-6}}{(150 \times 10^6)(750 \times 10^{-12})} e^{-t/0.113}$$

$\boxed{I = (53.3\ \mu\text{A})e^{-t/0.113}}$

$$q = Qe^{-t/RC}$$

$\boxed{q = (6.00\ \mu\text{C})e^{-t/0.113}}$

28.47 (a) Call the voltage at the left V_L and at the right V_R.

After a "long" time the capacitor is fully charged.

$V_L = 8$ V because of voltage divider

$$I_L = \frac{10\ \text{V}}{5\ \Omega} = 2\ \text{A}; \quad V_L = 10\ \text{V} - (2\ \text{A})(1\ \Omega) = 8\ \text{V}$$

Likewise, $V_R = (\dfrac{2\ \Omega}{2\ \Omega + 8\ \Omega})10\ \text{V} = 2\ \text{V}$ or

$$I_R = \frac{10\ \text{V}}{10\ \Omega} = 1\ \text{A};\ \text{voltage drop} = 10\ \text{V}(8\ \Omega)(1\ \text{A}) = 2\ \text{V}$$

Therefore $\Delta V = V_R - V_L = 8 - 2 = \boxed{6\ \text{V}}$

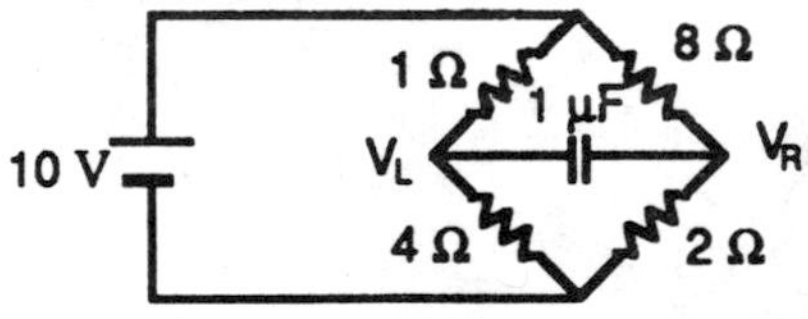

28.47a

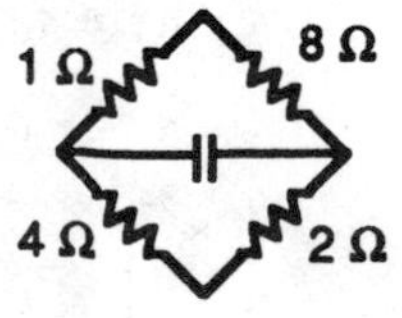

28.47b

(b) Redraw circuit

$$R = \frac{9(6)}{9+6} = 3.6\ \Omega \qquad RC = 3.6 \times 10^{-6}\ \text{s, and}$$

$$e^{-t/RC} = \frac{1}{10} \quad \text{so} \quad t = RC \ln 10 = \boxed{8.29 \times 10^{-6}\ \text{s}}$$

28.48 (a) $I(t) = I_0 e^{-t/RC}$

$$I_0 = \frac{Q}{RC} = \frac{5.1\times 10^{-6}\ \text{C}}{(1300\ \Omega)(2\times 10^{-3}\times 10^{-6}\ \text{F})} = 1.96\ \text{A}$$

$$I(t) = (1.96\ \text{A})\exp[\frac{-9\times 10^{-6}\ \text{s}}{(1300\ \Omega)(2\times 10^{-9}\ \text{F})} = \boxed{61.5\ \text{mA}}$$

(b) $q(t) = Qe^{-t/RC} = (5.11\ \mu\text{C})\exp[\frac{-8\times 10^{-6}\ \text{s}}{(1300\ \Omega)(2\times 10^{-9}\ \text{F})} = \boxed{0.235\ \mu\text{C}}$

(c) $\boxed{I_0 = 1.96\ \text{A}}$

28.49 (a) $U = \frac{Q^2}{2C} = \frac{(5.1\times 10^{-6}\ \text{C})^2}{2(2\times 10^{-9}\ \text{F})} = \boxed{6.5\times 10^{-3}\ \text{J}}$

(b) All of it, same as part (a).

28.50 $q(t) = Q[1 - e^{-t/RC}]$

$$\frac{q(t)}{Q} = 1 - e^{-t/RC}$$

$$0.6 = 1 - e^{-0.9/RC}$$

$$e^{-0.9/RC} = 1 - 0.6 = 0.4$$

$$\frac{-0.9}{RC} = \ln(0.4)$$

$$RC = \frac{-0.9}{\ln(0.4)} = \boxed{0.982\ \text{s}}$$

28.51 $v = \frac{Q}{C}$

$$q(t) = Qe^{-t/RC}$$

$$v(t) = ve^{-t/RC}$$

$$\frac{v(t)}{v} = e^{-t/RC}$$

$$\frac{1}{2} = \exp[-\frac{4}{R(3.6\times 10^{-6})}]$$

$$\ln(\frac{1}{2}) = -\frac{-4}{R(3.6\times 10^{-6})}$$

$$R = \boxed{1.60\ \text{M}\,\Omega}$$

28.52 Shunt Resistor ⟶ Ammeter

$V = IR$

$(1.5 \times 10^{-3})(0.75) = (0.9985)R_p$

$\boxed{R_p = 0.113\ \Omega}$

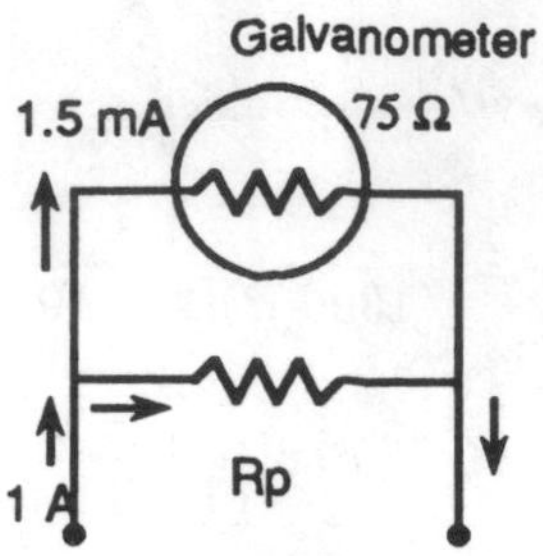

28.52

28.53 Series Resistor ⟶ Voltmeter

$V = IR$

$25 = 1.5 \times 10^{-3}(R_s + 75)$

$\boxed{R_s = 16,600\ \ \Omega}$

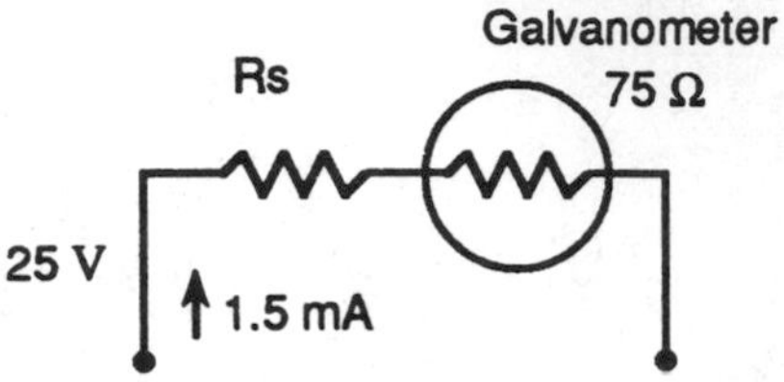

28.53

28.54 $V_{Fs} = I_g(R + r_g)$

$$R = \frac{V_{Fs}}{I_g} - r_g = \frac{1.0}{0.5 \times 10^{-3}} - 60 = 2000 - 60 = \boxed{1940\ \Omega}$$

28.55 $V = I_g r_g = I_s r_s$ where $I_{Fs} = I_g + I_s$

$$r_s = \frac{I_g r_g}{I_s} = \frac{I_g r_g}{(I_{Fs} - I_g)} = \frac{(0.5 \times 10^{-3})(60)}{0.1 - 0.5 \times 10^{-3}} = \boxed{0.302\ \ \Omega}$$

***28.56** $\boxed{R = 0.01\ \Omega}$

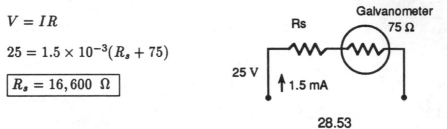

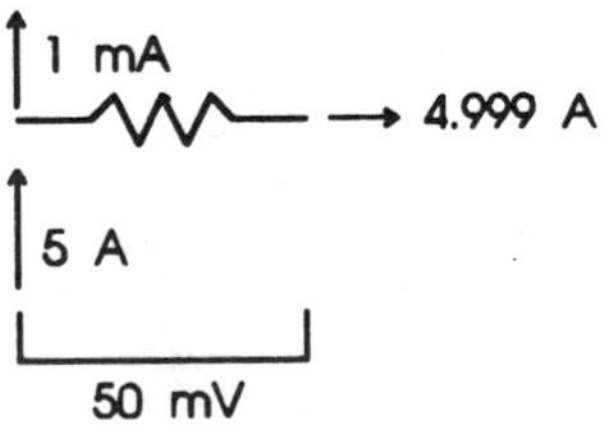

28.56

***28.57** We will use the values required for the 1-V voltmeter toobtain the internal resistance of the galvanometer.

$$V = I_G(R + R_G)$$

solve for R_G:

$$R_G = \frac{V}{I_G} - R = \frac{1\text{ V}}{0.001\text{ A}} - 900\ \Omega = 100\ \Omega$$

We then obtain the series resistance required for the 50-V voltmeter:

$$R = \frac{V}{I_G} - R_G = \frac{50\text{ V}}{0.001\text{ A}} - 100\ \Omega = \boxed{49,900\ \Omega}$$

28.58

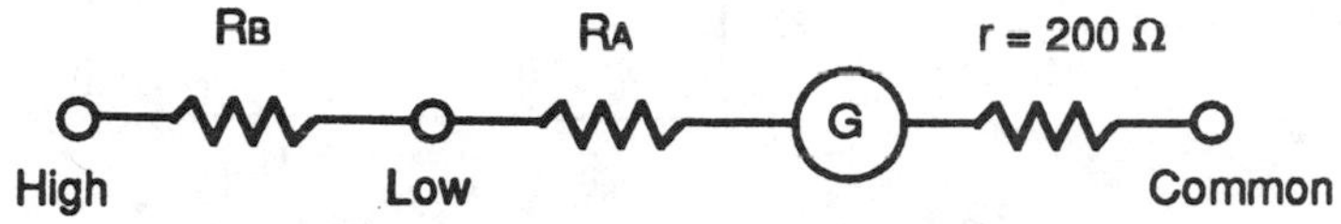

28.58

$$V_{\text{low}} = I(R_A + r)$$

$$R_A = \frac{20\text{ V}}{2.5\text{ mA}} - 200 = \boxed{7.80\text{ k}\Omega}$$

$$V_{\text{high}} = I(R_A + R_B + r)$$

$$R_B = \frac{200\text{ V}}{2.5\text{ mA}} - 7.8\text{ k}\Omega - 0.2\text{ k}\Omega = \boxed{72.0\text{ k}\Omega}$$

28.59

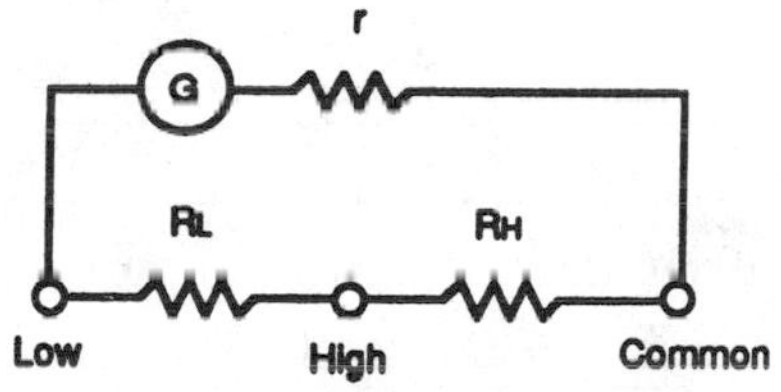

28.59

$$V_H = I_H R_H = (2.5\text{ mA})(R_L + 200\ \Omega)$$

$$V_H = (0.25 \times 10^{-3}\text{ A})(R_L + 200\ \Omega) = (10\text{ A})R_H$$

$$V_L = I_L(R_L + R_H) = (2.5 \times 10^{-3}\text{ A})(200\ \Omega) = (1\text{ A})(R_L + R_H)$$

Substitute for R_H and solve for R_L :

$$R_L = \boxed{0.450\ \Omega}$$

$$R_H = \boxed{0.0501\ \Omega}$$

28.60 $R_x = \frac{R_2R_3}{R_1} = \frac{R_2R_3}{2.5R_2} = \frac{1000\ \Omega}{2.5} = \boxed{400\ \Omega}$

***28.61** Using Kirchoff's Laws with $R_G \ll 1$,

$-21I_2 + 14I_1 = 0 \qquad I_2 = \frac{2}{3}I_1$

$70 - 14I_1 - 7(I_1 - I) = 0$
$70 - 21I_1 - 7(I_2 + I_1) = 0$

$70 - 21I_1 = -7I$
$70 - 28I_2 = 7I$

$70 - 21I_1 = -7I$

$70 - \frac{56}{3}I_1 = 7I$

Solving, $I = \frac{10}{17}\ \text{A} = \boxed{0.588\ \text{A}}$

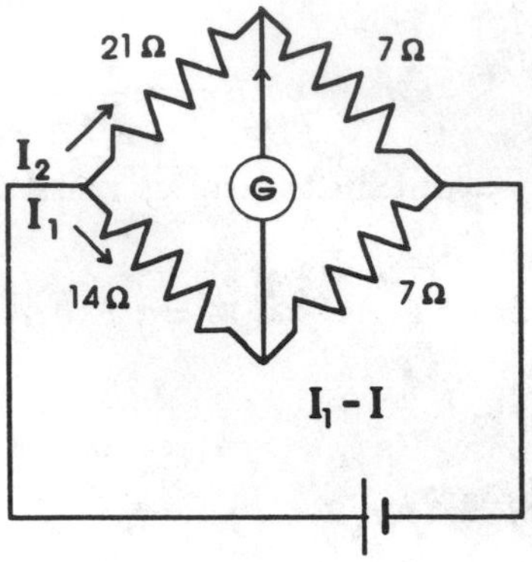

28.61

28.62 $R_x = \frac{V}{I_2} = \frac{3.2\ \text{V}}{300 \times 10^{-6}\ \text{A}} = \boxed{10.7\ \text{k}\Omega}$

28.63 $R_x = \frac{R_2R_3}{R_1} = \frac{(20)(30)}{10} = \boxed{60.0\ \Omega}$

28.64 $\frac{\mathcal{E}_x}{R_x} = \frac{\mathcal{E}_s}{R_s}; \qquad \mathcal{E}_x = \frac{\mathcal{E}_sR_x}{R_s}$

$\mathcal{E}_x = (\frac{48\ \Omega}{36\ \Omega})(1.0186\ \text{V}) = \boxed{1.36\ \text{V}}$

28.65 $P = IV$

$$I = \frac{P}{V} = \frac{1500\text{ W}}{120\text{ V}} = \boxed{12.5\text{ A}}\ \text{(Heater)}$$

$$I = \frac{750\text{ W}}{120\text{ V}} = \boxed{6.25\text{ A}}\ \text{(Toaster)}$$

$$I = \frac{1000\text{ W}}{120\text{ V}} = \boxed{8.33\text{ A}}\ \text{(Grill)}$$

(b) $12.5 + 6.25 + 8.33 = \boxed{27.1\text{ A}}$

No, it would not be sufficient since the current drawn is greater than 25 Amps.

28.66 total $P = 800 + 500 + 1000 = 2300\ \text{W}$

$P = IV$

$2300 = I(120)$

$I = 19.2\ \text{A}$

$\boxed{\text{No, but it sure is close!}}$

28.67 (a) $P = I^2R = I^2\left(\frac{\rho L}{A}\right) = \frac{(1A)^2(1.7\times10^{-8}\ \Omega\cdot\text{m})(16\text{ ft})(0.3048\text{ m/ft})}{\pi(0.512\times10^{-3}\text{ m})^2} = \boxed{0.101\text{ W}}$

(b) $P = I^2R = 100(0.101\text{ W}) = \boxed{10.1\text{ W}}$

28.68 $I_{\text{Al}}^2 R_{\text{Al}} = I_{\text{Cu}}^2 R_{\text{Cu}}$

$$I_{\text{Al}} = \sqrt{\frac{R_{\text{Cu}}}{R_{\text{Al}}}} I_{\text{Cu}} = \sqrt{\frac{\rho_{\text{Cu}}}{\rho_{\text{Al}}}} I_{\text{Cu}} = \sqrt{\frac{1.7}{2.82}}(20) = 0.776(20) = \boxed{15.5\text{ A}}$$

28.69 (a) $I = \frac{P}{V} = \frac{4000 \text{ W}}{240 \text{ V}} = \boxed{16.7 \text{ A}}$

(b) $I = \frac{4000 \text{ W}}{120 \text{ V}} = \boxed{33.3 \text{ A}}$

(c) $P_2 = P_1$

$$\frac{V_2^2}{R_2} = \frac{V_1^2}{R_1}$$

$R = \frac{\rho \ell}{A}$; ρ and ℓ are equal; substitute for R_1 and R_2.

$$V_2^2 A_2 = V_1^2 A_1$$

$$(240 \text{ V})^2 A_2 = (120 \text{ V})^2 A_1$$

$$\therefore \quad \frac{A_2}{A_1} = \frac{1}{4}$$

$$A_1 = 4A_2$$

Since the lengths are the same, but the cross-sectional area of the 120 V system is four times the area, the mass of the 120 V system is also $\boxed{\text{four times larger}}$

***28.70** Using Kirchoff's Law around the loop,

$12 - 2i - 4i = 0$

$i = 2 \text{ A}$

$V_{ab} = +4 \text{ V} - (2 \text{ A})(4\ \Omega) = 4.0 \text{ V}$

a is at the higher potential.

***28.71** $225\text{ W} = I^2 R_s \qquad R_s = x + y = 9\ \Omega$

$50\text{ W} = I^2 R_p \qquad R_p = \frac{1}{x} + \frac{1}{y} = 2\ \Omega$

$\frac{1}{x} + \frac{1}{9 - x} = 2$

$x^2 - 9x + 18 = 0$

$(x - 6)(x - 3) = 0$

The values of the resistors are $\boxed{6\ \Omega \text{ and } 3\ \Omega}$

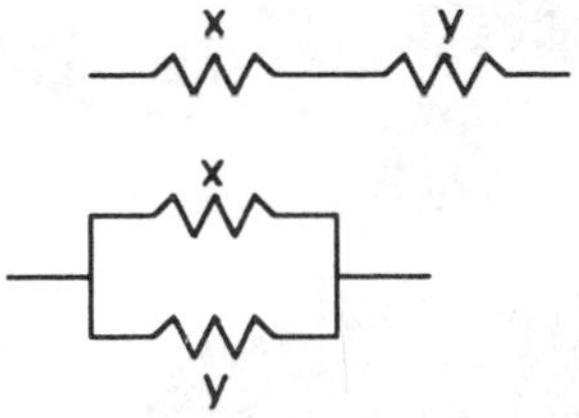

28.71

***28.72** (a) $10\text{ V} - (10\text{ k}\Omega)i - 0 = 0$

$i = \boxed{1.00\text{ mA, } 0\text{, } 1.00\text{ mA}}$

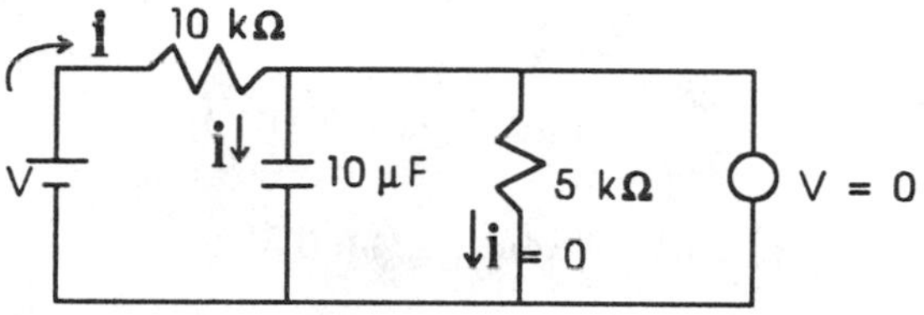

28.72(a)

(b) $t = \infty$

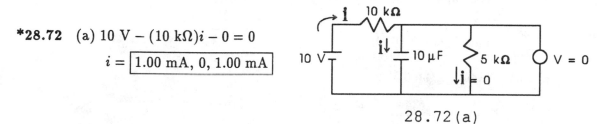

$10\text{V} - (15\ k\Omega)i = 0$

$i = \boxed{667\ \mu\text{A},\ 667\ \mu\text{A},\ 0}$

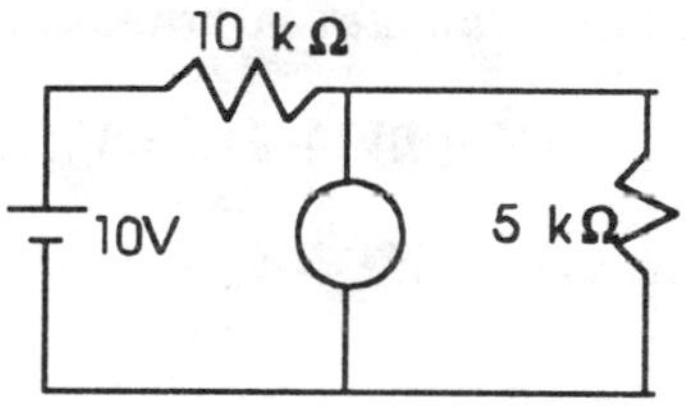

28.72(b)

28.73 $P = I^2 R$ and $I_m = \sqrt{\frac{P_m}{R}} = \sqrt{\frac{48\text{ W}}{3\ \Omega}} = 4\text{ A}$

Since the maximum current for any resistor is 4 A

(a) in circuit (a) the maximum current delivered to the group of resistors will be 6 A (2 A in the top branch and 4 A in the bottom branch.) The equivalent resistance is

$R_{eq} = [(\frac{1}{3\ \Omega}) + (\frac{1}{6\ \Omega})]^{-1} = 2\ \Omega$ so

$P = I^2 R = (6\text{ A})^2(2\ \Omega) = \boxed{72.0\text{ W}}$

(b) in circuit (b) the total current delivered to the group of resistors is 4 A (limited by the 3 Ω series resistor). The equivalent resistance of the circuit is $R_{eq} = [(\frac{1}{3\ \Omega}) + (\frac{1}{3\ \Omega})]^{-1} + 3\ \Omega = 4.5\ \Omega$ and

$P = I^2 R = (4\text{ A})^2(4.5\ \Omega) = \boxed{72.0\text{ W}}$

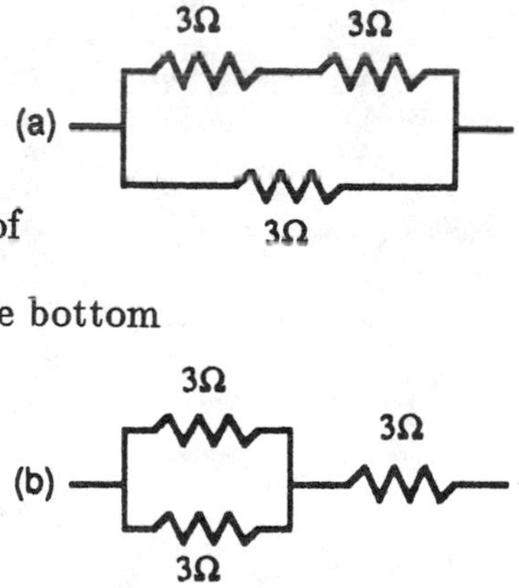

28.73

28.74 Choosing directions and labeling currents as shown in the figure, we have the following equations from Kirchhoff's rules:

$6 - I_1 - 2I_2 = 0$

$2 - 3I_3 + I_1 = 0$

$4 - 4I_4 - 2I_2 = 0$

$I_1 - I_2 + I_3 + I_4 = 0$

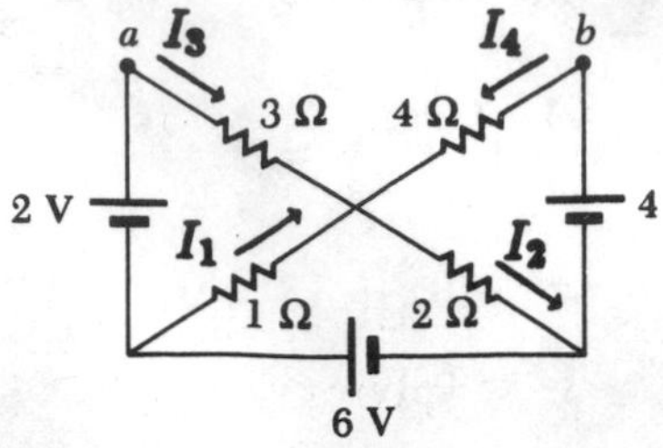

28.74

Solving for the currents we find $I_1 = \frac{34}{25}$ A, $I_2 = 2.32$ A,

$I_3 = \frac{28}{25}$ A and $I_4 = -0.16$ A

(a) The current in the 6 V battery is

$$I = I_1 + I_3 + = \frac{(34+28)}{25} = \boxed{2.48 \text{ A}}$$

(b) Adding changes in potential from point a to point b we find

$V_a - 2V - 6V + 4V = V_b$

Therefore $V_{ab} = V_a - V_b = (6 + 2 - 4)$ V $= \boxed{4.00 \text{ V}}$

***28.75** (a) The first step is to determine the resistance of each light bulb.

$$P = \frac{V^2}{R}$$

Thus:

$$R = \frac{V^2}{P} = \frac{(120\ \text{V})^2}{60\ \text{W}} = 240\ \Omega$$

We obtain the equivalent resistance R_{eq} of the network of light bulbs by applying Equations (28.6) and (28.7):

$$R_{eq} = R_1 + \frac{1}{\left(\frac{1}{R_2} + \frac{1}{R_3}\right)} = 240\ \Omega + 120\ \Omega = 360\ \Omega$$

The total power dissipated in the equivalent resistance of 360 Ω is

$$P = \frac{V^2}{R_{eq}} = \frac{(120\ \text{V})^2}{360\ \Omega} = \boxed{40.0\ \text{W}}$$

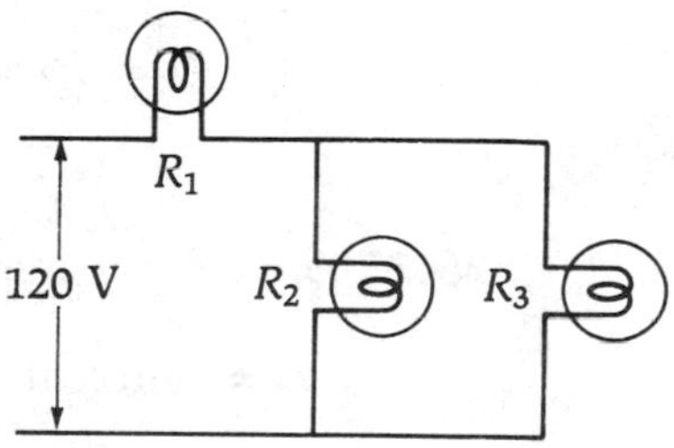

28.75

(b) The current through the network is given by:

$$P = I^2 R_{eq}$$

Solving for I gives $$I = \sqrt{\frac{P}{R_{eq}}} = \sqrt{\frac{40\ \text{W}}{360\ \Omega}} = \frac{1}{3}\ \text{A}$$

The potential difference across R_1 is

$$V_1 = IR_1 = \left(\frac{1}{3}\ \text{A}\right)(240\ \Omega) = 80.0\ \text{V}$$

The potential difference V_{23} across the parallel combination of R_2 and R_3 is

$$V_{23} = IR_{23} = \left(\frac{1}{3}\ \text{A}\right)\left(\frac{1}{\frac{1}{240\ \Omega} + \frac{1}{240\ \Omega}}\right) = \boxed{40.0\ \text{V}}$$

28.76 (a) Assume a clockwise current I and write the loop equation starting at point a going clockwise.

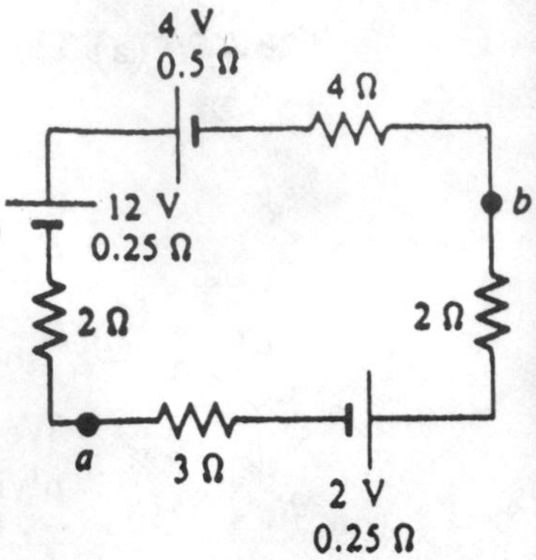

28.76

$$12\text{ V} - 4\text{ V} - 2\text{ V} - I[(2 + 0.25 + 0.5 + 4 + 2 + 0.25 + 3)\ \Omega] = 0$$

Thus $I = \dfrac{6\text{ V}}{12\ \Omega} = \boxed{0.500\text{ A}}$

(b) $V_a - (0.5\text{ A})[(2 + 0.25 + 0.5 + 4)\ \Omega] + 12\text{ V} - 4\text{ V} = V_b$

Therefore $V_a - V_b = V_{ab} = \boxed{4.63\text{ V}}$

(c) Across the 4–V battery $\Delta V = V_t = 4\text{ V} + (0.5\text{ A})(0.5\ \Omega) = \boxed{4.25\text{ V}}$

Note that the current through this battery is directed opposite the "sense" of the emf.

(d) $U = Pt = I^2Rt = (0.5\text{ A})^2(3\ \Omega)(600\text{ s}) = \boxed{450\text{ J}}$

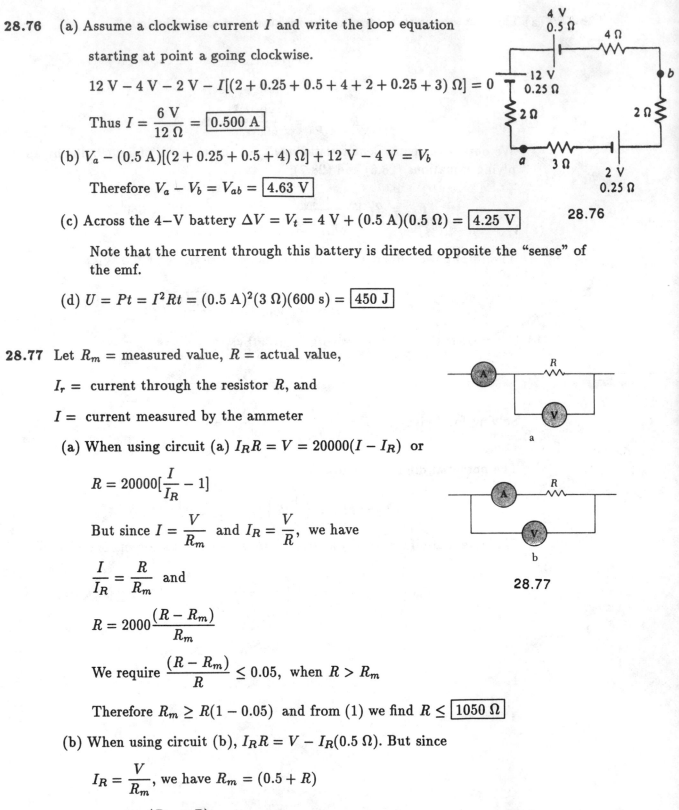

28.77 Let R_m = measured value, R = actual value,

I_r = current through the resistor R, and

I = current measured by the ammeter

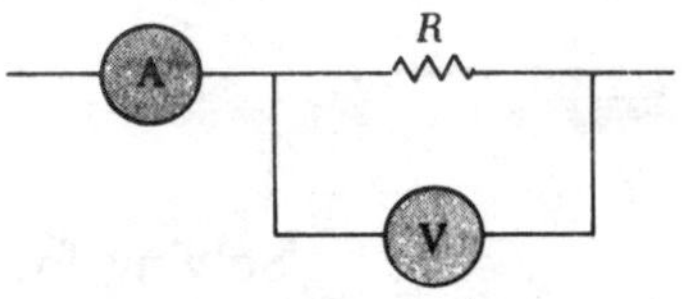

a

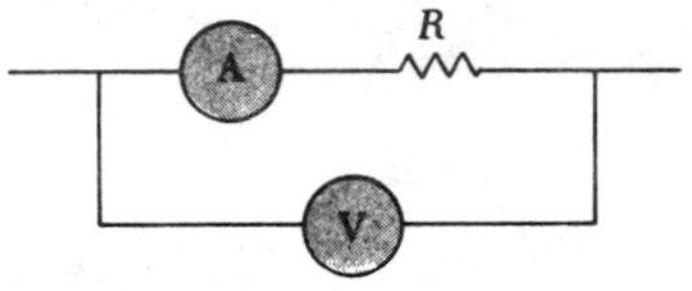

b

28.77

(a) When using circuit (a) $I_R R = V = 20000(I - I_R)$ or

$$R = 20000[\frac{I}{I_R} - 1]$$

But since $I = \dfrac{V}{R_m}$ and $I_R = \dfrac{V}{R}$, we have

$$\frac{I}{I_R} = \frac{R}{R_m} \text{ and}$$

$$R = 2000\frac{(R - R_m)}{R_m}$$

We require $\dfrac{(R - R_m)}{R} \le 0.05$, when $R > R_m$

Therefore $R_m \ge R(1 - 0.05)$ and from (1) we find $R \le \boxed{1050\ \Omega}$

(b) When using circuit (b), $I_R R = V - I_R(0.5\ \Omega)$. But since

$I_R = \dfrac{V}{R_m}$, we have $R_m = (0.5 + R)$

Require $\dfrac{(R_m - R)}{R} \le 0.05$ where $R_m > R$ and from (2) we find $\boxed{R \ge 10\ \Omega}$

28.78 (a) $\mathcal{E} - I(\Sigma R) - (\mathcal{E}_1 + \mathcal{E}_2) = 0$

$$40\text{ V} - (4\text{ A})[(2 + 0.3 + 0.3 + R)\ \Omega] - (6 + 6)\text{ V} = 0; \quad R = \boxed{4.40\ \Omega}$$

(b) $P = I^2R = (4\text{ A})^2[(2 + 0.3 + 0.3 + 4.4)\ \Omega] = \boxed{112\text{ W}}$

(c) $P = I(\mathcal{E}_1 + \mathcal{E}_2) = (4\text{ A})[(6 + 6)\text{ V}] = \boxed{48\text{ W}}$

28.79 The current in the simple loop circuit will be $I = \dfrac{\mathcal{E}}{R + r}$

(a) $V_{\text{ter}} = \mathcal{E} - Ir = \dfrac{\mathcal{E}R}{R + r}$ and $V_{\text{ter}} \longrightarrow \mathcal{E}$ as $R \longrightarrow \infty$

(b) $I = \dfrac{\mathcal{E}}{R + r}$ and $I \longrightarrow \dfrac{\mathcal{E}}{r}$ as $R \longrightarrow 0$

(c) $P = I^2R = \mathcal{E}^2 \dfrac{R}{(R + r)^2}$ and $P \longrightarrow \dfrac{\mathcal{E}^2}{4r}$ as $R \longrightarrow r$

28.80 First determine the equivalent resistance of the circuit as shown in the steps below.

(a) The current through the 5 Ω resistor is the same as the total current delivered by the battery $I = \dfrac{28\ V}{14\ \Omega} = \boxed{2.00\text{ A}}$

(b) Therefore $P = I^2R = (2\text{ A})^2(14\ \Omega) = \boxed{56.0\text{ W}}$

(c) Applying the loop rule to the simplified circuit

$$28\text{ V} - 5I - 3I' - 5I' - 2I' - 4I = 0$$

Since from part (a) $I = 2$ A, we find $I' = 1$ A

Therefore (refer to circuit as in step ii again)

$$V_a - 5I' - 2I' = V_b \text{ or } V_{ab} = V_a - V_b = 7I' = (7\ \Omega)(1\text{ A}) = \boxed{7.00\text{ V}}$$

Since $V_a - V_b > 0$, point a is at the higher potential.

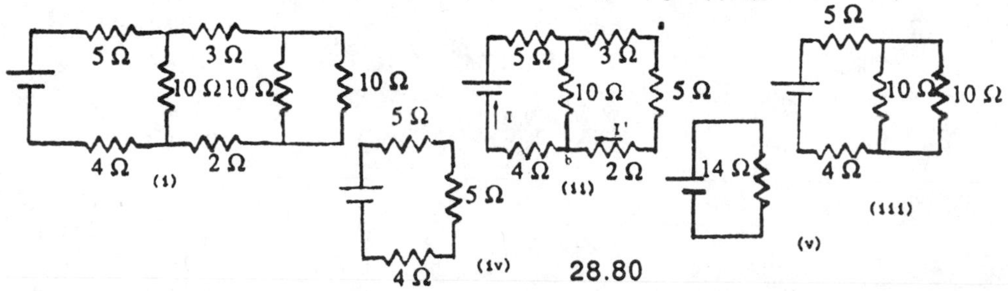

28.80

28.81 (a) $q = CV(1 - e^{-t/RC})$

$$= (10^{-6}\ \text{F})(10\ \text{V})[1 - e^{-(10\ \text{s})/(2\times10^{6}\ \Omega)(10^{-6}\ \text{F})}] = \boxed{9.93\ \mu\text{C}}$$

(b) $I = \dfrac{dq}{dt} = (\dfrac{V}{R})e^{-t/RC} = [\dfrac{10\ \text{V}}{2\times10^{-6}\ \Omega}]e^{-10/2} = \boxed{3.37\times10^{-8}\ \text{A}}$

(c) $\dfrac{dU}{dt} = \dfrac{d}{dt}(\dfrac{q^2}{C}) = \dfrac{q}{C}(\dfrac{dq}{dt}) = (\ ds\dfrac{q}{C})I$

$$= (\frac{9.9\times10^{-6}\ \text{C}}{1\times10^{-6}\ \text{F}})(3.37\times10^{-6}\ \text{A}) = \boxed{3.34\times10^{-7}\ \text{W}}$$

(d) $P_{\text{batt}} = I\mathcal{E} = (3.37\times10^{-6}\ \text{A})(10\ \text{V}) = \boxed{3.37\times10^{-7}\ \text{W}}$

28.82 The energy dissipated in the resistor is given by

$$U_R = \int_0^\infty I^2 R dt = (\frac{V}{R})^2 \int R dt = \frac{1}{(RC)^2}\int_0^\infty q^2 dt$$

$$= \frac{1}{(RC)^2}\int_0^\infty q_0^2 e^{-2t/RC} dt \quad \text{or} \quad U_R = \frac{q_0^2}{2C}$$

But from Eq. 28.14, energy in charged capacitor is $U_C = \dfrac{q_0^2}{2C}$.

Therefore one-half of energy supplied by the battery is stored in the capacitor.

28.83 Start at the point when the voltage has just reached $\frac{2}{3}V$ and the switch has just closed.

The voltage is $\frac{2}{3}V$ and is decaying towards 0 V with a time constant $R_B C$

$V(t) = [\frac{2}{3}V]e^{-t/R_B C}$ We want to know when $V(t)$ will reach $\frac{1}{3}V$

Therefore $(\frac{1}{3})V = [\frac{2}{3}V]e^{-t/R_B C}$ or $e^{-t/R_B C} = \frac{1}{2}$ or

$t_1 = R_B C \ln 2$

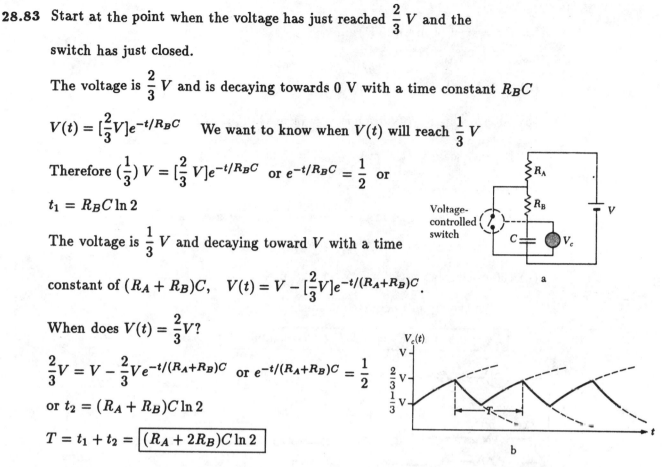

The voltage is $\frac{1}{3}V$ and decaying toward V with a time constant of $(R_A + R_B)C$, $V(t) = V - [\frac{2}{3}V]e^{-t/(R_A+R_B)C}$.

When does $V(t) = \frac{2}{3}V$?

$\frac{2}{3}V = V - \frac{2}{3}Ve^{-t/(R_A+R_B)C}$ or $e^{-t/(R_A+R_B)C} = \frac{1}{2}$

or $t_2 = (R_A + R_B)C \ln 2$

$T = t_1 + t_2 = \boxed{(R_A + 2R_B)C \ln 2}$

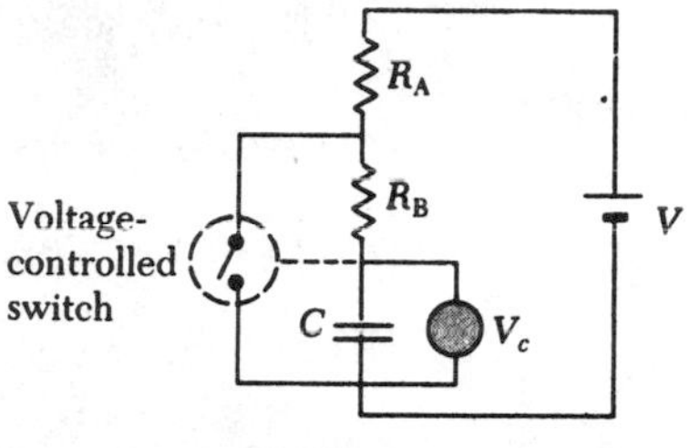

a

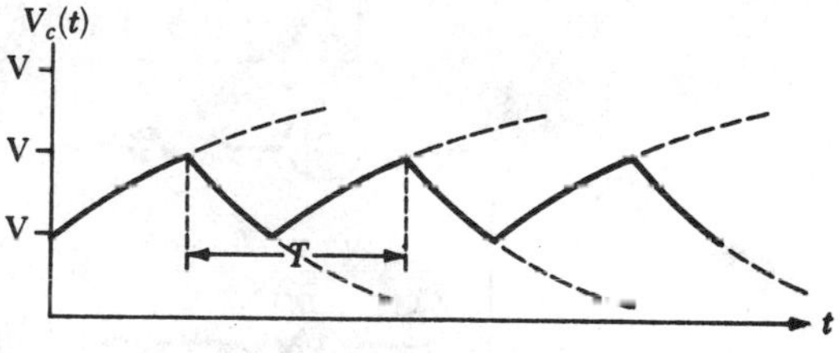

b

28.83

28.84 $V = IR$

(a) $20 = (1 \times 10^{-3})(R_1 + 60)$ $R_1 = 1.994 \times 10^4\ \Omega$

(b) $50 = (1 \times 10^{-3})(R_2 + R_1 + 60)$ $R_2 = 30.0\ \text{k}\Omega$

(c) $100 = (1 \times 10^{-3})(R_3 + R_1 + 60)$ $R_3 = 50.0\ \text{k}\Omega$

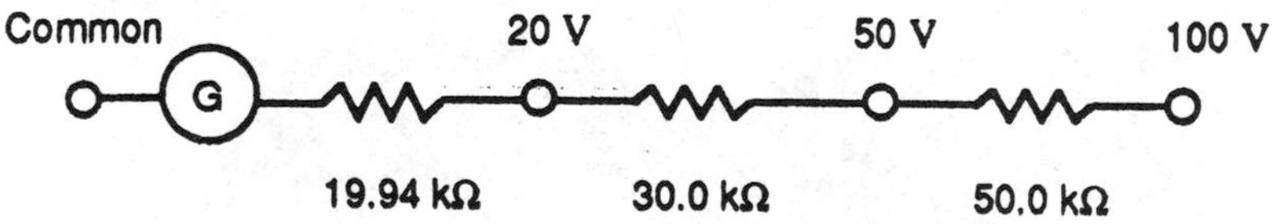

28.84

28.85 *Method 1:*

$V = IR = ir = (1\text{ mA})(25\ \Omega)$

$I_{\text{Range}} = I + i$

(a) 25 mA scale : $(24\text{ mA})(R_{25}) = (1\text{ mA})\ (25\ \Omega)$; $\boxed{R_{25} = 1.04\ \Omega}$

(b) 50 mA scale : $(49\text{ mA})(R_{50}) = (1\text{ mA})\ (25\ \Omega)$; $\boxed{R_{50} = 0.510\ \Omega}$

(c) 100 mA scale : $(99\text{ mA})(R_{100}) = (1\text{ mA})\ (25\ \Omega)$; $\boxed{R_{100} = 0.253\ \Omega}$

Method 2:

(a) 25 mA scale : $(24\text{ mA})(R_1 + R_2 + R_3) = (1\text{ mA})\ (25\ \Omega)$;

(b) 50 mA scale : $(49\text{ mA})(R_1 + R_2) = (1\text{ mA})\ (R_3 + 25\ \Omega)$;

(c) 100 mA scale : $(99\text{ mA})(R_1) = (1\text{ mA})\ (R_2 + R_3 + 25\ \Omega)$;

Solve the simultaneous equations.

$\boxed{R_3 = 0.521\ \Omega,\ R_2 = 0.261\ \Omega,\ R_1 = 0.260\ \Omega}$

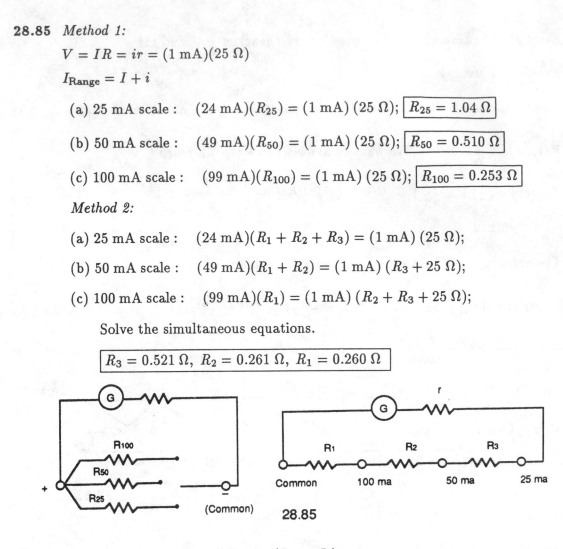

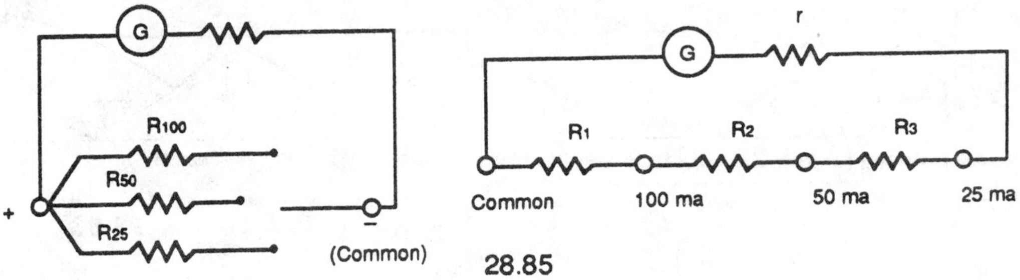

28.85

28.86 Parallel $V = I_g r_g = I_s r_s = (I_{Fs} - I_g) r_s$

$$I_g(r_g + r_s) = I_{Fs} r_s$$

$$V_{Fs}\frac{r_g + r_s}{R + r_g} = I_{Fs} r_s$$

$$\frac{V_{Fs}}{I_{Fs}} r_g + \frac{V_{Fs}}{I_{Fs}} = R r_s + r_g r_s$$

Series $V_{fs} = I_g(R + r_g)$

$$\therefore I_g = \frac{V_{Fs}}{R + r_g}$$

$$r_g = \frac{R - V_{Fs}/I_{Fs}}{V_{Fs}/I_{Fs} - r_s} \qquad r_s = \frac{2500 - 2/0.5}{2/0.5 - 0.22}(0.22) = \frac{2496}{3.78}(0.22) = \boxed{145\ \Omega}$$

$$I_g = \frac{V_{Fs}}{R + r_g} = \frac{2.0}{2500 + 145.3} = \boxed{0.756\text{ mA}}$$

***28.87** (a) After steady-state conditions have been reached, there is no DC current through the capacitor. Thus:

For R_3 : $\boxed{I_{R_3} = 0 \quad \text{(steady-state)}}$

For the other two resistors, the steady-state current is simply determined by the 9-V emf across the 12-kΩ and 15-kΩ resistors in series:

$$\text{For } R_1 \text{ and } r_2 : \; I_{(R_1+R_2)} = \frac{\mathcal{E}}{R_1+R_2} = \frac{9\text{ V}}{(12\text{ k}\Omega + 15\text{ k}\Omega)}$$

$$= \boxed{0.333\text{ mA} \quad \text{(steady-state)}}$$

(b) After the transient currents have ceased, the voltage across C is the same as the voltage across $R_2(= IR_2)$ because there is no voltage drop across R_3. Therefore, the charge Q on C is

$$Q = CV_{R_2} = C(IR_2) = (10\ \mu\text{F})(0.333\text{ mA})(15\text{ k}\Omega) = \boxed{50.0\ \mu C}$$

(c) When the switch is opened, the branch containing R_1 is no longer part of the circuit. The capacitor discharges through $(R_2 + R_3)$ with a time constant of $(R_2 + R_3)C = (15\text{ k}\Omega + 3\text{ k}\Omega)(10\ \mu F) = 0.180$ s. The initial current I_0 in this discharge circuit is determined by the initial voltage across the capacitor applied to $(R_2 + R_3)$ in series:

$$I_0 = \frac{V_C}{(R_2+R_3)} = \frac{IR_2}{(R_2+R_3)} = \frac{(0.333\text{ mA})(15\text{ k}\Omega)}{(15\text{ k}\Omega + 3\text{ k}\Omega)} = \boxed{0.278\text{ mA}}$$

Thus, when the switch is opened, the current through R_2 changes instantaneously from 0.333 mA (downward) to 0.278 mA (downward) as shown in Figure 28.87.
Thereafter, it decays according to

$$t_{R_2} = I_0 e^{-t/R_2+R_3)C}$$

$$= \boxed{(0.278\text{ mA})e^{-t/(0.180\text{ s})} \quad (\text{for } t > 0)}$$

(d) The charge q on the capacitor decays from Q_0 to $Q_0/5$ according to

$$q = Q_0 e^{-t/(R_2+R_3)C}$$

$$\frac{Q_0}{5} = Q_0 e^{(-t/0.180\text{ s})}$$

$$5 = e^{t/(0.180\text{ s})}$$

$$\ln 5 = \frac{t}{180\text{ s}}$$

$$t = (0.108\text{ s})(\ln 5) = \boxed{0.290\text{ s}}$$

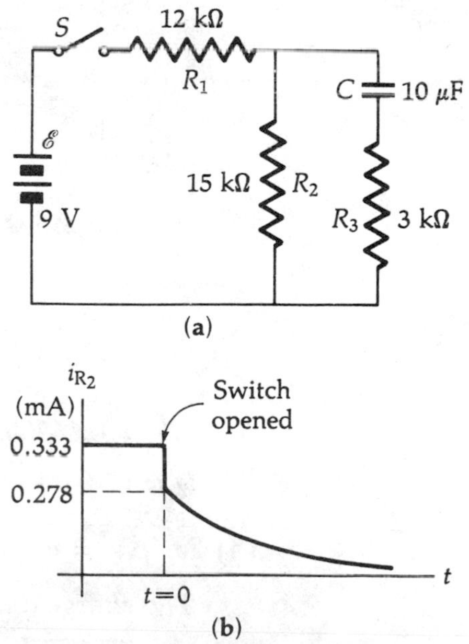

28.87

***28.88** $V = (10\ \text{V})(1 - e^{-t/RC})$

$0.4 = 1 - e^{-3/R\times10^{-5}}$

$e^{-3/R\times10^{-5}} = 0.6$

$\dfrac{+3}{R\times10^{-5}} = 0.510$

$\dfrac{3\times10^{5}}{0.510} = R = \boxed{587\ \text{k}\Omega}$

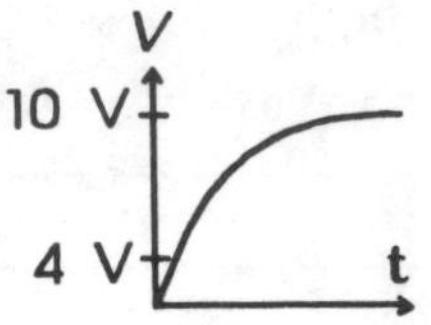

28.88

***28.89**

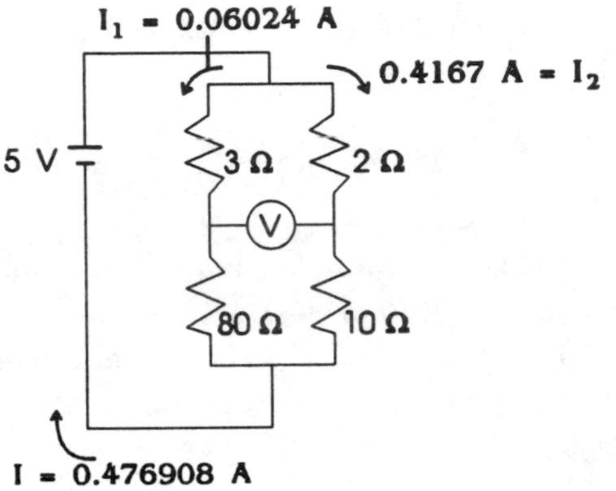

28.89

(a)

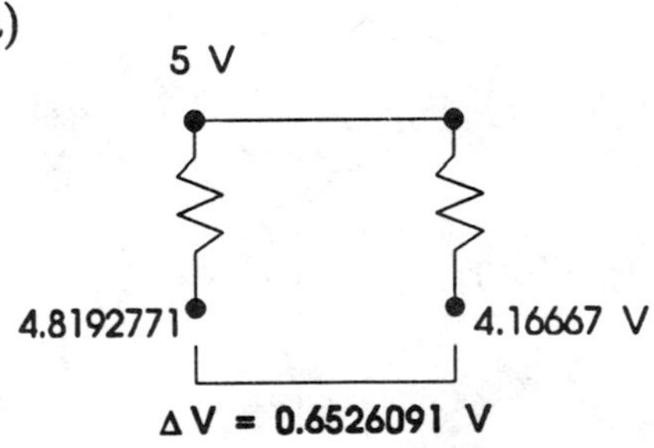

28.89(a)

$\Delta V = 0.6526091\ \text{V}$

$Q = CV = \boxed{1.96\ \mu\text{C}}$

(b) For $\Delta V = 0$, $I_1(83\ \Omega) = I_2(R+2)$

The charge on the capacitor is zero when

$R = \boxed{53.3\ \Omega}$

***28.90**

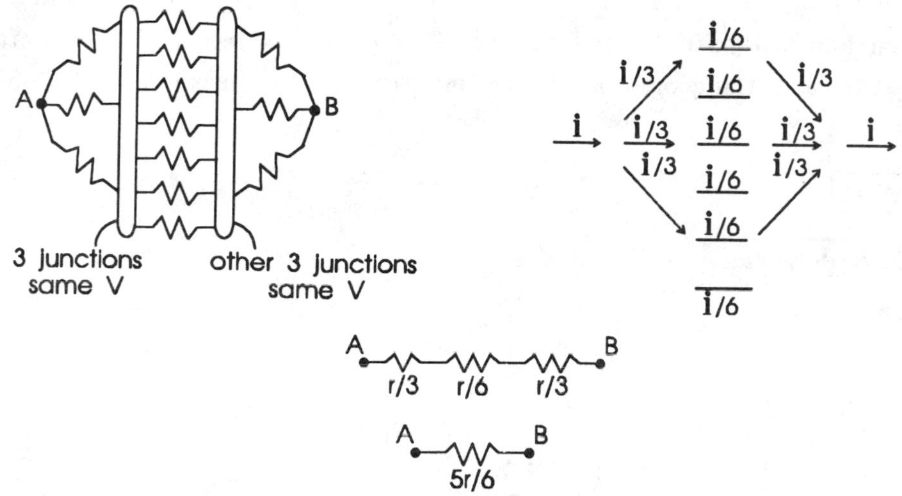

28.90

***28.91** $V = \mathcal{E}e^{-t/RC}$

$$ln\left(\frac{\mathcal{E}}{V}\right) = t/RC$$

V	$ln(\mathcal{E}/V)$	t(s)
6.19	0	0
5.55	+0.10914	4.87
4.93	0.22760	11.1
4.34	+0.35506	19.4
3.72	0.50921	30.8
3.09	+0.69476	46.6
2.47	+0.91872	67.3
1.83	1.21862	102.2

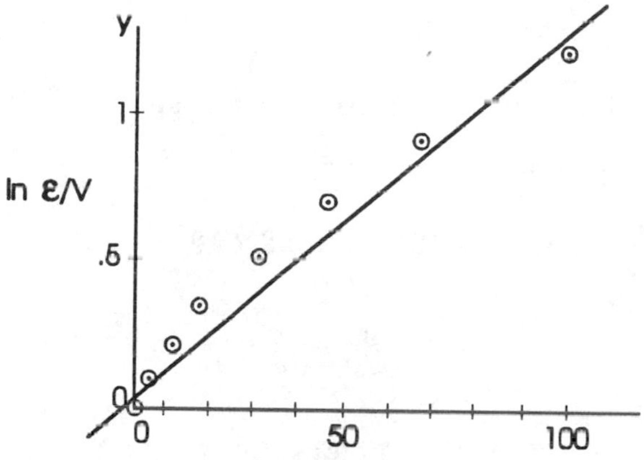

28.91

$$\Sigma x = 282.27$$
$$\Sigma x^2 = 18618$$
$$\Sigma xy = 244.38$$
$$\Sigma y = 4.0331$$
$$n = 8$$
$$n\Sigma x^2 - (\Sigma x)^2 = 69268$$

$$a = \frac{816.62}{69268} = 0.011789$$

84.823

(a) $\ln\frac{\mathcal{E}}{V} = 0.0811t + 0.0882$

(b) $RC = \boxed{85\text{s} \pm 6\%}$

$C = \boxed{8.5\mu F \pm 6\%}$

CHAPTER 29

29.1 Electron has a *negative* charge and use $F = qv \times B$ where $\boldsymbol{B}$ is horizontal, and directed towards the geographic North (magnetic South) (use left hand for negative charge).

(a) $\boxed{\text{West}}$

(b) $\boxed{\text{Zero deflection}}$

(c) $\boxed{\text{Up}}$

(d) $\boxed{\text{Down}}$

29.2 $\boldsymbol{F} = q\boldsymbol{v} \times \boldsymbol{B}$; $|\mathbf{F}|(-\boldsymbol{j}) = -e|\boldsymbol{v}|\boldsymbol{i} \times \boldsymbol{B}$

Therefore $\boldsymbol{B} = |\boldsymbol{B}|(-\boldsymbol{k})$ which indicates the $\boxed{\text{negative z direction}}$

29.3 $v = 3.8 \times 10^5$ m/s

$B = 1.9$ T

direction given by the right hand rule: vertically downward

$F = qvB \sin\theta$

$F = (2)(1.602 \times 10^{-19}\ \text{C})(3.8 \times 10^5\ \text{m/s})(1.9\ \text{T}) \sin 90°$

$F = \boxed{2.31 \times 10^{-13}\ \text{N}}$

29.4 $F = qvB\sin\theta = (1.602 \times 10^{-19}\ \text{C})(4.8 \times 10^6\ \text{m/s})(75 \times 10^{-6}\ \text{T}) \sin 90°$

$= \boxed{5.77 \times 10^{-17}\ \text{N, East}}$

29.5 $F = qvB \sin\theta$

$8.2 \times 10^{-13}\ \text{N} = (1.602 \times 10^{-19}\ \text{C})(4 \times 10^6\ \text{m/s})(1.7\ \text{T}) \sin\theta$

$\sin\theta = 0.753$

$\theta = \sin^{-1}(0.753) = \boxed{48.8° \text{ or } 131°}$

29.6 $V = 2.4 \times 10^3 \text{ V}$

$B = 1.7 \text{ T}$

$\frac{1}{2}mv^2 = qV$

$\frac{1}{2}(9.11 \times 10^{-31} \text{ kg})v^2 = (1.602 \times 10^{-19} \text{ C})(2.4 \times 10^3 \text{ V})$

$v = 2.91 \times 10^7 \text{ m/s}$

(a) $F = qvB\sin\theta \qquad \theta = 90^\circ$ maximum force

$F = (1.602 \times 10^{-19})(2.91 \times 10^7)(1.7)\sin 90^\circ$

$F_{\text{max}} = \boxed{7.90 \times 10^{-12} \text{ N}}$

(b) $\boxed{\theta = 0^\circ, 180^\circ \longrightarrow \mathbf{F}_{\text{min}} = 0}$

29.7 $$\boldsymbol{F} = q\boldsymbol{v} \times \boldsymbol{B} = q\begin{vmatrix} \boldsymbol{i} & \boldsymbol{j} & \boldsymbol{k} \\ -2 & 3 & -7 \\ 4 & -11 & 0 \end{vmatrix}$$

$$= (-1.6 \times 10^{-19})\{\boldsymbol{i}[(3)(0) - (-11)(-7)] - \boldsymbol{j}[(-2)(0) - (4)(-7)] + \boldsymbol{k}[(-2)(-11) - (4)(3)]\}$$

$$= \boxed{(12.3\boldsymbol{i} + 4.48\boldsymbol{j} - 1.60\boldsymbol{k}) \times 10^{-18} \text{ N}}$$

29.8 $$\boldsymbol{F} = q\boldsymbol{v} \times \boldsymbol{B} = (-1.6 \times 10^{-19})\begin{vmatrix} \boldsymbol{i} & \boldsymbol{j} & \boldsymbol{k} \\ 0 & 3.7 \times 10^5 & 0 \\ 1.4 & 2.1 & 0 \end{vmatrix}$$

$$= -1.6 \times 10^{-19}(-1.4)(3.7 \times 10^5)\boldsymbol{k} = \boxed{(8.29 \times 10^{-14}\ \boldsymbol{k}) \text{ N}}$$

29.9 $\boldsymbol{F} = q\boldsymbol{v} \times \boldsymbol{B}$

$$\boldsymbol{v} \times \boldsymbol{B} = \begin{vmatrix} \boldsymbol{i} & \boldsymbol{j} & \boldsymbol{k} \\ +2 & -4 & +1 \\ +1 & +2 & -3 \end{vmatrix} = (12-2)\boldsymbol{i} + (1+6)\boldsymbol{j} + (4+4)\boldsymbol{k} = 10\boldsymbol{i} + 7\boldsymbol{j} + 8\boldsymbol{k}$$

$$|\boldsymbol{v} \times \boldsymbol{B}| = \sqrt{10^2 + 7^2 + 8^2} = 14.6\ \mathrm{T \cdot m/s}$$

$$|\boldsymbol{F}| = q\boldsymbol{v} \times \boldsymbol{B} = (1.602 \times 10^{-19}\ \mathrm{C})(14.6\ \mathrm{T \cdot m/s}) = \boxed{2.34 \times 10^{-18}\ \mathrm{N}}$$

29.10 $\boldsymbol{v} = 10^7\ \boldsymbol{k}\ \mathrm{m/s}$

$$\boldsymbol{F} = m\boldsymbol{a} = (1.67265 \times 10^{27}\ \mathrm{kg})(2 \times 10^{13}\ \mathrm{m/s^2})\boldsymbol{i} = 3.345 \times 10^{-14}\boldsymbol{i}\ \mathrm{N}$$

$$\boldsymbol{F} = e\boldsymbol{v} \times \boldsymbol{B}$$

$$3.345 \times 10^{-14}\ \mathrm{N}\ \boldsymbol{i} = (1.6 \times 10^{-19}\ \mathrm{C})(10^7\ \boldsymbol{k}\ \mathrm{m/s}) \times \boldsymbol{B}$$

$$0.029\boldsymbol{i}\ \mathrm{T} = \boldsymbol{k} \times \boldsymbol{B}$$

$$\boxed{\boldsymbol{B} = 20.9\ \mathrm{mT}(-\boldsymbol{j})}$$

29.11 $W = \int \boldsymbol{F} \cdot d\boldsymbol{s}$ and $\boldsymbol{F} = q(\boldsymbol{v} \times \boldsymbol{B}) = q[\frac{d\boldsymbol{s}}{dt} \times \boldsymbol{B}]$ therefore

$$W = q\int [\frac{d\boldsymbol{s}}{dt} \times \boldsymbol{B}] \cdot d\boldsymbol{s}$$

But $d\boldsymbol{s}$ is perpendicular to the direction of $q[\frac{d\boldsymbol{s}}{dt} \times \boldsymbol{B}]$, therefore

$W = 0$ (the scalar product of two perpendicular vector is zero).

29.12 $F = I\ell B$

$$\frac{F}{\ell} = IB = (22\ \mathrm{A})(0.77\ \mathrm{T}) = \boxed{16.9\ \mathrm{N/m}}$$

29.13 $d\boldsymbol{F} = Id\boldsymbol{\ell} \times \boldsymbol{B}$

$$= (2.4\ \mathrm{A})(dx\boldsymbol{i}) \times (1.6\boldsymbol{k}\ \mathrm{T})$$

$$= (-3.84\ dx\ \boldsymbol{j})$$

$$\mathbf{F} = \int_0^{0.75\ \mathrm{m}} -3.84\ dx\boldsymbol{j} = \boxed{-2.88\ \boldsymbol{j}\ \mathrm{N}}$$

29.14 $\dfrac{|\mathbf{F}|}{\ell} = \dfrac{mg}{\ell} = \dfrac{I|\boldsymbol{\ell} \times \mathbf{B}|}{\ell}$;

so $I = \dfrac{mg}{B\ell} = \dfrac{(0.04\text{ kg/m})(9.80\text{ m/s}^2)}{3.6\text{ T}} = \boxed{0.109\text{ A}}$

The direction of I in the bar is $\boxed{\text{to the right}}$

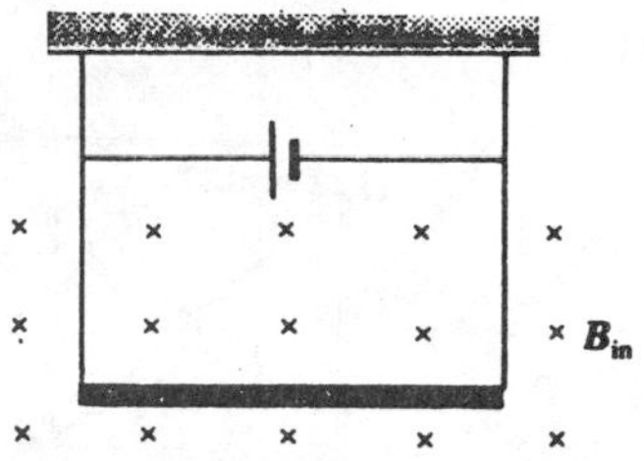

29.14

29.15 $\dfrac{m}{\ell} = (0.5\,\dfrac{\text{g}}{\text{cm}})(\dfrac{\text{kg}}{1000\text{ g}})(\dfrac{100\text{ cm}}{\text{m}}) = 5 \times 10^{-2}\text{ kg/m}$

$I = 2$ A direction given by right hand rule: eastward

$F = I\ell B \sin\theta$ $\qquad W = mg$

$mg = I\ell B \sin\theta$

$\dfrac{m}{\ell}g = IB \sin\theta$

$(5 \times 10^{-2})(9.8) = (2)\, B \sin 90°$

$B = \boxed{0.25\text{ Tesla}}$

29.16 For each segment of the rectangular loop within the region of the field $\mathbf{F} = I(\boldsymbol{\ell} \times \mathbf{B})$. For a fixed direction of the field, the forces on the two vertical segments of the loop will be equal and oppositely directed. Therefore the net magnetic force on the loop is due to $\mathbf{F} = I(\boldsymbol{\ell} \times \mathbf{B})$ on the horizontal segment. By use of the right hand rule we determine that the direction of $\mathbf{B}$ must be $\boxed{\text{into the page}}$ and

$B = \dfrac{F}{I\ell} = \dfrac{(4 \times 10^{-2}\text{ N})}{(3\text{ A})(0.1\text{ m})} = \boxed{0.133\text{ T}}$

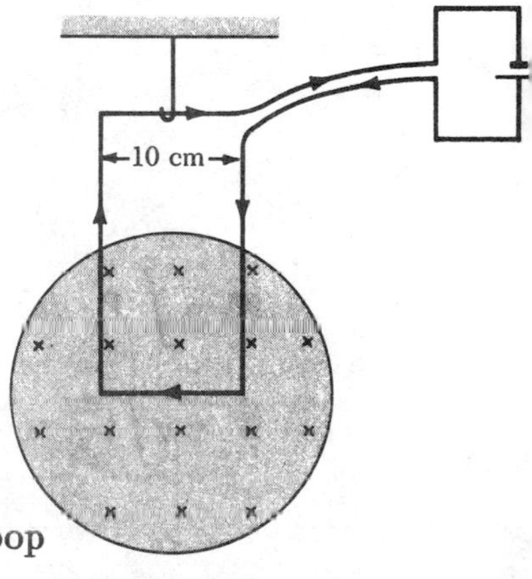

29.16

29.17 (a) $F = I\ell B \sin\theta$

$F = (5\text{ A})(2.8\text{ m})(0.39\text{ T}) \sin 60° = \boxed{4.73\text{ N}}$

(b) $F = (5\text{ A})(2.8\text{ m})(0.39\text{ T}) \sin 90° = \boxed{5.46\text{ N}}$

(c) $F = (5\text{ A})(2.8\text{ m})(0.39\text{ T}) \sin 120° = \boxed{4.73\text{ N}}$

***29.18**

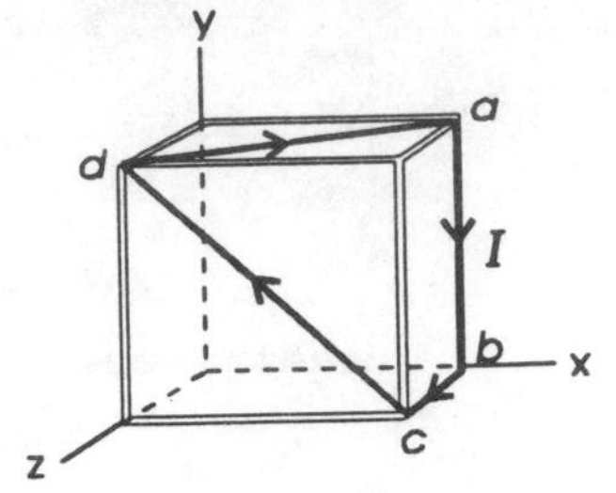

29.18

segment	i	L	B	$\mathbf{F} = i\ell \times B$
ab	5 A	(0.4 m)(−j)	$0.02 \frac{\text{N}}{\text{A}\cdot\text{m}}\mathbf{j}$	0
bc	5 A	(0.4 m)**k**	$0.02 \frac{\text{N}}{\text{A}\cdot\text{m}}\mathbf{j}$	(40.0 mN)(−i)
cd	5 A	(0.4 m)(−j)	$0.02 \frac{\text{N}}{\text{A}\cdot\text{m}}\mathbf{j}$	(40.0 mN)(−**k**) + 0
da	5 A	(0.4 m)**i** + (0.4 m)(−**k**)	$0.02 \frac{\text{N}}{\text{A}\cdot\text{m}}\mathbf{j}$	(40.0 mN)(**k** + **j**)

29.19 $F = I\ell B$

$$\frac{F}{\ell} = IB$$

$0.63\ \text{N/m} = (15\ \text{A})B$

$\boxed{B = 0.042\mathbf{k}\ \text{T}}$ (Use right hand rule for direction)

The direction of the magnetic field is in the z direction.

29.20 (a) (looking west)

$$F = I\ell B \sin\theta$$

$$= (15\ \text{A})(10\ \text{m})(0.60 \times 10^{-4}\ \text{T}) \sin 90° = \boxed{9.00\ \ \text{mN}}$$

The force points 15° above North

(b) (looking west)

$$F = I\ell B \sin\theta = (15\ \text{A})(10\ \text{m})(0.60 \times 10^{-4}\ \text{T}) \sin 165°$$

$\boxed{F = 0.00233\ \ \text{N}}$ The force is into the page, or west

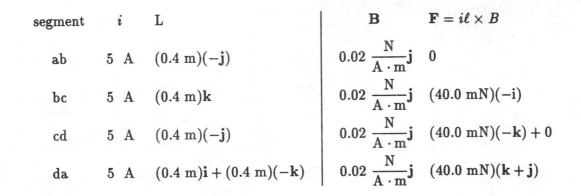

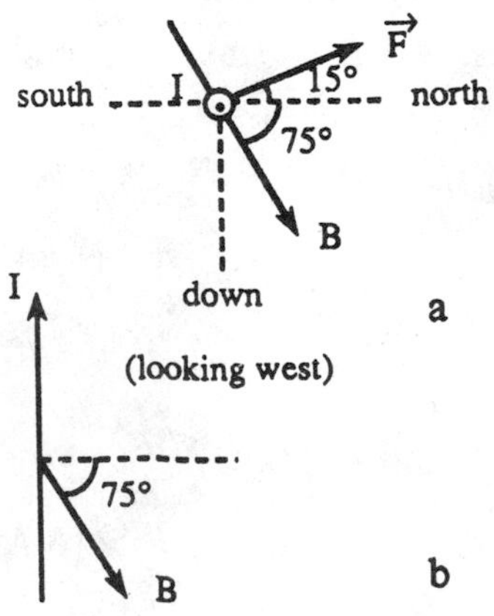

29.20

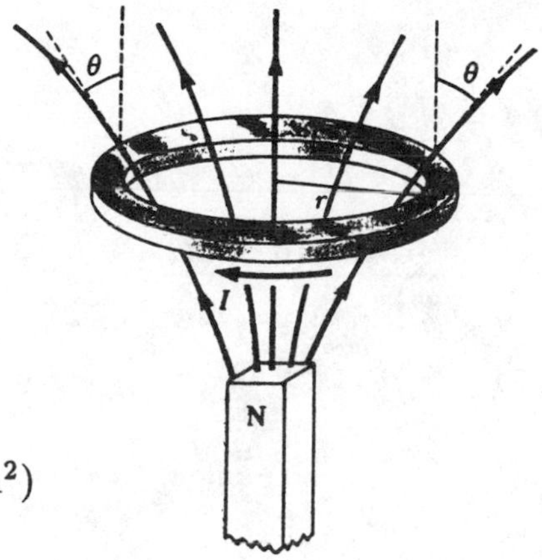

29.21

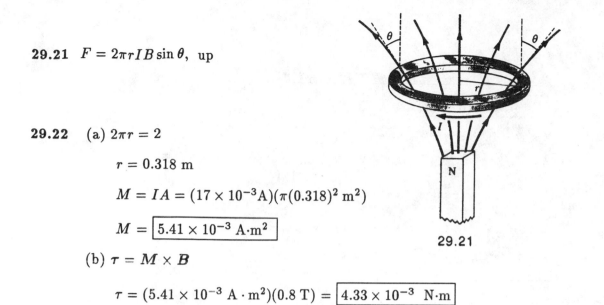

29.21 $F = 2\pi r I B \sin\theta$, up

29.22 (a) $2\pi r = 2$

$r = 0.318$ m

$M = IA = (17 \times 10^{-3}\text{A})(\pi(0.318)^2\ \text{m}^2)$

$M = \boxed{5.41 \times 10^{-3}\ \text{A}\cdot\text{m}^2}$

(b) $\boldsymbol{\tau} = \mathbf{M} \times \mathbf{B}$

$\tau = (5.41 \times 10^{-3}\ \text{A}\cdot\text{m}^2)(0.8\ \text{T}) = \boxed{4.33 \times 10^{-3}\ \text{N}\cdot\text{m}}$

29.23 $\tau = NBAI \sin\theta$

$\tau = (100)(0.8\ \text{T})(0.4 \times 0.3\ \text{m}^2)(1.2\ \text{A}) \sin 60° = \boxed{9.98\ \text{N}\cdot\text{m}}$

Note θ is the angle between the magnetic moment and the **B** field. Loop will rotate such to align the magnetic moment with the **B** field. Looking down along the y axis, loop will rotate in clockwise direction.

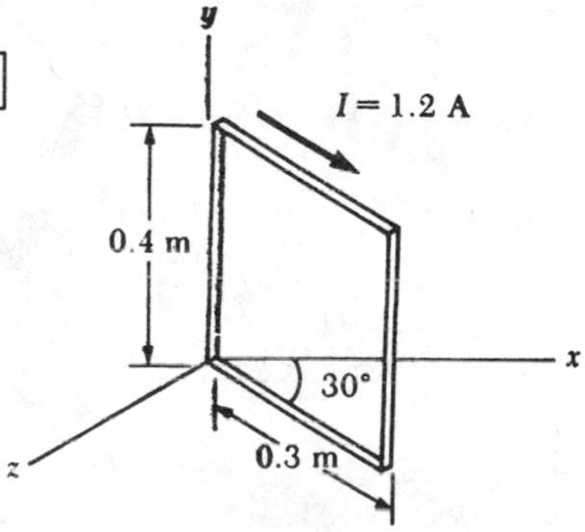

29.23

29.24 $\tau = \mu B \sin\theta$

$4.6 \times 10^{-3}\ \text{N}\cdot\text{m} = \mu(0.25) \sin 90°$

$\mu = \boxed{1.84 \times 10^{-2}\ \text{A}\cdot\text{m}^2}$

29.25 (a) $\tau = NBA\,I$

$8 \times 10^{-3}\ \text{N} \cdot \text{m} = (225)(0.21\ \text{T})(0.45\ \text{m}^2)I$

$\boxed{I = 3.76 \times 10^{-4}\ \text{A}}$

(b) Yes $A = 0.45 = \pi r^2$ $\quad r = 0.378\ \text{m}$

$\ell = N(2\pi r) = 225(2\pi(0.378)) = 535\ \text{m}$

$\ell = 2\pi R \quad 535 = 2\pi R$

$R = 85.2\ \text{m}$

$\tau = NBA\,I$

$8 \times 10^{-3}\ \text{N} \cdot \text{m} = (1)(0.21\ \text{T})(\pi[85.2]^2\ \text{m}^2)I$

$\boxed{I = 1.67 \times 10^{-6}\ \text{A}}$

A smaller current is required. The current decreases in the same ratio as the number of turns in the original coil.

***29.26** (a)

$$\tau = \boldsymbol{\mu} \times \mathbf{B} = NIAB$$
$$= 1(5A)\pi(0.5\ \text{m})^2(3 \times 10^{-3})\frac{\text{N} \cdot \text{s}}{\text{cm}} = \boxed{118\ \mu\text{N} \cdot \text{m}}$$

(b)

$$U = \boldsymbol{\mu} \cdot \mathbf{B}$$
$$\Delta U = 2\mu B = \boxed{236\ \mu\text{J}}$$

29.27

$$W = NIAB \int_0^{\pi} \sin\theta\, d\theta$$
$$= +2NIAB = +2(100)(0.1\ \text{A})(0.025\ \text{m})^2\pi(1.5\ \text{T}) = \boxed{0.0589\ \text{J}}$$

29.28 (a) $B = 0.5$ Gauss $\quad v = 6.2 \times 10^6\ \text{m/s}$

Direction is given by the right-hand-rule: southward

$F = qvB\sin\theta$

$F = (1.062 \times 10^{-19})(6.2 \times 10^6)(0.5 \times 10^{-4}\ \text{T})\sin 90°$

$F = \boxed{4.97 \times 10^{-17}\ \text{N}}$

(b) $F = \dfrac{mv^2}{r} \quad r = \dfrac{mv^2}{F}$

$$r = \frac{(1.67 \times 10^{-27}\ \text{kg})(6.2 \times 10^6\ \text{m/s})^2}{4.97 \times 10^{-17}\ \text{N}} = \boxed{1.29 \times 10^3\ \text{m}}$$

29.29 $\frac{1}{2}mv^2 = q\Delta V$

$\frac{1}{2}(3.2 \times 10^{-26})v^2 = (1.602 \times 10^{-19})(833)$

$v = 9.13 \times 10^4$ m/s

$$r = \frac{mv}{qB} = \frac{(3.2 \times 10^{-26}\text{ kg})(9.13 \times 10^4\text{ m/s})}{(1.602 \times 10^{-19}\text{ C})(0.92\text{ T})} = \boxed{1.98 \times 10^{-2}\text{ m}}$$

***29.30** (a) $\frac{mv^2}{r} = qvB \qquad \frac{mv^2}{2} = 3.2 \times 10^{-16}$ J

$$r = \frac{mv}{qB} = \frac{\sqrt{2mE}}{qB} = \boxed{3.02\text{ m}}$$

(b) $t = \frac{d}{v} = \frac{2\pi r}{v} = \boxed{7.15 \times 10^{-7}\text{ s}}$

(c) $f = \frac{1}{t} = \frac{qB}{2\pi m} = \boxed{1.4 \times 10^6\text{ Hz}}$

29.31 $K = \frac{1}{2}mv^2$

$(725\text{ eV})(1.602 \times 10^{-19}\text{ J/eV}) = \frac{1}{2}(9.11 \times 10^{-31}\text{ kg})v^2$

$v = 1.6 \times 10^7$ m/s

$r = \frac{mv}{qB}$

$$0.5 = \frac{(9.11 \times 10^{-31})(1.6 \times 10^7)}{(1.602 \times 10^{-19})B}$$

$\boxed{B = 1.82 \times 10^{-4}\text{ T}}$

29.32 (a) $m\frac{v^2}{R} = evB$

$$v = \frac{eBR}{m}$$

$$v = \frac{(1.6 \times 10^{-19}\text{ C})(0.8\text{ T})(0.45\text{ m})}{1.6727 \times 10^{-27}\text{ kg}} = \boxed{3.44 \times 10^7\text{ m/s}}$$

(b) $t = \frac{\theta}{\omega} = \frac{\theta R}{v} = \frac{\frac{\pi}{2}(0.45\text{ m})}{3.44 \times 10^7\text{ m/s}} = \boxed{20.5\text{ ns}}$

(c) $E = \frac{1}{2}mv^2 = \frac{1}{2}(1.6727 \times 10^{-27}\text{ kg})(3.44 \times 10^7\text{ m/s})^2 = 9.92 \times 10^{-13}\text{ J}$

$= \boxed{6.20\text{ MeV}}$

29.33 $q_pV = \frac{1}{2}m_pv^2;\; q_pvB = \frac{m_pv^2}{r_p}$ so $r_p = \frac{1}{B}(\frac{2m_pv}{q_p})$ and

$\frac{m_d}{m_p} = 2$ so $\boxed{r_d = r_p\sqrt{2}}$

$\frac{m_\alpha}{m_p} = 4;\quad \frac{q_\alpha}{q_p} = 2$ so $\boxed{r_\alpha = r_p\sqrt{2}}$

29.34 $\omega = \frac{qB}{m} = \frac{(1.602 \times 10^{-19}\text{ C})(5.2\text{ T})}{1.67 \times 10^{-27}\text{ kg}} = \boxed{4.99 \times 10^8\text{ rad/s}}$

29.35 $E = \frac{1}{2}mv^2 = eV$

$$B = \frac{mv}{eR} = \frac{m}{eR}\sqrt{\frac{2eV}{m}} = \frac{1}{R}\sqrt{\frac{2mV}{e}}$$

$$= \frac{1}{5.8 \times 10^{10}\text{ m}}\sqrt{\frac{2(1.6727 \times 10^{-27}\text{ kg})(10^7\text{ V})}{1.6 \times 10^{-19}\text{ C}}} = \boxed{7.884 \times 10^{-12}\text{ T}}$$

29.36 $r = \frac{mv}{qB}$

$$\frac{1}{2}mv^2 = qV \quad v = \sqrt{\frac{2qV}{m}}$$

$$r = \frac{m\sqrt{2qV/m}}{qB}$$

$$r^2 = \frac{m}{q} \cdot \frac{2V}{B^2}$$

$$r' = \sqrt{\frac{m'}{q'}}\frac{\sqrt{2V}}{B} : \quad r'^2 = \frac{m'}{q'} \cdot \frac{2V}{B^2}$$

$$\left.\begin{array}{l} m' = \dfrac{q'B^2r'^2}{2V} \\ m = \dfrac{qB^2r^2}{2V} \end{array}\right\} \frac{m'}{m} = \frac{q'}{q} \cdot \frac{r'^2}{r^2} = (\frac{2e}{e})(\frac{2R}{R})^2 = \boxed{8}$$

29.37 $r = \frac{mv}{qB}$

$$7.94 \times 10^{-3}\ \text{m} = \frac{m(4.6 \times 10^5\ \text{m/s})}{(1.602 \times 10^{-19}\ \text{C})(1.8\ \text{T})}$$

$$m = 4.98 \times 10^{-27}\ \text{kg} = 2.99\ u$$

$$\left(\frac{\text{u}}{1.66 \times 10^{-27}\ \text{kg}}\right) \qquad \text{u} \longrightarrow \text{atomic mass unit.}$$

$m = 2.99$ u nucleus of singly charged tritium atom $^3H^+$,
or a singly charged ^{3} He, $^3_2\text{He}^+$

29.38 $x = \frac{1}{2}\, at^2 = \frac{1}{2}\frac{evB}{m}(\frac{d}{v})^2 = \frac{eBd^2}{2mv}$

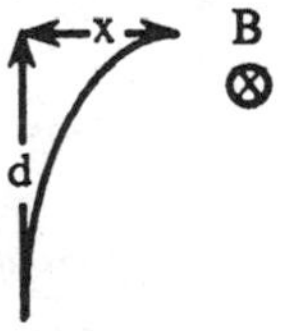

where $\frac{1}{2}mv^2 = eV$ or $v = \sqrt{\frac{2eV}{m}}$, so

$$x = \frac{(1.6 \times 10^{-19}\text{C})(4 \times 10^{-5}\text{T})(0.35\ \text{m})^2}{[8(9.1 \times 10^{-31}\ \text{kg})(1.6 \times 10^{-19}\ \text{C})(15 \times 10^3\ \text{V})]^{\frac{1}{2}}} = \boxed{5.93\ \text{mm}}$$

29.38

29.39 $\frac{1}{2}mv^2 = eV \quad v = \sqrt{\frac{2eV}{m}}$

$$E = B\sqrt{\frac{2eV}{m}}$$

$$= (10^{-2}\ \text{T})\left[\frac{2(1.6\times10^{-19}\ \text{C})(10^4\ \text{V})}{(9.1\times10^{-31}\ \text{kg})}\right]^{\frac{1}{2}} = \boxed{5.93\times10^5\ \text{V/m}}$$

***29.40** $F_M = F_E$

$qvB = qE$ where $v = \sqrt{\frac{2K}{m}}$. K is kinetic energy of the electrons.

$$E = vB = \sqrt{\frac{2K}{m}}B = \left[\frac{2(705)(1.602\times10^{-19})}{(9.11\times10^{-31})}\right]^{1/2}(0.015) = \boxed{2.44\times10^5\ \frac{\text{V}}{\text{m}}}$$

***29.41** $mg = \boxed{8.93\times10^{-30}\ \text{N down}}$

$qE = \boxed{1.60\times10^{-17}\ \text{N up}}$

$qvB = q\sqrt{\frac{2qU}{m}}B = \boxed{4.74\times10^{-17}\ \text{N down}}$

29.42 $K = \frac{1}{2}mv^2 = qV \quad v = \sqrt{\frac{2qV}{m}}$

$$|\mathbf{F}| = |q\mathbf{v}\times\mathbf{B}| = \frac{mv^2}{r} \quad r = \frac{mv}{qB} = \frac{m}{q}\frac{\sqrt{2qV/m}}{B} = \frac{1}{B}\sqrt{\frac{2mV}{q}}$$

(a) $r_{238} = \sqrt{\frac{2(238\times1.66\times10^{-27})2000}{1.6\times10^{-19}}}(\frac{1}{1.2}) = 8.28\times10^{-2}\ \text{m} = \boxed{8.28\ \text{cm}}$

(b) $r_{235} = \boxed{8.23\ \text{cm}}$

$$\frac{r_{238}}{r_{235}} = \sqrt{\frac{\text{m}_{238}}{\text{m}_{235}}} = \sqrt{\frac{238.05}{235.04}} = \boxed{1.0064}$$

Independent of all other common variables.

***29.43** $F_e = F_m$

$qE = qvB$

$E = vB \quad (E = 2500\ V/\text{m},\ \text{B} = 0.035\ \text{T})$

$2500 = v(0.035)$

$v = 7.14 \times 10^4\ \text{m/s}$

$$r = \frac{mv}{qB} = \frac{(2.18 \times 10^{-26}\ \text{kg})(7.14 \times 10^4\ \text{m/s})}{(1.602 \times 10^{-19}\ \text{C})(0.035\ \text{T})} = \boxed{0.278\ \text{m}}$$

29.44 $K = \frac{1}{2}mv^2$

$$(34 \times 10^6\ \text{eV})(1.602 \times 10^{-19}\ \frac{\text{J}}{\text{eV}}) = \frac{1}{2}(1.67 \times 10^{-27}\ \text{kg})v^2$$

$v = 8.08 \times 10^7\ \text{m/s}$

$$r = \frac{mv}{qB} = \frac{(1.67 \times 10^{-27}\ \text{kg})(8.08 \times 10^7\ \text{m/s})}{(1.062 \times 10^{-19}\ \text{C})(5.2\ \text{T})} = \boxed{0.162\ \text{m}}$$

29.45 $K = \frac{1}{2}\,mv^2 = \left(\frac{q^2B^2}{2m}\right)R^2 \qquad f = \frac{qB}{2\pi m}$

$$2\pi^2 m f^2 = \frac{q^2B^2}{2m}$$

$K = (2\pi^2 m f^2)R^2$

$$(18 \times 10^6\ \text{eV})(1.602 \times 10^{-19}\ \text{J/eV}) = 2\pi^2(1.67 \times 10^{-27}\ \text{kg})(3 \times 10^7\ \text{Hz})^2 R^2$$

$R = \boxed{31.2\ \text{cm}}$

***29.46** $F = qvB = \frac{mv^2}{r}$

$$B = \frac{mv}{qr} = \frac{4.8 \times 10^{-16}\ kg \cdot \text{m/s}}{(1.6 \times 10^{-19}\ \text{C})(1000\ \text{m})} = \boxed{3.00\ \text{T}}$$

29.47 (a) $F = qvB = \frac{mv^2}{R}$

$$\omega = \frac{v}{R} = \frac{qBR}{mR} = \frac{qB}{m} = \frac{(1.602 \times 10^{-19}\ \text{C})(0.45\ \text{T})}{1.67 \times 10^{-27}\ \text{kg}} = \boxed{4.32 \times 10^7\ \text{rad/s}}$$

(b) $$v = \frac{qBR}{m} = \frac{(1.6 \times 10^{-19}\ \text{C})(0.45\ \text{T})(1.2\ \text{m})}{1.67 \times 10^{-27}\ \text{kg}} = \boxed{5.17 \times 10^7\ \text{m/s}}$$

29.48 (a) $K = \dfrac{q^2B^2R^2}{2m}$

$$B = \frac{\sqrt{2mK}}{qR} = \frac{\sqrt{2(1.67 \times 10^{-27}\text{ kg})(10.5 \times 10^6)(1.6 \times 10^{-19})\text{ J}}}{(1.6 \times 10^{-19}\text{ C})(30)(2.54/100)\text{ m}} = \boxed{0.614\ \text{T}}$$

(b) $f = \dfrac{\omega}{2\pi} = \dfrac{qB}{2\pi m} = \dfrac{(1.6 \times 10^{-18}\text{ C})(0.614\text{ T})}{2\pi(1.67 \times 10^{-27}\text{ kg})} = \boxed{9.37\ \text{MHz}}$

(c) $f\ \alpha\ \dfrac{1}{m}$; $\dfrac{f_1}{f_2} = \dfrac{B_1/m_1}{B_2/m_2}$; $B_2 = B_1(\dfrac{m_2}{m_1}) = 2B_1 = \boxed{1.23\ \text{T}}$

(d) $\dfrac{K_2}{K_1} = \dfrac{B_2^2/m_2}{B_1^2/m_1}$; $K_2 = K_1(\dfrac{B_2}{B_1})^2(\dfrac{m_1}{m_2}) = K_1(4)(\dfrac{1}{2}) = \boxed{21.0\ \text{MeV}}$

29.49 $\theta = \tan^{-1}\dfrac{25}{10.5} = 67.2°$

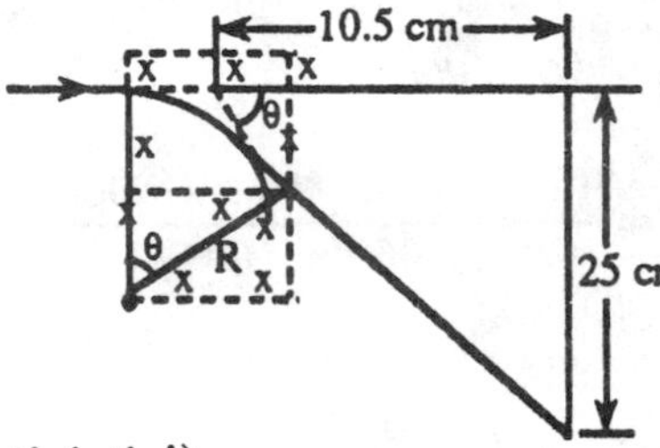

29.49

$R = \dfrac{1.0\text{ cm}}{\sin 67.2°} = 1.085\ \text{cm}$

$\dfrac{1}{2}mv^2 = qV$

$v = \sqrt{\dfrac{2qV}{m}} = 1.33 \times 10^8\ \text{m/s}$ (This is relativistic!)

$\dfrac{mv^2}{R} = qvB$;

$$B = \frac{mv}{qR} = \sqrt{\frac{m2V}{qR^2}} = \sqrt{\frac{(9.11 \times 10^{-31}\text{ kg})(2)(50,000\text{ V})}{(1.6 \times 10^{-19}\text{ C})(1.085 \times 10^{-2}\text{ m})^2}} = \boxed{69.5\ \text{mT}}$$

29.50 (a) $n_- = -\dfrac{1}{eR_H} = -\dfrac{1}{(1.60 \times 10^{-19}\text{ C})(-0.84 \times 10^{-10}\text{ m}^3/\text{C})} = \boxed{7.44 \times 10^{28}\ \text{m}^{-3}}$

On the basis of a valence of *one* for silver, we expect a charge carrier density of $5.86 \times 10^{28}\ \text{m}^{-3}$. Thus, in the Hall effect, the effective number of electrons per atom of silver is

$\dfrac{(7.44 \times 10^{28}\ \text{m}^{-3})}{(5.86 \times 10^{28}\ \text{m}^{-3})} = 1.27.$

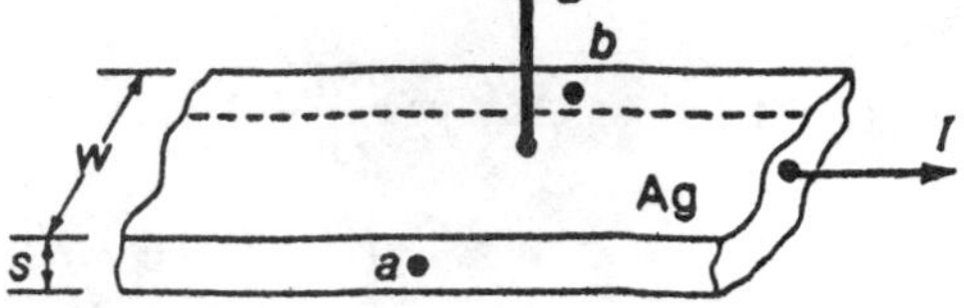

29.50

(b) $B_z = -\dfrac{E_x}{J_yR_H} = -\dfrac{\mathcal{E}_{ab}/d}{(I/td)R_H} = -\dfrac{\mathcal{E}_{ab}t}{IR_H}$

$$= -\frac{(15 \times 10^{-6}\text{ V})(0.20 \times 10^{-3}\text{ m})}{(20\text{ A})(-0.84 \times 10^{-10}\text{ m}^3/\text{C})} = \boxed{1.79\ \text{T}}$$

29.51 $\dfrac{1}{nq} = \dfrac{V_H t}{IB} = \dfrac{(35\ \mu\text{V})(0.4\times10^{-2}\text{ m})}{(21\text{ A})(1.8\text{ T})} = \boxed{3.70\times10^{-9}\text{ m}^3/\text{C}}$

***29.52** $V_H = \dfrac{IB}{nqt}$ (*Eq.* 29.26)

$$\text{For copper, } n = \frac{(8.96\times10^6\text{ g/m}^3)(6.02\times10^{23}\text{ electrons/mol})}{(63.546\text{ g/mol})}$$

$$= 8.48\times10^{28}\text{ electrons/m}^3$$

Substituting in, $V_H = \dfrac{IB}{nqt} = \boxed{3.69\times10^{-7}\text{ V}}$

29.53 $R_H = \dfrac{1}{nq} = \dfrac{1}{(8.48\times10^{28})(1.602\times10^{-19})} = 7.36\times10^{-11}\text{ m}^3/\text{C}$

$$B = \frac{nqtV_H}{I} = \frac{(8.48\times10^{28}/\text{m}^3)(1.602\times10^{-19}\text{ C})(0.005\text{ m})(5.1\times10^{-12}\text{ V})}{8\text{ A}}$$

$$= \boxed{4.32\times10^{-5}\text{ T}}$$

29.54 $n = \dfrac{JB}{eE} = \dfrac{I}{t\omega}\dfrac{B}{e(\frac{V}{\omega})} = \dfrac{IB}{teV}$

$$n = \frac{(50\text{ A})(1.3\text{ T})}{(\frac{1}{3}\times10^{-3}\text{ m})(1.6\times10^{-19}\text{ C})(9.6\times10^{-6}\text{ V})} = \boxed{1.27\times10^{29}\text{ m}^{-3}}$$

$n_0 =$ atomic number density $= 8.459\times10^{28}\text{ m}^{-3}$

$$\frac{n}{n_0} = \frac{1.27}{0.8459} = \boxed{1.50}$$

29.55 $V_H = \dfrac{IB}{nqt}$

$$0.122\times10^{-6} = \frac{(12)(1.8)}{n(1.602\times10^{-19})(15\times10^{-3})}$$

$$n = \boxed{7.37\times10^{28}\text{ electrons/m}^3}$$

***29.56** (a) $V_H = \frac{BI}{net} = \frac{B}{V_H} = \frac{0.08\ T}{(0.7 \times 10^{-6}\ \text{V})} = 1.143 \times 10^5\ \frac{\text{T}}{\text{V}}$

$$B = (1.143 \times 10^5)V_H = (1.143 \times 10^5)(0.33 \times 10^{-6}) = \boxed{37.7\ \text{mT}}$$

(b) $\frac{net}{I} = 1.143 \times 10^5 \rightarrow n = \frac{(1.143 \times 10^5)(120 \times 10^{-3})}{(1.602 \times 10^{-19})(0.002)}$

$$n = \boxed{4.28 \times 10^{25}\ \text{m}^{-3}}$$

29.57 A key to solving this problem is to notice that reducing the normal force will reduce the friction...

$F_m = I\ell B$

$f = 0.2N = F_m \cos\theta$

$0.2(W - F_m \sin\theta) = F_m \cos\theta$

$0.2W = F_m(\cos\theta + 0.2\sin\theta)$

$F_m = \frac{0.2W}{\cos\theta + 0.2\sin\theta}$

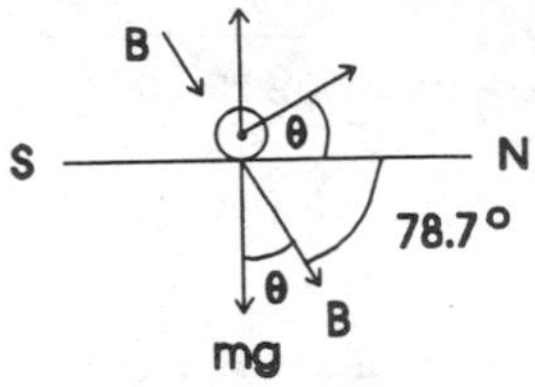

29.57

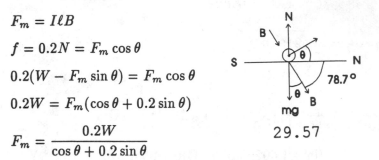

Minimize B by minimizing F_m, $0 = \frac{dF_m}{d\theta} = (0.2W)\frac{(-1)(-\sin\theta) + 0.2\cos\theta)}{(\cos\theta + 0.2\sin\theta)^2}$

$\sin\theta = 0.2\cos\theta$ $\quad\theta = 11.31^\circ$ is the angle for minimum $F_m = I\ell B$

$\frac{F_m}{\ell} = \frac{0.2(0.1\ \text{kg/m})(9.8\ \text{m/s}^2)}{1.02} = 0.192\ \text{N/m} = (1.5\ \text{A})B$

$B = \boxed{0.128\ \text{T (pointing north) at an angle of } 78.7^\circ \text{ below the horizontal}}$

29.58 (a) up; (b) out; (c) no deflection; (d) in; (e) no detection; (f) down

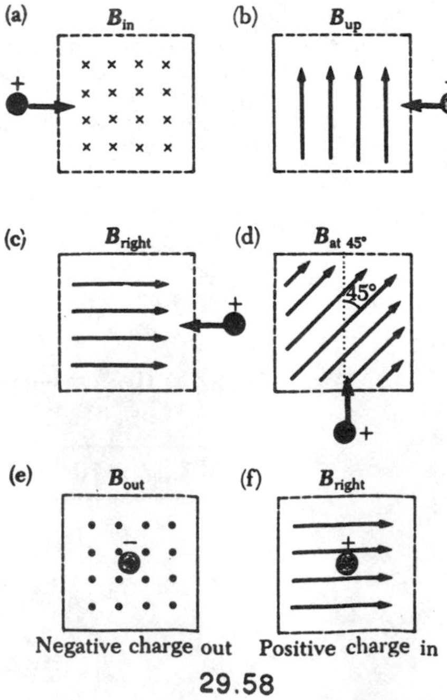

29.58

29.59 (a) The net force is the Lorentz force given by Eq. 29.18

$\boldsymbol{F} = q\boldsymbol{E} + q\boldsymbol{v} \times \boldsymbol{B} = q(\boldsymbol{E} + \boldsymbol{v} \times \boldsymbol{B})$

$\boldsymbol{F} = (3.2 \times 10^{-19})[(4\boldsymbol{i} - \boldsymbol{j} - 2\boldsymbol{k}) + (2\boldsymbol{i} + 3\boldsymbol{j} - \boldsymbol{k})$

$\times (2\boldsymbol{i} + 4\boldsymbol{j} + \boldsymbol{k})]$

Carrying out the indicated operations we find

$\boldsymbol{F} = \boxed{(3.52\boldsymbol{i} - 1.60\boldsymbol{j}) \times 10^{-18}\ \text{N}}$

(b) $\theta = \cos^{-1}(\frac{F_x}{F}) = \cos^{-1}(\frac{3.52}{3.87}) = \boxed{24.4^\circ}$

***29.60** Ignoring relativistic corrections,

$$r = \frac{mv}{qB} = \frac{(1.67 \times 10^{-27})(1.5 \times 10^{8})}{(1.6 \times 10^{-19})(5 \times 10^{-5})} \text{ m}$$

$$r = \boxed{3.13 \times 10^{4} \text{ m}} = 31.3 \text{ km}$$

No, the proton will not hit the Earth.

29.61 Let Δx_1 be the elongation due to the weight of the wire and let Δx_2 be the additional elongation of the springs when the magnetic field is turned on. Then $F_{\text{magnetic}} = 2k\Delta x_2$ where k is the force constant of the spring and can be determined from $k = mg/2\Delta x_1$. (The factor 2 is included in the two previous equations since there are 2 springs in parallel.) Combining these two equations we find

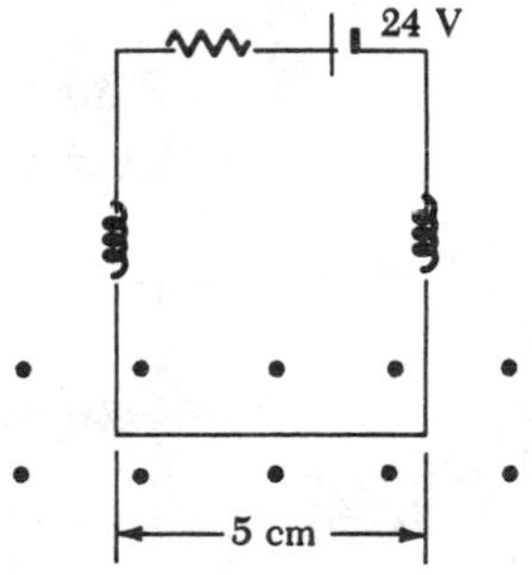

29.61

$F_{\text{magnetic}} = 2(\frac{mg}{2\Delta x_1})\Delta x_2 = \frac{mg\Delta x_2}{\Delta x_1}$; But

$|F| = I|\boldsymbol{\ell} \times \boldsymbol{B}| = I\ell B$;

Therefore $B = \frac{mg\Delta x_2}{I\ell\Delta x_1}$ where $I = \frac{24 \text{ V}}{12\ \Omega} = 2 \text{ A}$

$$B = \frac{(0.01)(9.80)(0.003)}{(2)(0.05)(0.005)} = \boxed{0.588 \text{ T}}$$

***29.62** (a) $\boxed{\text{k}}$

(b) Ignoring relativistic corrections

$$r = \frac{mv}{qB} = \frac{(1.67 \times 10^{-27})(2 \times 10^{8})}{(1.6 \times 10^{-19})(1)} \text{ m}$$

$$= \boxed{2.09 \text{ m}}$$

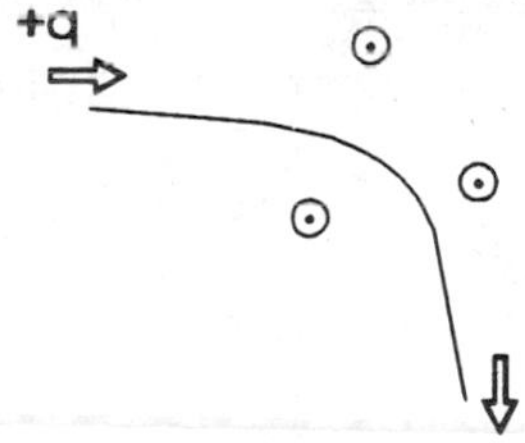

29.62

(c) $\frac{1}{4}(2\pi r) = \boxed{3.28 \text{ m}}$

(d) $t = \frac{3.28 \text{ m}}{2 \times 10^{8} \text{ m/s}} = \boxed{1.64 \times 10^{-8} \text{ s}}$

***29.63** The electric current carried by the material feels a force.

(a) $I\mathbf{w} \times \mathbf{B}$ in the direction of L.

(b) The sodium, consisting of ions and electrons, flows along the pipe transparting no net charge. But inside the section of length L electrons drift upward to consititute downward electric current J×(area)=Jlw.
uThe current then feels a magnetic force

$$i\ell \times \mathbf{B} = \mathrm{JL}whB \ \sin 90°$$

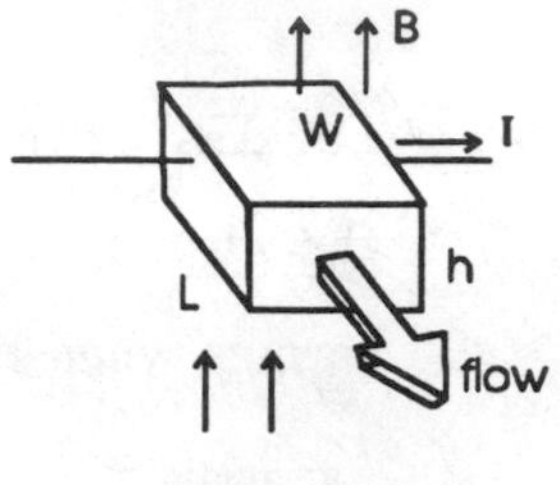

29.63

This force along the pipe axis will make the fluid move, exerting pressure

$$\frac{F}{\text{area}} = \frac{\mathrm{J}LwhB}{hw} = JLB$$

***29.64** $= \int NIdA \quad I = \frac{q}{t}\frac{q\omega}{2\pi}$

$$= \int_0^{\ell/2} \lambda\frac{\omega}{2\pi}\pi\ x^2 dx$$

$$= \lambda\omega\frac{x^3}{3}\Big|_0^{\ell/2} = \lambda\omega\frac{\ell^3}{24}$$

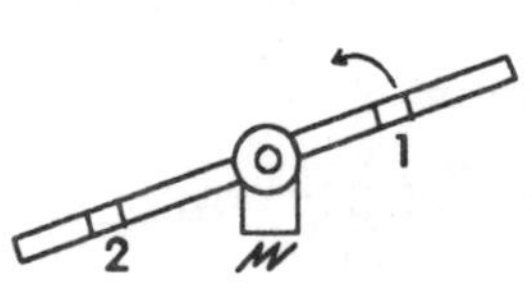

29.64

29.65 $R_1 = \dfrac{m_1 v}{Bq}$ and $R_2 = \dfrac{m_2 v}{Bq}$. Ions of the two isotopes will impact on the plate at points separated by a distance $d = 2(R_2 - R_1)$. This is due to the fact that the circular paths followed by the two types of ions have a point in common on their circumference where the ions enter the deflection chamber; but their centers are not at the same point.

$$d = \frac{2v(m_2 - m_1)}{Bq} = \frac{2(3 \times 10^5)(238 - 235)(1.67 \times 10^{-27})}{0.6(1.6 \times 10^{-19})} = \boxed{3.13\ \text{cm}}$$

29.66 Total time required for deuterons to reach maximum energy,

$t =$ (The number of orbits) $\times$ (period)

The number of orbits, $N =$ final energy/increase in energy per orbit

The final energy at maximum radius is:

$E_{max} = \frac{mv^2}{2} = \frac{q^2B^2R^2}{2m}$ and the energy gain per orbit $= 2qV$ Therefore

$N = \frac{q^2B^2R^2/2m}{2qV} = \frac{q^2B^2R^2}{4mV}$ Also the period of the ion is $T = \frac{2\pi m}{Bq}$.

Therefore the required time is

$$t = NT = (\frac{qB^2R^2}{4mV})(\frac{2\pi m}{Bq}) = \pi\frac{BR^2}{2V}$$

Substituting the given values we have

$$t = \frac{\pi(1.5\text{ T})(0.45\text{ m})^2}{(2)(15\times 10^3\text{ V})} = 3.18\times 10^{-5}\text{ s} = \boxed{31.8\ \mu\text{s}}$$

29.67 Use the equation for cyclotron frequency (Eq. 29.16) $\omega = \frac{qB}{m}$ or

$$m = \frac{qB}{\omega} = \frac{qB}{2\pi f}$$

$$m = \frac{(1.6\times 10^{-19}\text{ C})(5\times 10^{-2}\text{ T})}{(2\pi)(5\text{ rev}/1.5\times 10^{-3}\text{ s})} = \boxed{3.82\times 10^{-25}\text{ kg}}$$

29.68 Let $v_{||}$ and $v_{\perp}$ be the components of the velocity of the positron parallel to and perpendicular to the direction of the magnetic field.

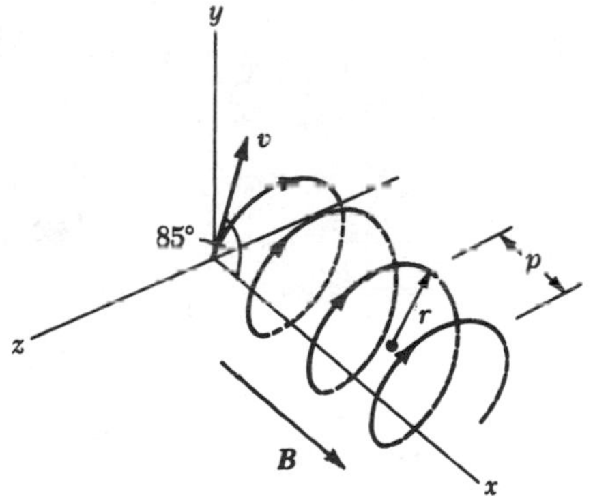

29.68

(a) The pitch of trajectory is the distance moved along x by the position during each period, T (see EQ. 29.16). Therefore

$$p = v_{||}T = (v\cos 85°)(\frac{2\pi m}{Bq})$$

$$p = \frac{(5\times 10^6)(\cos 85°)(2\pi)(9.1\times 10^{-31})}{(0.15)(1.6\times 10^{-19})} = \boxed{1.04\times 10^{-4}\text{ m}}$$

(b) From Eq. 29.15; $R = \frac{mv_{\perp}}{Bq} = \frac{mv\sin 85°}{Bq}$ or

$$R = \frac{(9.1\times 10^{-31})(5\times 10^6)(\sin 85°)}{(0.15)(1.6\times 10^{-19})} = \boxed{1.88\times 10^{-4}\text{ m}}$$

29.69 $|\tau| = IAB$ where the effective current due to the orbiting electron is $I = \frac{\Delta q}{\Delta t} = \frac{q}{T}$ and the period of the motion is $T = \frac{2\pi R}{v}$. The speed of the electron in its orbit is found by requiring $\frac{kq^2}{R^2} = \frac{mv^2}{R}$ or

$v = q\sqrt{\frac{k}{mR}}$. Substituting this expression for v into the equation for T we find $T = 2\pi\sqrt{\frac{mR^3}{q^2k}}$ or

$$T = 2\pi\sqrt{\frac{(9.1\times10^{-31})(5.29\times10^{-11})^3}{(1.6\times10^{-19})^2(9\times10^9)}} = 1.52\times10^{-16}\text{ s}.$$

Therefore

$$|\tau| = \left(\frac{q}{T}\right)AB = \frac{1.6\times10^{-19}}{1.52\times10^{-16}}\pi(5.29\times10^{-11})^2(0.4) = \boxed{3.70\times10^{-24}\text{ N·m}}$$

29.70 (a) $\frac{1}{2}mv^2 = 6\text{ MeV} = (6\times10^6)(1.6\times10^{-19}\text{ C})(\text{J/C})$

$$v = \sqrt{\frac{2(6)(10^6)(1.6\times10^{-19}\text{ C})(\text{J/C})}{1.67\times10^{-27}\text{ kg}}} = 3.39\times10^7\text{ m/s}$$

$$F = \frac{mv^2}{R} = qvB$$

$$R = \frac{mv}{qB} = \frac{(1.67\times10^{-27}\text{ kg})(3.39\times10^7\text{ m/s})}{(1.6\times10^{-19}\text{ C})(1\text{ T})} = 0.354\text{ m}$$

$$x = 2R\cos45° = 2(0.354\text{ m})(\cos45°) = \boxed{0.501\text{ m}}$$

(b) $\theta' = 45°$ (see figure).

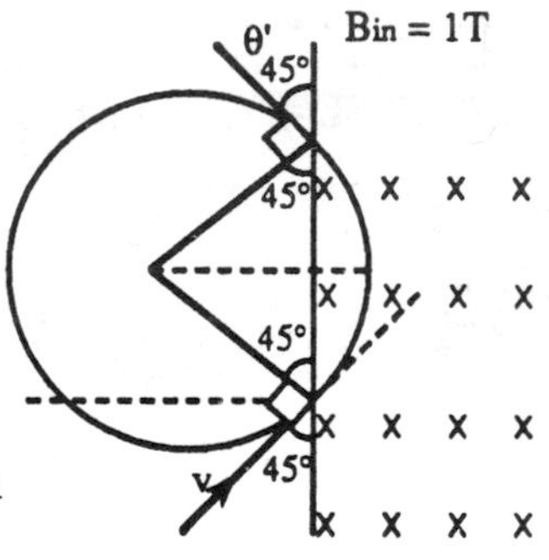

29.70

***29.71** (a) $$\frac{1}{2}mv^2 = 5.0 \text{ MeV} = 8.0 \times 10^{-13} \text{ J}$$

$$v = \sqrt{\frac{2(8 \times 10^{-13})}{1.67 \times 10^{-27}}} = 3.09 \times 10^7 \text{ m/s}$$

Although v is approximately 10% of c, we will ignore relativistic effects,

$$F = qvB = \frac{mv^2}{R} \qquad R = \frac{mv}{qB} = 6.46 \text{ m}$$

$$\alpha = \sin^{-1}\left(\frac{1}{6.46}\right) = \boxed{8.91°}$$

(b) Since the magnetic force is always perpendicular to the particle's velocity,

$$p_y = mv \sin\alpha = \boxed{8.00 \times 10^{-21} \text{ kg} \cdot \text{m/s}}$$

***29.72** (a) $$\frac{V_H}{B} = \left(100.3 \frac{\mu\text{V}}{\text{T}} \pm 5\%\right)$$

(b) $$\frac{V_H}{B} = \frac{I}{nqt} = 100.3 \times 10^{-6}$$

$$t = \frac{I}{nq(100.3 \times 10^{-6})} \text{ m}$$

$$t = \boxed{0.125 \text{ mm}}$$

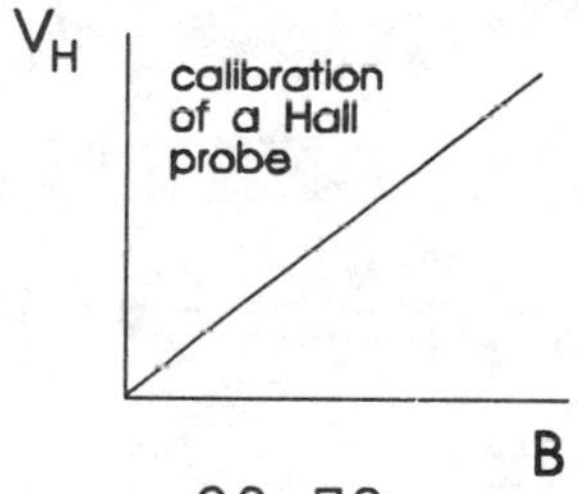

29.72

CHAPTER 30

30.1 $B = \frac{\mu_0 I}{2\pi r} = \frac{4\pi \times 10^{-7}(1)}{(2\pi)(1)} = \boxed{2.00 \times 10^{-7}\ \text{T}}$

30.2 $B = \frac{\mu_0 I}{2\pi r} \qquad r = \frac{\mu_0 I}{2\pi B} = 2 \times 10^{-2}\ \text{m} = \boxed{2.00\ \text{cm}}$

30.3 $B = \frac{\mu_0 I}{2R} \qquad R = \frac{\mu_0 I}{2B} = \frac{20\pi \times 10^{-7}}{2 \times 10^{-5}} = \boxed{31.4\ \text{cm}}$

30.4 $B = \frac{\mu_0 I}{2R} = \frac{\mu_0 q(v/2\pi R)}{2R} = \boxed{12.5\ \text{T}}$

30.5

$$B = \frac{4\mu_0 I}{4\pi a}(\cos\frac{\pi}{4} - \cos\frac{3\pi}{4})$$

$$= \frac{4 \times 10^{-6}}{0.2}(\frac{\sqrt{2}}{2} + \frac{\sqrt{2}}{2}) = 2\sqrt{2} \times 10^{-5}\ \text{T}$$

$$B = \boxed{28\ \mu\text{T}}$$

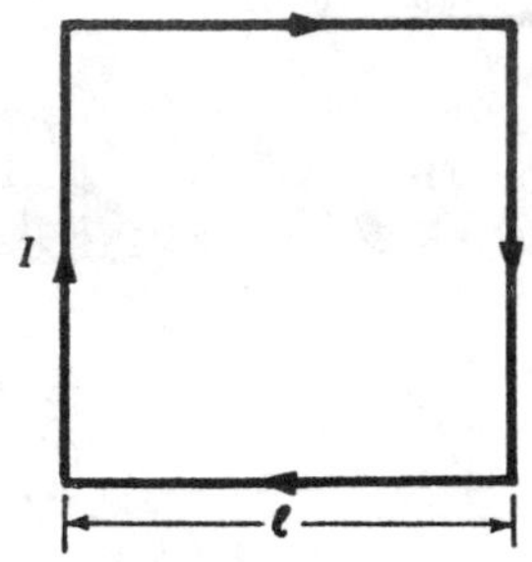

30.5 and 30.7

30.6 $B = \frac{2\mu_0 I}{4\pi a}(\cos\theta_1 - \cos\theta_2) + \frac{2\mu_0 I}{4\pi b}(\cos\phi_1 - \cos\phi_2)$

$B = \boxed{2.5 \times 10^{-4}\ \text{T}}$

30.7 The circumference must equal $4\ell = 4(0.3\ \text{m}) = 1.2\ \text{m} = 2\pi\text{R}$, so we find that $R = 0.191$ m. From Eq. 30.10, the field at the center of a circular turn of wire is

$$B = \frac{\mu_0 I}{2R} = \frac{(4\pi \times 10^{-7})(2.5)}{2(0.191)} = 8.22\ \mu\text{T}$$

$$B = \frac{\mu_0 I}{2R} \quad (R = \frac{1.6\ \text{m}}{2\pi})$$

$$B = \frac{8\pi^2 \times 10^{-6}}{3.2} = \boxed{24.7\ \mu\text{T}}$$

30.8 $B = \dfrac{\mu_0 NI}{2R}$ $\quad N = \dfrac{2RB}{\mu_0 I} \cong \boxed{47.7 \text{ Turns}}$

30.9 For leg A, $d\ell \times \hat{r} = 0$

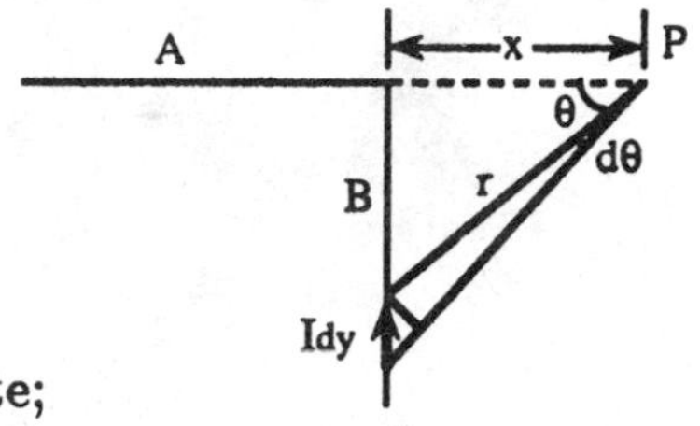

30.9

so there is no contribution to the field from this segment.

For leg B, the geometry is the same as Figure 34.2 (see the derivation of Eq. 34.4), but the wire is only semi-infinite; thus (note the limits of integration)

$$B = \frac{\mu_0 I}{2\pi x} \int_0^{\pi/2} \cos\theta d\theta = \boxed{\frac{\mu_0 I}{4\pi x}}$$

direction: into the paper

30.10 $B = \dfrac{\mu_0 I}{4R} = \boxed{3 \times 10^{-5} \text{ T}}$ into the paper

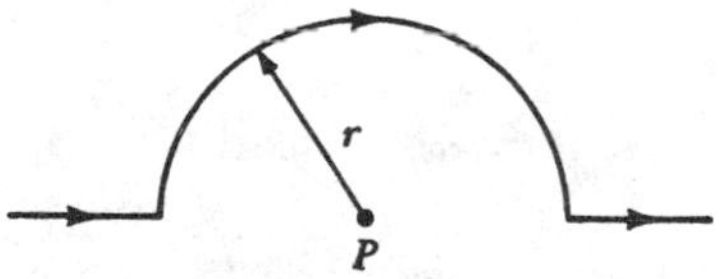

30.10

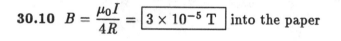

30.11 Over the radial segments $ds \times \hat{r} = 0$ and along the arc, B is given by Eq. 30.8,

$$B = \frac{\mu_0 I\theta}{4\pi r}.$$

If the total length of the closed path is ℓ, $r = \dfrac{\ell}{2+\theta}$ Therefore at point P;

$$B = \frac{\mu_0 I\theta(2+\theta)}{4\pi\ell}, \text{ where } \theta = \frac{\pi}{6}. \quad \text{Using given values we find}$$

$$B = \frac{\mu_0 (3 \text{ A})(\frac{\pi}{6})(2+\frac{\pi}{6})}{(4\pi)(1.2 \text{ m})} = \boxed{0.33\ \mu\text{T}}$$

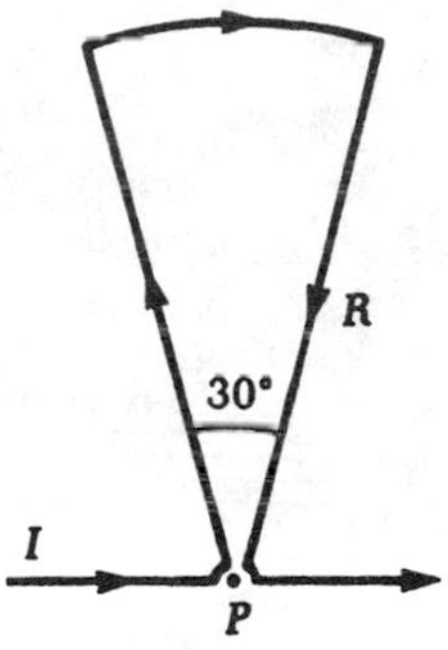

30.11

***30.12** $dB = \dfrac{\mu_0}{4\pi} I \dfrac{d\ell \times \mathbf{r}}{r^2}$

$$B = \frac{\mu_0}{4\pi} I \left(\frac{\frac{1}{6}2\pi a}{a^2} - \frac{\frac{1}{6}2\pi b}{b^2} \right)$$

$$B = \frac{\mu_0 I}{12} \left(\frac{1}{a} - \frac{1}{b} \right) \text{ directed out of the paper.}$$

***30.13** $B = \dfrac{N\mu_0 I R^2}{2(r^2 + x^2)^{3/2}}$ (Eq. 30.9)

(a) At the center of the coil, $x = 0$, and

$$B = \frac{N\mu_0 I}{2R} = \frac{100(4\pi \times 10^{-7})(0.3)}{2(0.1)} \quad \boxed{189\ \mu T}$$

(b) $B = \dfrac{B_0}{2}$ When

$$\frac{R^2}{(R^2 + x^2)^{3/2}} = \frac{1}{2R}$$

or when

$$2R^3 = (R^2 + x^2)^{3/2}$$

$$2^{2/3}R^2 = R^2 + x^2$$

$$x^2 = (\sqrt[3]{4} - 1)R^2 \quad \boxed{x = 7.66 \text{ cm}}$$

30.14 The Biot-Savart law is stated as $dB = \dfrac{\mu_0}{4\pi}\dfrac{(I ds \times \hat{r})}{r^2}$.

But $J = nqv_d$ and also $J = \dfrac{I\ ds}{A\ ds}$. Combining these expressions for J we have

$$ds = nqv_d \frac{Ads}{I} = \frac{(nqv_d/l)}{dV}, \text{ since } dV = Ads$$

Substituting this form for ds into the Biot-Savart law, we find $dB = \dfrac{\mu_0}{4\pi}(\dfrac{qv_d \times \hat{r}}{r^2})ndV$

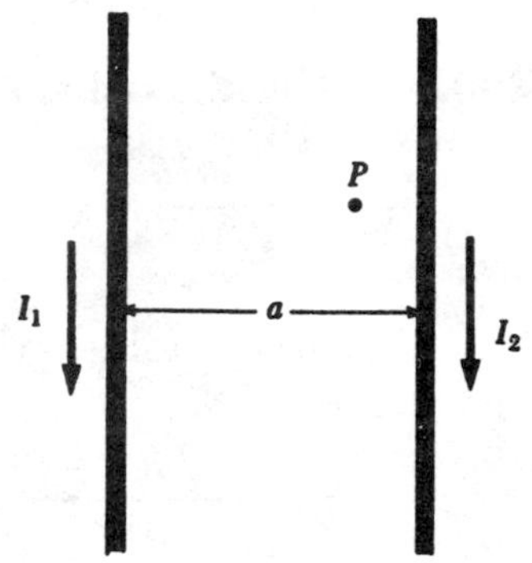

30.15

30.15 $\dfrac{F}{\ell} = \dfrac{\mu_0 I_1 I_2}{2\pi a} = \boxed{8.00 \times 10^{-5}\ \text{N/m}}$

***30.16** The separation between the wires is $a = 2(6 \text{ cm}) \sin 8° = 1.67$ cm.

(a) Because the wires repel, the currents are in opposite directions.

(b) Because the magnetic force acts horizontally,

$$\frac{F_{\text{mag}}}{F_{\text{grav}}} = \frac{\mu_0 I^2 \ell}{2\pi a\ mg} = \tan 8°$$

$$I^2 = \frac{mg\ 2\pi a}{\ell \mu_0} \tan 8°$$

$$I = \boxed{67.8 \text{ A}}$$

***30.17** From Equation 30.13

$$\frac{F}{\ell} = \frac{\text{force}}{\text{meter}} = \frac{\mu_0 I_1 I_2}{2\pi d}$$

$$= \frac{1.26 \times 10^{-6}\ \text{T}\cdot\text{m/A} \times 10^4\ \text{A} \times 10^4\ \text{A}}{2\pi \times 10^{-2}\ \text{m}}$$

$$= 2000\ \text{T}\cdot\text{A}$$

$$\frac{F}{\ell} = \boxed{2000\ \text{N/m}}\quad \text{Attractive}$$

This is about 140 pounds per foot. This force, together with the joule heat generated, might weld the two conductors together.

30.18 $\frac{F}{\ell} = \frac{\mu_0 I_1 I_2}{2\pi a} = \boxed{0.500\ \text{N/m, Compressive}}$

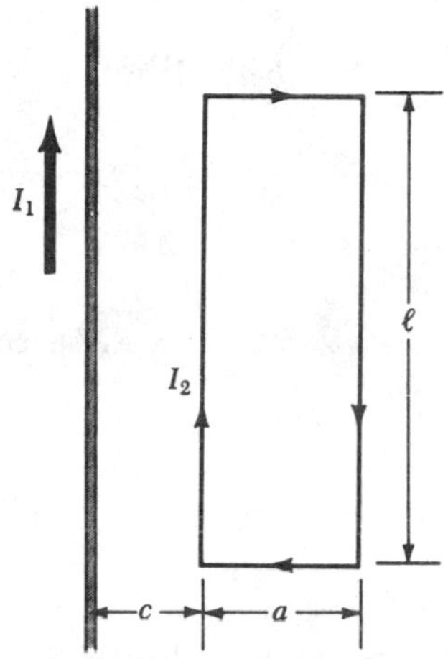

30.19

30.19 By application of Eq. 29.5 we note that the magnetic forces on the top and bottom segments of the rectangle cancel. The net force on the vertical segments of the rectangle is (using Eq. 30.13):

$$F = \frac{\mu_0 I_1 I_2 \ell}{2\pi}\left(\frac{1}{c+a} - \frac{1}{c}\right)i$$

Substituting given values $F = \boxed{-2.70 \times 10^{-5}\ i\ \text{N}}$

30.20 $B = \boxed{20.0\ \mu\text{T}}$ Toward the top of the page.

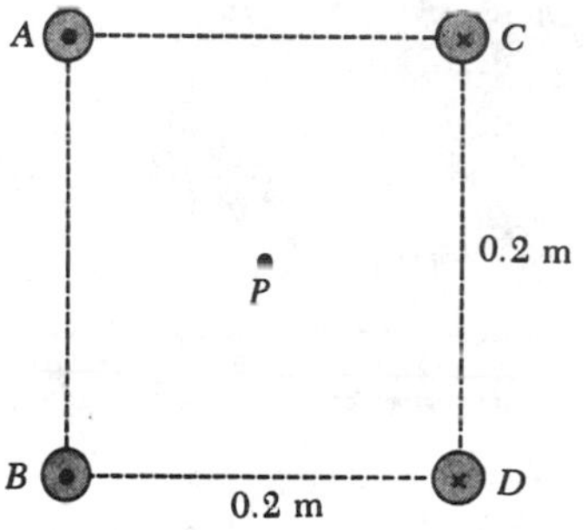

30.20

30.21 $B = \boxed{13.0\ \mu\text{T}}$ directed to bottom of page.

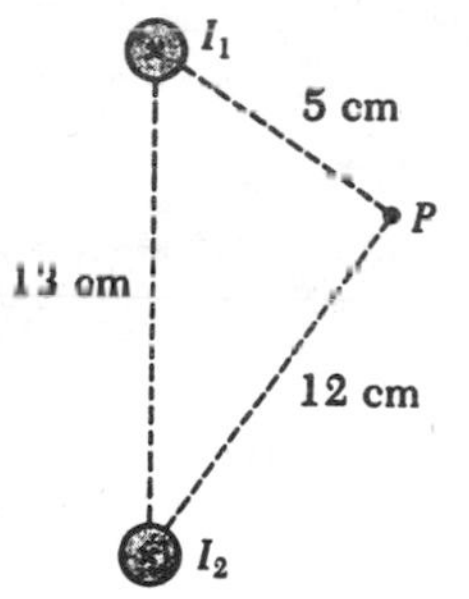

30.21

30.22 $B = \frac{\mu_0 N I}{\ell}$, $N = \frac{B\ell}{\mu_0 I} = \boxed{120\ \text{Turns}}$

30.23 (a) $I = \frac{10}{(4\pi \times 10^{-7})(2000)} = \boxed{3980\ \text{A}}$

(b) $\frac{F}{\ell} = IB = 39{,}800$ N/m radically outward.

Although the force per length is non-zero (in an outward direction) the $\boxed{\textit{net}\ \text{force per unit length will be zero}}$

30.24 $B = \mu_0 \frac{N}{\ell} I$, $I = \frac{B}{\mu_0 n} = \boxed{32.0\ \text{mA}}$

30.25 $B = \mu_0 \dfrac{N}{\ell} I = (4\pi \times 10^{-7})(4000)(1000) \cong \boxed{5.00\ \text{T}}$

30.26 $B = \dfrac{\mu_0 N I}{2\pi r} = \boxed{8.00 \times 10^{-4}\ \text{T}}$

30.27 $B = \dfrac{\mu_0 N I}{2\pi r}$

(a) $B_{\text{inner}} = \boxed{3.60\ \text{T}}$

(b) $B_{\text{outer}} = \boxed{1.94\ \text{T}}$

30.28
$$B = \frac{\mu_0 I}{2\pi a^2} r \quad \text{for } r \le a$$
$$B = \frac{\mu_0 (2.5\ \text{A})}{2\pi (0.025\ \text{m})^2}(0.0125\ \text{m}) = \boxed{10.0\ \mu\text{T}}$$

30.29
$$B = \frac{\mu_0 I}{2\pi r}; \quad \text{for } r \ge a$$
$$r = \frac{\mu_0 I}{2\pi B} = \frac{\mu_0 (2.5\ \text{A})}{2\pi (10 \times 10^{-6}\ \text{T})} = 0.05\ \text{m} = \boxed{5.00\ \text{cm}}$$

30.30 From $\oint \mathbf{B} \cdot d\boldsymbol{\ell} = \mu_0 I$,

$$I = \frac{2\pi r B}{\mu_0} = \frac{(2\pi)(0.001)(0.1)}{4\pi \times 10^{-7}} = \boxed{500\ \text{A}}$$

30.31 (a) Within the bundle, $B = \left(\dfrac{\mu_0 I}{2\pi R^2}\right) r = 3.2 \times 10^{-3}\ \text{T}$

the force, *acting inward*, is $F = I\ell B$,

and the force per unit length is

$$\frac{F}{\ell} = \boxed{6.4 \times 10^{-3}\ \text{N/m} \quad \text{inward}}$$

(b) $B \propto r$, so B is greatest at the outside of the bundle.

Since each wire carries the same current, F is greatest at the outer surface.

***30.32** From each wire, $B = \frac{\mu_0 I}{2\pi\sqrt{a^2+z^2}}$

Combining fields, $B = \frac{2\mu_0 I}{2\pi\sqrt{a^2+z^2}}(\sin\theta)$

$$B = \frac{2\mu_0 I}{2\pi\sqrt{a^2+z^2}} \frac{z}{\sqrt{a^2+z^2}} = \frac{\mu_0 I z}{\pi(a^2+z^2)}$$

$$\frac{dB}{dz} = \frac{-\mu_0 I z(2z)}{\pi(a^2+z^2)^2} + \frac{\mu_0 I}{\pi(a^2+z^2)} = 0$$

$$\frac{\mu_0 I}{\pi}\frac{(a^2-z^2)}{(a^2+z^2)^2} = 0$$

Maximum B at $\boxed{z = a.}$

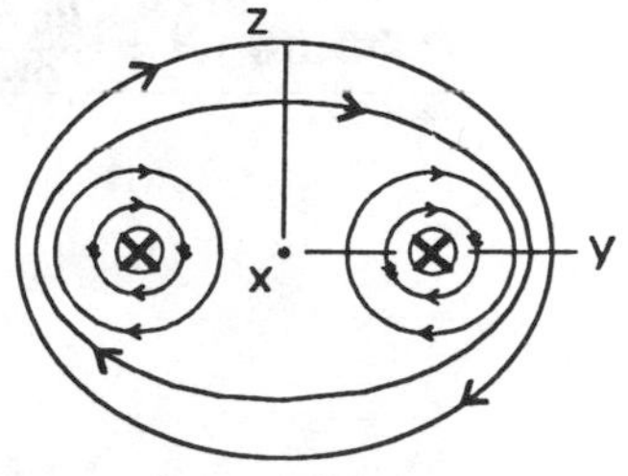

(Currents are into the paper.)

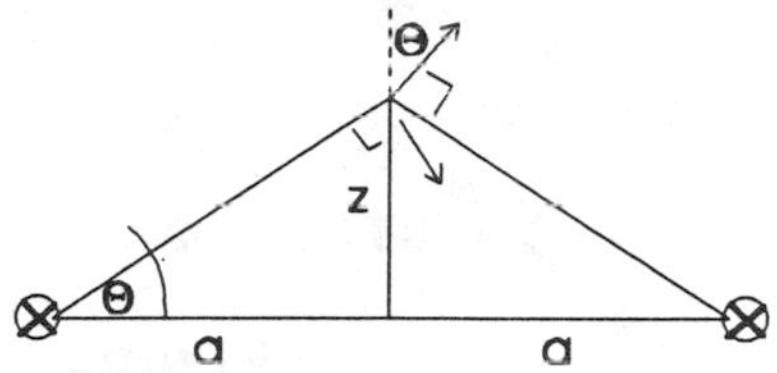

At a distance z above the plane of the conductors

30.32

30.33 $\mathbf{B} = -\mu_0 nI(\cos\theta_1 - \cos\theta_2)\mathbf{k} = \frac{\mu_0 NI}{2\ell}\mathbf{k}$

$$= \frac{(4\pi\times10^{-7}\ \mathrm{T\cdot m/A})(200)(15\ \mathrm{A})}{2(0.1\ \mathrm{m})} = \boxed{26.7\ \mathrm{mT}}$$

For $\ell \longrightarrow \infty, n = 200$ turns/m

$$B = \mu_0 nI = (4\pi\times10^{-7}\ \mathrm{T\cdot m/A})(2000\ \mathrm{m^{-1}})(15\ \mathrm{A}) = 0.0377\ \mathrm{T} = \boxed{37.7\ \mathrm{mT}}$$

30.34 (a) $B \cong \mu_0 nI = \boxed{4.24\times10^{-3}\ \mathrm{T}}$ (at the center)

(b) $B \cong \frac{\mu_0 nI}{2} = \boxed{2.12\times10^{-3}\ \mathrm{T}}$ (at the end)

30.35 $B = \frac{\mu_0 NI}{2\ell}(\sin\phi_2 - \sin\phi_1) = \boxed{0.00474\ \mathrm{T}}$

30.36 $B = \dfrac{\mu_0 N I}{2\pi r}$

(a) $\Phi_m = \int \mathbf{B} \cdot d\mathbf{A} = \int_a^b Bhdr = \dfrac{\mu_0 N I h}{2\pi} \int_a^b \dfrac{dr}{r}$

$\Phi_m = \boxed{\dfrac{\mu_0 N I h}{2\pi} \ln \dfrac{b}{a}}$

(b) $\Phi_m = \dfrac{(4\pi \times 10^{-7})}{2\pi} 200(2)(0.015) \ln(\frac{5}{2}) = \boxed{1.1 \times 10^{-6} \text{ Wb}}$

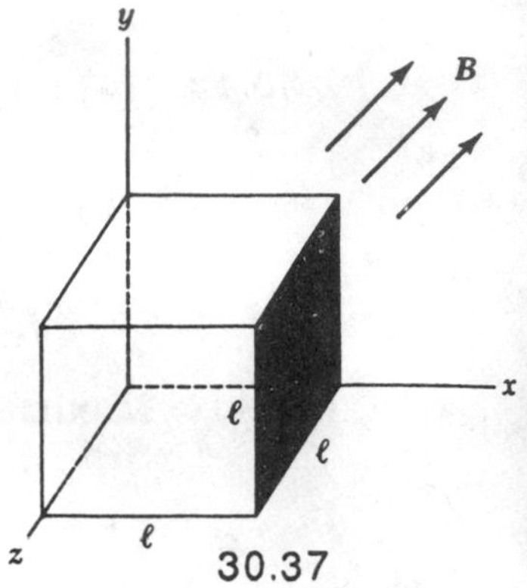

30.37

30.37 (a) $\Phi = 5(0.025)^2 = \boxed{3.13 \text{ mWb}}$

(b) $\Phi_{total} = \boxed{\text{Zero}}$

30.38 $\Phi = \mathbf{B} \cdot \mathbf{A} = \dfrac{\mu_0 N I}{\ell} \pi r^2 = \boxed{7.4 \times 10^{-6} \text{ Wb}}$

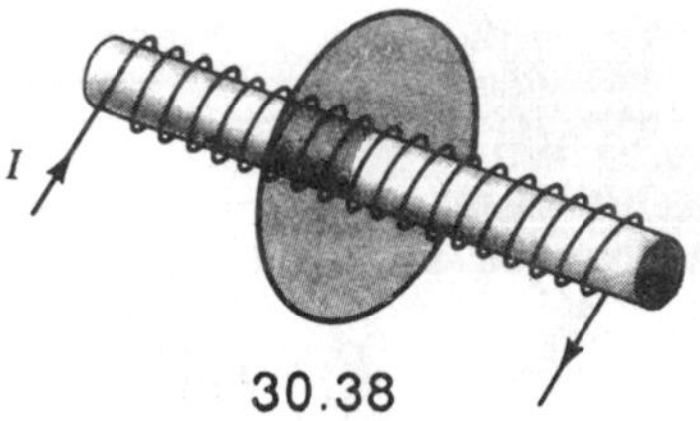

30.38

30.39 $\Phi = \mathbf{B} \cdot \mathbf{A} = \dfrac{\mu_0 N I}{\ell} \pi (r_2^2 - r_1^2) = \boxed{2.27 \times 10^{-6} \text{ Wb}}$

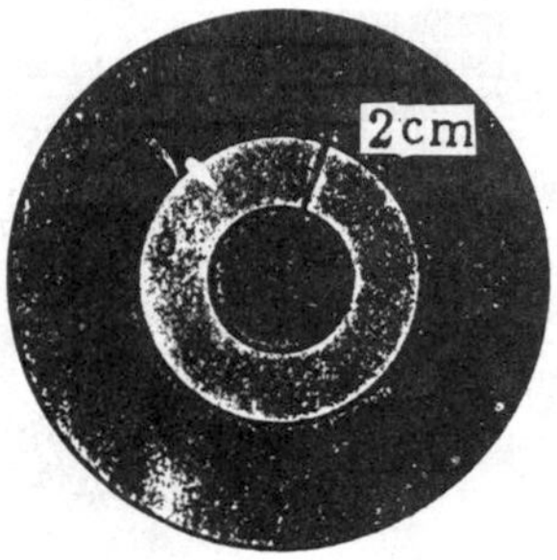

30.39

30.40 $\Phi_m = \int \mathbf{B} \cdot d\mathbf{A} = BA \cos\theta = B\pi R^2 \cos\theta$

(a) $\theta = \omega t$ if start timing when normal is aligned with $\mathbf{B}$.

$\Phi_m = \boxed{B\pi R^2 \cos(\omega t)}$

(b) $\Phi_m = BA \cos \dfrac{\pi}{2} = \boxed{0}$

30.41 (a) $I_d = C\dfrac{dV}{dt} = \boxed{(8 \times 10^{-6}\ \text{A})(e^{-t/4})}$

(b) $I_d(4) = \boxed{2.94 \times 10^{-6}\ \text{A}}$

30.42 (a) $q(t) = Qe^{-t/RC}$ $\boxed{I_d = \dfrac{Q}{RC}e^{-t/RC}}$

(b) Characteristic time $RC = (500 \times 10^3)(2 \times 10^{-6}) = 1.00$ s

$$I_d = \frac{-20 \times 10^{-6}}{1.0}e^{-0.1/1.0} = \boxed{-18.1\ \mu\text{A}}$$

(c) Displacement current $= \epsilon_0 \dfrac{d\Phi_E}{dt}$, so

$$\frac{d\Phi_E}{dt} = \frac{-18.1 \times 10^{-6}}{8.85 \times 10^{-12}} = \boxed{-2.04 \times 10^6\ \text{V·m/s}}$$

30.43 (a) $\dfrac{d\Phi_E}{dt} = \dfrac{d\phi/dt}{\epsilon_0} = \dfrac{I}{\epsilon_0} = \dfrac{(0.1)}{(8.85 \times 10^{-12})} = \boxed{11.3 \times 10^9\ \text{V·m/s}}$

(b) $I_d = \epsilon_0 \dfrac{d\Phi_E}{dt} = I = \boxed{0.10\ \text{A}}$

30.44 $\dfrac{d\Phi_E}{dt} = \dfrac{d}{dt}(EA) = \dfrac{dQ/dt}{\epsilon_0} = \dfrac{I}{\epsilon_0}$

(a) $\dfrac{dE}{dt} = \dfrac{I}{\epsilon_0 A} = \boxed{7.2 \times 10^{11}\ \text{V/m·s}}$

(b) $\oint \mathbf{B} \cdot d\mathbf{s} = \epsilon_0 \mu_0 \Phi_E$

$$2\pi r B = \epsilon_0 \mu_0 \frac{d}{dt}\left[\frac{Q}{\epsilon_0 A} \cdot \pi r^2\right]$$

$$B = \frac{\mu_0 I r}{2A} = \frac{\mu_0(0.2)(0.05)}{2\pi(0.10)^2} = \boxed{2 \times 10^{-7}\ \text{T}}$$

30.45 $\mu = \mu_0(1 + \chi)$

$$\frac{\mu}{\mu_0} = \boxed{1.0001}$$

30.46 (a) For a toroid $H = nI = \boxed{2000 \text{ A}\cdot \text{ Turns/m}}$

(b) $B = \mu H = (5001)(2000)(4\pi \times 10^{-7}) = \boxed{12.6 \text{ T}}$

30.47 Assuming a uniform $\boldsymbol{B}$ inside the toroid in equivalent to assuming $r << R$, then $B_0 \cong \mu_0 \dfrac{NI}{2\pi R}$ and a *tightly* wound solenoid.

$$B_0 = \mu_0 \frac{(630)(3)}{2\pi(0.20)} = 0.00189 \text{ T}$$

With the steel, $B = \kappa_m B_0 = (1+\chi)B_0 = (101)(0.00189 \text{ T})$

$\boxed{B = 0.191 \text{ T}}$

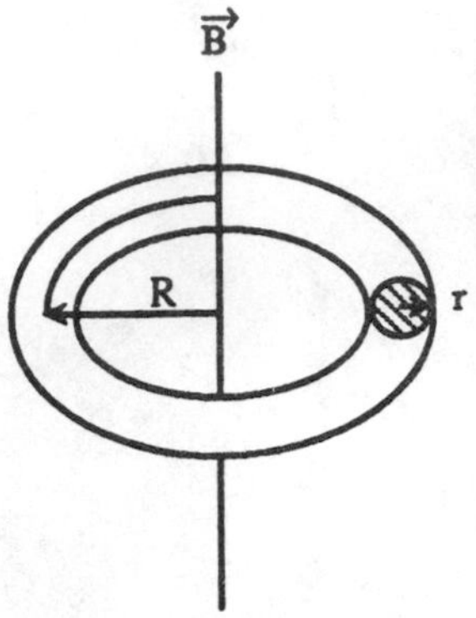

30.47

30.48 $H = \dfrac{NI}{2\pi r}$ $\boxed{\text{N} = 792 \text{ turns}}$

30.49 $B = \mu n I,$

$$I = \frac{1.30 \text{ T}}{5000(4\pi \times 10^{-7} \text{ Wb/A}\cdot\text{m})(\frac{470 \text{ turns}}{2\pi(0.1 \text{ cm})})} = \boxed{277 \text{ mA}}$$

30.50 $B = \dfrac{\mu I}{2\pi R}$ $\Phi = N \displaystyle\int \boldsymbol{B} \cdot d\boldsymbol{A} \approx \dfrac{N\mu I A}{2\pi R}$ if the magnetic field does not change much inside the toroidal solenoid

$$I = \frac{\Phi(2\pi R)}{\mu N A} = \frac{(5 \times 10^{-4} \text{ Wb})(2\pi)(10 \times 10^{-2} \text{ m})}{800(4\pi \times 10^{-7} \text{ N/A}^2)(400)(1 \times 10^{-2} \text{ m})^2} = \boxed{7.81 \text{ A}}$$

30.51 $\Phi = \mu n I A$

$$B = \mu n I = (750 \times 4\pi \times 10^{-7})(\frac{500}{2\pi(0.20)})(0.5) = 0.1875 \text{ T}$$

$$A = 8 \times 10^{-4} \text{ m}^2$$

$$\Phi = (0.1875 \text{ T})(8 \times 10^{-4} \text{ m}^2) = \boxed{1.50 \times 10^{-4} \text{ Wb}}$$

30.52 $HB = [\frac{\text{A}}{\text{m}}][\frac{\text{kg}}{\text{A}\cdot\text{s}^2}] = \frac{\text{kg}}{\text{m}\cdot\text{s}^2}$

$$\frac{\text{kg}}{\text{m}\cdot\text{s}^2}\frac{\text{m}^2}{\text{m}^2} = \frac{\text{kg}\cdot\text{m}^2}{\text{m}^3\cdot\text{s}^2} = \boxed{\text{J/m}^3}$$

30.53 $|\mathbf{M}| = \chi|\mathbf{H}|$

$$B = \mu H = \mu_0(1+\chi)H = \mu_0 H + \mu_0\chi H = \mu_0(H+M)$$

$$(1+\chi)H = H + M$$

$$1 + \chi = 1 + \frac{M}{H}$$

$$\boxed{\chi = \frac{M}{H}}$$

30.54 $B = \mu_0(H+M), \quad H = \frac{B}{\mu_0} - M = \boxed{2.62\times10^6\ \text{A/m}}$

30.55 $B_{\text{solenoid}} = \frac{\mu_0 N}{\ell} I$

$\boxed{\text{N} = 1273\ \text{Turns}}$

30.56 (a) $I = \frac{ev}{2\pi r}$

$$M = IA = (\frac{ev}{2\pi R})\pi r^2 = \boxed{9.3\times10^{-24}\ \text{A}\cdot\text{m}^2}$$

The Bohr model predicts the correct magnetic moment. However, the "planetary model" is seriously deficient in other regards.

(b) Because the electron is (−), its [conventional] current is clockwise, and **M** points downward.

30.57 $B = \mu_0(H + M)$

If $\mu_0 M = 2$ T, $M = \dfrac{2 \times 10^7}{4\pi} = 1.6 \times 10^6\ \text{A} \cdot \text{m}^2$

$M = x\eta\mu = x(8.5 \times 10^{28})(9.27 \times 10^{-24})$

$\boxed{x = 2.02}$

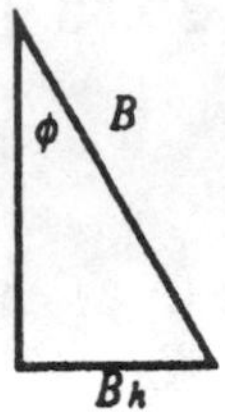

30.58

30.58 (a) $B_h = B_{\text{coil}} = \dfrac{\mu_0 NI}{2R} = \dfrac{(4\pi \times 10^{-7})(5)(0.60)}{0.30} = \boxed{1.26 \times 10^{-5}\ \text{T}}$

(b) $B_h = B \sin\phi \longrightarrow B = \dfrac{B_h}{\sin\phi} = \dfrac{12.6}{\sin 13°} = \boxed{56.0\ \mu\text{T}}$

30.59 (a) Number of unpaired electrons $= \dfrac{8.7 \times 10^{22}\text{A} \cdot \text{m}^2}{9.27 \times 10^{-24}\ \text{A} \cdot \text{m}^2} = 9.39 \times 10^{45}$

Each iron atom has two unpaired electrons, so the

number of iron atoms required $\dfrac{1}{2}(9.39 \times 10^{45})$.

(b) Mass $= \dfrac{4.69 \times 10^{45}\ \text{atoms}(7900\ \text{kg/m}^3)}{8.5 \times 10^{28}\ \text{atoms/m}^3} = \boxed{4.36 \times 10^{20}\ \text{kg}}$

30.60 $B = \dfrac{\mu_0 I}{2\pi R} = \boxed{2 \times 10^{-5}\ \text{T}}$

30.61 $I = \dfrac{2\pi r B}{\mu_0} = \dfrac{2\pi(9000)(1.5 \times 10^{-8})}{4\pi \times 10^{-7}} = \boxed{675\ \text{A}}$ (Conventional) current is downward *or* negative charge flows upward

***30.62** $B = \mu n I = \mu_0(1 + \chi)nI$

$0.13\ \text{T} = \left(4\pi \times 10^{-7}\ \dfrac{\text{T} \cdot \text{m}}{\text{A}}\right)\left(\dfrac{250}{\text{m}}\right)(2\ \text{A})(1 + \chi)$

$206.9 = 1 + \chi$

$\chi = \boxed{206}$

$\boxed{\text{ferromagnetic material}}$

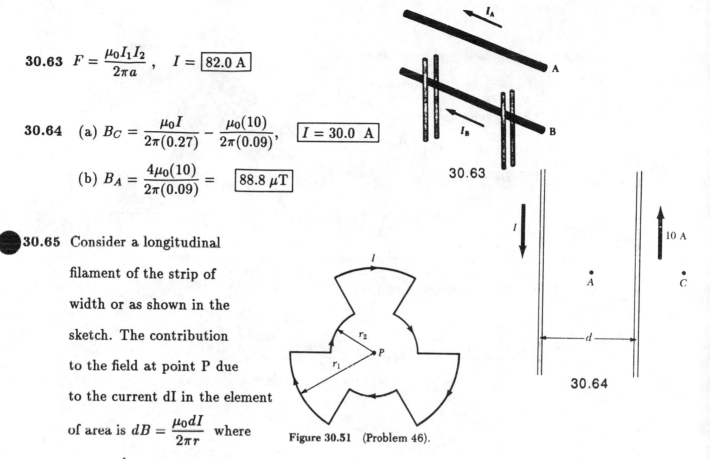

30.63 $F = \dfrac{\mu_0 I_1 I_2}{2\pi a}$, $I = \boxed{82.0\text{ A}}$

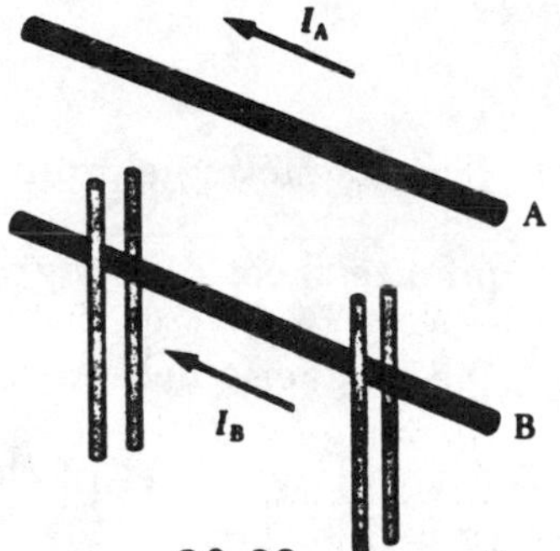

30.63

30.64 (a) $B_C = \dfrac{\mu_0 I}{2\pi(0.27)} - \dfrac{\mu_0(10)}{2\pi(0.09)}$, $\boxed{I = 30.0\text{ A}}$

(b) $B_A = \dfrac{4\mu_0(10)}{2\pi(0.09)} = \boxed{88.8\ \mu\text{T}}$

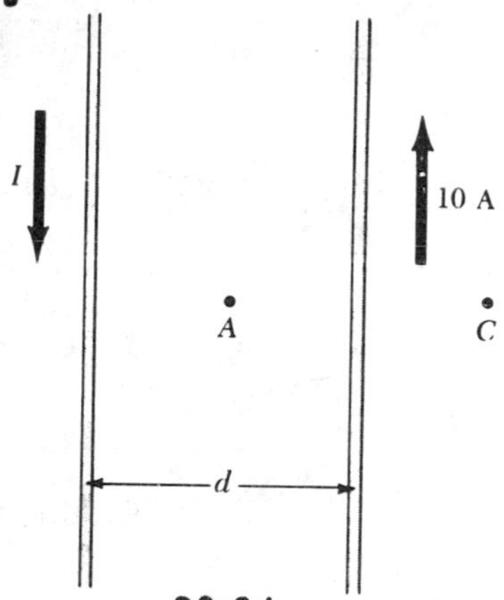

30.64

30.65 Consider a longitudinal filament of the strip of width or as shown in the sketch. The contribution to the field at point P due to the current dI in the element of area is $dB = \dfrac{\mu_0 dI}{2\pi r}$ where

$dI = I(\dfrac{dr}{\omega})$ so

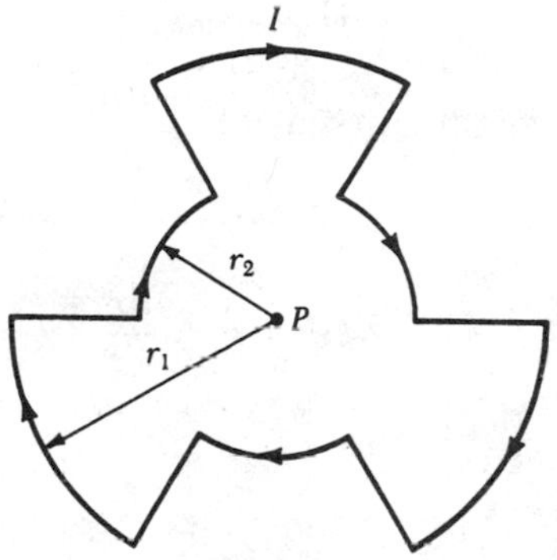

Figure 30.51 (Problem 46).

30.65

$$B = \int dB = \int_b^{b+w} \frac{\mu_0 I dr}{2\pi\omega r}\mathbf{k} = \boxed{\frac{\mu_0 I}{2\pi w}\ln(1 + \frac{w}{b})\mathbf{k}}$$

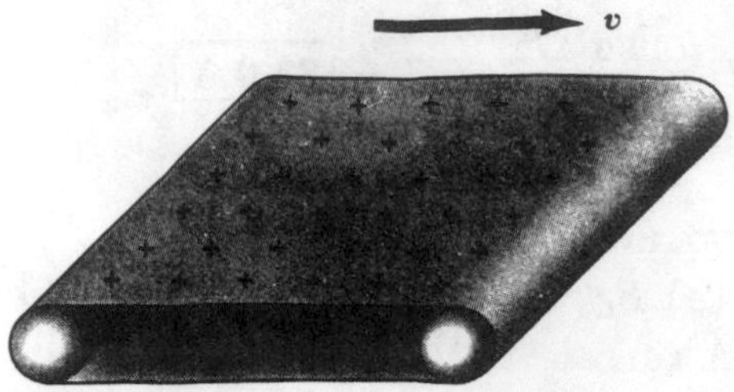

30.66

30.66 The magnetic field due to an infinite sheet of charge (or the magnetic field at points near a large sheet of charge) is given by Eq. 30.19:

$B = \frac{\mu_0 J_s}{2}$. The current density $J_s = \frac{I}{\ell}$ and in this case the equivalent current of the moving charged belt is

$$I = \frac{dq}{dt} = \frac{d}{dt}(\sigma \ell x) = \sigma \ell v; \quad v = \frac{dx}{dt}$$

Therefore $J_s = \sigma v$ and

$$\boxed{B = \frac{\mu_0 \sigma v}{2}}$$

30.67 $mg = I\ell B$ $\boxed{I = 594 \text{ A, East}}$

30.68 $B = \frac{\mu_0 I R}{2(R^2 + R^2)^{3/2}}$, $\boxed{I = 2.00 \times 10^9 \text{ A}}$

30.69 On the axis of a current loop the magnetic field is given by

$$B = \frac{\mu_0 I R^2}{2(x^2 + R^2)^{3/2}} \text{ where in this case } I = \frac{q}{(2\pi/\omega)}. \text{ Therefore}$$

$$B = \frac{\mu_0 \omega R^2 q}{4\pi(x^2 + R^2)^{3/2}}$$

$$B = \frac{\mu_0 (20)(0.1)^2(10 \times 10^{-6})}{4\pi[(0.05)^2 + (0.1)^2]^{3/2}}$$

$$= \boxed{1.43 \times 10^{-10} \text{ T, directed away from the center}}$$

30.70 From Eq. 30.10 the magnetic field at the center of a current loop is given by $B = \dfrac{\mu_0 I}{2R}$.

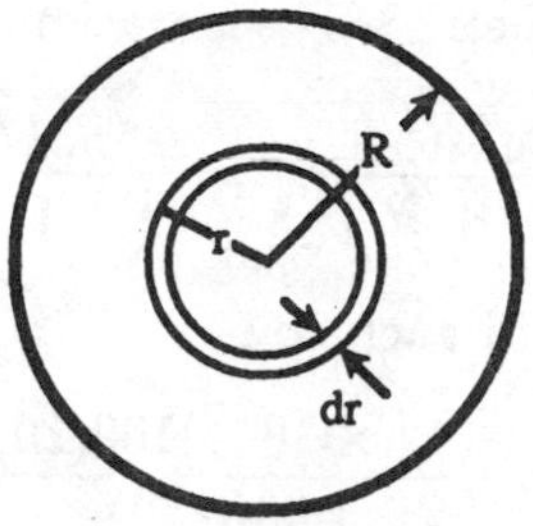

30.70

A surface element in the shape of a thin ring of radius r and width dr will have a magnetic field contribution of

$$dB = \frac{\mu_0 dI}{2R} \quad \text{where}$$

$$dI = \frac{dq}{T} = \frac{\sigma dA}{(2\pi/\omega)} \quad \text{so}$$

$$dB = \frac{\mu_0}{2}\frac{\sigma}{2\pi/\omega}(2\pi r dr)$$

Therefore

$$B = \int_0^R dB = \frac{\mu_0 \sigma \omega}{2}\int_0^R dr = \boxed{\frac{\mu_0 \sigma \omega R}{2}}$$

30.71 (a) Use Eq. 30.9 twice:

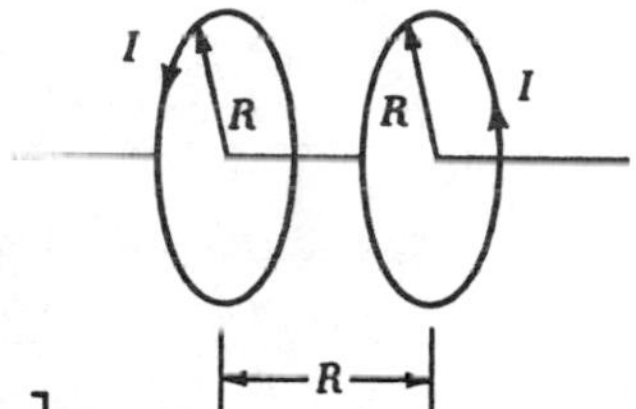

30.71

$$B_x = \frac{\mu_0 I R^2}{2(x^2 + R^3)^{2/3}}$$

$$B = B_{x_1} + B_{x_2} = \frac{\mu_0 I R^2}{2}\left[\frac{1}{(x^2+R^2)^{3/2}} + \frac{1}{((R-x)^2+R^2)^{3/2}}\right]$$

$$= \frac{\mu_0 I R^2}{2}\left[\frac{1}{(x^2+R^2)^{3/2}} + \frac{1}{(2R^2+x^2-2xR)^{3/2}}\right]$$

(b) $$\frac{dB}{dx} = \frac{\mu_0 I R^2}{2}\left[\frac{-\frac{3}{2}\sqrt{x^2+R^2}}{(x^2+R^2)^3} \frac{-\frac{3}{2}\sqrt{2R^2+x^2-2xR}}{(2R^2+x^2-2xR)^3}\right] = 0 \text{ at } x = R/2$$

$$\frac{d^2B}{dx^2} = \frac{-3\mu_0 I R^2}{4}\left[\frac{(x^2+R^2)^3(\frac{1}{2})(x^2+R^2)^{-1/2}(2x) - (x^2+R^2)^{1/2}(3)(x^2+R^2)^2(2x)}{(x^2+R^2)^6}\right.$$

$$\left. + \frac{(2R^2+x^2-2xR)^3(\frac{1}{2})(2R^2+x^2-2xR)^{-1/2}(2x-2R) - (2R^2+x^2-2xR)\cdot(3)(2R^2+x^2-2xR)^2(2x-2R)}{(2R^2+x^2-2xR)^6}\right]$$

$$= 0 \text{ at } x = R/2$$

30.72 "Helmholtz pair" $\longrightarrow$ separation distance = radius

$$B = \frac{2\mu_0 I R^2}{2[(R/2)^2 + R^2]^{3/2}} = \frac{\mu_0 I R^2}{[\frac{1}{4}+1]^{3/2} R^3} = \frac{\mu_0 I}{1.40R} \text{ for 1 turn}$$

For N turns in each coil

$$B = \frac{\mu_0 N I}{1.40R} = \frac{(4\pi \times 10^{-7})100(10)}{1.40(0.50)} = \boxed{1.80 \times 10^{-3}\ \text{T}}$$

30.73 Use Ampere's law $\oint \mathbf{B} \cdot d\mathbf{s} = \mu_0 I$. For uniform current density, J, this becomes

$$\oint \mathbf{B} \cdot d\mathbf{s} = \mu_0 \int \mathbf{J} \cdot d\mathbf{A}$$

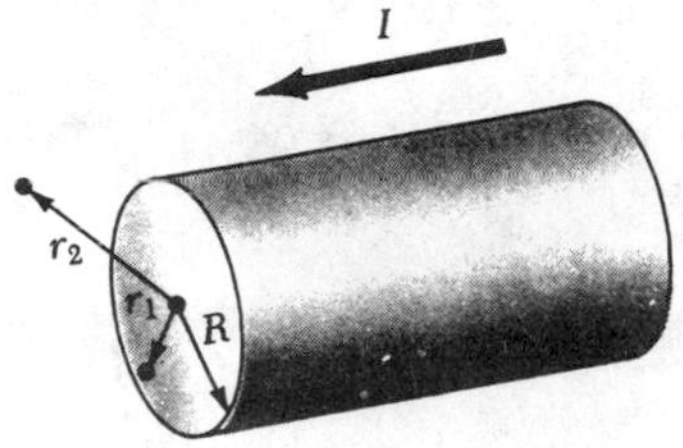

30.73

(a) When $r_1 < R$ this becomes

$$2\pi r_1 B = \mu_0 \int_0^{r_1} (br)(2\pi r dr) \text{ and}$$

$$\boxed{B_{\text{in}} = \frac{\mu_0 b r_1^2}{3}} \quad \text{(inside)}$$

(b) When $r_2 > R$ this becomes

$$2\pi r_2 B = \mu_0 \int_0^{R} (br)(2\pi r dr) \text{ and}$$

$$\boxed{B_{\text{out}} = \frac{\mu_0 b R^3}{3r_2}} \quad \text{(outside)}$$

***30.74** Torques balance

$$\tau_{\text{mag}} = \mu \times B \qquad \tau_g = mg\frac{L}{2}\cos 5°$$

$$\mu B \sin 5° = mg\frac{L}{2}\cos 5°$$

$$B = \frac{mgL}{\mu \tan 5°} = \boxed{28.8 \times 10^{-3}\ \text{T}}$$

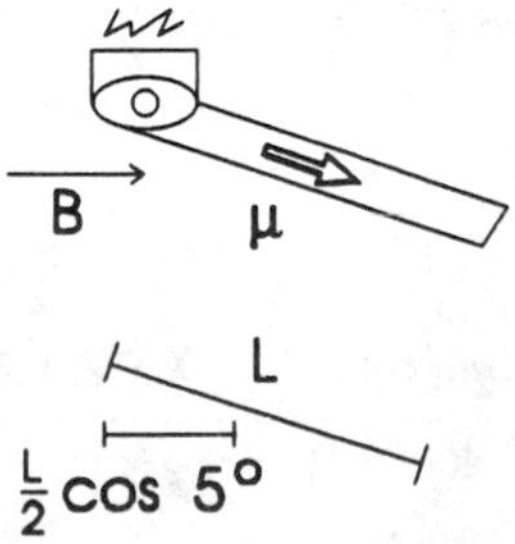

30.74

***30.75** Model the two wires as straight parallel wires(!)

$$\text{(a)}\ F = \frac{\mu_0 I^2 L}{2\pi a} \quad (\textit{Equation } 30.13)$$

$$= \frac{(4\pi\times 10^{-7})(140)^2 2\pi(0.1)}{2\pi(10^{-3})} = \boxed{2.46\text{ N}}$$

$$\text{(b)}\ a_{\text{loop}} = \frac{2.46\text{ N} - m_{\text{loop}}g}{m_{\text{loop}}} = \boxed{107.3\text{ m/s}^2}\uparrow$$

***30.76**

$$B = \mu_0 n I = \mu_0 \frac{N}{L} I$$

$$0.03\text{ T} = \frac{(4\pi\times 10^{-7}\frac{\text{T}\cdot\text{m}}{\text{A}})(1\text{A})}{0.1\text{ m}}\text{N}$$

$$N = \boxed{2387\text{ turns}}$$

Since each layer has $\frac{10\text{ cm}}{0.5\text{ mm}} = 200$ turns, it will take 12 layers to complete the solenoid.

Total length of wire = (2387 turns)2π(1.3 cm)

Total length = $\boxed{195\text{ m}}$

30.77 (a) $H = nI = (\frac{N}{2\pi r})I = \frac{1505}{2\pi(0.04\text{ m})}(2\text{ A}) = (5988\ \frac{\text{turns}}{\text{m}})(2\text{ A})$

or $H = 11,976\ \frac{\text{A}\cdot\text{turn}}{\text{m}} \approx \boxed{1.20\times 10^4\ \frac{\text{A}\cdot\text{turn}}{\text{m}}}$

(b) $B = \frac{\Phi}{A} = \frac{3\times 10^{-5}\text{ Wb}}{1.21\times 10^{-4}\text{ m}^2} = 0.248\text{ Wb/m}^2$

$$B = \kappa_m H \implies \kappa_m = \frac{B}{H} = \frac{0.248\text{ Wb/m}^2}{1.2\times 10^4\text{ A}\cdot\text{turn/m}} = \boxed{2.07\times 10^{-5}\text{ Wb/A}\cdot\text{m}}$$

30.78 $C = \frac{TM}{B} = \frac{(4\text{ K})(10\%)(8\times10^{27}\text{ atoms/m}^3)(5)(9.27\times10^{-24}\text{ J/T}^2)}{5\text{ T}}$

$= \boxed{2.97\times10^4\text{ K}\cdot\text{J/T}^2\cdot\text{m}^3}$

30.79 $n = \frac{M_s}{\mu}$

$= \frac{(7.6\times10^4\text{ A/m})}{1.2(9.27\times10^{-24}\text{ A}\cdot\text{m}^2)}$

$= 6.83\times10^{27}\text{ atoms/m}^3 = 6.83\times10^{21}\text{ atoms/cm}^3$

$At.wt. = \rho(1/n)N_A$

$= (4.15\text{ g/cm}^3)(1/6.83\times10^{21}\text{ atoms/cm}^3)(6.02\times10^{23}\text{ atoms/mol}) = \boxed{366\text{ g/mol}}$

30.80 (a) $B = \frac{\mu_0}{2\pi}\frac{M}{x^3}$ where $M = IA = I\pi R^2$

$|F| = M\frac{dB}{dx} = \frac{M^2\mu_0}{2\pi}(\frac{3}{x^4}) = \boxed{\frac{3\pi}{2}\frac{\mu_0 I^2 R^4}{x^4}}$

(b) $|F| = (I\pi R^2)^2\frac{\mu_0}{2\pi}\frac{3}{x^4} = (10\pi)^2(\frac{0.5}{5})^4(\frac{4\pi\times10^{-7}}{2\pi})3 = \boxed{5.92\times10^{-8}\text{ N}}$

30.81 By symmetry of the arrangement, the magnitude of the net magnetic field at point P is $B = 8B_0$ where B_0 is the contribution to the field due to current in an edge length equal to $L/2$. In order to calculate B_0, we use the Biot-Savart law and consider the plane of the square to be the yz–plane with point P on the x-axis. The contribution to the magnetic field at point P due to a current element of length dz and located a distance z along the axis is given by Eq. 30.5.

$$B_0 = \frac{\mu_0 I}{4\pi}\int \frac{d\boldsymbol{\ell} \times \hat{\boldsymbol{r}}}{r^2}$$

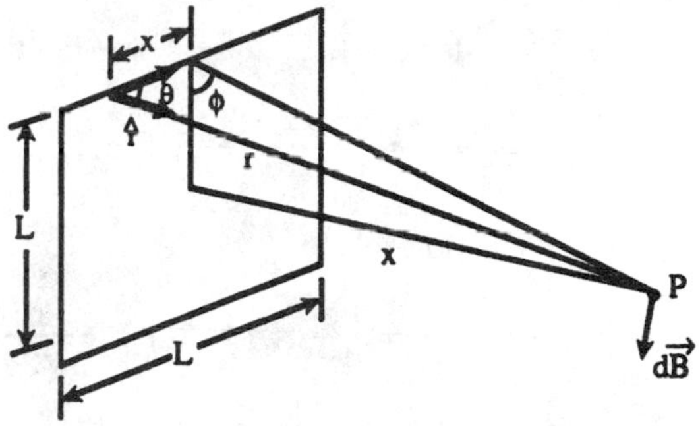

30.81

From the figure we see that

$r = \sqrt{x^2 + (L^2/4) + z^2}$ and

$$|d\boldsymbol{\ell} \times \hat{\boldsymbol{r}}| = dz \sin\theta = dz\sqrt{\frac{L^2/4 + x^2}{L^2/4 + x^2 + z^2}}$$

By symmetry all components of the field B at P cancel except the components along x (perpendicular to the plane of the square); and

$B_x = B_0 \sin\phi$ where

$$\sin\phi = \frac{L/2}{\sqrt{L^2/4 + x^2}}.$$

Therefore

$$B_0 = \frac{\mu_0 I}{4\pi}\int_0^{L/2} \frac{\sin\theta \sin\phi dz}{r^2}$$

and $B = 8B_0$.

Using the expressions given above for $\sin\theta\sin\phi$, and r we find

$$B = \frac{\mu_0 I L^2}{2\pi(x^2 + \frac{L^2}{4})\sqrt{x^2 + \frac{L^2}{2}}}$$

30.82 When the conductor is in the rectangular shape shown in Figure 30.54(a), the net magnetic field at point P_1 is due to the current in the horizontal segment of length 2ℓ. The contribution to the field at P_1 due to the two vertical segments of length ℓ cancel. To calculate the magnitude of the field at P_1, we use Eq. 30.6,

$$B = \frac{\mu_0 I}{4\pi a}(\cos\theta_1 - \cos\theta_2)$$

In this case (with point P_1 on the perpendicular bisector of the segment of length 2ℓ), $\theta_2 = \pi - \theta_1$ and $\cos\theta_2 = -\cos\theta_1$. Also from the geometry we see that $\cos\theta_1 = \frac{1}{\sqrt{2}}$ and $a = \ell$.

Therefore

$$B_1 = \frac{\mu_0 I}{4\pi\ell}(2\cos\theta_1) = \frac{\mu_0 I}{2\sqrt{2}\pi\ell}$$

When the conductor is in the shape of a circular arc, the magnitude or the field at the center is given by Eq. 30.8,

$$B = \frac{\mu_0 I}{4\pi R}\theta.$$

From the geometry in this case we find

$$R = \frac{4\ell}{\pi} \text{ and } \theta = \pi.$$

Therefore $B_2 = \frac{\mu_0 I\pi}{4\pi(4\ell/\pi)} = \frac{\mu_0 I\pi}{16\ell}$

So that $\boxed{\frac{B_1}{B_2} = \frac{4\sqrt{2}}{\pi^2}}$

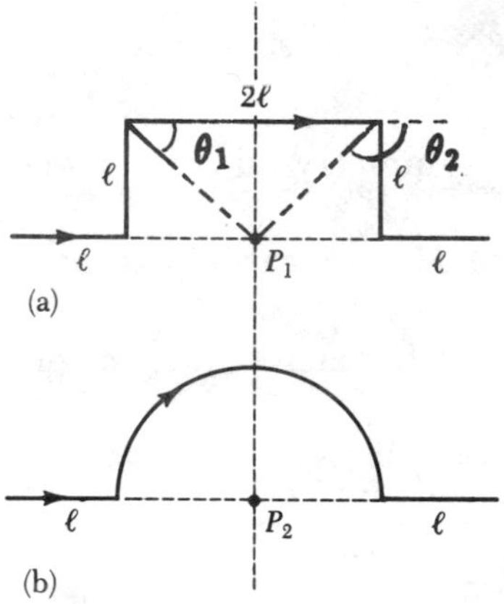

30.82

30.83 There is no contribution from the straight portion of the wire since $ds \times \hat{r} = 0$. For the field of the spiral

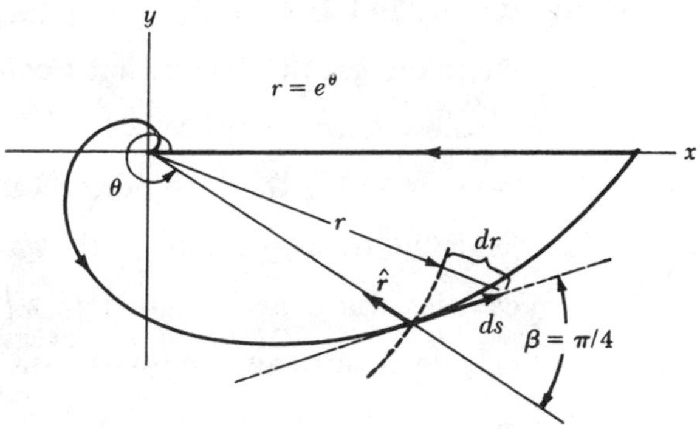

30.83

$$dB = \frac{\mu_0 I}{(4\pi)} \frac{(ds \times \hat{r})}{r^2}$$

$$B = \frac{\mu_0 I}{4\pi} \int_{\theta=0}^{2\pi} \frac{|ds| \sin\theta |\hat{r}|}{r^2}$$

$$= \frac{\mu_0 I}{4\pi} \int_{\theta=0}^{2\pi} (\sqrt{2}dr)[\sin(\frac{3\pi}{4})]\frac{1}{r^2}$$

$$= \frac{\mu_0 I}{4\pi} \int_{\theta=0}^{2\pi} r^{-2} dr = -\frac{\mu_0 I}{4\pi}(r^{-1})\Big|_{\theta=0}^{2\pi}$$

Substitute $r = e^{\theta}$

$$B = -\frac{\mu_0 I}{4\pi}[3^{-\theta}]_0^{2\pi} = -\frac{\mu_0 I}{4\pi}[e^{-2\pi} - e^0] = \boxed{\frac{\mu_0 I}{4\pi}(1 - e^{-2\pi})}$$

30.84 At P_1 find B as if conductor were solid using Ampere's law. Next find B that *would* be due to the conductors of radius $\frac{a}{2}$ that *could* occupy the void where the holes exist. Then use the superposition principle and subtract the field that would be due to the part of the conductor where the holes exist from the field of a solid cylindrical conductor. Note the current I exists in the conductor with a current density

$$J = \frac{I}{A}, \text{ where } A = \pi[a^2 - \frac{a^2}{4} - \frac{a^2}{4}] = \frac{\pi a^2}{2}.$$

Therefore $J = \frac{2I}{\pi a^2}$. The current in the solid conductor is $I_a = J\pi a^2$ and the current through conductor of radius, $a/2$ is $I_{a/2} = J\pi(\frac{3}{2})^2$. Thus

$$B = \frac{\mu_0 J \pi a^2}{2\pi r} - \mu_0 J \pi \frac{(\frac{a}{2})^2}{2\pi(r - \frac{a}{2})} - \mu_0 J \pi \frac{(\frac{a}{2})^2}{2\pi(r + \frac{a}{2})}$$

$$B = \frac{\mu_0 J a^2}{2r} \frac{(2r^2 - a^2)}{(4r^2 - a^2)}$$

$$B = \boxed{\frac{\mu_0 I}{\pi r} \frac{(2r^2 - a^2)}{(4r^2 - a^2)} \text{ directed to the left}}$$

30.85 At P_2, find B as if the conductor were solid. Next subtract the field that *would* be due to the two conductors that would fill the two cavities. Note that the horizontal components of the field due to the conductor that *could* fill the cavities will cancel. Therefore we need only to calculate vertical components on B.

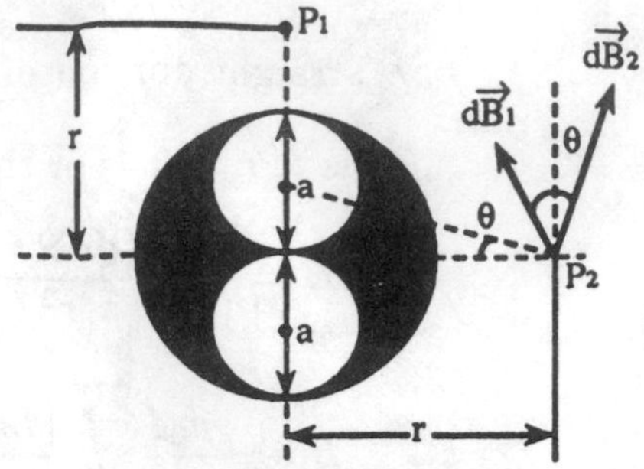

30.85

$$B_v = B\cos\theta = \frac{Br}{\sqrt{(a^2/4)+r^2}}$$

Also $J = \dfrac{I}{A} = \dfrac{2I}{\pi a^2}$ and

$I_a = J\pi a^2,\quad I_{(a/2)} = J\pi(\frac{a}{2})^2$. Thus

$$B = \frac{\mu_0 J\pi a^2}{2\pi r} - 2[\mu_0 J\pi(\frac{a}{2})^2/2\pi\sqrt{(a^2/4)+r^2}]r/\text{sqrt}(a^2/4)+r^2]$$

$$B = \frac{\mu_0 J a^2}{2r}\frac{(a^2+2r^2)}{(a^2+4r^2)}$$

$$\boxed{B = \frac{\mu_0 I}{\pi r}\frac{(a^2+2r^2)}{(a^2+4r^2)}}$$ directed in the positive y−direction.

30.86 At the center of the loop, $B_0 = \dfrac{\mu_0 I}{2R}$ (Eq. 30.10)

At points along the x-axis,

$$B(x) = \frac{\mu_0 I R^2}{2(x^2+R^2)^{3/2}} \quad \text{(Eq. 30.9)}$$

x	$B(x)$
0	$B_0/1$
R	0.53 B_0
$2R$	$0.089B_0$
$3R$	$0.032B_0$
$4R$	$0.14B_0$
$5R$	$0.0075B_0$

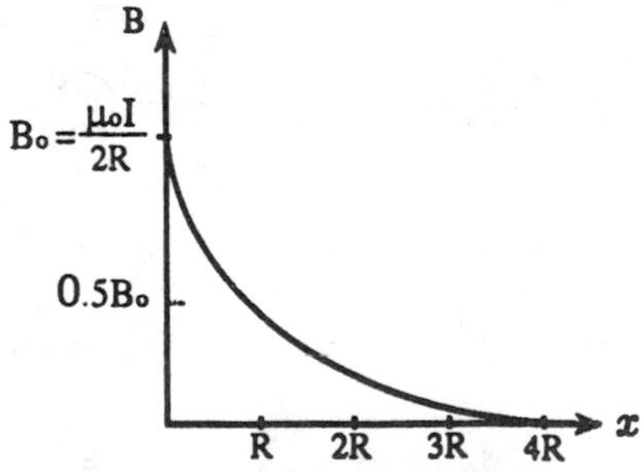

30.86

Magnetic field B as a function of distance x from center of loop.

***30.87** Consider the sphere as being built up of little rings of radius r, centered on the rotation axis. The contribution to the B-field from each ring is

$$dB = \frac{\mu_0 I r^2}{2(x^2+r^2)^{3/2}} \quad \text{where } I = \frac{Q}{t} = \frac{Q\omega}{2\pi}$$

$$dB = \frac{\mu_0}{2}\frac{\rho 2\pi r dr\, dx}{(x^2+r^2)^{3/2}}\frac{r^2\omega}{2\pi} \quad \text{and } \rho = \frac{Q}{\frac{4}{3}\pi R^3}$$

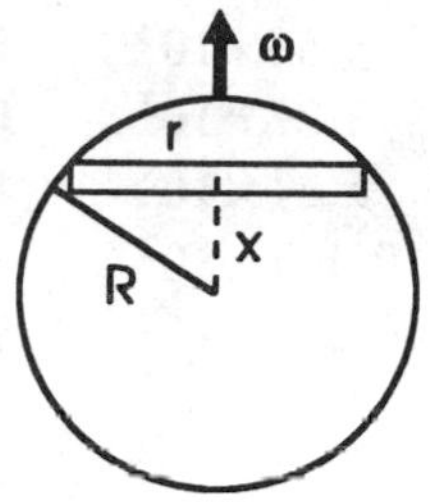

30.87

$$dB = \int_{r=0}^{R} \frac{\mu_0}{2}\frac{\rho\omega r^3 dr\, dx}{(r^2+x^2)^{3/2}}$$

$$B = \int_{x=-R}^{+R}\int_{r=0}^{\sqrt{R^2-x^2}} \frac{\mu_0\rho\omega}{2}\frac{r^3 dr dx}{(r^2+x^2)^{3/2}}$$

Let $v = r^2+x^2, \quad dv = 2rdr, \quad r^2 = v - x^2$

$$B = \int_{x=-R}^{+R}\int_{v=x^2}^{R^2} \frac{\mu_0\rho\omega}{2}\frac{(v-x^2)dv}{v^{3/2}}\,dx$$

$$B = \frac{4}{3}\rho\mu_0\omega R^2$$

***30.88**

B/B_0	B_0, mT
4.17×10^3	0.048
5.71×10^3	0.070
6.82×10^3	0.088
6.67×10^3	0.12
5.56×10^3	0.18
3.87×10^3	0.31
1.61×10^3	0.87
0.471×10^3	3.4
0.015×10^3	120.0

(b) Relative permability of a ferromagnetic sample as it depends on applied field.

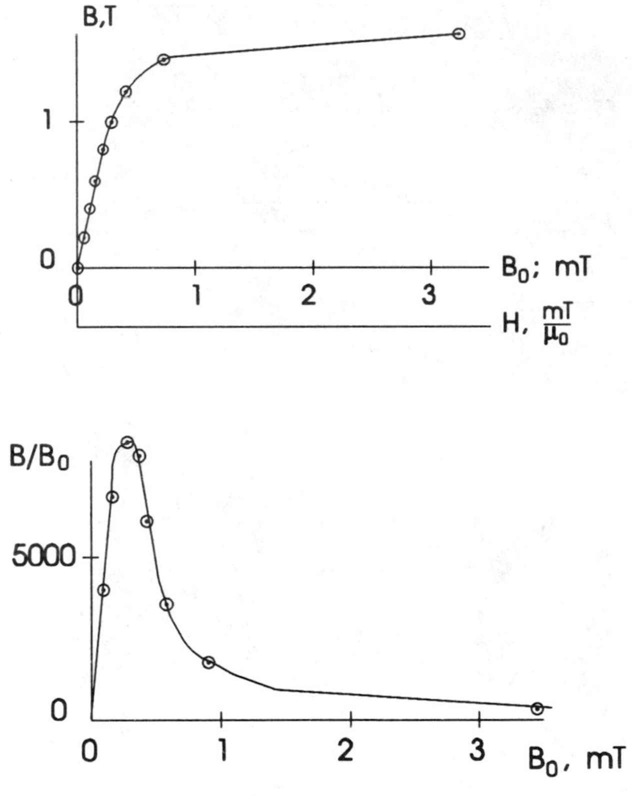

30.88

***30.89** $$I = \frac{Q}{t} = \frac{2\pi r\ dr\ dx\ \rho\ \omega}{2\pi}$$

$$\mu = IA = \int r\ dr\ dx\ \rho\ \omega\ \pi\ r^2$$

$$= \int_x \int_{r=0}^{\sqrt{R^2-x^2}} \rho\omega \cdot \pi r^3\ dr\ dx$$

$$\mu = \int_{x=-R}^{R} \rho\ \omega\ \pi \frac{(\sqrt{R^2-x^2})^4}{4}\ dx$$

$$= \frac{\rho\ \omega\ \pi}{4} \int_{-R}^{R} (R^2 - x^2)^2\ dx$$

$$= \frac{\rho\ \omega\ \pi}{4} \int_{-R}^{R} (R^4 - 2R^2x^2 + x^4)dx$$

$$= \frac{\rho\ \omega\ \pi}{4} \left(R^4\ 2R - 2R^2\ \frac{2R^3}{3} + \frac{2R^5}{5} \right)$$

$$= \frac{\rho\ \omega\ \pi}{4}\ R^5 \left(2 - \frac{4}{3} + \frac{2}{5} \right)$$

$$\mu = \frac{\rho\ \omega\ \pi}{4}\ R^5\ \frac{16}{15} = \boxed{\frac{4\rho\omega\pi}{15}\ R^5}$$

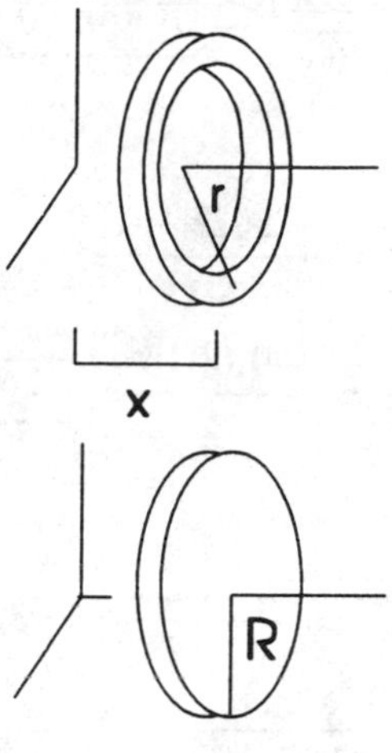

30.89

CHAPTER 31

31.1 $V = \frac{\Delta(NBA)}{\Delta t} = \boxed{0.500\ \text{V}}$

31.2 $V = \frac{\Delta\Phi}{\Delta t} = \frac{-\Delta(B \cdot A)}{\Delta t} = -0.0016\ \text{V}$

$$I_{\text{loop}} = \frac{V}{R} = -\frac{0.0016}{2} = \boxed{-0.800\ \text{mA}}$$

31.3 $\mathcal{E} = N\frac{d\Phi}{dt} = \frac{\Delta(NBA)}{\Delta t} = 3200\ \text{V}$

$$I = \frac{\mathcal{E}}{R} = \boxed{160\ \text{A}}$$

31.4 $V = NB\frac{\Delta A}{\Delta t}, \quad \boxed{B = 0.180\ \text{T}}$

31.5 $I = \frac{V}{R} = \frac{\Delta(NBA)}{R\Delta t}, \quad \frac{\Delta B}{\Delta t} = \boxed{2.67\ \text{T/s}}$

31.6 $V = \frac{\Delta(NBA)}{\Delta t} = \boxed{4.71\ \text{V}}$

31.7 $V = N\frac{dB}{dt}A = (30)(0.41)(\pi)(0.0016) = \boxed{61.8\ \text{mV}}$

31.8 $|\mathcal{E}| = \frac{d}{dt}(NBA\sin(60\pi t)) = \boxed{1.32\ \cos(60\pi t)\ \text{V}}$

31.9 $\Phi = NBA$

$$\mathcal{E} = \frac{d\Phi}{dt} = \boxed{0.0002\, e^{-t/7}\ \text{V}}$$

31.10 (a) $\mathcal{E} = \frac{d\phi}{dt} = A\frac{dB}{dt} = \boxed{\frac{AB_0}{\tau}e^{-t/\tau}}$

(b) $\mathcal{E} = \frac{(0.16\text{ m}^2)(0.35\text{ T})}{2\text{ s}}e^{-4/2} = \boxed{3.79\text{ mV}}$

(c) At $t = 0$, $\mathcal{E} = \boxed{28.0\text{ mV}}$

31.11 $B = \mu_0 nI = \mu_0 nI_0(1 - e^{-\alpha t})$

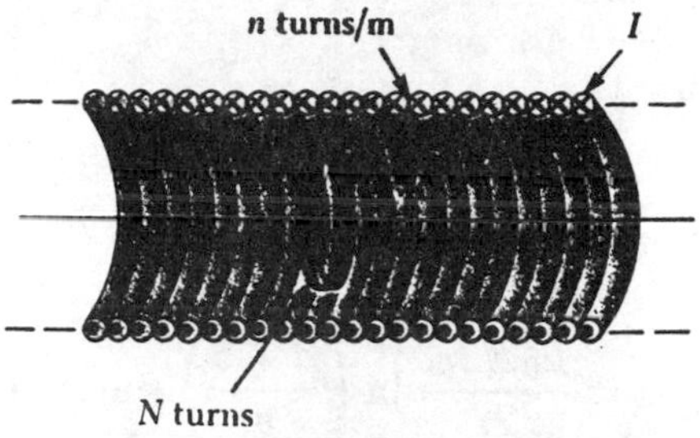

31.11

$$\Phi_m = \int BdA$$
$$= \mu_0 nI_0(1 - e^{-\alpha t})\int dA$$
$$= \mu_0 nI_0(1 - e^{-\alpha t})\pi R^2$$
$$\mathcal{E} = -N\frac{d\Phi_m}{dt} = N\mu_0 nI_0\pi R^2\alpha e^{-\alpha t}$$
$$= (250)(4\pi \times 10^{-7}\text{N/A}^2)(400\text{ m}^{-1})(30\text{ A})(\pi(0.06\text{ m})^2)(1.6\text{ s}^{-1})\text{e}^{-1.6\text{t}}$$
$$= \boxed{68.2\, e^{-1.6t}\text{ mV}}$$

31.12 $\mathcal{E} = \frac{-d\Phi_m}{dt} = -N\frac{d\Phi_m}{dt} = -\frac{N(BA - 0)}{\Delta t}$

$$\Delta t = \frac{NBA}{\mathcal{E}} = \frac{NB(\pi r^2)}{\mathcal{E}} = \frac{500(0.2)\pi(0.05)^2}{10 \times 10^3} = \boxed{7.85 \times 10^{-5}\text{ s}}$$

31.13 $\mathcal{E} = \frac{d}{dt}(NB\ell^2\cos\theta) = \frac{N\ell^2\Delta B\cos\theta}{\Delta t}$

$$\ell = \sqrt{\frac{\mathcal{E}\Delta t}{N\Delta B\cos\theta}}$$
$$= \sqrt{\frac{(80 \times 10^{-3}\text{ V})(0.4\text{ s})}{(50)(600 \times 10^{-6}\text{ T} - 200 \times 10^{-6}\text{ T})\cos(30°)}} = 1.36\text{ m}$$

Length $= 4\ell N = 4(1.36\text{ m})(50) = \boxed{272\text{ m}}$

31.14 The loop is the boundary of the plane surface S. The magnetic field produced by the current in the straight wire is perpendicular to S at all points on the surface. The magnitude of the field is

$$B = \frac{\mu_0 I}{2\pi r}$$

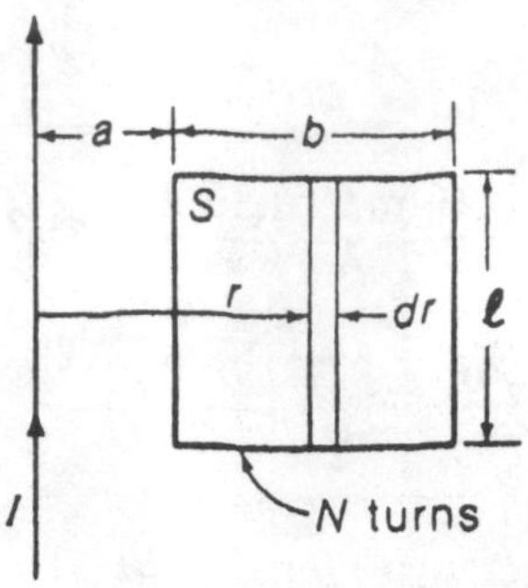

31.14

Thus, the flux linkage is

$$\Phi_m = N\Phi'_m = \frac{\mu_0 N I \ell}{2\pi}\int_a^{a+b}\frac{dr}{r}$$

$$= \frac{\mu_0 N I_0 \ell}{2\pi}\ln\left(\frac{a+b}{a}\right)\sin(\omega t + \delta)$$

Finally, the induced EMF is

$$\mathcal{E} = \frac{d\Phi_m}{dt} = \frac{\mu_0 N I_0 \ell \omega}{2\pi} ln\left(\frac{a+b}{a}\right)\cos(\omega t + \delta)$$

$$= (2\times10^{-7}\ \mathrm{T\cdot m/A})(100)(50\ \mathrm{A})(0.20\ \mathrm{m})(200\pi\ \mathrm{s}^{-1})\ln\left(\frac{5+5}{5}\right)\cos(\omega t + \delta)$$

$$= \boxed{(87.1\ \mathrm{mV})\cos(200\pi t + \delta)}$$

The term $\sin(\omega t + \delta)$ in the expression for the current in the straight wire does not change appreciably when ωt changes by 0.1 rad or less. Thus, the current does not change appreciably during a time interval $\tau < 0.1/(200\pi\ \mathrm{s}^{-1}) = 1.6\times10^{-4}$ s We define a critical length, $c\tau = (3\times10^8\ \mathrm{m/s})(1.6\times10^{-4}\ \mathrm{s}) = 4.8\times10^4$ m, equal to the distance to which field changes could be propagated during an interval of 1.6×10^{-4} s. This length is so much larger than any dimension of the loop or its distance from the wire that, although we consider the straight wire to be infinitely long, we can also safely ignore the field propagation effects in the vicinity of the loop. Moreover, the phase angle can be considered to be constant along the wire in the vicinity of the loop.

If the frequency ω were much larger, say, $200\pi\times10^5\ \mathrm{s}^{-1}$, the corresponding critical length would be only 48 cm. In this situation propagation effects would be important and the above expression for $\mathcal{E}$ would require modification. As a "rule of thumb" we can consider field propagation effects for circuits of laboratory size to be negligible for frequencies, $f = \omega/2\pi$, that are less about 10^6 Hz.

31.15
$$\Phi_m = N\Phi'_m = NB_0 \cos\omega t \int_0^R \left(1 - \frac{r}{2R}\right) 2\pi r dr$$
$$= \frac{2\pi}{3} R^2 N B_0 \cos\omega t$$
$$\mathcal{E} = \frac{d\Phi_m}{dt} = \boxed{\frac{2\pi}{3}\omega R^2 N B_0 \sin\omega t}$$

counterclockwise, looking to the left

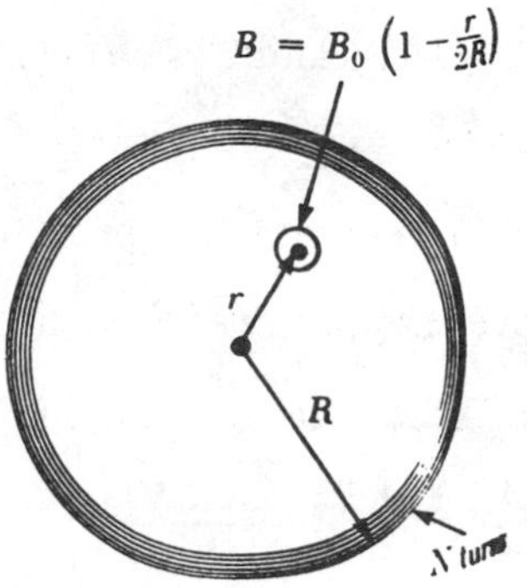

31.15

31.16 In a toroid, all the flux is confined to the inside of the toroid.

$$B = \frac{\mu_0 \text{NI}}{2\pi \text{r}} = \frac{500\mu_0 I}{2\pi r}$$
$$\Phi_m = \int B dA = \frac{500\mu_0 I_0}{2\pi} \sin\omega t \int \frac{dzdr}{r}$$
$$= \frac{500\mu_0 I_0}{2\pi} a \sin\omega t \ln\left(\frac{b+R}{R}\right)$$
$$\mathcal{E} = N' \frac{d\Phi_m}{dt}$$
$$\mathcal{E} = 20 \frac{500\mu_0 I_0}{2\pi} \omega a \ln\left(\frac{b+R}{R}\right) \cos\omega t$$
$$= \frac{10^4}{2\pi}(4\pi \times 10^{-7}\ \text{N/A}^2)(50\ \text{A})(377\ \text{rad/s})(0.02\ \text{m})\ell n\left(\frac{3\ \text{cm} + 4\ \text{cm}}{4\ \text{cm}}\right) \cos\omega t$$
$$= \boxed{(0.422\ \text{V}) \cos\omega t}$$

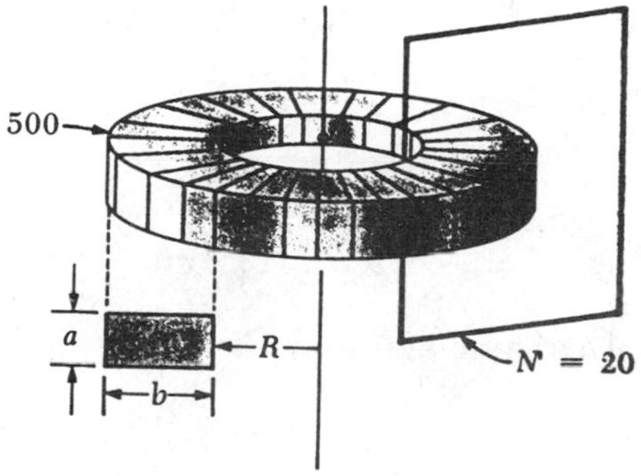

31.16

31.17 $\mathcal{E} = \dfrac{\Delta(NBA)}{\Delta t} = NB\dfrac{\Delta A}{\Delta t}$, $\quad B = \boxed{2.81 \times 10^{-3}\ \text{T}}$

31.18 $I = \dfrac{\mathcal{E}}{R} = \dfrac{B\ell v}{R}$ $\quad \boxed{v = 1.00\ \text{m/s}}$

31.19 (a) $|\boldsymbol{F}| = I|\boldsymbol{\ell} \times \boldsymbol{B}| = I\ell B$. When $I = \dfrac{\mathcal{E}}{R}$ and $\mathcal{E} = B\ell v$, we get

$$F = \frac{B\ell v}{R}(\ell B) = \frac{B^2 \ell^2 v}{R} = \frac{(2.5)^2(1.2)^2(2)}{6} = \boxed{3.00\ \text{N}}$$

(b) $P = I^2 R = \dfrac{B^2 \ell^2 v^2}{R} = 6\ \text{W}$ or $P = Fv = \boxed{6.00\ \text{W}}$

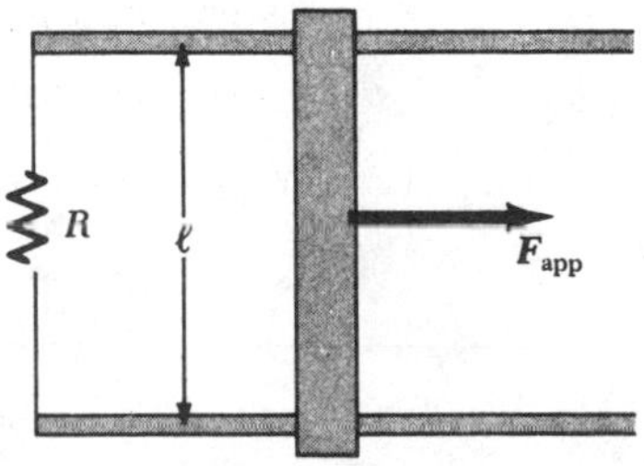

31.19

31.20 $F = I\ell B$ and $\mathcal{E} = B\ell v$

$$I = \frac{\mathcal{E}}{R} = \frac{B\ell v}{R}, \text{ so } B = \frac{IR}{\ell v}$$

(a) $\therefore \quad F = \dfrac{I^2 \ell R}{\ell v} \quad \therefore \; I = \sqrt{\dfrac{Fv}{R}} = \boxed{\dfrac{1}{2} \text{ A}}$

(b) $I^2 R = \boxed{2.00 \text{ W}}$

(c) For constant force, $P = \mathbf{F} \cdot \boldsymbol{v} = (1 \text{ N})(2 \text{ m/s}) = \boxed{2.00 \text{ W}}$

31.21 $\mathcal{E} = -B\ell v = (4 \times 10^{-5})(5)(10) = \boxed{2.00 \text{ mV}}$

The west end is positive

31.22 (a) $\mathcal{E} = -B\ell v = (1.2 \times 10^{-6})(14)(70) = \boxed{1.18 \text{ mV}}$

(b) Same emf, but the north wingtip is now positive.

31.23 $\omega = (2 \text{ rev/s})(2\pi \text{ rad/s}) = 12.57 \text{ rad/s}$

$$\mathcal{E} = \frac{1}{2} B\omega\ell^2 = \boxed{2.83 \text{ mV}}$$

31.24 $\mathcal{E} = \dfrac{1}{2} B\ell^2\omega = \boxed{0.26 \text{ mV}}$

31.25 (a) $|\boldsymbol{F}| = |q\boldsymbol{v} \times \boldsymbol{B}| = qvB = qr\omega B = q\omega Br \implies E = \omega Br$

$$|\Delta V| = \int \mathbf{E} \cdot d\boldsymbol{r} = \omega B \int_0^{L/2} r\,dr = \frac{\omega B}{2}\left(\frac{L}{2}\right)^2 = \boxed{\frac{\omega B}{8} L^2}$$

(b) $|\Delta V| = \dfrac{60(1.2)}{8}(0.2)^2 = \boxed{0.36 \text{ V}}$

31.26 (a) $\mathcal{E} = N\frac{d}{dt}(BA\cos\theta) \approx NBA|\frac{\Delta \cos\theta}{\Delta t}|$

$$= (200)(0.8\text{ T})\pi(0.1\text{ m})^2\frac{(\cos 0° - \cos 90°)}{(1.5\text{ s})} = \boxed{3.35\text{ V}}$$

(b) $\mathcal{E} = NBA|\frac{d(\cos\theta)}{dt}| = NBA\omega\sin\theta$

$$= 200(0.8\text{ T})\pi(0.1\text{ m})^2\frac{(\pi/2)}{(1.5\text{ s})}\sin(45\text{ co}) = \boxed{3.72\text{ V}}$$

31.27 (a) $\mathbf{B}_{ext} = B_{ext}\mathbf{i}$ and B_{ext} decreases; therefore the induced field is $\boldsymbol{B}_0 = B_0\boldsymbol{i}$ (to the right)

Therefore the current is $\boxed{\text{to the right}}$ in the resistor

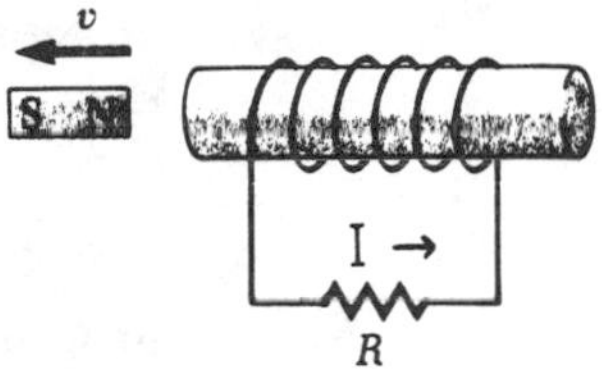

a

(b) $\boldsymbol{B}_{ext} = B_{ext}(+\boldsymbol{i})$; increases; therefore the induced field $\boldsymbol{B}_0 = B_0(-\boldsymbol{i})$ is to the left, and the current goes $\boxed{\text{to the right}}$ in the resistor.

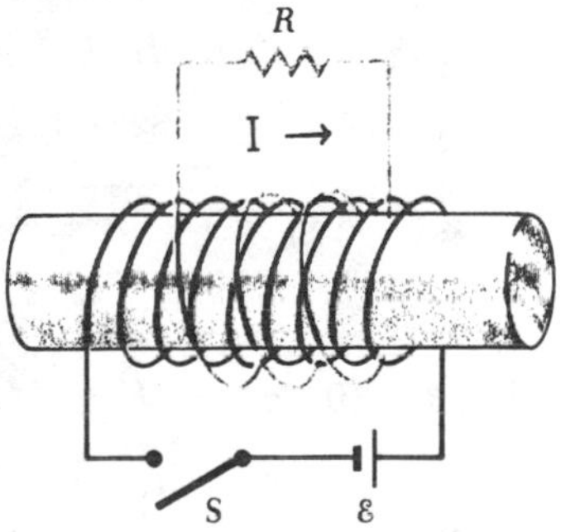

b

(c) $\boldsymbol{B}_{ext} = B_{ext}(-\boldsymbol{j})$ into the paper and B_{ext} decreases;

therefore the induced field is
$\boldsymbol{B}_0 = B_0(-\boldsymbol{j})$ into the paper.

Therefore the current is $\boxed{\text{to the right}}$ in the resistor.

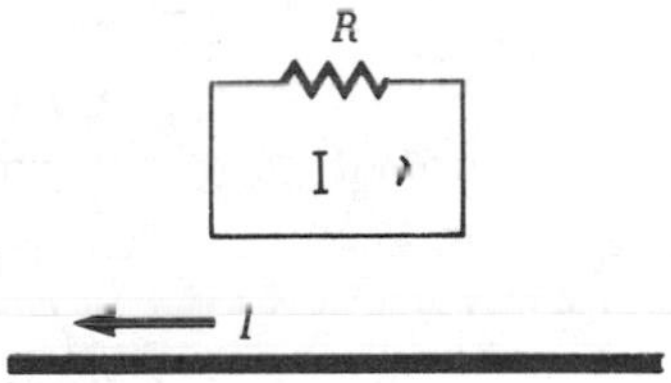

c

(d) According to the right-hand rule $\boldsymbol{F} = q\boldsymbol{v} \times \boldsymbol{B}$; $B_{ext} = B_{ext}(-\boldsymbol{j})$

$\boxed{\text{into the paper}}$

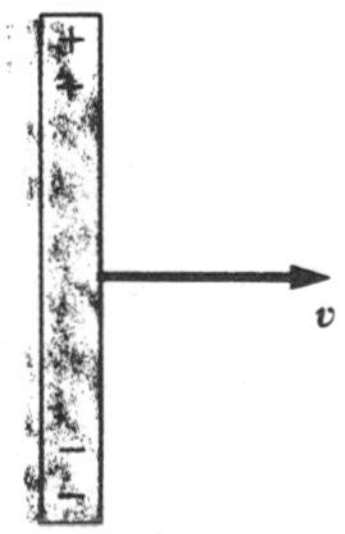

d

31.27

31.28 (a) $F_{\text{magnetic}} = ILB = mg$

$$IR = BLv$$

$$v = \frac{mgR}{B^2L^2} = \frac{mgR}{B^2w^2}$$

(b) The EMF is directly proportional to v, but the current is inversely proportional to R. A large R means a small current at a given speed, so the loop must travel faster to get F_{mag} = weight.

(c) At a given speed, the current is directly proportional to the magnetic field. But the force is proportional to the product of the current and the field. For a small B, the speed must increase to compensate for both the small B and also the current, so $v \propto B^{-2}$.

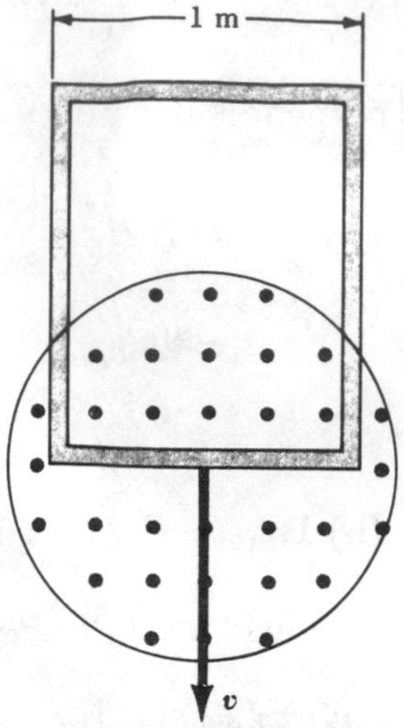

31.28 and 31.29

31.29 $mg = F = I\ell B = \dfrac{\mathcal{E}}{R}\ell B = \dfrac{B\ell v}{R}\ell B,$ $\boxed{B = 0.742\ \text{T}}$

31.30 $\mathcal{E} = -N\dfrac{d\Phi}{dt} = -N\dfrac{d(BA)}{dt}$

$$\mathcal{E} = -\frac{\mu_0 N^2 A}{L}\cdot\frac{dI}{dt}\ :\quad |\mathcal{E}| = \boxed{2.37\ \text{mV}}$$

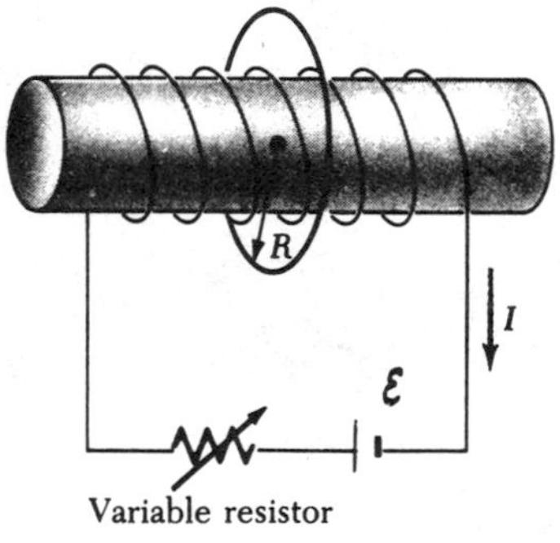

31.31 $\mathcal{E} = \dfrac{-\Delta B}{\Delta t}A = \boxed{114\ \mu\text{V}}$

31.32 $\Phi_{\text{solenoid}} = (\mu_0 n I)A$

$$\mathcal{E} = -N\frac{d\Phi}{dt} = -N\mu_0 n(\pi r^2_{\text{solenoid}})\frac{dI}{dt}$$

$$= -N\mu_0 n(\pi r^2)600\cos(120\,t) = -(15)\mu_0(10^3)n(0.02)^2 600\cos(120\,t)$$

$|\mathcal{E}| = 14.2\cos(120\,t)$ mV

31.33 $|\mathcal{E}| = \dfrac{d\Phi}{dt}$, $E = \pi r_1^2 (\dfrac{dB}{\pi r_1 dt}) = 1.8 \times 10^{-3}$ N/C,

$\boxed{\text{perpendicular to } R_1 \text{ and Counterclockwise}}$

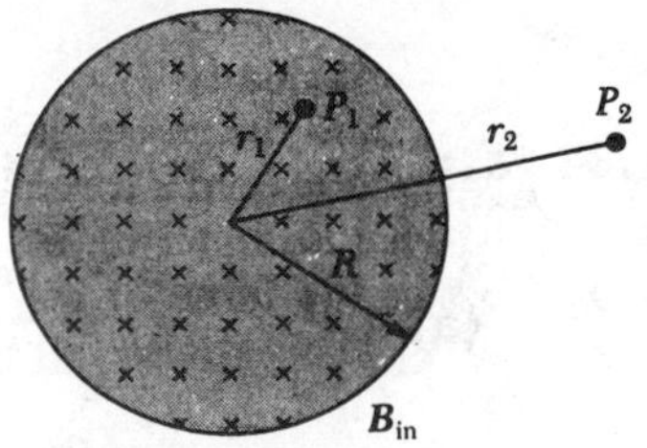

31.33 and 31.34

31.34 (a) $|\mathcal{E}| = \dfrac{d\Phi}{dt}, E = \dfrac{\pi R^2 (dB/dt)}{2\pi r_2} = \dfrac{8\pi (0.025)^2}{2\pi (0.05)}$

$F = qE = \boxed{8.00 \times 10^{-21} \text{ N}}$ Clockwise for electron

(b) When $6t^2 - 8t = 0$, $t = \boxed{1.33 \text{ s}}$

31.35 $\oint \mathbf{E} \cdot d\boldsymbol{\ell} = \dfrac{d\Phi}{dt}$

$$2\pi r E = (\pi r^2) \frac{dB}{dt}$$

$$E = \boxed{(9.87 \times 10^{-3}) \cos(100\pi t) \text{ V/m}}$$

The E field is always opposite to increasing B. $\therefore$ $\boxed{\text{clockwise}}$

31.36 $\mathcal{E} = \dfrac{d\phi}{dt} = \pi r^2 \dfrac{dB}{dt} = \oint \mathbf{E} \cdot d\boldsymbol{\ell}$

$$E(2\pi R) = \pi r^2 \frac{dB}{dt}$$

$$E = \frac{\pi r^2}{2\pi R} \frac{dB}{dt}$$

$$B = \frac{N\mu_0 I}{L}; \quad \frac{dB}{dt} = \mu_0 \frac{N}{L} \frac{dI}{dt}$$

$$I = 3e^{0.2t}; \quad \frac{dI}{dt} = 0.6e^{0.2t}$$

$$E = \frac{\pi r^2}{2\pi R} (\mu_0 \frac{N}{L})(0.6e^{0.2t})$$

$$= \frac{(0.02 \text{ m})^2}{2(0.05 \text{ m})} (4\pi \times 10^{-7} \text{N/A}^2)(1000 \text{ turns/m})(0.6)e^2$$

$$= \boxed{2.23 \times 10^{-5} \text{ N/C}}$$

31.37 $\mathcal{E} = -\frac{d(BA)}{dt} = 0.5\mu_0 nA\frac{dI}{dt} = 0.48 \times 10^{-3}$ V

(a) $I_{ring} = \frac{\mathcal{E}}{R} = \frac{0.00048}{0.0003} = \boxed{1.60\text{ A}}$

(b) $B_{ring} = \frac{\mu_0 I}{2R} = \boxed{2.01 \times 10^{-5}\text{ T}}$

(c) Coils field points downward, and is increasing, so

$\boxed{B_{ring}\text{ points upward}}$

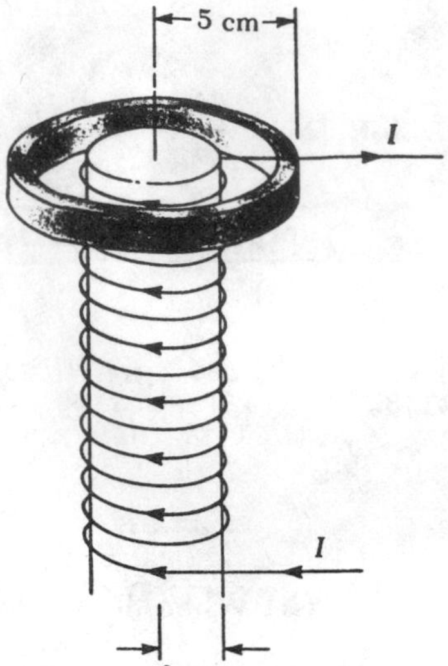

31.37

31.38 $\mathcal{E} = -N\frac{d\phi_B}{dt}$

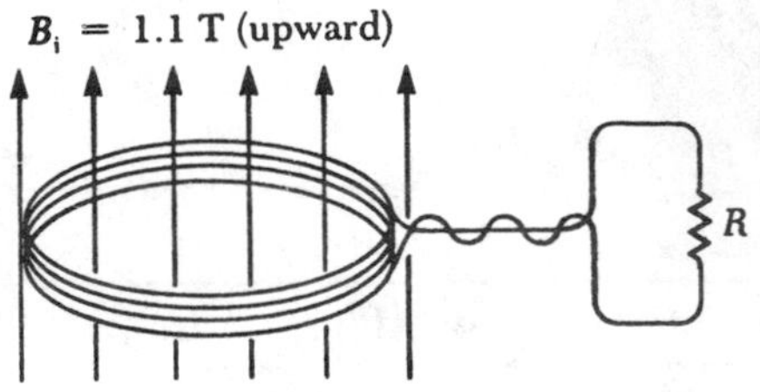

31.38

$IR = -N\frac{d\phi_B}{dt}$

$Idt = -\frac{N}{R}d\phi_B$

$\int Idt = -\frac{N}{R}\int d\phi_B$

$Q = -\frac{N}{R}\Delta\phi_B = -\frac{N}{R}A(B_f - B_i)$

$Q = -(\frac{200}{5\,\Omega})(100 \times 10^{-4}\text{ m}^2)(-1.1 - 1.1)$ T

$Q = \boxed{0.88\text{ C}}$

31.39 $\frac{d\phi}{dt} = \frac{\omega\mu_0 m_0 a^2 \cos\omega t}{2(a^2 + b^2)^{3/2}}$

$A = A_0 \sin\omega t$

$A_0 = (0.2\text{ m})^2 = 0.04\text{ m}^2$

$A = (0.04\text{ m}^2)\sin 50\pi t$

$\phi = NBA = 100(2 \times 10^{-5}\text{ T})(4 \times 10^{-2}\text{ m}^2)\sin 50\pi t$

$= (8 \times 10^{-5}\text{ T}\cdot\text{m}^2)\sin 50\pi t$

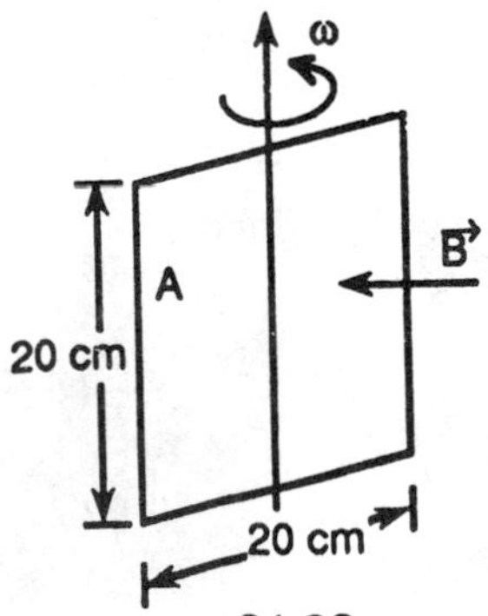

31.39

$|\mathcal{E}| = \frac{d\phi}{dt} = 50\pi(8 \times 10^{-5}\text{ V})\cos 50\pi t = (4\pi \times 10^{-3}\text{ V})\cos 50\pi t$

$|\mathcal{E}|_{max} = 4\pi \times 10^{-3}\text{ V} = \boxed{12.6\text{ mV}}$

31.40 $\omega = \dfrac{\mathcal{E}_{\max}}{NBA} = \boxed{7.07 \text{ rad/s}}$

31.41 (a) $\mathcal{E}_{\max} = NAB\omega = (10^3)(0.1)(0.2)(120\pi) = \boxed{7540 \text{ V}}$

(b) $\mathcal{E}(t) = -NBA\omega \cdot \sin \omega t = -NBA\omega \sin \theta$

$|\mathcal{E}|$ is max when $|\sin \theta| = 1$, or $\theta = \pm\dfrac{\pi}{2}$, so the

$\boxed{\text{plane of loop is parallel to } \mathbf{B}}$

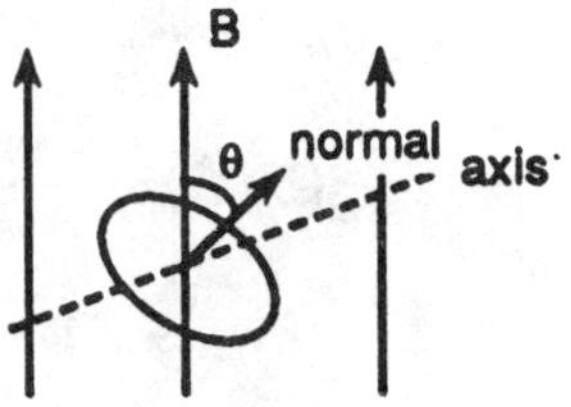

31.41

31.42 $\mathcal{E} = NBA\omega$

$$N = \frac{\mathcal{E}}{BA\omega} = \frac{90.4 \text{ V}}{(0.1 \text{ T})(0.1 \text{ m})(0.2 \text{ m})(2\pi)(60 \text{ Hz})} = \boxed{12.0 \text{ turns}}$$

31.43 $B = \mu_0 nI = (4\pi \times 10^{-7} \text{ T} \cdot \text{m/A})(200 \text{ m}^{-1})(15 \text{ A})$

$= 3.77 \times 10^{-3} \text{ T}$

For the small solenoid $A = A_0 \cos \omega t$

$A_0 = \pi R^2 = \pi(0.08 \text{ m})^2 = 2.011 \times 10^{-2} \text{ m}^2$

$A = (2.011 \times 10^{-2} \text{ m}^2) \cos 4\pi t$

$\phi = NBA = 30(3.77 \times 10^{-3} \text{ T})(2.011 \times 10^{-2} \text{ m}^2) \cos 4\pi t$

$= (2.274 \times 10^{-3} \text{ Wb}) \cos 4\pi t$

$\dfrac{d\phi}{dt} = 4\pi(2.274 \times 10^{-3} \text{ V}) \sin 4\pi t$

$= (2.858 \times 10^{-2} \text{ V}) \sin 4\pi t = \boxed{(28.6 \text{ mV}) \sin 4\pi t}$

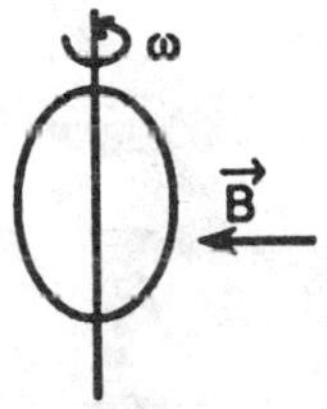

31.43

***31.44** (a) $\Phi_m = BA\cos\theta = BA\cos\omega t$

$$= (0.80\text{ T})(0.01\text{ m}^2)\cos 2\pi(60)t$$

$$\Phi_m = \boxed{0.008\ \cos(377t)\ \text{T}\cdot\text{m}^2}$$

(b) $\mathcal{E} = -\dfrac{d\Phi_m}{dt} = \boxed{3.02\sin(377t)\text{ V}}$

(c) $I = \mathcal{E}R = \boxed{3.02\sin(377t)\text{ A}}$

(d) $P = I^2R = \boxed{9.10\sin^2(377t)\text{ W}}$

(e) $P = Fv = \tau\omega$

$$\tau = \frac{P}{\omega} = \boxed{0.024\sin^2(377t)\text{ N}\cdot\text{m}}$$

31.45 (a) $F = NI\ell B$

$$\tau_{max} = 2Fr = NI\ell wB = \boxed{0.640\text{ N}\cdot\text{m}}$$

(b) $P = \tau\omega = (0.640\text{ N}\cdot\text{m})(120\pi\text{ rad/s})$

$$P_{max} = \boxed{241\text{ W}}\ (\text{about } \tfrac{1}{3}\text{ H. P. })$$

31.46 (a) $\mathcal{E}_{max} = BA\omega = (1.3\text{ T})(\frac{1}{2})(\pi)(0.25\text{ m})^2(120\text{ rev})(2\pi\frac{\text{rad}}{\text{rev}})(\frac{1}{60\text{ s}}) = 1.60\text{ V}$

(b) $\mathcal{E}_{avg} = \displaystyle\int_0^{2\pi}(\frac{\mathcal{E}}{2\pi})d\theta = \frac{BA\omega}{2\pi}\int_{\pi/2}^{3\pi/2}\sin\theta d\theta = 0$

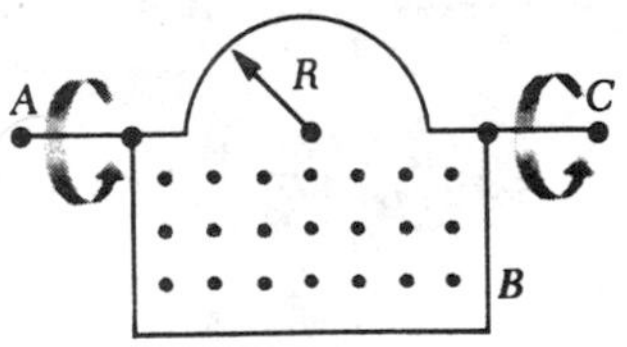

31.46

(c) The maximum and average $\mathcal{E}$ would remain unchanged.

(d)

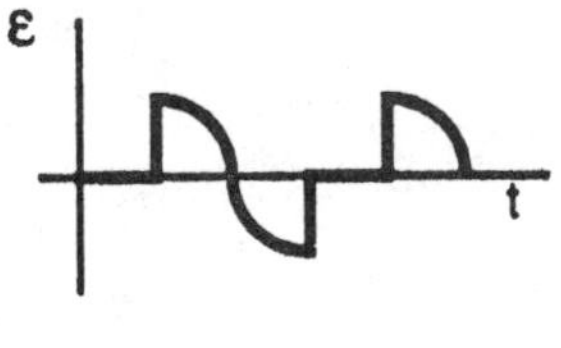

31.47 $\tau = (2F_1)(r\cos\theta), \quad F_1 = I_1 \ell B$

$$\tau = NI_1BA\cos\theta = 50(1.5\text{ A})(B)(30\times 10^{-4}\text{ m}^2)\cos 30°$$

$$= 0.1\text{ N}\cdot\text{m}$$

$$\boxed{B = 0.513\text{ T}}$$

31.48 $\tau = 0$

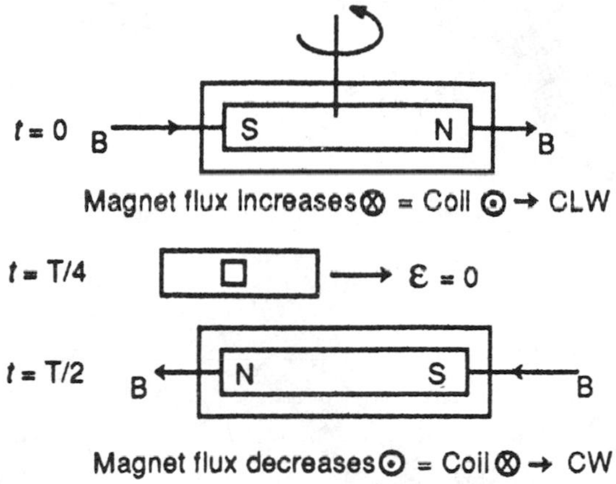

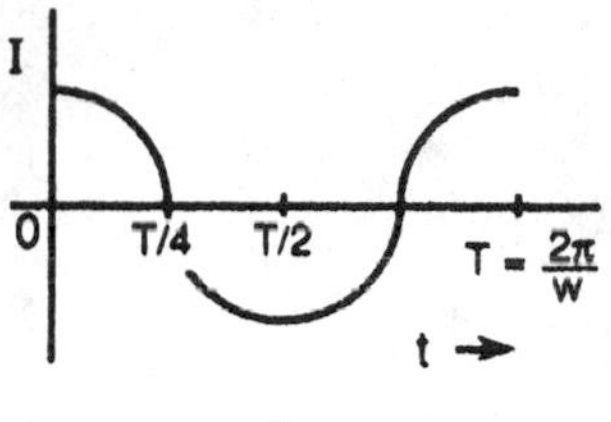

b

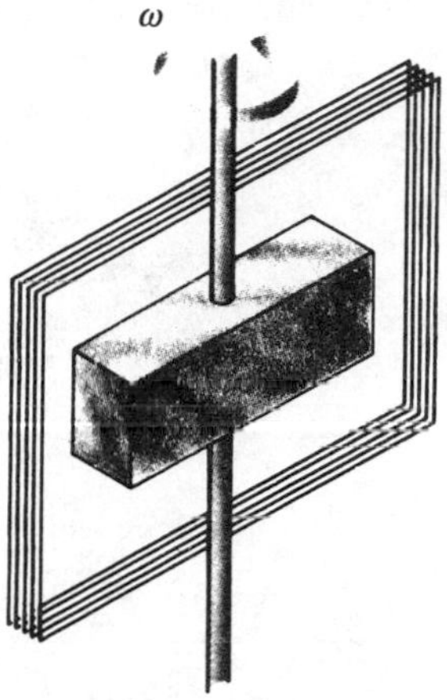

31.48

31.49 (a) $F_1 = I\ell B \quad F_N = NI\ell B$

$$\mathcal{E}_1 = -\frac{d\phi}{dt} = -\frac{d}{dt}(B\omega x) = -B\omega\frac{dx}{dt} = -Bwv$$

$$\mathcal{E}_N = -NBwv$$

$$I = \frac{\mathcal{E}_N}{R} = -\frac{NBwv}{R}$$

$$F = -N\left(\frac{NBwv}{R}\right)wB = \boxed{\frac{N^2B^2w^2v}{R}, \text{ to the left}}$$

(b) Inside the B field, $\Phi = NBA =$ constant, so $\mathcal{E} = 0$,

$I = 0$, and $F = \boxed{0}$

(c) As it leaves the field the flux *decreases* at the rate

Bwv, so the same current appears, but now CW, so

$$F = \boxed{\frac{N^2B^2w^2v}{R}, \text{ to the left again}}$$

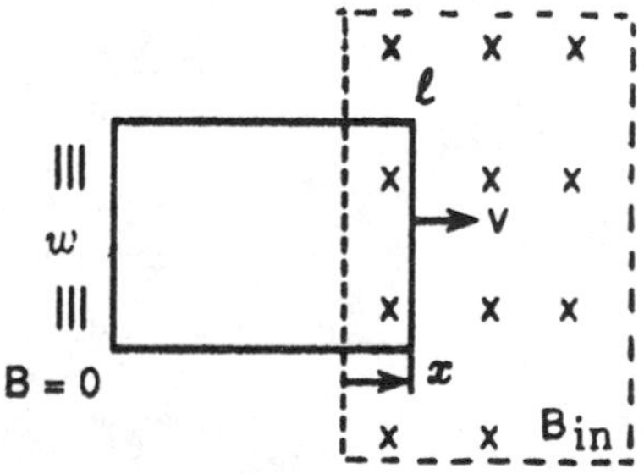

31.49

31.50 $\Phi = BA\cos\theta \qquad \frac{d\Phi}{dt} = -\omega BA\sin\theta;$

$I \propto -\sin\theta$

$\tau \propto IB\sin\theta \propto -\sin^2\theta$

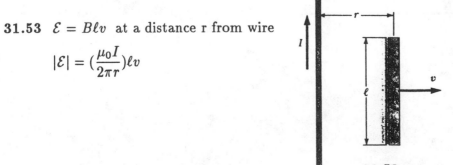

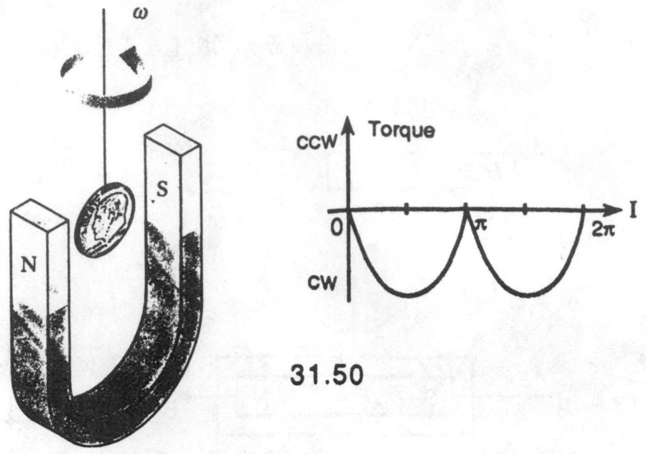

31.50

31.51 $\boldsymbol{F} = m\boldsymbol{a} = q\boldsymbol{E} + q\boldsymbol{v}\times\boldsymbol{B}$

$\boldsymbol{a} = \frac{e}{m}[\boldsymbol{E} + \boldsymbol{v}\times\boldsymbol{B}]$ where

$$\boldsymbol{v}\times\boldsymbol{B} = \begin{vmatrix} \boldsymbol{i} & \boldsymbol{j} & \boldsymbol{k} \\ 200 & 0 & 0 \\ 0.2 & 0.3 & 0.4 \end{vmatrix} = -200(0.4)\boldsymbol{j} + 200(0.3)\boldsymbol{k}$$

$$\boldsymbol{a} = \frac{1.6\times10^{-19}}{1.67\times10^{-27}}[50\boldsymbol{j} - 80\boldsymbol{j} + 60\boldsymbol{k}] = 9.58\times10^{7}[-30\boldsymbol{j} + 60\boldsymbol{k}]$$

$$\boldsymbol{a} = 2.87\times10^{9}[-\boldsymbol{j} + 2\boldsymbol{k}]\ \text{m/s}^2 = \boxed{(-2.87\times10^{9}\boldsymbol{j} + 5.75\times10^{9}\boldsymbol{k})\ \text{m/s}^2}$$

31.52 $\boldsymbol{F} = m\boldsymbol{a} = q\boldsymbol{E} + q\boldsymbol{v}\times\boldsymbol{B}$ (Lorentz Force)

$\boldsymbol{a} = \frac{q}{m}[\boldsymbol{E} + \boldsymbol{v}\times\boldsymbol{B}]$ where

$$\boldsymbol{v}\times\boldsymbol{B} = \begin{vmatrix} \boldsymbol{i} & \boldsymbol{j} & \boldsymbol{k} \\ 10 & 0 & 0 \\ 0 & 0 & 0.4 \end{vmatrix} = -4\boldsymbol{j}$$

$$\boldsymbol{a} = -\frac{1.6\times10^{-19}}{9.1\times10^{-31}}[2.5\boldsymbol{i} + 5.0\boldsymbol{j} - 4\boldsymbol{j}] = \frac{-1.6\times10^{-19}}{9.1\times10^{-31}}[2.5\boldsymbol{i} + 1.0\boldsymbol{j}]$$

$$\boldsymbol{a} = \boxed{(-4.40\times10^{11}\boldsymbol{i} - 1.76\times10^{11}\boldsymbol{j})\ \text{m/s}^2}$$

Thus, $|\boldsymbol{a}| = 4.74\times10^{11}\ \text{m/s}^2$ and is at an angle of 201.8° with the $+x$ axis.

31.53 $\mathcal{E} = B\ell v$ at a distance r from wire

$|\mathcal{E}| = (\frac{\mu_0 I}{2\pi r})\ell v$

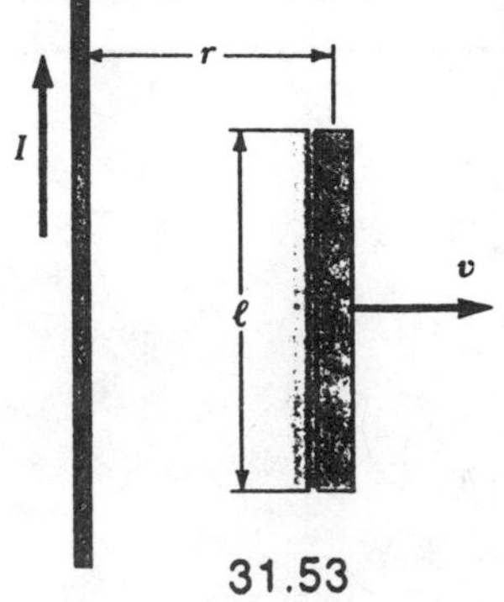

31.53

***31.54** (a) $\Phi_m = BA\cos\theta = (0.2 + 0.32t)\pi r^2$ At $t = 0$

$$\Phi_m = \boxed{1.57 \times 10^{-3}\ \mathrm{T \cdot m^2}}$$

(b) $\mathcal{E} = -\dfrac{d\Phi}{dt} = -b(\pi r^2) = \boxed{-2.51\ \mathrm{mV}}$

(c) $I = \dfrac{\mathcal{E}}{R} = \boxed{-2.09\ \mathrm{mA}}$

(d) $P = I^2 R = \boxed{5.26\ \mu\mathrm{W}}$

31.55 (a) $\dfrac{dW}{dt} = I\mathcal{E} = IN\dfrac{d}{dt}(B \cdot A) = INA\dfrac{dB}{dt}$

But $H = nI = \dfrac{NI}{\ell}$

$$\frac{dW}{dt} = \frac{\ell H}{N} NA\frac{dB}{dt} = \boxed{HA\ell\frac{dB}{dt}}$$

(b) $W = \displaystyle\int HA\ell\frac{dB}{dt}dt = A\ell\int H\,dB$

The integral corresponds to the area under the B vs H

curve in one complete hysteresis cycle.

***31.56** $\mathcal{E} = -\dfrac{d}{dt}(NBA) = -1\dfrac{dB}{dt}\pi a^2 = \pi a^2 k$

(a) $Q = C\mathcal{E} = \boxed{C\pi a^2 k}$

(b) **B** into the paper is decreasing therefore current will attempt to counteract this. Positive charge will go to upper plate.

(c) The changing magntic field through the enclosed area induces an electric field, surrounding the B-field, and this pushes on charges in the wire.

31.57 (a) $\mathcal{E}_{\max} = NAB\omega = \boxed{36.0 \text{ V}}$

(b) $\dfrac{\mathcal{E}_{\max}}{N} = \dfrac{d\Phi}{dt} = \boxed{0.60 \text{ Wb/s}}$

(c) $\mathcal{E}_{0.05} = NAB\omega \sin \omega t = \boxed{35.9 \text{ V}}$

(d) $\tau_{\max} = NI\ell Bw = \boxed{4.32 \text{ N}\cdot\text{m}}$

***31.58** $I = \dfrac{\mathcal{E} + \mathcal{E}_{\text{induced}}}{R}$ and $\mathcal{E}_{\text{induced}} = -\dfrac{d}{dt}(BA)$

$$F = m\frac{dv}{dt} = IBd$$

The acceleration of the wire is

$$\frac{dv}{dt} = \frac{IBd}{m} = \frac{Bd}{mR}(\mathcal{E} + \mathcal{E}_{\text{induced}})$$

$$\frac{dv}{dt} = \frac{Bd}{mR}(\mathcal{E} - Bvd)$$

To solve this differential equation, let $u = (\mathcal{E} - Bvd)$

then, $\dfrac{du}{dt} = -Bd\dfrac{dv}{dt}$

$$-\frac{1}{Bd}\frac{du}{dt} = \frac{Bd}{mR}u$$

$$\int_{u}^{u_0} \frac{du}{u} = -\int_{t=0}^{t} \frac{(Bd)^2}{mR}dt$$

Integrating from $t = 0$ to $t = t$,

$$ln\frac{u}{u_0} = -\frac{(Bd)^2}{mR}t$$

$$\frac{u}{u_0} = e^{-B^2d^2t/mR}$$

Since $v = 0$ when $t = 0$, $u_0 = \mathcal{E}$ and $u = \mathcal{E} - Bvd$.

$\therefore\ \mathcal{E} - Bvd = \mathcal{E}e^{B^2d^2t/mR}$

and $v = \dfrac{\mathcal{E}}{Bd}(1 - e^{-B^2d^2t/mR})$

31.59 (a) $\mathcal{E} = -N\frac{d\Phi}{dt} = -NA\frac{dB}{dt} = -NA\frac{d}{dt}(\mu_0 nI)$

where $A =$ radius of coil, $N =$ number of turns in coil, and

$n =$ number of turns per unit length in solenoid. Therefore

$$\mathcal{E} = N\mu_0 An\frac{d}{dt}[4\sin(120\pi t)] = N\mu_0 An(480\pi)\cos(120\pi t)$$

$$\mathcal{E} = 40(4\pi \times 10^{-7}\ \text{H/m})[\pi(0.05\ \text{m})^2](2 \times 10^3)(480\pi)\cos(120\pi t)$$

$$\mathcal{E} = \boxed{1.19\cos(120\pi t)}$$

(b) $P_{av} = \frac{\mathcal{E}^2_{av}}{R} = \frac{[(1.19\ \text{V})\cos(120\pi t)]^2_{av}}{8\ \Omega} = \boxed{88.5\ \text{mW}}$

***31.60**
$$\mathcal{E} = -N\frac{d}{dt}(BA)\cos\theta$$
$$= -N\frac{\Delta B}{\Delta t}A\cos 62°$$
$$= -(200)\frac{(50 \times 10^{-6}\ \text{T})}{(1.8\ \text{s})}(39 \times 10^{-4}\ \text{m}^2)\cos 62°$$
$$\mathcal{E} = \boxed{-10.2\ \mu\text{V}}$$

***31.61** (a) For maximum induced emf, with positive charge at the top of the antenna, $\mathbf{F}_+ = q_+(\mathbf{v} \times \mathbf{B})$, so the auto must move east.

(b) $\mathcal{E} = B\ell v = (5 \times 10^{-5}\ \text{T})(1.2\ \text{m})\left(\frac{65 \times 10^3\ \text{m}}{3600\ \text{s}}\right)\cos 65°$

$$\mathcal{E} = \boxed{4.58 \times 10^{-4}\ \text{V}}$$

31.62 (a) $\mathcal{E} = -\frac{d\phi}{dt} = -\frac{d}{dt}\int \mathbf{B}\cdot d\mathbf{A}$

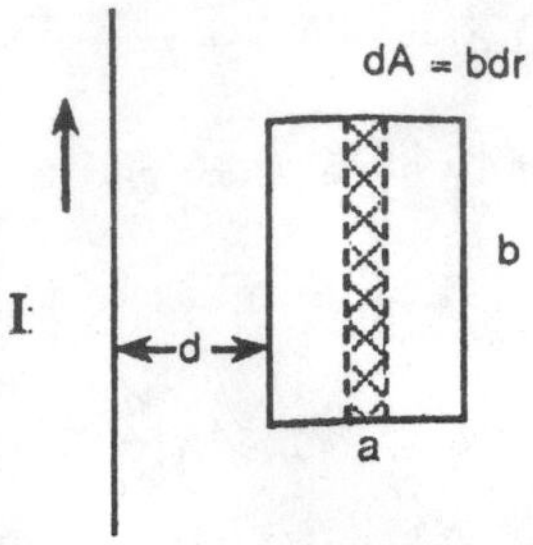

31.62

$$B = \frac{\mu_0 I}{2\pi r}; \quad I = I_0 e^{-t/\tau}; \quad \frac{dI}{dt} = -\frac{I_0}{\tau}e^{-t/\tau}$$

$$\mathcal{E} = -\frac{d}{dt}\int_d^{d+a} \frac{\mu_0 I}{2\pi r}(bdr)$$

$$= -\frac{d}{dt}\left[\frac{\mu_0 I b}{2\pi}\ln\left(\frac{d+a}{d}\right)\right]$$

$$= -\frac{\mu_0 b}{2\pi}\ln\left(1+\frac{a}{d}\right)\frac{dI}{dt}$$

$$\boxed{\mathcal{E} = \frac{\mu_0 b I}{2\pi\tau}\ln\left(1+\frac{a}{d}\right)}$$

(b) $$\mathcal{E} = \frac{\mu_0 b I_0 e^{-t/\tau}}{2\pi\tau}\ln\left(1+\frac{a}{d}\right)$$

$$= \frac{4\pi\times10^{-7}\ \text{N/A}^2(0.15\ \text{m})(10\ \text{A})e^{-5/5}}{2\pi(5\ \text{s})}\ell n\left(1+\frac{6}{3}\right)$$

$$= \boxed{2.42\times10^{-8}\ \text{V}}\ \text{Clockwise.}$$

31.63 Find an expression for the flux through a rectangular area "swept out" by the bar in time t. The magnetic field at a distance x from wire is

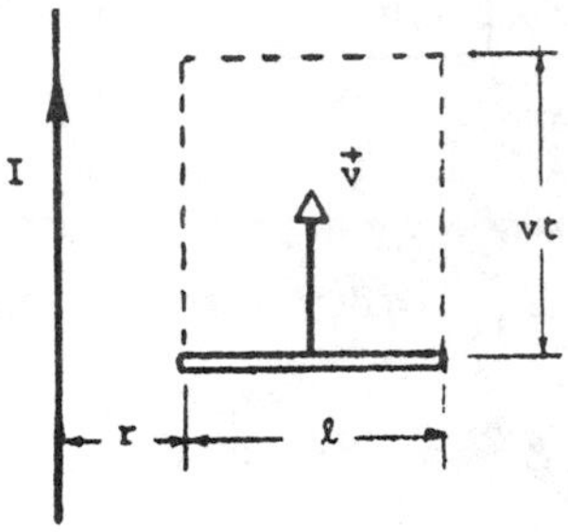

31.63

$B = \frac{\mu_0 I}{2\pi x}$ and $\Phi = \int BdA$. Therefore

$$\Phi = \frac{\mu_0 I vt}{2\pi}\int_r^{r+\ell}\frac{dx}{x}$$

where vt is the distance the bar has moved in time t. Then

$$|\mathcal{E}| = \frac{d\Phi}{dt} = \frac{\mu_0 I v}{2\pi}\ln\left(1+\frac{\ell}{r}\right)$$

31.64 The magnetic field at a distance x from a long wire is $B = \dfrac{\mu_0 I}{2\pi x}$. Find an expression for the flux through the loop.

$$d\Phi = \frac{\mu_0 I}{2\pi x}(\ell dx)$$

$$\Phi = \frac{\mu_0 I \ell}{2\pi}\int_r^{r+w} \frac{dx}{x}$$

$$\Phi = \frac{\mu_0 I \ell}{2\pi}\ln\left(1+\frac{w}{r}\right)$$

$$\mathcal{E} = -\frac{d\Phi}{dt} = \frac{\mu_0 I \ell v}{2\pi r}\,\frac{w}{(r+w)}$$

$$I = \frac{\mathcal{E}}{R} = \boxed{\frac{\mu_0 I \ell v}{2\pi R r}\,\frac{w}{(r+w)}}$$

31.65 $I = \dfrac{\mathcal{E}}{R} = \dfrac{B\,\Delta A}{R\,\Delta t}$

$$q = I\Delta t = \frac{(15\ \mu T)(0.2\ \text{m})^2}{0.5\ \Omega} = \boxed{1.20\ \mu\text{C}}$$

31.66 (a) $I = \dfrac{dq}{dt} = \dfrac{\mathcal{E}}{R}$ where $\mathcal{E} = -N\dfrac{d\Phi}{dt}$ so

$$\int dq = -\frac{N}{R}\int_{\Phi_1}^{\Phi_2} d\Phi \quad \text{and}$$

the charge through the circuit will be

$$|Q| = \frac{N}{R}(\Phi_2 - \Phi_1)$$

(b) $q = \dfrac{N}{R}[BA\cos 0 - BA\cos(\frac{\pi}{2})] = \dfrac{BAN}{R}$ so

$$B = \frac{Rq}{NA} = \frac{(200\ \Omega)(5\times 10^{-4}\ \text{C})}{(100)(40\times 10^{-4}\ \text{m}^2)} = \boxed{0.250\ \text{T}}$$

***31.67** $\Phi_m = (6t^3 - 18t^2)\ \mathrm{T\cdot m^2}$

$$\mathcal{E} = -\frac{d\Phi_m}{dt} = -18t^2 + 36t$$

Maximum $\mathcal{E}$ at $\dfrac{d\mathcal{E}}{dt} = -36t + 36 = 0,$ at $t = 1$ s.

$\therefore$ Maximum current $I = \dfrac{\mathcal{E}}{R} = \dfrac{(-18 + 36)\ \mathrm{V}}{3\ \Omega} = \boxed{6.0\ \mathrm{A}}$

(at $t = 1$ s)

31.68 For the suspended mass, M : $\Sigma F = Mg - T = Ma$

For the sliding bar, $m : \Sigma F = T - I\ell B = ma$: where

$$I = \frac{\mathcal{E}}{R} = \frac{B\ell v}{R}$$

$$Mg - \frac{B^2\ell^2 v}{R} = (m + M)a$$

$$a = \frac{dv}{dt} = \frac{Mg}{m + M} - \frac{B^2\ell^2 v}{R(M + m)} \quad \text{or}$$

$$\int_0^v \frac{dv}{(\alpha - \beta v)} = \int_0^t dt :$$

where $\alpha = \dfrac{Mg}{M + m}$ and $\beta = \dfrac{B^2\ell^2}{R(M + m)}$.

Therefore the velocity varies with time according to

$$v = \frac{\alpha}{\beta}(1 - e^{-\beta t}) = \boxed{\frac{mgR}{B^2\ell^2}[1 - e^{-B^2\ell^2 t/R(M+m)}]}$$

***31.69** (a) $\mathcal{E} = B\ell v = 0.36\ \mathrm{V}$

$$I = \frac{\mathcal{E}}{R} = \boxed{0.900\ \mathrm{A}}$$

(b) $F = I\ell B = \boxed{0.108\ \mathrm{N}}$

(c) Since the magnetic flux $B \cdot A$ is in effect decreasing, the induced current flow through R is from b to a. $\underline{b}$ is at higher potential.

(d) No.

31.70 Loop 1 on the left (B_{in});

$$\mathcal{E} = \frac{d\Phi}{dt} = A\frac{dB}{dt} = \pi(0.1\text{ m})^2(100\text{ T/s}) = \pi\text{ V};$$

and $-6I_1 - 3I_3 - \pi = 0$

Loop 2 on the right (B_{out});

$$\mathcal{E} = \frac{d\Phi}{dt} = \pi(0.15\text{ m})^2(100\text{ T/s}) = 2.25\pi\text{ V}$$

and $3I_3 + 5I_2 + 2.25\pi = 0$

From the junction rule: $I_1 + I_2 = I_3$

Solving these three simultaneous equations yields

$\boxed{I_1 = -0.062\text{ A},\ I_2 = -0.860\text{ A},\ I_3 = -0.922\text{ A}}$

***31.71** (a) $\boxed{\text{counterclockwise}}$

(b) $\boxed{\dfrac{k\pi r^2}{R}}$

(c) $\boxed{\text{There is no single-valued potential function}}$

(d) The changing magnetic field within the loop induces an electric field in the circumference.

***31.72**

$$\mathcal{E} = B(y)\ell v(t) \qquad \text{In SI units, } v = 9.8t;\ \ y = 0.8 - 4.9t^2$$

$$\mathcal{E} = \frac{\mu_0 I}{2\pi y}\ell(9.8t)$$

$$\mathcal{E} = \frac{(4\pi \times 10^{-7})(200)(0.3)(9.8)t}{2\pi(0.8 - 4.9t^2)}$$

$$\mathcal{E}(\text{at } t = 0.3\text{ s}) = \boxed{9.83 \times 10^{-5}\text{ V}}$$

***31.73** (a)

$$d\Phi = B \cdot dA = \frac{\mu_0 I}{2\pi x}\, L dx$$

$$\Phi = \int_{x=h}^{h+w} \frac{\mu_0 I L}{2\pi x} dx = \frac{\mu_0 I L}{2\pi} \ln\left(\frac{h+w}{h}\right)$$

(b)

$$\mathcal{E} = -\frac{d\Phi}{dt} = -\frac{d}{dt}\left[\frac{\mu_0 I L}{2\pi} \ln\left(\frac{h+w}{h}\right)\right]$$

$$= -\frac{\mu_0}{2\pi}(10\ \text{A/s}) \ln\left(\frac{h+w}{h}\right)$$

$$\mathcal{E} = \frac{-4\pi\times 10^{-7}}{2\pi}(1)(10)\ln\left(\frac{11}{1}\right) = \boxed{-4.8\times 10^{-6}\ \text{V}}$$

CHAPTER 32

32.1 $|\mathcal{E}| = +L\frac{dI}{dt} = (2\text{ H})\left(\frac{0.5\text{ A}}{0.01\text{ s}}\right) = \boxed{100\text{ V}}$

32.2 $L = \frac{\mu_0 N^2 A}{\ell} \longrightarrow N = \sqrt{\frac{L\ell}{\mu_0 A}} = \boxed{199\text{ turns}}$

32.3 $L = \frac{\mu_0 N^2 A}{\ell} = \boxed{4.69\text{ mH}}$

32.4 $L = \mu_0 n^2 A\ell \longrightarrow n = \sqrt{\frac{L}{\mu_0 A\ell}} = \boxed{7800\text{ turns/m}}$

32.5 $[L] = \left[\frac{N\Phi_m}{I}\right] = \frac{\text{T}\cdot\text{m}^2}{\text{A}} = \frac{\frac{\text{N}}{\text{C}\cdot\text{m/s}}\cdot\text{m}^2}{\text{C/s}} = \frac{\text{N}\cdot\text{m}}{(\text{C/s})^2}$

$[L] = \left[\frac{\mathcal{E}}{dI/dt}\right] = \frac{\text{V}}{\text{A/s}} = \frac{\text{N}\cdot\text{m/C}}{(\text{C/s})/\text{s}} = \frac{\text{N}\cdot\text{m}}{(\text{C/s})^2}$

32.6 $L = \frac{N\Phi}{I} \longrightarrow \Phi = \frac{LI}{N} = \boxed{2.4\times 10^{-7}\text{ Wb}}$ (through each turn)

32.7 (a) $B = \mu_0 nI = \mu_0\left(\frac{450}{0.12\text{ m}}\right)(0.040\text{ rmA}) = \boxed{1.88\times 10^{-4}\text{ T}}$

(b) $\Phi = BA = \boxed{3.33\times 10^{-8}\text{ Wb}}$

(c) $L = \frac{N\Phi}{I} = \boxed{0.375\text{ mH}}$

(d) $\boxed{B \text{ and } \Phi \text{ are proportional to current; } L \text{ is independent of current}}$

32.8 $L = \mu_0 \frac{N^2 A}{\ell}$: $A = \pi r^2 = \pi (\frac{\ell}{8})^2$

$$L = \frac{\mu_0 N^2 \pi \ell^2}{64 \ell} = \frac{\mu_0 n^2 \ell^3 \pi}{64}$$

$$\ell^3 = \frac{64L}{\pi \mu_0 n^2} \longrightarrow \ell = \boxed{0.109 \text{ m}}$$

32.9 $|\mathcal{E}| = L\frac{dI}{dt} \longrightarrow L = \frac{0.036 \text{ V}}{12 \text{ A/s}} = 3 \text{ mH}$

The flux through each loop is: $\Phi = \frac{LI}{N} = \frac{(0.003 \text{ H})(2.8 \text{ A})}{400} = \boxed{21.0 \ \mu\text{Wb}}$

***32.10** $|\mathcal{E}| = L\frac{dI}{dt} = 0.09\frac{d}{dt}(t^2 - 6t) \text{ V}$

(a) At $t = 1$ s, $\mathcal{E} = \boxed{360 \text{ mV}}$

(b) At $t = 4$ s, $\mathcal{E} = \boxed{180 \text{ mV}}$

(c) $\mathcal{E} = 0.09(2t - 6) = 0$ when $\boxed{t = 3 \text{ s}}$

32.11 $\mathcal{E}_{\text{back}} = -\mathcal{E} = L\frac{dI}{dt} = L\frac{d}{dt}(I_0 \sin \omega t)$

$$= L\omega I_0 \cos \omega t = (0.01)(120\pi)(5) \cos \omega t$$

$$= (6.0\pi) \cos(120\pi t) = \boxed{(18.8 \text{ V}) \cos(377\ t)}$$

32.12 $L = \frac{\mu_0 N^2 A}{\ell} = \frac{\mu_0 \pi (0.01)^2}{0.05} N^2 = 7.90 \times 10^{-9} N^2$

$$\left.\begin{array}{l} L_1 = 7.11 \times 10^{-4} \text{ H} \\ L_2 - 3.16 \times 10^{-4} \text{ H} \\ L_3 = 7.90 \times 10^{-5} \text{ H} \end{array}\right\} L_{\text{tot}} = \boxed{1.1 \times 10^{-3} \text{ H}}$$

32.13 Twice as many turns $\Longrightarrow \ell_A = 2\ell_B$

$$\Longrightarrow N_A \cdot 2\pi r_A = N_B \cdot 2\pi r_B, \text{ so } \quad r_A = \frac{1}{2} r_B$$

$$\frac{L_A}{L_B} = \frac{\mu_0 n^2 A_A \ell_A}{\mu_0 n^2 A_B \ell_B} = \frac{A_A}{A_B} \cdot \frac{\ell_A}{\ell_B} = \frac{\pi r^2}{\pi r_B^2} \cdot \frac{\ell_A}{\ell_B} = (\frac{1}{2})^2(\frac{2}{1}) = \boxed{\frac{1}{2}}$$

32.14 $$L = \frac{N\Phi}{I} = \frac{NBA}{I} \cong \frac{NA}{I} \cdot \frac{\mu_0 NI}{2\pi R} = \frac{1}{2\pi}\mu_0 N^2 (\frac{A}{R})$$

32.15 (a) $$L = \frac{\mu_0 N^2 A}{\ell} = \frac{\mu_0 (120)^2 \pi (5 \times 10^{-3})^2}{0.09} = \boxed{1.58 \times 10^{-5} \text{ H}}$$

(b) $$\Phi' = \frac{\mu}{\mu_0}\Phi_0 \longrightarrow L = \frac{\mu N^2 A}{\ell} = 800(1.58 \times 10^{-5} \text{ H}) = \boxed{1.26 \times 10^{-2} \text{ H}}$$

32.16 $$L = \frac{\mu_0 N^2 A}{\ell} = \frac{\mu_0 (420)^2 (3 \times 10^{-4})}{0.16} = 4.16 \times 10^{-4} \text{ H}$$

$$\mathcal{E} = -L\frac{dI}{dt} \longrightarrow \frac{dI}{dt} = \frac{-\mathcal{E}}{L} = \frac{-175 \times 10^{-6} \text{ V}}{4.16 \times 10^{-4} \text{ H}} = \boxed{-0.421 \text{ A/s}}$$

32.17 $$I = \frac{\mathcal{E}}{R}(1 - e^{-t/\tau}); \quad \frac{dI}{dt} = \frac{\mathcal{E}}{R}(e^{-t/\tau})(-\frac{1}{\tau})$$

$$\mathcal{E} - IR - L\frac{dI}{dt} = 0$$

$$\mathcal{E} - \frac{\mathcal{E}}{R}(1 - e^{-t/\tau})R - L(\frac{\mathcal{E}}{R})(e^{-t/\tau})(-\frac{1}{\tau}) = \boxed{0}$$

32.18 $$I = I_0 e^{-t/\tau}; \quad \tau = \frac{L}{R}; \quad I_0 = \frac{\mathcal{E}}{R}$$

$$\frac{dI}{dt} = I_0 e^{-t/\tau}(-\frac{1}{\tau})$$

$$IR + L\frac{dI}{dt} = 0$$

$$I_0 R e^{-t/\tau} + L(I_0 e^{-t/\tau})(-\frac{1}{\tau}) = 0$$

$$0 = 0$$

32.19 $I = I_0(1 - e^{-t/\tau})$

$$0.25 = 1 - e^{-1.5/\tau} \longrightarrow e^{-1.5/\tau} = 0.75$$

$$\tau = \frac{-1.5}{\ln(0.75)} = 5.214 \text{ s}$$

$$L = \tau R = (5.214 \text{ s})(0.5\ \Omega) = \boxed{2.61 \text{ H}}$$

32.20 $I_{\text{max}} = \dfrac{\mathcal{E}}{R} \longrightarrow R = \dfrac{\mathcal{E}}{I_{\text{max}}} = \dfrac{12 \text{ V}}{0.200 \text{ A}} = 60\ \Omega$

$$\tau = \frac{L}{R} \longrightarrow L = \tau R = (500 \times 10^{-6} \text{ s})(60\ \Omega) = \boxed{3.0 \times 10^{-2} \text{ H}}$$

32.21 $[\tau] = \dfrac{[L]}{[R]} = \dfrac{[\mathcal{E}/dI/dt]}{[V/I]} = \dfrac{\frac{\text{V}}{\text{A/s}}}{\frac{\text{V}}{\text{A}}} = \text{s}$

32.22 $I = I_0(1 - e^{-t/\tau}):\quad \dfrac{dI}{dt} = -I_0(e^{-t/\tau})(-\dfrac{1}{\tau})$

$$\frac{dI}{dt} = \frac{R}{L} I_0 e^{-t/\tau}\ ; \quad I_0 = \frac{\mathcal{E}}{R}$$

(a) $t = 0: \quad \dfrac{dI}{dt} = \dfrac{R}{L} I_0 e^0 = \dfrac{\mathcal{E}}{L} = \dfrac{100 \text{ V}}{15 \text{ H}} = \boxed{6.67 \text{ A/s}}$

(b) $t = 1.5 \text{ s}: \quad \dfrac{dI}{dt} = \dfrac{\mathcal{E}}{L} e^{-t/\tau} = (6.67 \text{ A/s}) e^{-\frac{1.5}{15/30}} = (6.67 \text{ A/s}) e^{-3} = \boxed{0.332 \text{ A/s}}$

32.23 $\tau = \dfrac{L}{R} = 0.2 \text{ s}: \quad \dfrac{I}{I_0} = 1 - e^{-t/\tau}$

(a) $0.50 = 1e^{-t/0.2} \longrightarrow t = \tau \ln 2 = \boxed{0.139 \text{ s}}$

(b) $0.90 = 1 - e^{-t/0.2} \longrightarrow t = \tau \ln 10 = \boxed{0.461 \text{ s}}$

32.24 (a) $\tau = \frac{L}{R} = 0.002\text{ s} = \boxed{2.00\text{ ms}}$

(b) $I = I_0(1 - e^{-t/\tau}) = (\frac{6\text{ V}}{4\ \Omega})[1 - e^{-\frac{0.250}{2}}] = \boxed{0.176\text{ A}}$

(c) $I_0 = \frac{\mathcal{E}}{R} = \frac{6\text{ V}}{4\ \Omega} = \boxed{1.50\text{ A}}$

(d) $0.80 = 1 - e^{-t/2\text{ ms}} \longrightarrow t = -(2\text{ ms})\ln(0.20) = \boxed{3.22\text{ ms}}$

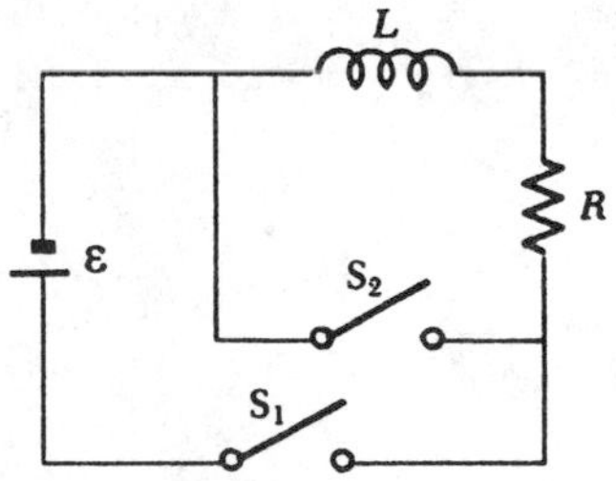

32.24

32.25 $\tau = \frac{L}{R} = \frac{0.140}{4.9} = 28.57\text{ ms};\quad ;\mathrm{I_0} = \frac{\mathcal{E}}{\mathrm{R}} = \frac{6\text{ V}}{4.9\ \Omega} = 1.224\text{ A}$

(a) $I = I_0(1 - e^{-t/\tau})$

$0.220 = 1.224(1 - e^{-t/\tau})$

$e^{-t/\tau} = 0.8203$

$t = -\tau\ln(0.8203) = \boxed{5.66\text{ ms}}$

(b) $I = I_0(1 - e^{-\frac{10}{0.0286}}) = (1.224\text{ A})(1 - e^{-350}) = \boxed{1.22\text{ A}}$

(c) $I = I_0 e^{-t/\tau}$

$0.160 = 1.224e^{-t/\tau}$

$t = -\tau\ln(0.1307) = \boxed{58.1\text{ ms}}$

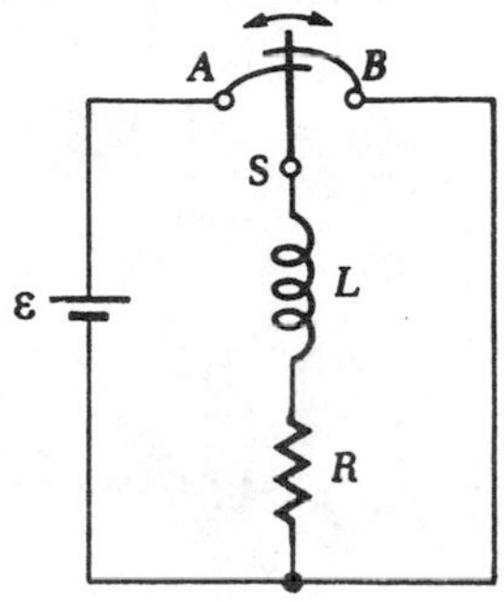

32.25

32.26 $I = I_0(1 - e^{-t/\tau})$

$0.98 = 1 - e^{-3\times10^{-3}/\tau}$

$0.02 = e^{-3\times10^{-3}/\tau}$

$\tau = -\frac{3\times10^{-3}}{\ln(0.02)} = 7.67\times10^{-4}\text{ s}$

$\tau = \frac{L}{R}$

$L = \tau R = (7.67\times10^{-4})(10) = \boxed{7.67\text{ mH}}$

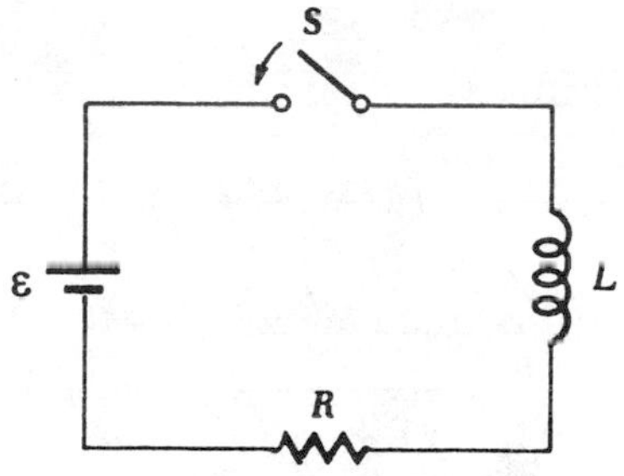

32.26 , 32.29 , 32.30 and 32.35

32.27 $\tau = \frac{L}{R} = \frac{24\text{ mH}}{10\ \Omega} = 2.4\text{ ms}\ :\quad \mathrm{I_0} = \frac{\mathcal{E}}{\mathrm{R}} = \frac{6\text{ V}}{10\ \Omega} = 0.60\text{ A}$

(a) $I = I_0(1 - e^{-t/\tau}) = (0.60\text{ A})[1 - e^{-\frac{0.5}{2.4}}] = \boxed{0.113\text{ A}}$

(b) $I_0 = \frac{\mathcal{E}}{R} = \boxed{0.600\text{ A}}$

32.28 $I = I_0 e^{-t/t}$

$$0.25 = e^{-t/2.4}$$

$$\frac{t}{2.4\text{ ms}} = \ln(0.25)$$

$$t = (-2.4\text{ ms})\ln(0.25) = \boxed{3.33\text{ ms}}$$

32.29 (a)
$$\left.\begin{aligned} V_R &= IR = (8\ \Omega)(2\text{ A}) = 16\text{ V} \\ V_L &= \mathcal{E} - V_R = 36\text{ V} - 16\text{ V} = 20\text{ V} \end{aligned}\right\} \frac{V_R}{V_L} = \frac{16}{20} = \boxed{0.800}$$

(b) $V_R = IR = (4.5\text{ A})(8\ \Omega) = 36\text{ V}$

$$V_L = \mathcal{E} - V_R = \boxed{0}$$

32.30 $I = \dfrac{\mathcal{E}}{R}(1 - e^{-t/\tau}) = \dfrac{120}{9}(1 - e^{-1.8/7}) = 3.02\text{ A}$

$$V_R = IR = (3.02)(9) = 2.72\text{ V}$$

$$V_L = \mathcal{E} - V_R = 120 - 27.2 = \boxed{92.8\text{ V}}$$

32.31 (a) $I = \dfrac{\mathcal{E}}{R} = \dfrac{12\text{ V}}{12\ \Omega} = \boxed{1.00\text{ A}}$

(b) Initial current is 1 A, so

$$V_{12} = (1\text{ A})(12\ \Omega) = \boxed{12.0\text{ V}}$$

$$V_{1200} = (1\text{ A})(1200\ \Omega) = \boxed{1.20\text{ kV}}$$

$$V_L = \boxed{1.21\text{ kV}}$$

(c) $I = I_0 e^{-Rt/L}$

$$\frac{dI}{dt} = -I_0 \frac{R}{L} e^{-Rt/L}$$

$$-L\frac{dI}{dt} = V_L = I_0 R e^{-Rt/L}$$

$$12\text{ V} = (1212\text{ V})e^{-1212t/2}$$

$$0.009901 = e^{-606t}$$

$$\boxed{t = 7.62\text{ ms}}$$

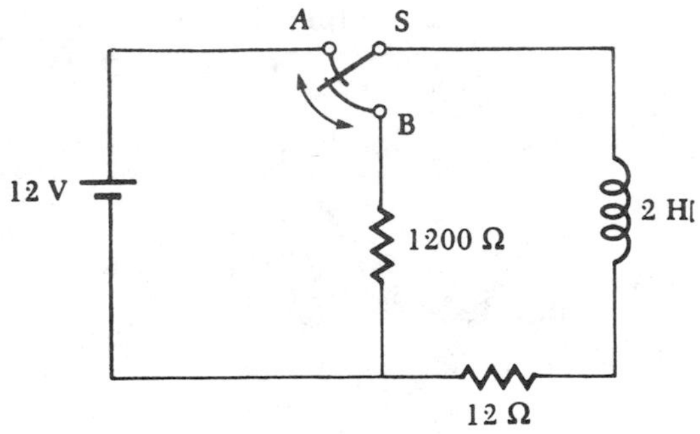

32.31

32.32 $L = \frac{N\Phi}{I} = \frac{200(3.7 \times 10^{-4})}{1.75} = 42.3 \text{ mH}$

$$U = \frac{1}{2}LI^2 = \frac{1}{2}(0.0423 \text{ H})(1.75 \text{ A})^2 = \boxed{0.0648 \text{ J}}$$

32.33 $L = \mu_0 \frac{N^2 A}{\ell} = \mu_0 \frac{(68)^2 \pi (0.6 \times 10^{-2})^2}{0.08} = 8.21\ \mu\text{H}$

$$U = \frac{1}{2}LI^2 = \frac{1}{2}(8.21 \times 10^{-6} \text{ H})(0.77 \text{ A})^2 = \boxed{2.44 \times 10^{-6} \text{ J}}$$

32.34 $I = \frac{\mathcal{E}}{R} = \frac{24 \text{ V}}{8\ \Omega} = 3 \text{ A}$

$$U = \frac{1}{2}LI^2 = \frac{1}{2}(4 \text{ H})(3 \text{ A})^2 = \boxed{18.0 \text{ J}}$$

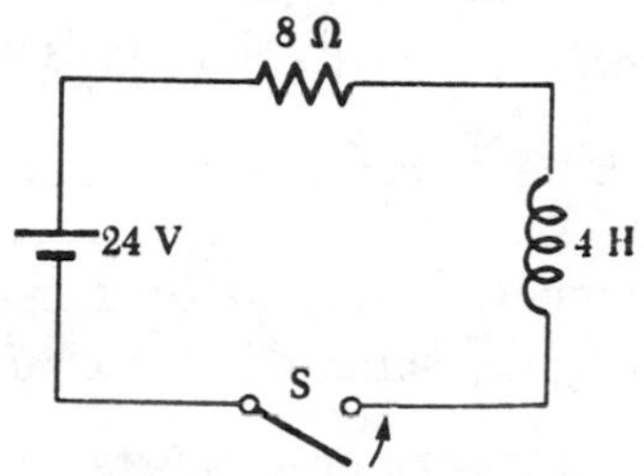

32.34 and 32.42

***32.35** From Equation 32.7,

$$I = \frac{\mathcal{E}}{R}(1 - e^{-Rt/L})$$

(a) The maximum current is reached after a long time t and is $I = \frac{\mathcal{E}}{R} = 2$ A.
At that time, the inductor is fully charged and
$P = IV = (2 \text{ A})(10 \text{ V}) = \boxed{20 \text{ W}}$

(b) $P_{\text{lost}} = I^2 R = (2 \text{ A})^2(5\ \Omega) = \boxed{20 \text{ W}}$

(c) $P_{\text{inductor}} = IV_{\text{drop}} = \boxed{0}$

(d) $E_{\text{stored}} = \frac{LI^2}{2} = \frac{(10 \text{ H})(2 \text{ A})^2}{2} = \boxed{20 \text{ J}}$

***32.36** (a) $U_L = \frac{1}{2}LI^2 = \frac{1}{2}L\left(\frac{\mathcal{E}}{2R}\right)^2 = \frac{L\mathcal{E}^2}{8R^2} = \frac{(0.80)(500)^2}{8(30)^2} = \boxed{27.8 \text{ J}}$

(b)

$$I = \left(\frac{\mathcal{E}}{R}\right)\left[1 - e^{-\left(\frac{R}{L}\right)t}\right]$$

$$\frac{\mathcal{E}}{2R} = \left(\frac{\mathcal{E}}{R}\right)\left[1 - e^{-\left(\frac{R}{L}\right)t}\right] \to e^{-\left(\frac{R}{L}\right)t} = \frac{1}{2}$$

$$\frac{R}{L}t = \ln 2 \to \quad t = \frac{L}{R}\ln 2 = \frac{0.80}{30}\ln 2 = \boxed{18.5 \text{ ms}}$$

***32.37** (a) The magnetic energy density is given by Equation 32.15,

$$u_M = B^2/2\mu_0 = (4.5 \text{ T})^2/(1.26 \times 10^{-6} \text{ T}\cdot\text{m/A}) = \boxed{8.06 \times 10^6 \text{ J/m}^3}$$

(b) The magnetic energy stored in the field equals u_M times the volume of the solenoid (the volume in which B is non-zero).

$$U_M = u_M V = (8.06 \times 10^6 \text{ J/m}^3)\{(0.26 \text{ m})\ \pi(0.031 \text{ m})^2\} = \boxed{6.32 \text{ kJ}}$$

32.38 $u_E = \epsilon_0 \frac{E^2}{2}$; $\quad u_B = \frac{B^2}{2\mu_0}$

$$\epsilon_0 \frac{E^2}{2} = \frac{B^2}{2\mu_0}$$

$$B^2 = \epsilon_0 \mu_0 E^2$$

$$B = E\sqrt{\epsilon_0 \mu_0} = \frac{6.8 \times 10^5 \text{ V/m}}{2.998 \times 10^8 \text{ m/s}} = \boxed{2.27 \times 10^{-3} \text{ T}}$$

32.39 $u_E = \epsilon_0 \frac{E^2}{2} = \boxed{4.43 \times 10^{-8} \text{ J/m}^3}$

$$u_B = \frac{B^2}{2\mu_0} = \boxed{9.95 \times 10^{-4} \text{ J/m}^3}$$

32.40 $I_0 = \frac{\mathcal{E}}{R} = \frac{15 \text{ V}}{7\ \Omega} = 2.14 \text{ A} \longrightarrow I = \frac{1}{2}I_0 = 1.07 \text{ A}$

$$U = \frac{1}{2}LI^2 = \frac{1}{2}(0.6)(1.07)^2 = \boxed{0.344 \text{ J}}$$

32.41 $U_1 = \frac{1}{2}(85 \times 10^{-6})(0.850)^2 = \boxed{30.7\ \mu\text{J}}$

$$U_2 = \frac{1}{2}(200 \times 10^{-6})(0.850)^2 = \boxed{72.2\ \mu\text{J}}$$

32.42 $I = \frac{\mathcal{E}}{R}(1 - e^{-t/\tau}) = \frac{\mathcal{E}}{R}(1 - e^{-1}) = \frac{24 \text{ V}}{8\ \Omega}(1 - \frac{1}{e}) = 1.896 \text{ A}$

(a) $U_L = \frac{1}{2}LI^2 : \ P_L = \frac{dU}{dt} = LI \cdot \frac{dI}{dt} = LI \cdot \frac{\mathcal{E}}{R}(\frac{1}{\tau}e^{-t/\tau})$

$$P_L = \frac{LI\mathcal{E}}{R} \cdot \frac{R}{L}e^{-1} = (1.896 \text{ A})(24 \text{ V})e^{-1} = \boxed{16.7 \text{ W}}$$

(b) $P_R = I^2R = (1.896 \text{ A})^2(8\ \Omega) = \boxed{28.8 \text{ W}}$

(c) $U_L = \frac{1}{2}(4 \text{ H})(1.896 \text{ A})^2 = \boxed{7.19 \text{ J}}$

32.43 (a) $U_L = \frac{1}{2}(4 \text{ H})(0.5 \text{ A})^2 = \boxed{0.500 \text{ J}}$

(b) $I = I_0(1 - e^{-t/\tau}); \quad \tau = \frac{L}{R} = 0.8 \text{ s}$

$$1 = \frac{22}{5}(1 - e^{-t/0.8})$$

$$t = 0.2063 \text{ s}$$

$$P_L = LI\frac{dI}{dt} = \mathcal{E}Ie^{-t/\tau} = (22 \text{ V})(1 \text{ A})e^{-\frac{0.2063}{0.8}} = \boxed{17.0 \text{ W}}$$

(c) $P_{\text{batt}} = \mathcal{E}I = (22 \text{ V})(0.5 \text{ A}) = \boxed{11.0 \text{ W}}$

***32.44** The total magnetic energy is the volume integral of the energy density,

$$mu_B = B^2/2\mu_0$$

Because B changes with position u_B is not constant. For $B = B_0(R/r)^2$,

$$u_B = (B_0^2/2\mu_0)(R/r)^4$$

Next, we set up an expression for the magnetic energy in a spherical shell of radius r and thickness dr. Such a shell has a volume $4\pi r^2 dr$, so the energy stored in it is

$$dU_B = 4\pi r^2 dr\ u_B = (2\pi B_0^2 R^4/\mu_0)dr/r^2$$

We integrate this expression for r = R to r = ∞ to obtain the total magnetic energy outside the sphere. This gives

$$\begin{aligned} U_B &= 2\pi B_0^2 R^3/\mu_0 \\ &= 2\pi(5\times10^{-5}\text{ T})^2(6\times10^6\text{ m})^3/(1.26\times10^{-7}\text{ T}\cdot\text{m/A}) \\ &= \boxed{2.7\times10^{18}\text{ J}} \end{aligned}$$

32.45 $$\begin{aligned} \mathcal{E}_2 &= -M\frac{dI_1}{dt} = -M\frac{d}{dt}(3t^2 - 4t + 5) \\ &= -(0.028\text{ H})(6t-4) = \boxed{(0.112 - 0.168\,t)\text{ V}} \end{aligned}$$

32.46 $$\mathcal{E}_2 = -M\frac{dI_1}{dt} = -(10^{-4}\text{ H})10^4\cos(1000t)$$

$$(\mathcal{E}_2)_{\max} = \boxed{1.00\text{ V}}$$

32.47 $$M = \left|\frac{\mathcal{E}_2}{dI_1/dt}\right| = \frac{96\text{ mV}}{1.2\text{ A/s}} = \boxed{80.0\text{ mH}}$$

32.48 (a) $$M = \frac{\Phi_2}{I_1} = \frac{N_2B_1A_2}{I_1} = \frac{N_2(\mu_0\frac{N_1}{\ell}I_1)\pi r_2^2}{I_1} = \boxed{\pi\mu_0N_1N_2\frac{r_2^2}{\ell}}$$

(b) $$M = \frac{\Phi_1}{I_2} = \frac{N_1B_2A_2}{I_2} = \frac{N_1(\mu_0\frac{N_2}{\ell}I_2)\pi r_2^2}{I_2} = \boxed{\pi\mu_0N_1N_2\frac{r_2^2}{\ell}\text{ [same]}}$$

32.49 $M = \frac{\Phi_2}{I_1} = \frac{N_2 B_1 A_2}{I_1} = \frac{(50)\mu_0(1000)(8.8 \times 10^{-3})I}{I} = \boxed{5.53 \times 10^{-4}\ \text{H}}$

32.50 $M = \frac{\Phi_2}{I_1} = \frac{B_1 A_1 N_2}{I_1} = \frac{(\mu_0 \frac{70}{0.05} I_1)[\pi(0.5 \times 10^{-2})^2](1)}{I_1} = \boxed{1.38 \times 10^{-7}\ \text{H}}$

32.51 (a) $M = \frac{\Phi_B}{I_A} = \frac{700(90 \times 10^{-6})}{3.5} = \boxed{18.0\ \text{mH}}$

(b) $L_A = \frac{\Phi_A}{I_A} = \frac{400(300 \times 10^{-6})}{3.5} = \boxed{0.0343\ \text{H}}$

(c) $\mathcal{E}_B = -M\frac{dI_A}{dt} = -(0.018\ \text{H})(0.5\ \text{A/s}) = \boxed{-0.009\ \text{V}}$

32.52 B at center of (larger) loop: $B_1 = \frac{\mu_0 I_1}{2R}$

(a) $M = \frac{\Phi_2}{I_1} = \frac{B_1 A_2}{I_1} = \frac{(\mu_0 I_1/2R)(\pi r^2)}{I_1} = \boxed{\frac{\mu_0 \pi r^2}{2R}}$

(b) $M = \frac{\mu_0 \pi (0.02)^2}{2(0.20)} = \boxed{3.95\ \text{nH}}$

32.53 $(U_c)_{\text{max}} = (U_L)_{\text{max}}$ (not at the same instant, though!)

$(\frac{1}{2}CV^2)_{\text{max}} = (\frac{1}{2}LI^2)_{\text{max}}$

$I_{\text{max}} = \sqrt{\frac{C}{L}}V_{\text{max}} = \sqrt{\frac{10^{-6}\ \text{F}}{10^{-2}\ \text{H}}}(40\ \text{V}) = \boxed{0.400\ \text{A}}$

32.54 $(\frac{1}{2}CV_c^2)_{\text{max}} = (\frac{1}{2}LI^2)_{\text{max}}$

$(V_c)_{\text{max}} = \sqrt{\frac{L}{C}}I_{\text{max}} = \sqrt{\frac{0.020\ \text{H}}{0.5 \times 10^{-6}\ \text{F}}}(0.1\ \text{A}) = \boxed{20.0\ \text{V}}$

32.63 (a) $\omega_d = \sqrt{\frac{1}{LC} - (\frac{R}{2L})^2} = \sqrt{\frac{1}{(2.2\times10^{-3})(1.8\times10^{-6})} - (\frac{7.6}{2(2.2\times10^{-3})})^2}$

$$\omega_d = 1.580 \times 10^4 \text{ rad/s} \longrightarrow f_d = \frac{\omega_d}{2\pi} = \boxed{2.51 \text{ kHz}}$$

(b) $R_c = \sqrt{\frac{4L}{C}} = \boxed{69.9\ \Omega}$

32.64 $R_{\text{max}} = R_c = \sqrt{\frac{4L}{C}} = \sqrt{\frac{4(2.18)}{6\times10^{-9}}} = \boxed{38.1\ k\Omega}$

32.65 (a) $\omega_0 = \frac{1}{\sqrt{LC}} = \frac{1}{\sqrt{(0.500)(10^{-7})}} = \boxed{4472 \text{ rad/s}}$

(b) $\omega_d = \sqrt{\frac{1}{LC} - (\frac{R}{2L})^2} = \boxed{4358 \text{ rad/s}}$

(c) $\frac{\Delta\omega}{\omega_0} = \boxed{2.53\% \text{ lower}}$

32.66 (a) $Q = Q_0 e^{-\frac{Rt}{2L}} \cos\omega_d t \longrightarrow I_0 \propto e^{-\frac{Rt}{2L}}$

$$0.50 = e^{-\frac{Rt}{2L}}$$

$$\frac{Rt}{2L} = -\ln(0.50)$$

$$t = -\frac{2L}{R}\ln(0.50) = \boxed{0.693(\frac{2L}{R})}$$

(b) $U_0 \propto Q_0^2 \longrightarrow U = 0.50U_0$

$$Q = \sqrt{0.50}\, Q_0 = 0.707Q_0$$

$$t = -\frac{2L}{R}\ln(0.707) = \boxed{0.347(\frac{2L}{R})} \text{ (half as long)}$$

32.67 (a) $\frac{\omega_d}{\omega_0} = \frac{\sqrt{\frac{1}{LC} - (\frac{R}{2L})^2}}{\sqrt{\frac{1}{LC}}} = \sqrt{1 - LC(\frac{R^2}{4L^2})} = \sqrt{1 - \frac{R^2C}{4L}}$

(b) $L < 4R^2C \longrightarrow \frac{R^2C}{4L} > 1 :$ $\frac{\omega_d}{\omega_0}$ becomes imaginary

[If $L < 4R^2C$, then $R > R_C$, so no oscillations occur!]

32.68 (a) $\omega_0 = \sqrt{\frac{1}{LC}} = 250$ rad/s: $f_0 = \boxed{39.8 \text{ Hz}}$

(b) $\omega_d = 0$ $\boxed{\text{no oscillations}}$

(c) $\omega_d = \sqrt{\frac{1}{LC} - (\frac{R}{2L})^2} = 242$ rad/s: $f_d = \boxed{38.5 \text{ Hz}}$

(d) ω_d is imaginary $\boxed{\text{no oscillations}}$

32.69 $I = \frac{\mathcal{E}}{R}(1 - e^{-t/\tau})$ $\qquad \tau = \frac{L}{R}$

$4 = \frac{5}{0.5}(1 - e^{-1/\tau})$ $\qquad L = R\tau = (0.5\ \Omega)(1.96\ \text{s}) = \boxed{0.979 \text{ H}}$

$e^{-1/\tau} = 0.6$

$\tau = 1.96$ s

32.70 (a) If unrolled, the wire forms the diagonal of a 10-cm wide rectangle

$\ell = \sqrt{9.80^2 - 0.10^2} = 9.7995$ m

Now ℓ represents $N \cdot C$, where N = # of turns and C = (mean) circumference of each turn:

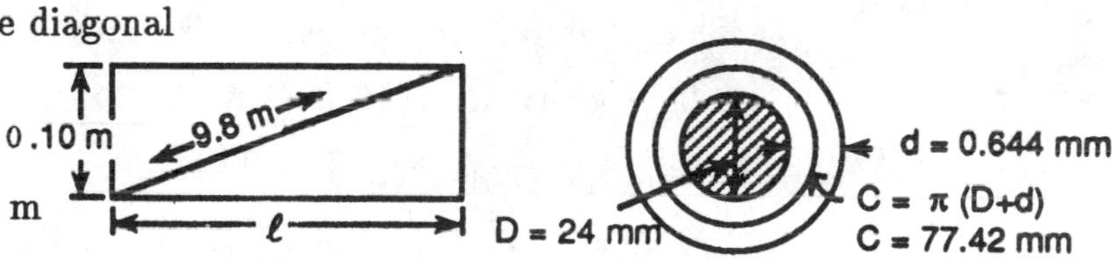

a 32.70 b

$$\therefore N = \frac{\ell}{C} = \frac{9.7995 \text{ m}}{77.42 \times 10^{-3} \text{ m}} = \boxed{127 \text{ turns}}$$

(b) $R = \rho\frac{\ell}{A} = (1.7 \times 10^{-8}\ \Omega \cdot \text{m})\frac{10 \text{ m}}{\pi(0.322 \times 10^{-3} \text{ m})^2} = \boxed{0.522\ \Omega}$

(c) $L = \mu\frac{N^2 A}{\ell} = 800\mu_0\frac{(126.6)^2\pi(12.322 \times 10^{-3} \text{ m})^2}{0.10 \text{ m}} = \boxed{76.8 \text{ mH}}$

***32.71** For $0 < t < 1$ ms,

$$\frac{dI}{dt} = \frac{2\text{ mA}}{1\text{ ms}} = 2\ \frac{\text{A}}{\text{s}}$$

$$\mathcal{E} = -L\frac{dI}{dt} = -\left(5\ \frac{V\cdot s}{\text{A}}\right)\left(2\ \frac{\text{A}}{\text{s}}\right) = -10\text{ V}$$

a at higher V: ± 10 V

$1 < t < 2 \quad \mathcal{E} = 0$

$$2 < t < 3 \quad \frac{dI}{dt} = 1\ \frac{\text{A}}{\text{s}}$$

$$V_a = +5\text{ V}$$

$$3 < t < 4 \quad \frac{dI}{dt} = -3\ \frac{\text{A}}{\text{s}}$$

$$V_a = -15\text{ V}$$

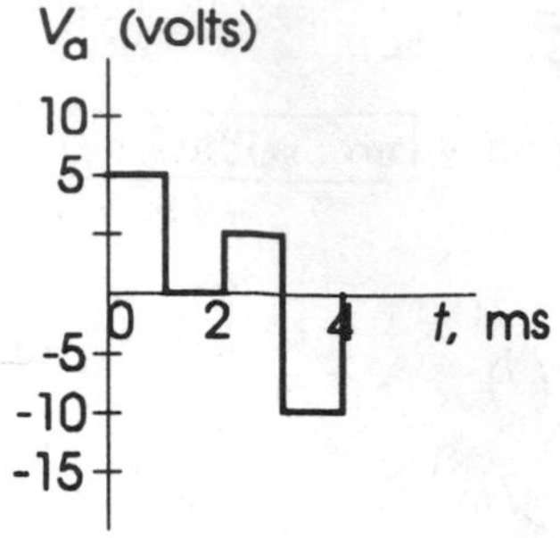

32.71

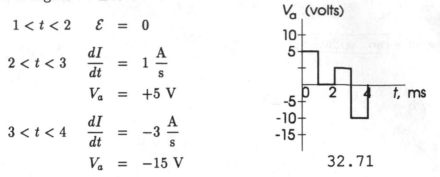

***32.72** (a) Kirchhoff's loop equation is

$L(dI/dt) + RI = 0$

The potential drop across the inductor is

$-L(dI/dt) = RI = (6\ \Omega)(5\text{ A}) = \boxed{30\text{ V}}$

(b) Solving for dI/dt gives

$dI/dt = -RI/L = -(30\text{ V})/(0.1\text{ H}) = \boxed{-300\text{ A/s}}$

***32.73** When switch is closed, steady current $I_0 = 1.2$ A

$$I = I_0 \exp -\frac{Rt}{L}$$

$$0.25\text{ A} = (1.2\text{ A}) \exp -\frac{(1\ \Omega)(0.15\text{ s})}{\text{L}}$$

$$\ln\left(\frac{0.25}{1.2}\right) = -1.5686 = -\frac{(1\ \Omega)(0.15\text{ s})}{L}$$

$$L = \frac{0.15\text{ V}\cdot\text{s}}{1.5686\text{ A}} = \boxed{95.6\text{ mH}}$$

32.74 $R_{max} = R_c = \sqrt{\frac{4L}{C}} = \sqrt{\frac{4(1.2 \times 10^{-9}\text{ H})}{10^{-4}\text{ F}}} = 6.93\text{ m}\Omega$

$$R = \rho\frac{\ell}{A} \longrightarrow \ell = \frac{RA}{\rho} = \frac{(6.93 \times 10^{-3})\pi(1.25 \times 10^{-3})^2}{(11 \times 10^{-8})} = \boxed{0.31\text{ m}}$$

32.75 $U_L = \frac{1}{2}LI_0^2 = \frac{1}{2}L(\frac{\mathcal{E}}{R})^2$

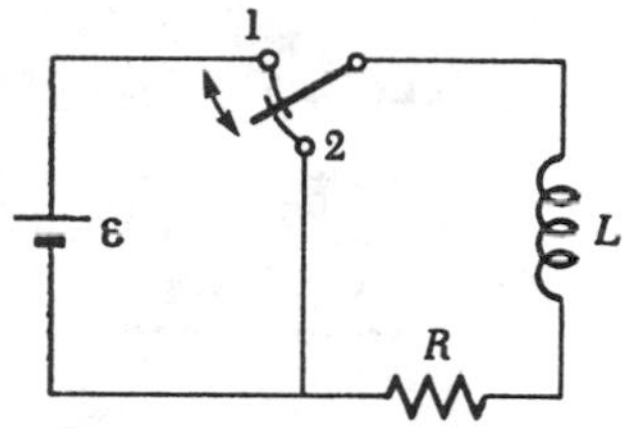

32.75, 32.85, and 32.86

after switch $\longrightarrow$ 2, $I = I_0 e^{-t/\tau}$: $\tau = \frac{L}{R}$

$$P_R = I^2R \longrightarrow U_R = \int_0^\infty P_R dt = \int_0^\infty I_0^2 e^{-2t/\tau} R dt$$

$$U_R = I_0^2 R \int_0^\infty e^{-2t/\tau} dt = (\frac{\mathcal{E}}{R})^2 R \left[\frac{e^{-2t/\tau}}{-2/\tau}\right]_0^\infty$$

$$U_R = \frac{\mathcal{E}^2}{R}(-\frac{L}{2R})[e^{-2t/\tau}]_0^\infty = -\frac{\mathcal{E}^2 L}{2R^2}[0 - 1] = \frac{1}{2}L(\frac{\mathcal{E}}{R})^2$$

***32.76** (a) It has a magnetic field, and it stores energy, so $L = \frac{2U}{I^2}$ is non-zero.

(b) Every field line goes through the rectangle between the conductors.

(c) $\Phi = LI$

$$L = \frac{\Phi}{I} = \frac{1}{I}\int_{y=a}^{w-a} B\, da$$

$$= \frac{1}{I}\int_a^{w-a} x\, dy \left(\frac{\mu_0 I}{2\pi y} + \frac{\mu_0 I}{w - y}\right)$$

$$= \frac{2}{I}\int \frac{\mu_0 I x}{2\pi y}\, dy = \frac{2\mu_0 x}{2\pi} ln\ y\Big|_a^{w-a}$$

$$L = \frac{\mu_0 x}{\pi} ln\left(\frac{w - a}{a}\right)$$

32.77 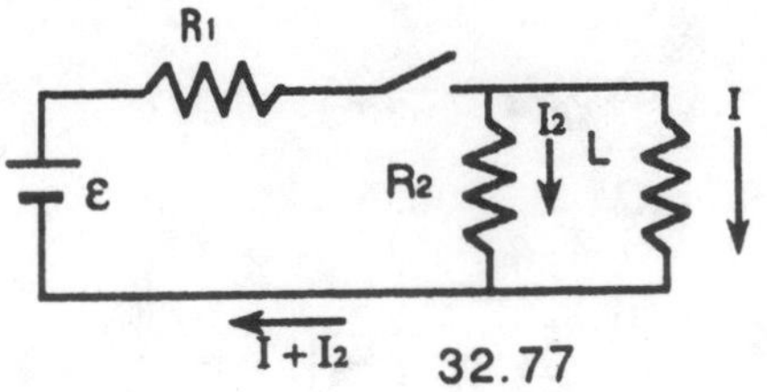

32.77

Left hand loop: $\mathcal{E} - (I + I_2)R_1 - I_2R_2 = 0$

outside loop: $\mathcal{E} - (I + I_2)R_1 - L\frac{dI}{dt} = 0$

(eliminate I_2, obtaining)

$$\underbrace{I\left(\frac{R_1R_2}{R_1 + R_2}\right)}_{R'} + L\frac{dI}{dt} = \underbrace{\left(\frac{R_2}{R_1 + R_2}\right)\mathcal{E}}_{\mathcal{E}'}$$

$$\therefore \mathcal{E}' - IR' - L\frac{dI}{dt} = 0$$

Same form as Eq. 32.6: $I = \frac{\mathcal{E}'}{R'}(1 - e^{-R't/L})$

$$\frac{\mathcal{E}'}{R'} = \frac{\mathcal{E}R_2/(R_1 + R_2)}{R_1R_2/(R_1 + R_2)} = \frac{\mathcal{E}}{R_1}: \quad I(t) = \frac{\mathcal{E}}{R_1}(1 - e^{-\frac{R't}{L}})$$

32.78 Eq. 30.18: $B = \frac{\mu_0 NI}{2\pi r}$

(a) $\Phi = \int BdA = \int_a^b \frac{\mu_0 NI}{2\pi r}hdr = \frac{\mu_0 NIh}{2\pi}\int_a^b \frac{dr}{r} = \frac{\mu_0 NIh}{2\pi}\ln(\frac{b}{a})$

$L = \frac{N\Phi}{I} = \frac{\mu_0 N^2 h}{2\pi}\ln(\frac{b}{a})$

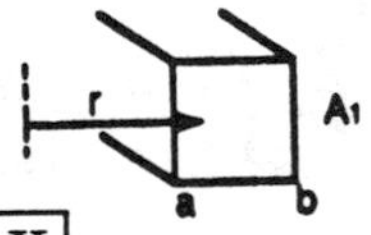

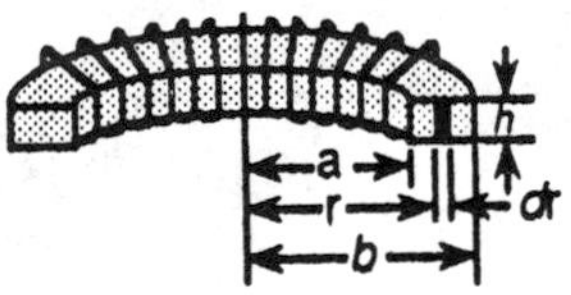

32.78

(b) $L = \frac{\mu_0(500)^2(0.01)}{2\pi}\ln(\frac{12}{10}) = \boxed{91.2\ \mu\text{H}}$

(c) $L_{\text{appx}} = \frac{\mu_0 N^2}{2\pi}(\frac{A}{R}) = \frac{\mu_0(500)^2}{2\pi}(\frac{2 \times 10^{-4}\ \text{m}^2}{0.11\ \text{m}}) = \boxed{90.9\ \mu\text{H}}$

***32.79** (a) steady state:

$t = 0$

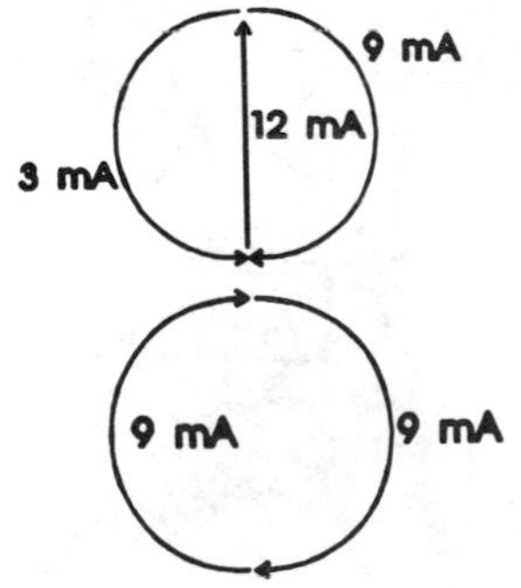

32.79(a)

$\mathcal{E}_0 = (8\text{ k}\Omega)(9\text{ mA}) = \boxed{72.0\text{ V}}$ with b at higher voltage

(b) Current in R_1

Current in R_2

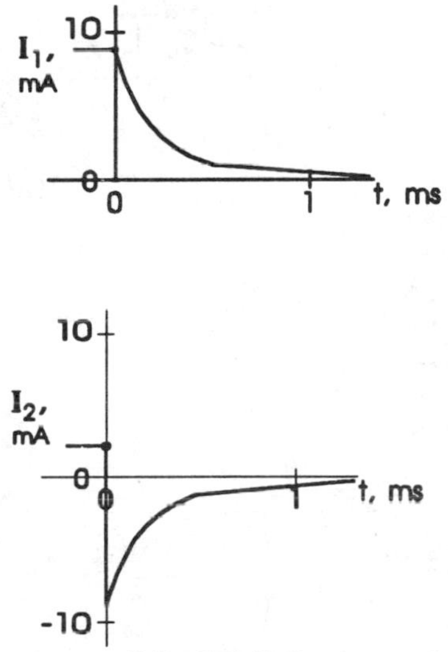

32.79(b)

(c)
$$\begin{aligned} I &= 2\text{ mA} = (9\text{ mA})\exp\left(-\frac{8\text{ k}\Omega\text{ t}}{0.4\text{ H}}\right) \\ \ln\left(\frac{2}{9}\right) &= -1.504 = \frac{-8000}{0.4}t \\ t &= \frac{(1.504)(0.4)}{8000}\text{ s} = \boxed{75.2\ \mu\text{s}} \end{aligned}$$

***32.80** (a) $I = 0 \qquad \dfrac{dI}{dt} = \dfrac{\mathcal{E}_0}{L}$

$$\boxed{0,\ \frac{\mathcal{E}_0}{R},\ \frac{\mathcal{E}_0}{R},\ \mathcal{E}_0,\ 0,\ \mathcal{E}_0}$$

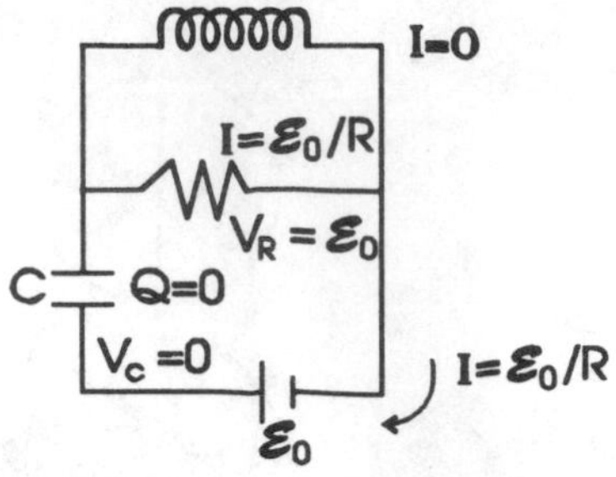

32.80(a)

(b) 0, 0, 0, 0, $\mathcal{E}_0$, 0

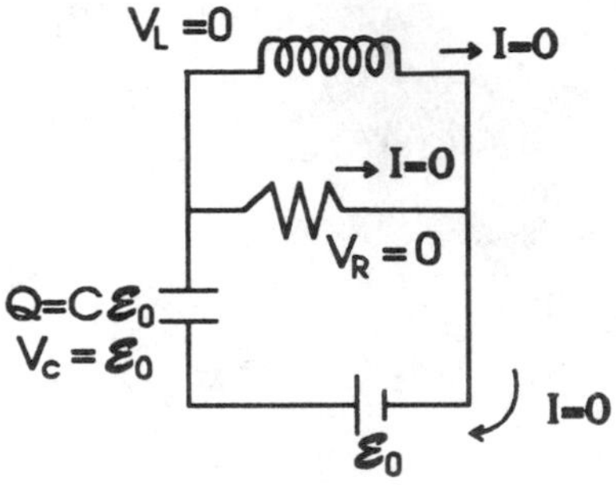

32.80(b)

32.81 $B_1 = \dfrac{\mu_0 I}{2\pi r} \qquad B_2 = \dfrac{\mu_0 I}{2\pi(d-r)}$

$$B_r = \frac{\mu_0 I}{2\pi}\left(\frac{1}{r} + \frac{1}{d-r}\right)$$

$$\Phi = \int_a^{d-a} B\ell dr: \quad L = \frac{\Phi}{I} = \frac{\mu_0 \ell}{2\pi}\int_a^{d-a}\left(\frac{1}{r} + \frac{1}{d-r}\right)dr$$

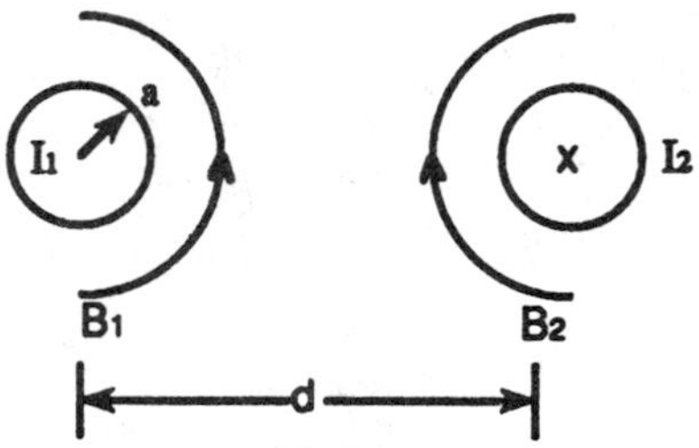

32.81

$$L = \frac{\mu_0 \ell}{2\pi}\left[\int_a^{d-a}\frac{dr}{r} + \int_a^{d-a}\frac{dr}{d-r}\right]$$

$u = d - r: \ du = -dr$

$$L = \frac{\mu_0 \ell}{2\pi}\left[\ln\left(\frac{d-a}{a}\right) + \int_{d-a}^{a}\frac{-du}{u}\right] = \frac{\mu_0 \ell}{2\pi}\left[\ln\left(\frac{d-a}{a}\right) - \ln\left(\frac{a}{d-a}\right)\right]$$

$$\boxed{\frac{L}{\ell} = \frac{\mu_0}{\pi}\cdot\ln\left(\frac{d-a}{a}\right)}$$

32.82 (a) $L = \dfrac{\mu_0 N^2 A}{\ell} = \dfrac{\mu_0(10^6)(10^{-4})}{0.5} = \boxed{2.51 \times 10^{-4}\ \text{H}}$

(b) $M = \dfrac{N\Phi_2}{I_1} = \dfrac{100\mu_0(2000)I(10^{-4})}{I} = \boxed{2.51 \times 10^{-5}\ \text{H}}$

(c) $\mathcal{E}_1 = -M\dfrac{dI_2}{dt}$ or $I_1 R_1 = -M\dfrac{dI_2}{dt}$

$$I_1 = -\frac{M}{R_1}\frac{dI_2}{dt}$$

$$\int I_1 dt = -\int \frac{M}{R_1} dI_2$$

$$Q_1 = -\frac{M}{R_1}(\Delta I_2) = -\frac{2.51 \times 10^{-5}\ \text{H}}{10^3\ \Omega}(-1\ \text{A}) = \boxed{2.51 \times 10^{-8}\ \text{C}}$$

32.83 When the switch is closed, as shown in (32.83a), the current in the inductor is I:

$12 - 7.5I - 10 = 0 \longrightarrow I = 0.267$ A

When the switch is opened, the initial current in the inductor remains at 0.267 A:

$IR = V$

$(0.267\ \text{A})R \le 80$ V

$\boxed{R \le 300\ \Omega}$

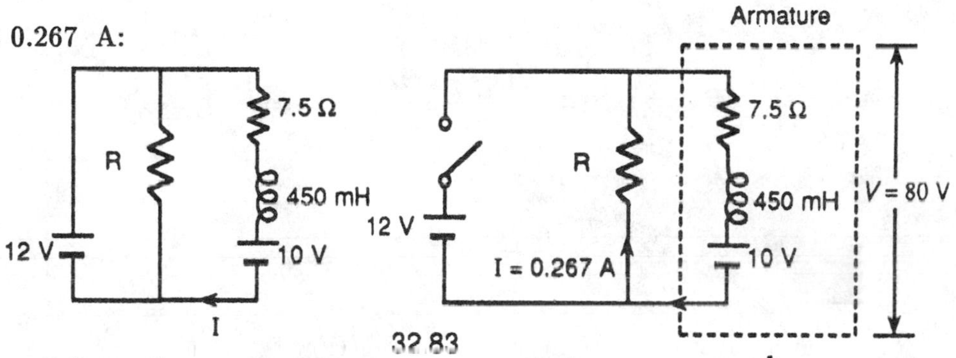

32.83

a b

***32.84**

$$I = I_0(1 - e^{-Rt/L})$$

$$\frac{I}{I_0} = 0.8 = (1 - e^{-0.4R/2})$$

$$0.2 = e^{-0.2R}$$

$$\ln(0.2) = -0.2R$$

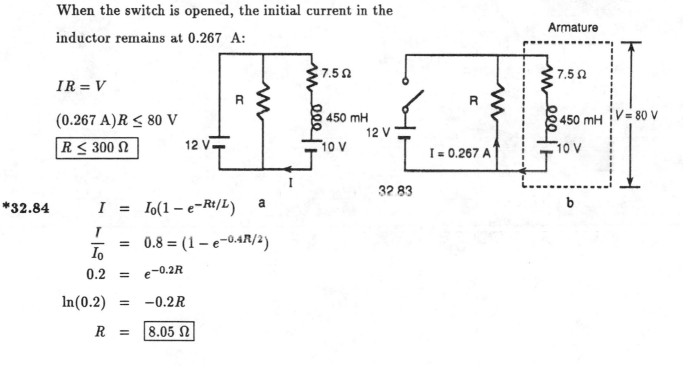

$$R = \boxed{8.05\ \Omega}$$

***32.85** $L = 2$ H, $r = 40\ \Omega$, $\mathcal{E} = 60$ V

For a series RL circuit, $I = \frac{\mathcal{E}}{R}(1 - e^{-t/\tau})$

$$\text{(a)}\quad P_{\mathcal{E}} = \mathcal{E}I = \frac{\mathcal{E}^2}{R}(1 - e^{-1})$$

$$= \frac{(60)^2}{40}(1 - e^{-1}) = \boxed{56.9 \text{ W}}$$

$$\text{(b)}\quad P_R = I^2R = \frac{\mathcal{E}^2}{R}(1 - e^{-1})^2$$

$$= \frac{(60)^2}{40}(1 - e^{-1})^2 = \boxed{36.0 \text{ W}}$$

$$\text{(c)}\quad P_L = LI\frac{dI}{dt} = L\left[\frac{\mathcal{E}}{R}(1 - e^{-1})\left(\frac{\mathcal{E}}{L}e^{-1}\right)\right]$$

$$P_L = \frac{\mathcal{E}^2}{R}(1 - e^{-1})\,e^{-1}$$

$$= \frac{60^2}{40}(1 - e^{-1})\,e^{-1} = \boxed{20.9 \text{ W}}$$

***32.86** $\ell B_1 = N_1\mu_0 I_1$

$$B_1 = \frac{N_1\mu_0 I_1}{\ell}$$

$$\Phi = \frac{N_1 A\mu_0 I_1}{\ell}$$

(a) $L_1 = \frac{N_1^2 A\mu_0}{\ell}$ $\qquad L_2 = \frac{N_2^2 A\mu_0}{\ell}$

(b) $M = \frac{N_1 N_2 A\mu_0}{\ell}$

(c) $M^2 = \frac{N_1^2 A\mu_0}{\ell}\cdot\frac{N_2^2 A\mu_0}{\ell} = L_1 L_2$

CHAPTER 33

33.1 Eqn for $V(t)$ during first period: $y = mx + b$

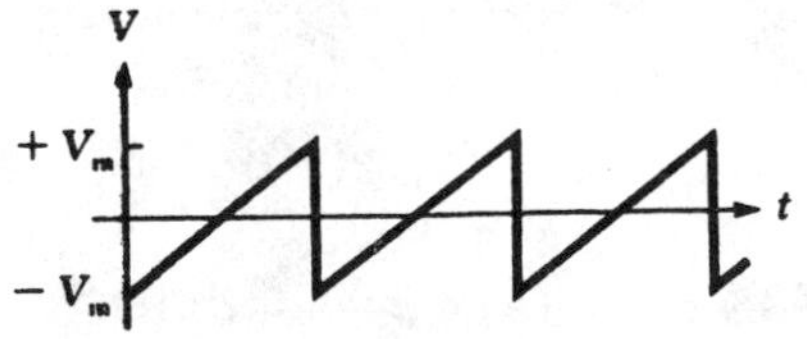

33.1

$$V = \frac{2V_m}{T}t - V_m$$

$$\overline{V^2} = \frac{1}{T}\int_0^T V^2 dt = \frac{1}{T}\int_0^T \left(\frac{2V_m}{T}t - V_m\right)^2 dt$$

$$= \frac{1}{T}\left[\int_0^T \left(\frac{2V_m}{T}\right)^2 t^2 dt - \frac{4V_m^2}{T}\int_0^T t dt + V_m^2 \int_0^T dt\right]$$

$$= \frac{1}{T}\left[\frac{4V_m^2}{T^2}\left(\frac{T^3}{3}\right) - \frac{4V_m^2}{T}\left(\frac{T^2}{2}\right) + V_m^2 T\right]$$

$$= \frac{4}{3}V_m^2 - 2V_m^2 + V_m^2 + V_m^2 = \frac{1}{3}V_m^2$$

$$V_{\text{rms}} = \sqrt{\overline{V^2}} = \frac{V_m}{\sqrt{3}}$$

33.2 $V_{\text{rms}} = \dfrac{170\ V}{\sqrt{2}} = 120\text{ V}$

(a) $P_{\text{av}} = \dfrac{(V_{\text{rms}})^2}{R} \longrightarrow R = \dfrac{(120\text{ V})^2}{75\text{ W}} = \boxed{193\ \Omega}$

(b) $R = \dfrac{(120\text{ V})^2}{100\text{ W}} = \boxed{144\ \Omega}$

33.3 Each meter reads the rms value.

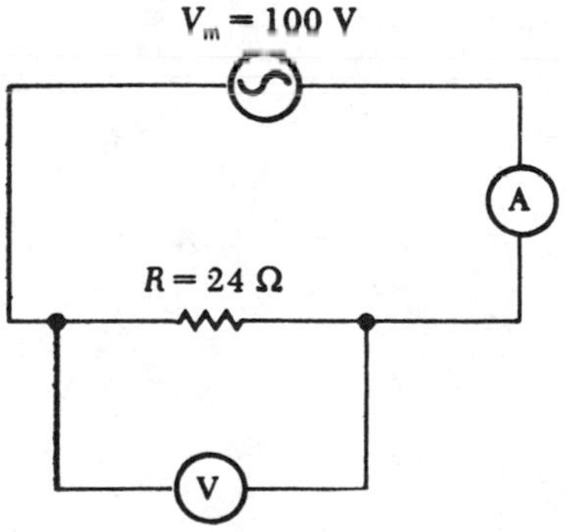

33.3

$$(V_{\text{app}})_{\text{rms}} = \frac{100\text{ V}}{\sqrt{2}} = 70.7\text{ V}$$

$$I_{\text{rms}} = \frac{V_{\text{rms}}}{R} = \frac{70.7\text{ V}}{24\ \Omega} = \boxed{2.95\text{ A}}$$

$$V_{\text{rms}} = \boxed{70.7\text{ V}}$$

33.4 (a) $I = \dfrac{V}{R} = \dfrac{100}{60} = \boxed{1.67\ \text{A}}$

(b) $\omega = 2\pi f = 2\pi(50) = \boxed{314\ \text{rad/s}}$

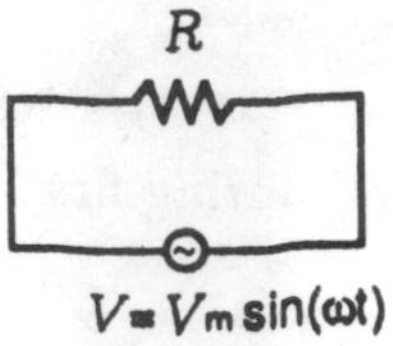

33.4 and 33.5

33.5 (a) $i_R = I_m \sin(\omega t)$

$$i_R = 1.67 \sin(\frac{314}{75}) = \boxed{-\ 1.44\ \text{A}}$$

(b) $i_R = 1.67 \sin(\dfrac{314}{150}) = \boxed{1.45\ \text{A}}$

33.6 $v_R = V_m \sin[\omega t]$

$$0.25V_m = V_m \sin[\omega(0.01)]$$

$$[0.01\omega] = \sin^{-1}(0.25) = 0.253$$

$$\boxed{\omega = 25.3\ \ \text{rad/s}}$$

(b) $\omega = 2\pi f \quad f = 4.02\ \ \text{Hz}$

$$T = \frac{1}{f} = \frac{1}{402\ \text{Hz}} = 0.249\ \text{s}$$

$$t = \frac{T}{2} - 0.01\ \text{s}$$

$$t = \frac{0.249}{2} - 0.01 = \boxed{0.114\ \text{s}}$$

$$\sin\theta = \sin\phi$$

$$\omega t' = \pi - \omega t$$

$$t' = \frac{\pi}{\omega} - t = \frac{\pi}{25.3} - 0.01$$

$$t' = 0.1243 - 0.0100 = 0.1143\ \text{s}$$

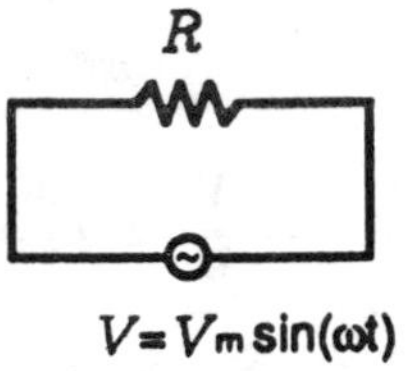

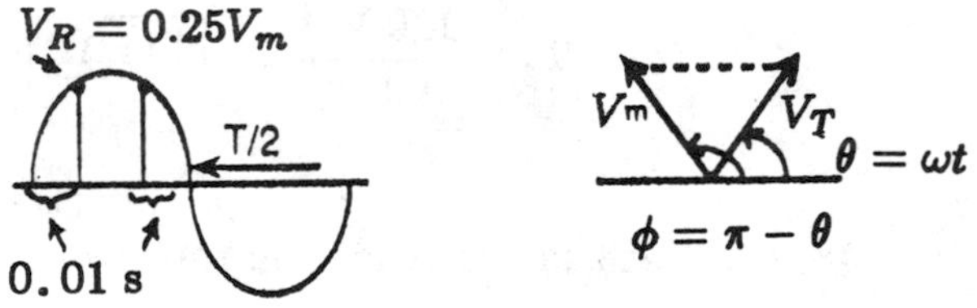

33.6 b

33.7 $I_R = I_m \sin\omega t$

$$0.6 = \sin(\omega\ 0.007)$$

$$\sin(0.007\ \omega) = 0.6$$

$$0.007\omega = \sin^{-1}(0.6) = 0.644$$

$$\omega = 91.9\ \ \text{rad/s} = 2\pi f$$

$$\boxed{f = 14.6\ \ \text{Hz}}$$

33.8 $|X_L| = [\omega L] \sim (\frac{1}{\text{s}})(\text{H}) \sim (\frac{1}{\text{s}})(\frac{\text{V}\cdot\text{s}}{\text{A}}) \sim \ \Omega$

33.9 (a) $X_L = \frac{V}{I} = \frac{100}{7.5} = 13.3\ \Omega$

$$L = \frac{X_L}{\omega} = \frac{13.3}{2\pi(50)} = 0.0424\ \text{H} = \boxed{42.4\ \text{mH}}$$

(b) $X_L = \frac{V}{I} = \frac{100}{2.5} = 40\ \Omega$

$$\omega = \frac{X_L}{L} = \frac{40}{42.4 \times 10^{-3}} = \boxed{943\ \text{rad/s}}$$

33.10 $I = \frac{V}{X_L} = \frac{V}{\omega L}$:

(a) $\omega \longrightarrow 2\omega$ gives $I \longrightarrow \frac{1}{2}I_0 :\ I = \boxed{1.50\ \text{A}}$

(b) $X_L = \frac{V}{I} = \frac{100\ \text{V}}{3\ \text{A}} = \boxed{36.7\ \Omega}$

$$X_L' = \frac{V}{I'} = \frac{100\ \text{V}}{1.5\ \text{A}} = \boxed{73.3\ \Omega}$$

33.11 For $I = 80$ mA, $I_{\text{rms}} = \frac{80\ \text{mA}}{\sqrt{2}} = 56.6\ \ \text{mA}$

$$(X_L)_{\text{min}} = \frac{V_{\text{rms}}}{I_{\text{rms}}} = \frac{50\ \text{V}}{0.0566\ \text{A}} = 884\ \Omega$$

$$X_L = 2\pi f L \longrightarrow L = \frac{X_L}{2\pi f} \geq \frac{884\ \Omega}{2\pi(20)} \geq \boxed{7.03\ \text{H}}$$

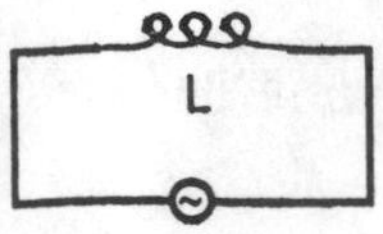

$V = V_m \sin(\omega t)$

33.12, 33.13, and 33.14

33.12 $V = V_{\text{rms}}\sqrt{2} = 141.4 \text{ V}$

$$X_L(50) = \frac{50}{60} X_L(60) = \frac{50}{60}(54 \ \Omega) = 45 \ \Omega$$

$$I = \frac{V}{X_L} = \frac{141.4 \text{ V}}{45 \ \Omega} = \boxed{3.14 \text{ A}}$$

33.13 $X_L = L\omega = (70 \times 10^{-3})(65\pi) = 14.3 \ \Omega$

$$I = \frac{V}{X_L} = \frac{80}{14.3} = 5.6 \text{ A}$$

$$I = I_m \sin \omega t = 5.6 \sin(65\pi(0.015)) = \boxed{5.6 \text{ A}}$$

33.14 (a) $X_L = \omega L$

$$40 = \omega(310 \times 10^{-3})$$

$$\omega = 129 \text{ rad/s}$$

$$\omega = 2\pi f = 129$$

$$f = \boxed{20.5 \text{ Hz}}$$

(b) $V = IX_L$

$$130 = I(40)$$

$$I = \boxed{3.25 \text{ A}}$$

33.15 $X_L = \omega L$

$$63 = (820)L$$

$$L = \boxed{76.8 \text{ mH}}$$

33.16 $[X_C] = [\frac{1}{\omega C}] \sim \text{s(F)}^{-1} \sim \text{s}(\frac{\text{C}}{\text{V}})^{-1} \sim \frac{\text{V}}{\text{(C/s)}} \sim \frac{\text{V}}{\text{A}} \sim \Omega$

33.17 (a) $X_C = \dfrac{1}{2\pi f C}$: $\dfrac{1}{2\pi f(22 \times 10^{-6})} < 175\ \Omega$

$$\frac{1}{2\pi(22 \times 10^{-6})(175)} < f$$

$$\boxed{f > 41.3\ \text{Hz}}$$

(b) $X_C \propto \dfrac{1}{C}$, so $X(44) = \dfrac{1}{2}X(22)$: $\boxed{X_C < 87.5\ \Omega}$

33.18 $X_C = \dfrac{1}{\omega C} = \dfrac{1}{(95\pi)(10 \times 10^{-6})} = \boxed{335\ \Omega}$

33.19 $V = \sqrt{2}V_{\text{rms}} = \sqrt{2}(20\ \text{V}) = 28.3\ \text{V}$

$$V_C = \frac{Q}{C} \longrightarrow Q_{\max} = CV_{\max} = (98 \times 10^{-12}\ \text{F})(28.3\ \text{V}) = \boxed{2.77\ \text{nC}}$$

33.20 (a) $q(t) = CV_C(t) = \boxed{CV_m \cos \omega t}$

(b) $i(t) = \dfrac{dq}{dt} = \boxed{-\omega C V_m \sin \omega t}$

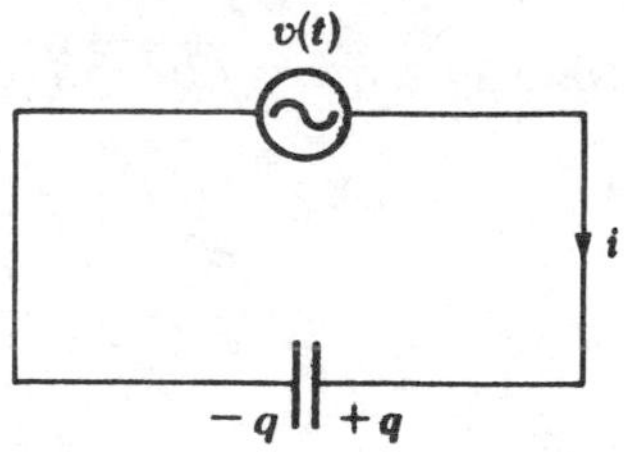

33.20

33.21 $I_m = V_m \omega C = (48\ \text{V})(2\pi)(90\ \text{s}^{-1})(3.7 \times 10^{-6}\ \text{F}) = \boxed{100\ \text{mA}}$

33.22 $I_m = V_m(\omega C) = V_m(2\pi f)C$

$$f = \frac{5\ \text{A}}{2\pi(18\ \text{V})(9.4 \times 10^{-8}\ \text{F})} = \boxed{4.7 \times 10^5\ \text{Hz}}$$

33.23 $I = \omega C \mathcal{E}_m \sin(\omega t + \pi/2)$

$$I = (100\pi\ \text{s}^{-1})(20 \times 10^{-6}\ \text{F})(220\ \text{V}) \sin(100\pi(0.004) + \pi/2)$$

$$= 1.382 \sin(72 + 90) = \boxed{0.427\ \text{A}}$$

33.24 $\omega L = \dfrac{1}{\omega C} \longrightarrow \omega = \dfrac{1}{\sqrt{LC}} = \dfrac{1}{\sqrt{(57 \times 10^{-6})(57 \times 10^{-6})}} = 1.75 \times 10^4 \text{ rad/s}$

$$f = \frac{\omega}{2\pi} = \boxed{2792 \text{ Hz}}$$

33.25 (a) $X_L = \omega L = 2\pi(50 \text{ s}^{-1})(250 \times 10^{-3} \text{ H}) = \boxed{78.5 \ \Omega}$

(b) $X_C = \dfrac{1}{\omega C} = [2\pi(50 \text{ s}^{-1})(2 \times 10^{-6} \text{ F})]^{-1} = \boxed{1.59 \times 10^3 \ \Omega}$

(c) $Z = \sqrt{R^2 + (X_L - X_C)^2} = \boxed{1.52 \times 10^3 \ \Omega}$

(d) $I_m = \dfrac{\mathcal{E}_m}{Z} = \dfrac{210 \text{ V}}{1.52 \times 10^3 \ \Omega} = \boxed{0.138 \text{ A}}$

(e) $\phi = \tan^{-1}[\dfrac{X_L - X_C}{R}] = \tan^{-1}(-10.1) = \boxed{-84.3°}$

33.26 (a) $Z = \sqrt{R^2 + (X_L - X_c)^2} = \sqrt{68^2 + (16 - 101)^2} = \boxed{109 \ \Omega}$

$$X_L = \omega L = (100)(0.160) = 16 \ \Omega$$

$$X_C = \frac{1}{\omega C} = \frac{1}{(100)(99 \times 10^{-6})} = 101 \ \Omega$$

(b) $I = \dfrac{V_{\text{app}}}{Z} = \dfrac{40 \text{ V}}{109 \ \Omega} = \boxed{0.367 \text{ A}}$

(c) $\tan\phi = \dfrac{X_L - X_C}{R} = \dfrac{16 - 101}{68} = -1.25 : \ \phi = -0.896 \text{ rad} = -51.3°$

$\therefore \boxed{I_m = 0.367 \text{ A}} \quad \boxed{\omega = 100 \ \text{rad/s}} \quad \boxed{\phi = -0.896 \text{ rad} = -51.3°}$

33.27 $X_L = 2\pi f L = 2\pi(60)(0.460) = 173.4 \ \Omega$

$$X_C = \frac{1}{2\pi f C} = \frac{1}{2\pi(60)(21 \times 10^{-6})} = 126.3 \ \Omega$$

(a) $\tan\phi = \dfrac{X_L - X_C}{R} = \dfrac{173.4 \ \Omega - 126.3 \ \Omega}{150 \ \Omega} = 0.314 \ : \ \phi = 0.304 \text{ rad} = \boxed{17.4°}$

(b) Since $X_L > X_C$, ϕ is positive, so $\boxed{V_{\text{app}} \text{ leads the current}}$

33.28 (a) $\omega = 2\pi f = 2\pi(240\ s^{-1}) = 1508\ \text{rad/s};$

$$X_L = \omega L = (1508\ s^{-1})(2.5\ H) = 3770\ \Omega$$

$$X_C = \frac{1}{\omega C} = \frac{1}{(1508\ s^{-1})(0.25\times10^{-6})} = 2652\ \Omega$$

$$Z = \sqrt{(R^2 + (X_L - X_C)^2} = \sqrt{(900\ \Omega)^2 + (3770\ \Omega - 2652\ \Omega)^2}$$

$$= 1.435\ k\Omega = \boxed{1.44\ k\Omega}$$

(b) $I_m = \frac{V_m}{Z} = \frac{140\ V}{1.435\times10^3\ \Omega} = \boxed{97.6\ mA}$

(c) $\phi = \tan^{-1}(\frac{X_L - X_C}{R}) = \tan^{-1}(\frac{3770\ \Omega - 2652\ \Omega}{900\ \Omega}) = \boxed{51.2^\circ}$

(d) $\boxed{\text{The current lags the voltage}}$

33.29 $\tan\phi = \frac{X_L - X_C}{R}$

$\tan 45^\circ = \frac{X_L - X_C}{7} = 1$

Since $X_C = 0, \quad X_L = 7 = \omega L$

$\omega(18.1\times10^{-3}) = 7$

$\omega = 387\ \text{rad/s or}$

$\boxed{f = 61.6\ Hz}$

33.30 $Z^2 = R^2 + (X_L - X_C)^2; \quad X_C = \frac{1}{2\pi f C} = X_L \mp \sqrt{Z^2 - R^2}$

$C = [2\pi f(X_L \mp \sqrt{Z^2 - R^2})]^{-1}$

$= [2\pi(\frac{600\ s}{\pi})(700\ \Omega \mp \sqrt{(910)^2 - (400)^2})]^{-1} = [2\pi(\frac{600\ s}{\pi})(700 \mp 817)]^{-1}$

We must choose the (+) sign since the r.h.s. of the equation is positive.

$\boxed{C = 5.49\times10^{-7}\ F}$

33.31 $X_C = \frac{1}{\omega C} = \frac{1}{2\pi(50)(65 \times 10^{-6})} = 49.0\ \Omega$

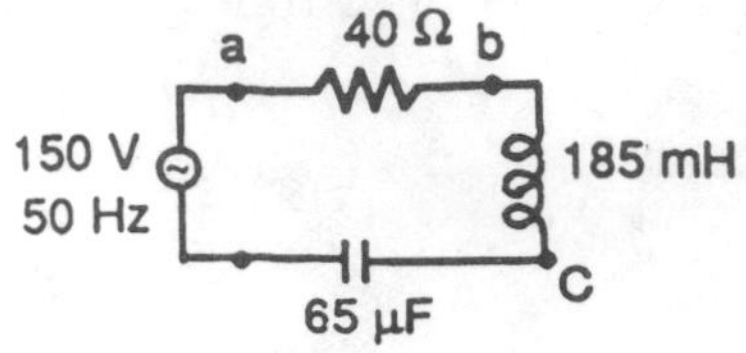

33.31

$X_L = \omega L = 2\pi(50)(185 \times 10^{-3}) = 58.1\ \Omega$

$Z = \sqrt{R^2 + (X_L - X_C)^2} = \sqrt{40^2 + (58.1 - 49.0)^2} = 41\ \Omega$

$I_m = \frac{V_m}{Z} = \frac{150}{41} = 3.66\ \text{A}$

(a) $V_R = I_m R = (3.66)(40) = \boxed{146\ \text{V}}$

(b) $V_L = I_m X_L = (3.66)(58.1) = 212.6 = \boxed{213\ \text{V}}$

(c) $V_C = I_m X_C = (3.66)(49.0) = 179.3\ \text{V} = \boxed{179\ \text{V}}$

(d) $V_L - V_C = 212.6 - 179.3 = \boxed{33.3\ \text{V}}$

33.32 $R = 300\ \Omega$

$X_C = \frac{1}{\omega C} = \frac{1}{2\pi(\frac{500}{\pi})(11 \times 10^{-6}\ \text{F})} = 90.9\ \Omega$

$X_L = \omega L = 2\pi(\frac{500}{\pi})(0.2) = 200\ \Omega$

The phasor diagram is shown at the right.

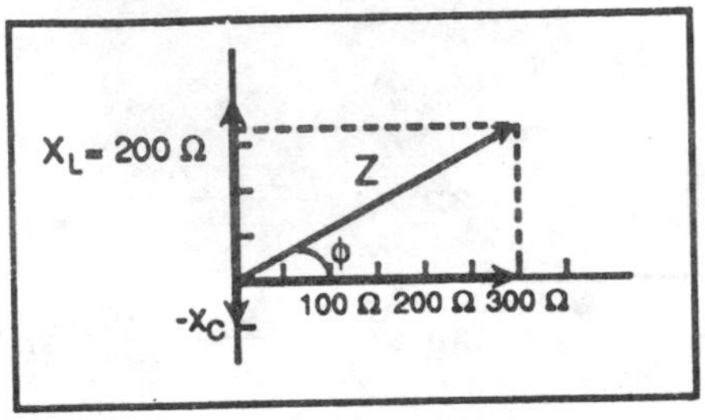

33.32

33.33 (a) $X_L = \omega L = 2\pi(50)(400 \times 10^{-3}) = 126\ \Omega$

$X_C = \frac{1}{\omega L} = \frac{1}{2\pi(50)(4.43 \times 10^{-6})} = 719\ \Omega$

$Z = \sqrt{R^2 + (X_L - X_C)^2} = \sqrt{500^2 + (126 - 719)^2} = 776\ \Omega$

$V_m = I_m\ Z = (250 \times 10^{-3})(776) = \boxed{194\ \text{V}}$

(b) $\phi = \tan^{-1}(\frac{X_L - X_C}{R}) = \tan^{-1}(\frac{126 - 719}{500}) = \boxed{-49.9^\circ}$

Current leads voltage

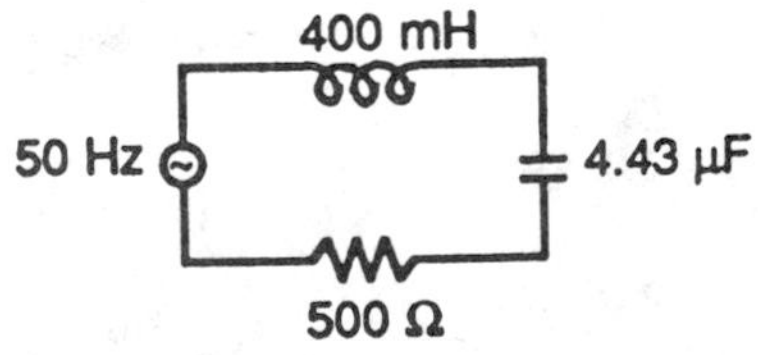

33.33

***33.34** From Equation 33.28, the current reaches a maximum when $\omega_0 L = \dfrac{1}{\omega_0 C}$

(a) $L = \dfrac{1}{\omega_0^2 C} = \dfrac{1}{(2\pi f)^2 C} = \boxed{662\ \mu\text{H}}$

(b) At resonance, $Z = R$ and $V_{\text{rms}} = I_{\text{rms}} R = (0.14\ \text{A})(1500\ \Omega) = \boxed{210\ \text{V}}$

33.35 $I_{\text{rms}} = 0.707 I_m = 0.707(0.138) = 97.6\ \text{mA}$

$V_{\text{rms}} = I_{\text{rms}} Z = (97.6 \times 10^{-3})(1521) = 148\ \text{V}$

$P_{\text{av}} = I_{\text{rms}}^2 R = (97.6 \times 10^{-3})^2 (150) = \boxed{1.43\ \text{W}}$

$P_{\text{av}} = I_{\text{rms}} V_{\text{rms}} \cos\phi = (97.6 \times 10^{-3})(148)\cos(-84.3°) = 1.43\ \text{W}$

33.36 (a) $\cos\phi = \cos(51°) = \boxed{0.627}$

(b) $I_{\text{rms}} = \dfrac{I_m}{\sqrt{2}} = \dfrac{0.097\ \text{A}}{\sqrt{2}} = \boxed{69.0\ \text{mA}}$

(c) $P_{\text{av}} = \dfrac{I_m V_m \cos\phi}{2} = \dfrac{(0.0972\ \text{A})(140\ \text{V})(0.627)}{2} = \boxed{4.27\ \text{W}}$

***33.37** $\omega = 1000\ \dfrac{\text{rad}}{\text{s}}$, $R = 400\ \Omega$, $C = 5 \times 10^{-6}\ \text{F}$, $L = 0.5\ \text{H}$

$V_{\text{max}} = 100\ \text{V}$, $\omega\text{L} = 500\ \Omega$, $\left(\dfrac{1}{\omega \text{C}}\right) = 200\ \Omega$

$$\text{Z} = \sqrt{\text{R}^2 + \left(\omega\text{L} - \frac{1}{\omega\text{C}}\right)^2} = \sqrt{400^2 + 300^2} = 500\ \Omega$$

$$\text{I}_{\text{max}} = \frac{\text{V}_{\text{max}}}{\text{Z}} = \frac{100}{500} = 0.2\ \text{A}$$

From Equation 33.36,

$P_{\text{AV}} = I_{\text{rms}}^2 R = (0.2)^2(400) = \boxed{8.0\ \text{W}}$

***33.38** $V_{max} = 100\text{ V},\ C = 2 \times 10^{-4}\text{ F},\ L = 0.1\text{ H},\ R = 20\ \Omega$

(a) $f = 60\text{ Hz},\ \omega = 377\ \dfrac{\text{rad}}{\text{s}},\ \omega L = 37.7\ \Omega,\ \dfrac{1}{\omega C} = 13.26\ \Omega$

$$Z = \sqrt{R^2 + \left(\omega L - \frac{1}{\omega C}\right)^2} = 31.58\ \Omega$$

$$I_{max} = \frac{V_{max}}{Z} = \frac{100\text{ V}}{31.58\ \Omega} = 3.17\text{ A}$$

$$P_{AV} = I_{rms}^2 R = \frac{I_{max}^2}{2} R = \boxed{100.3\text{ W}}$$

$$P_{AV} = \frac{1}{2} I_m V_m \cos\phi,\ \boxed{\cos\phi = 0.633}$$

(b) $f = 50\text{ Hz},\ \omega = 314\ \dfrac{\text{rad}}{\text{s}},\ \omega L = 31.4\ \Omega,\ \dfrac{1}{\omega C} = 15.9\ \Omega$

$$Z = \sqrt{20^2 - (31.4 - 15.9)^2} = 25.3\ \Omega$$

$$I_{max} = \frac{V_{max}}{Z} = \frac{100\ V}{23.3\ \Omega} = 3.95\text{ A}$$

$$P_{AV} = I_{rms}^2 R = \frac{I_{max}^2}{2} R = \boxed{156.0\text{ W}}$$

$$P_{AV} = \frac{1}{2} I_m V_m \cos\phi,\ \boxed{\cos\phi = 0.790}$$

33.39 $V = V_m \sin(\omega t) = \sqrt{2} V_{rms} \sin(\omega t) = 200\sqrt{2}\ \sin[2\pi(100\ t)] = (283\text{ V}) \sin(628\ t)$

33.40 $P_{av} = I_{rms}^2 R$

$$R = \frac{450}{5^2} = \boxed{18.0\ \Omega}$$

33.41 (a) $P_{av} = I_{rms}V_{rms}\cos\phi = (9)(180)\cos(-37°) = 1294\ \text{W}$

$$P_{av} = I_{rms}^2 R$$

$$1294 = (9)^2 R$$

$$R = \boxed{16.0\ \Omega}$$

(b) $\tan\phi = \dfrac{X_L - X_C}{R}$

$$\tan(-37°) = \frac{X_L - X_C}{16}$$

$$X_L - X_C = \boxed{-12.0\ \Omega}$$

33.42 $Z = \sqrt{R^2 + (X_L - X_C)^2}$

$$X_L - X_C = \sqrt{75^2 - 45^2} = 60\ \Omega$$

$$\phi = \tan^{-1}\left(\frac{X_L - X_C}{R}\right) = \tan^{-1}\left(\frac{60}{45}\right) = 53.1°$$

$$I_{rms} = \frac{V_{rms}}{Z} = \frac{210}{75} = 2.8\ \text{A}$$

$$P_{av} = I_{rms}V_{rms}\cos(53.1°) = \boxed{353\ \text{W}}$$

33.43 $f = \dfrac{1}{2\pi\sqrt{LC}} = \dfrac{1}{2\pi\sqrt{(120\times10^{-3})(8.4\times10^{-6})}} = \boxed{159\ \text{Hz}}$

33.44 $Q_s \cong \dfrac{\omega_0 L}{R} = \dfrac{1}{R}\sqrt{\dfrac{L}{C}}$ (Eq. 33.43)

(a) From problem 26: $Q_0 \cong \dfrac{1}{68}\sqrt{\dfrac{0.160}{99\times10^{-6}}} = \boxed{0.591}$

From problem 27: $Q_0 \cong \dfrac{1}{150}\sqrt{\dfrac{0.460}{21\times10^{-6}}} = \boxed{0.987}$

(b) High $Q_0 \Longrightarrow$ sharp resonance:

33.45 $\omega_0 = 2\pi(99.7\times10^6) = 6.264\times10^8\ \text{rad/s} = \dfrac{1}{\sqrt{LC}}$

$$C = \frac{1}{\omega_0^2 L} = \frac{1}{(6.264\times10^8)^2(1.40\times10^{-6})} = \boxed{1.82\ \text{pF}}$$

***33.46** At resonance,

$$\frac{1}{2\pi fC} = 2\pi fL$$

$$\frac{1}{(2\pi f)^2 L} = C$$

The range of values for C is

<u>46.5 pF</u> to <u>419 pF</u>

33.47 (a)

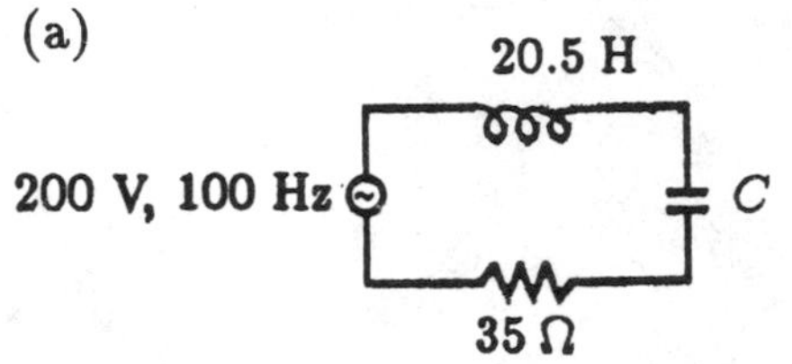

33.47

$$X_L = \omega L = 2\pi(100\text{ Hz})(20.5\text{ H}) = 12{,}880\ \Omega$$

$$Z = \frac{V_{\text{rms}}}{I_{\text{rms}}} = \frac{200}{4} = 50\ \Omega = \sqrt{R^2 + (X_L - X_C)^2} = \sqrt{35^2 + (12{,}880 - X_C)^2}$$

$$X_C = 12{,}915\ \Omega = \frac{1}{2\pi(100)C} \qquad C = 123 \times 10^{-9}\text{ F} = \boxed{123\text{ nF}}$$

(b) $V_{\text{rms}} = I_{\text{rms}} X_L = (4\text{ A})(12{,}880\ \Omega) = \boxed{51.5\text{ kV}}$

Notice, this is a large voltage!

***33.48** $L = 20\text{ mH},\ C = 10^{-7}\text{ F},\ R = 20\ \Omega,\ \text{V}_{\text{m}} = 100\text{ V}$

(a) The resonant frequency for a series–RLC circuit is

$$f = \frac{1}{2\pi}\sqrt{\frac{1}{LC}} = \boxed{3.56\text{ kHz}}$$

(b) At resonance,

$$I_{\text{max}} = \frac{V_{\text{max}}}{R} = \boxed{5.00\text{ A}}$$

(c) From Equation 33.43,

$$Q = \frac{\omega_0 L}{R} = \boxed{22.4}$$

(d) $\text{V}_{\text{L}} = \text{X}_{\text{L}} I = \omega L I = \boxed{2240\text{ V}}$

***33.49** $L = 10\text{ mH},\ C = 10^{-4}\text{ F},\ R = 10\ \Omega,\ V_{rms} = 50\text{ V}$

(a) At resonance, $I_{rms} = \dfrac{V_{rms}}{R} = \boxed{5.0\text{ A}}$

(b) At $\left(\dfrac{\omega_0}{2}\right) = \dfrac{1}{2}\dfrac{1}{\sqrt{LC}} = 500\ \dfrac{\text{rad}}{\text{s}}$

$$I_{rms} = \frac{V_{rms}}{Z} = \frac{50\ V}{18} = \boxed{2.77\text{ A}}$$

(c) At $2\omega_0 = \dfrac{2}{\sqrt{LC}} = 2000\ \dfrac{\text{rad}}{\text{s}}$

$$I_{rms} = \frac{V_{rms}}{Z} = \frac{50\text{ V}}{18\ \Omega} = \boxed{2.77\text{ A}}$$

33.50 (a)
$$\frac{V_{out}}{V_{in}} = \frac{R}{\sqrt{R^2 + (\frac{1}{\omega C})^2}} = \frac{800\ \Omega}{\sqrt{(800\ \Omega)^2 + (\frac{1}{300\text{ s}^{-1}(0.09\times10^{-6}\text{C})})^2}}$$
$$= \frac{800\ \Omega}{\sqrt{(800\ \Omega)^2 + (3.70\times10^4\ \Omega)^2}} = \boxed{2.16\times10^{-2}}$$

(b)
$$\frac{V_{out}}{V_{in}} = \frac{800\ \Omega}{\sqrt{(800\ \Omega)^2 + (\frac{1}{7\times10^5\text{ s}^{-1})(0.09\times10^{-6}\text{ F})})^2}} = \boxed{0.9998}$$

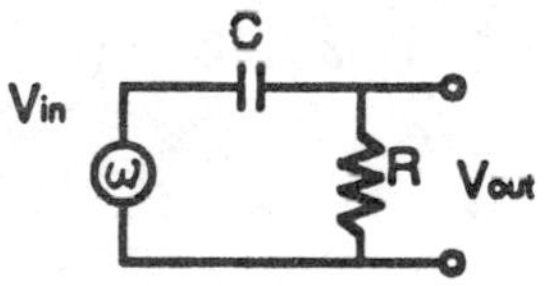

33.50

33.51 (a)
$$\frac{V_{out}}{V_{in}} = \frac{R}{\sqrt{R^2 + (\frac{1}{\omega C})^2}}$$

$$0.5 = \frac{0.50}{\sqrt{(0.50)^2 + (\frac{1}{\omega C})^2}}$$

$$(0.50)^2 + (\frac{1}{\omega C})^2 = 1$$

$$\left(\frac{1}{\omega C}\right)^2 = \frac{3}{4}$$

$$\omega C = \sqrt{\frac{4}{3}}$$

$$C = \sqrt{\frac{4}{3}}\frac{1}{2\pi(300)} = \boxed{613\ \mu\text{F}}$$

(b)
$$\frac{V_{out}}{V_{in}} = \frac{0.5}{\sqrt{(0.5)^2 + (\frac{1}{600\cdot 2\pi\cdot 613\ \mu\text{F}})^2}} = \boxed{0.756}$$

33.52 $\dfrac{V_{out}}{V_{in}} = \dfrac{\frac{1}{\omega C}}{\sqrt{R^2 + (\frac{1}{\omega C})^2}}$

(a) $f = 600$ Hz : $\dfrac{1}{\omega C} = \dfrac{1}{2\pi(600)(8 \times 10^{-9})} = 3.316 \times 10^4$

$$\frac{V_{out}}{V_{in}} = \frac{3.316 \times 10^4}{\sqrt{90^2 + (3.316 + 10^4)^2}} = \boxed{0.9999963 \cong 1}$$

(b) $f = 600$ kHz : $\dfrac{1}{\omega C} = 33.16$

$$\frac{V_{out}}{V_{in}} = \frac{33.16}{\sqrt{90^2 + 33.16^2}} = \boxed{0.346}$$

33.53 (a) $\dfrac{V_{out}}{V_{in}} = \dfrac{\frac{1}{\omega C}}{\sqrt{(\frac{1}{\omega C})^2 + (R)^2}} = \dfrac{3.70 \times 10^4\ \Omega}{\sqrt{(3.70 \times 10^4\ \Omega)^2 + (800\ \Omega)^2}}$

$= \boxed{0.9998}$

(b) $\dfrac{V_{out}}{V_{in}} = \dfrac{15.9}{\sqrt{(19.9)^2 + (800)^2}} = 1.99 \times 10^{-2}$

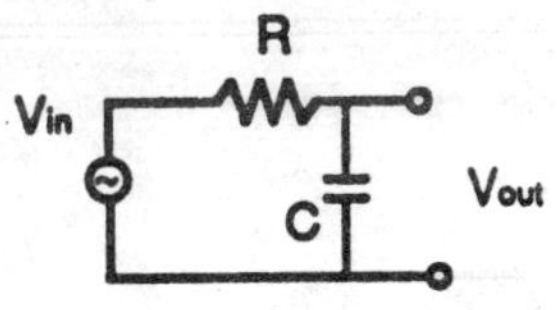

33.53

33.54 (a) $\left(\dfrac{V_{out}}{V_{in}}\right)$ is greatest when V_{LC} is smallest. Since V_L and V_C are 180° out of phase, their sum is smallest (viz, 0) when $X_L = X_C$. Then

$V_R = V_{in}$, and $(\dfrac{V_{out}}{V_{in}}) = 1$.

(b) $X_L = X_C$ at resonance: when $\boxed{f = \dfrac{1}{2\pi\sqrt{LC}}}$

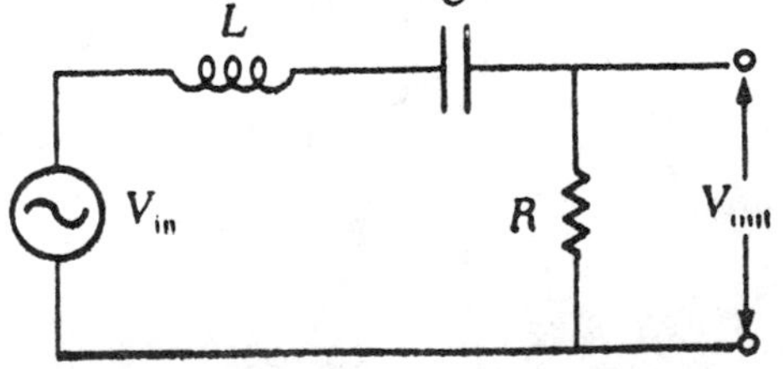

33.54 and 33.55

33.55 From Figure 33.55 b we obtain

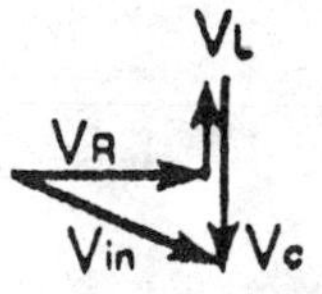

33.55

$$V_{\text{in}} = \sqrt{V_R^2 + (V_L - V_C)^2}$$

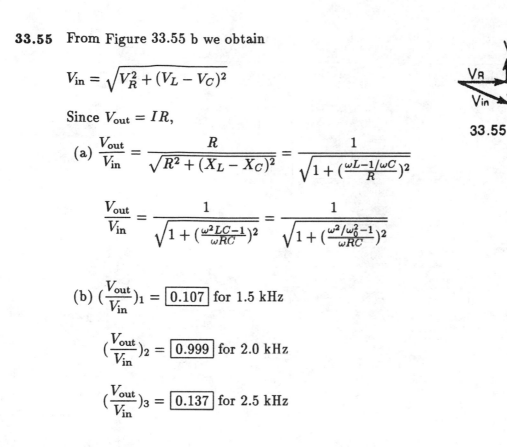

Since $V_{\text{out}} = IR$,

(a) $$\frac{V_{\text{out}}}{V_{\text{in}}} = \frac{R}{\sqrt{R^2 + (X_L - X_C)^2}} = \frac{1}{\sqrt{1 + (\frac{\omega L - 1/\omega C}{R})^2}}$$

$$\frac{V_{\text{out}}}{V_{\text{in}}} = \frac{1}{\sqrt{1 + (\frac{\omega^2 LC - 1}{\omega RC})^2}} = \frac{1}{\sqrt{1 + (\frac{\omega^2/\omega_0^2 - 1}{\omega RC})^2}}$$

(b) $(\frac{V_{\text{out}}}{V_{\text{in}}})_1 = \boxed{0.107}$ for 1.5 kHz

$(\frac{V_{\text{out}}}{V_{\text{in}}})_2 = \boxed{0.999}$ for 2.0 kHz

$(\frac{V_{\text{out}}}{V_{\text{in}}})_3 = \boxed{0.137}$ for 2.5 kHz

33.56 High-pass filter: $\frac{V_{\text{out}}}{V_{\text{in}}} = \frac{R}{\sqrt{R^2 + (\frac{1}{\omega C})^2}}$

$$\frac{(V_{\text{out}})_1}{(V_{\text{in}})_1} = \frac{R}{\sqrt{R^2 + (\frac{1}{\omega C})^2}}; \quad \frac{(V_{\text{out}})_2}{(V_{\text{in}})_2} = \frac{R}{\sqrt{R^2 + (\frac{1}{\omega C})^2}}$$

now $(V_{\text{in}})_2 = (V_{\text{out}})_1$, so

$$\frac{(V_{\text{out}})_2}{(V_{\text{in}})_1} = \frac{R^2}{R^2 + (\frac{1}{\omega C})^2} = \frac{1}{1 + (\frac{1}{\omega RC})^2}$$

33.57 Rewrite the circuit in terms of impedence. (See Fig. 33.57a)

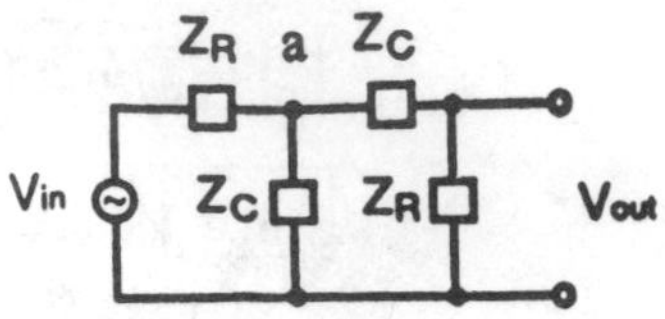

33.57a

Find $V_{out} = \dfrac{Z_R}{Z_R + Z_C} V_{ab}$ (See Fig. 33.57b)

$$V_{ab} = \frac{Z_C||(Z_C + Z_R)}{Z_C||(Z_C + Z_R) + Z_R} V_{in} \quad \text{(See Fig. 33.57c)}$$

$$\frac{V_{out}}{V_{in}} = \frac{Z_R[Z_C||(Z_C + Z_R)]}{(Z_R + Z_C)[Z_C||(Z_C + Z_R) + Z_R]}$$

$$= \frac{Z_R[\frac{Z_C(Z_C+Z_R)}{Z_C+Z_C+Z_R}]}{(Z_R + Z_C)[\frac{Z_C(Z_C+Z_R)}{Z_C+Z_C+Z_R} + Z_R]}$$

$$= \frac{Z_R Z_C}{Z_C(Z_C + Z_R) + Z_R(Z_R + 2Z_C)}$$

$$= \frac{Z_R}{3Z_R + Z_C + \frac{(Z_R)^2}{Z_C}}$$

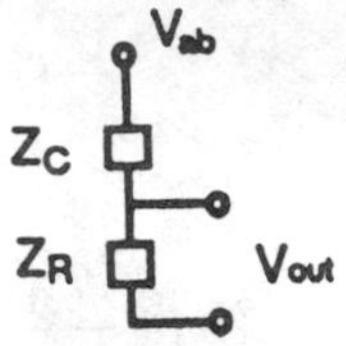

33.57b

Substitute for Z_C and Z_R in terms of phasors in the complex plane.

(See Fig. 33.57d)

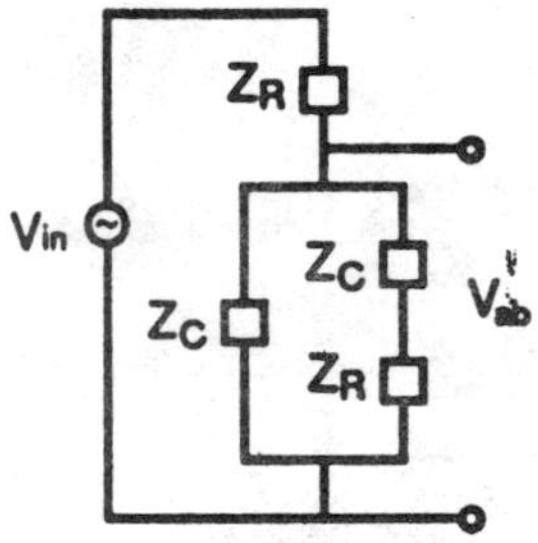

33.57c

$Z_R = R$ and $Z_C = \dfrac{-\hat{\jmath}}{\omega C}$, where $\hat{\jmath} = \sqrt{-1}$.

$$\frac{V_{out}}{V_{in}} = \frac{R}{3R - (\frac{1}{\omega C})\hat{\jmath} + R^2\omega C\hat{\jmath}}$$

where $\dfrac{1}{\hat{\jmath}} = -\hat{\jmath}$

$$\frac{V_{out}}{V_{in}} = \frac{R}{3R - (\frac{1}{\omega C} - R^2\omega C)\hat{\jmath}}$$

$$\frac{V_{out}}{V_{in}} = \frac{R}{\sqrt{(3R)^2 + (\frac{1}{\omega C} - R^2\omega C)}}$$

$$\frac{V_{out}}{V_{in}} = \frac{10^3}{\sqrt{(3 \times 10^3)^2 + (1592 - 628)^2}} = \boxed{0.317}$$

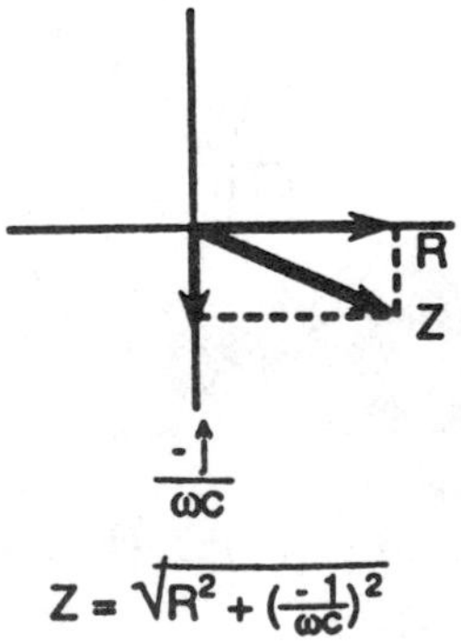

33.57d

***33.58** From Equation 33.48,

$$V_2 = \frac{N_2}{N_1} V_1 = \frac{50}{400}(120\ \text{V}_{\text{rms}})$$

$$\boxed{V_2 = 15.0\ \text{V (rms)}}$$

33.59 $V_{\text{out}} = \frac{N_2}{N_1} V_{\text{in}} = (\frac{2000}{350})(170\ \text{V}) = 971\text{V}$

$$(V_{\text{out}})_{\text{rms}} = \frac{(971\ \text{V})}{\sqrt{2}} = \boxed{687\ \text{V}}$$

33.60 "ideal" $\Longrightarrow P_{\text{out}} = P_{\text{in}}$

$$V_{\text{out}} I_{\text{out}} = V_{\text{in}} I_{\text{in}} \Longrightarrow \frac{I_{\text{out}}}{I_{\text{in}}} = \frac{V_{\text{in}}}{V_{\text{out}}} = \frac{N_1}{N_2}$$

33.61 $V_{\text{out}} = (\frac{2}{1}) V_{\text{in}} = \boxed{240\ \text{V (rms)}}$

$$P_{\text{out}} = 0.95 P_{\text{in}}$$

$$I_{\text{out}} V_{\text{out}} = 0.95 I_{\text{in}} V_{\text{in}}$$

$$I_{\text{out}} = \frac{0.95(5\ \text{A})(120\ \text{V})}{(240\ \text{V})} = \boxed{2.38\ \text{A}}$$

33.62 (a) $V_2 = \frac{N_2}{N_1} V_1$

$$N_2 = \frac{(2200)(80)}{110} = \boxed{1600\ \text{windings}}$$

(b) $I_1 V_1 = I_2 V_2$

$$I_1 = \frac{(1.5)(2200)}{110} = \boxed{30.0\ \text{A}}$$

33.63 $0.95 I_1 V_1 = I_2 V_2$

$$I_1 = \frac{(1.2)(2200)}{110(0.95)} = \boxed{25.3\ \text{A}}$$

33.64 $I_1V_1 = I_2V_2$

$$V_2 = \frac{(8.5)(77)}{1.4} = \boxed{468\ \text{V}}$$

33.65 $\omega_0 = \dfrac{1}{\sqrt{LC}} = \dfrac{1}{\sqrt{(0.05\ \text{H})(5 \times 10^{-6}\ \text{F})}} = 2000\ \text{s}^{-1}$

so the operating frequency of the circuit is $\omega = \dfrac{\omega_0}{2} = 1000\ \text{s}^{-1}$

Using Eq. 33.41 $P_{\text{av}} = \dfrac{V_{\text{rms}}^2 R\omega^2}{R^2\omega + L^2(\omega^2 - \omega_0^2)}$

$$P_{\text{av}} = \frac{(400)^2(8)(1000)^2}{(8)^2(1000)^2 + (0.05)^2(1-4) \times 10^6} = \boxed{56.7\ \text{W}}$$

***33.66** $R = 10\ \Omega$, $L = 2 \times 10^{-3}$ H, $C = 4 \times 10^{-6}$ F, $\omega = 2\pi f$

(a) $Z = \sqrt{R^2 + \left(\omega L - \dfrac{1}{\omega C}\right)^2} = \boxed{662\ \Omega}$

(b) $f_0 = \dfrac{1}{2\pi}\sqrt{\dfrac{1}{LC}} = \boxed{1.78\ \text{kHz}}$

(c) At resonance, $Z = R = \boxed{10\ \Omega}$

(d) At $\omega = \dfrac{1}{2}\sqrt{\dfrac{1}{LC}} = 5590\ \dfrac{\text{rad}}{\text{s}}$,

$$Z = \sqrt{10^2 + (11.2 - 44.7)^2} = \boxed{35.0\ \Omega}$$

33.67 (a) $I_m = \dfrac{\mathcal{E}_m}{\sqrt{R^2 + (X_L - X_C)^2}}$

where $X_L = \omega L = (\dfrac{2000}{\pi}\ \mathrm{s}^{-1})(0.025\ \mathrm{H}) = 15.9\ \Omega$

$X_C = (\omega C)^{-1} = [(2000\pi/\mathrm{s}^{-1})(17 \times 10^{-6}\ \mathrm{F})]^{-1} = 92.4\ \Omega$

so $I_m = \dfrac{150\ \mathrm{V}}{\sqrt{(21\ \Omega)^2 + (15.9\ \Omega - 92.4\ \Omega)^2}} = \boxed{1.89\ \mathrm{A}}$

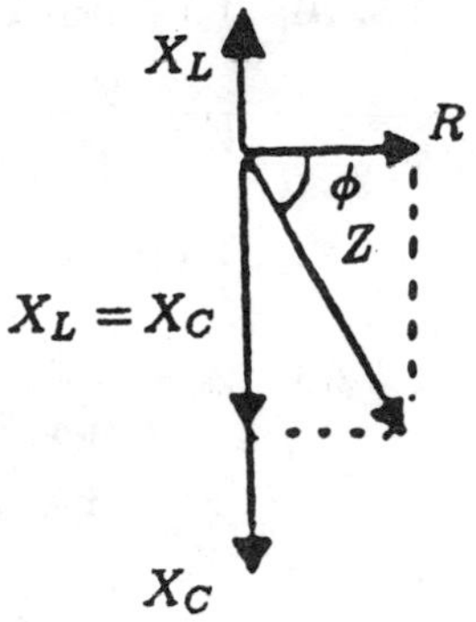

33.67

(b) $V_R = I_m R = (1.89\ \mathrm{A})(21\ \Omega) = \boxed{39.7\ \mathrm{V}}$

$V_L = I_m X_L = (1.89\ \mathrm{A})(15.9\ \Omega) = \boxed{30.1\ \mathrm{V}}$

$V_C = I_m X_C = (1.89\ \mathrm{A})(92.4\ \Omega) = \boxed{175\ \mathrm{V}}$

(c) Power Factor $= \cos\phi = \cos[\tan^{-1}(\dfrac{X_L - X_C}{R})]$

$\cos\phi = \cos[\tan^{-1}(\dfrac{15.9 - 92.4}{21})] = \boxed{0.265}$

(d) See phasor diagram at the right.

***33.68** $R = 1.5\ \Omega,\ L = 2.5\ \mathrm{mH},\ V_{\mathrm{rms}} = 12.5\ \mathrm{V},\ \mathrm{f} = 400\ \mathrm{Hz}$

(a) $Z = \sqrt{R^2 + \left(\omega L - \dfrac{1}{\omega C}\right)^2} = \boxed{6.46\ \Omega}$

(b) $I_{\mathrm{rms}} = \dfrac{V_{\mathrm{rms}}}{Z} = \boxed{1.94\ \mathrm{A}}$

(c) $V_{\mathrm{R}} = I_{\mathrm{rms}} R = \boxed{2.90\ \mathrm{V}}$

(d) $V_{\mathrm{L}} = I_{\mathrm{rms}} \omega L = \boxed{12.2\ \mathrm{V}}$

***33.69** The resistance of the circuit is

$$R = \frac{V}{I} = \frac{12\text{ V}}{0.63\text{ A}} = 19.05\ \Omega$$

The impedance of the circuit is

$$Z = \frac{V_{rms}}{I_{rms}} = \frac{24.0\text{ V}}{0.57\text{ A}} = 42.1\ \Omega$$

$$Z^2 = R^2 + \omega^2 L^2$$

$$L = \frac{1}{\omega}\sqrt{Z^2 - R^2} = \frac{1}{377}\sqrt{(42.1)^2 - (19.05)^2} = \boxed{99.6\text{ mH}}$$

***33.70** $R = 2500\ \Omega,\ C = 10^{-7}\text{ F},\ V_{rms} = 2.5\text{ V},\ \omega = 628/\text{s}$

(a) $Z = \sqrt{R^2 + \left(\frac{1}{\omega C}\right)^2} = \boxed{16.1\text{ k}\Omega}$

(b) $I_{rms} = \frac{V_{rms}}{Z} = \boxed{0.155\text{ mA}}$

33.71 (a) $R = (4.5 \times 10^{-4}\ \Omega/\text{m})(6.44 \times 10^5\text{ m}) = 290\ \Omega$ and

$$I = \frac{P}{V} = \frac{5 \times 10^6\text{ W}}{5 \times 10^5\text{ V}} = 10\text{ A};$$

$$P_{loss} = I^2 R = (10\text{ A})^2(290\ \Omega) = \boxed{2.90 \times 10^4\text{ W}}$$

(b) $\frac{P_{loss}}{P} = \frac{2.9 \times 10^4}{5 \times 10^6} = \boxed{5.8 \times 10^{-3}}$

(c) If the generator voltage is 4.6 V, and we again raise this voltage to 500 kV, the current in the transmission line is again 10 A. The terminal voltage is 4.5 kV−(10 A)(2.90 Ω) = 1.6 kV. The power available is

$IV = (10\text{ A})(1.6\text{ kV}) = 16\text{ kW}$, which is far below the required 5000 kW needed.

***33.72** Since the lights are installed in parallel, the voltage is the same across each.

For each light, $P = \frac{V^2}{R}$ and $R = \frac{(12\text{ V})^2}{40\text{ W}} = 3.6\ \Omega$

(a) For the 8 lights in parallel,

$$\frac{1}{R_{EQ}} = \frac{8}{R} = \frac{8}{3.6\ \Omega} \quad \boxed{R_{EQ} = 0.45\ \Omega}$$

(b) $I_2 = \frac{V_2}{R_{EQ}} = \frac{12\ V}{0.45\ \Omega} = \boxed{26.7\text{ A}}$

(c) From Equation 33.49,

$$I_1 = \frac{I_2 V_2}{V_1} = 2.67\text{ A}$$

The power consumed in the secondary is 320 W, therefore, $I_1^2 R_1 = 320$ W implies $\boxed{R_1 = 45.0\ \Omega}$

33.73 (b) First obtain an expression for the output/input formulas:

Circuit (a):

$$\boxed{V_{out} = \frac{\sqrt{R^2 + (\omega L)^2} V_{in}}{\sqrt{R^2 + (\omega L - \frac{1}{\omega C})^2}}}$$

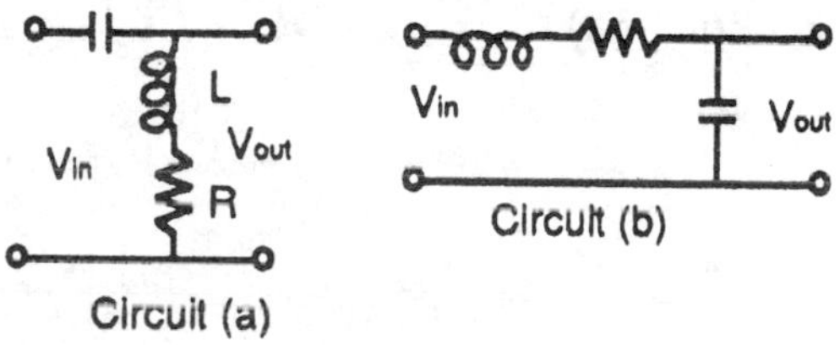

33.73

When $\omega \longrightarrow 0$, $\frac{V_{out}}{V_m} \approx \omega RC$

When $\omega \longrightarrow 0$, $\frac{V_{out}}{V_m} \approx 1$ (high-pass filter)

Circuit (b):

$$\boxed{V_{out} = \frac{\frac{1}{\omega C} V_{in}}{\sqrt{R^2 + (\omega L - \frac{1}{\omega C})^2}}}$$

When $\omega \longrightarrow 0$ $\frac{V_{out}}{V_{in}} \approx 1$

When $\omega \longrightarrow 0$ $\frac{V_{out}}{V_{in}} \approx \frac{1}{\omega^2 LC}$ (low pass filter)

(a) Circuit (a) is a high-pass filter, and circuit (b) is a low-pass filter.

33.74 (a) $I_{rms} = \frac{V_{rms}}{R} = \frac{100\text{ V}}{80\ \Omega} = \boxed{1.25\text{ A}}$

(b) Current *lags* the voltage. See sketch at right

$$I_L = \frac{V}{X_L} = \frac{V}{\omega L} = \frac{(100\text{ V})}{2\pi}(60\text{ s}^{-1})(0.2\text{ H}) = 1.33\text{ A}$$

$$\phi = \tan^{-1}(\frac{I_L}{I_R}) = \tan^{-1}(\frac{1.33}{1.25}) = \boxed{46.7°}$$

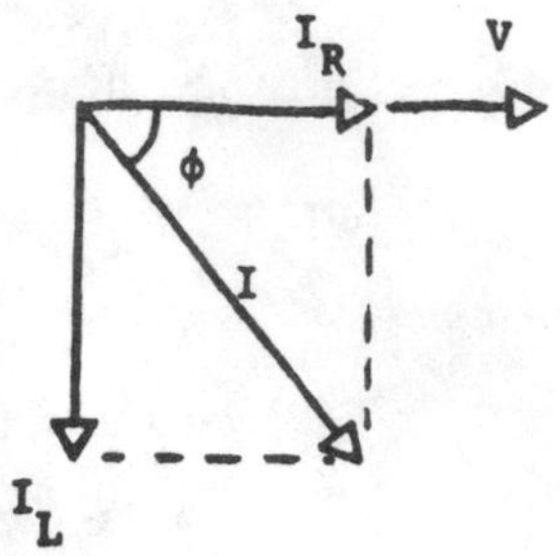

33.74

***33.75** $R = 80\ \Omega,\ V_{rms} = 110\text{ V},\ \omega = 377\ \frac{\text{rad}}{\text{s}}$

If $I_{rms}^2 R = 50$ W, then $I_{rms} = 0.79$ A.

Then $\frac{V_{rms}}{R_{rms}} = Z = 139.24\ \Omega$

$$Z^2 = R^2 + \omega^2 L^2$$

$$L = \frac{1}{\omega}\sqrt{Z^2 - R^2} = \frac{1}{377}\sqrt{(139.24)^2 - (80)^2} = \boxed{302\text{ mH}}$$

33.76 (a) $\mathcal{E}_m = I_m\sqrt{R^2 + (X_L + X_C)^2}$

where $(X_L - X_C)^2 = (\omega L - \frac{1}{\omega C})^2 = \frac{L^2}{\omega^2}(\omega_0^2 - \omega^2)^2$

therefore $\mathcal{E}_m = \frac{I_m}{\omega}\sqrt{\omega^2 R^2 + L^2(\omega_0^2 - \omega^2)^2}$

or $I_m = \frac{\omega \mathcal{E}_m}{\sqrt{L^2(\omega_0^2 - \omega^2)^2 + (\omega R)^2}}$

(b) $\phi = \tan^{-1}[\frac{X_L - X_C}{R}] = \tan^{-1}[\frac{L(\omega_0^2 - \omega^2)}{R\omega}]$

***33.77** $R = 200\ \Omega,\ L = 663\ \text{mH},\ C = 26.5\ \mu\text{F},\ \omega = 377\ \text{s}^{-1},\ \text{V}_{\text{max}} = 50\ \text{V},$

$$\text{wL} = 250\ \Omega, \quad \left(\frac{1}{\omega \text{C}}\right) = 100\ \Omega$$

(a) $I = \dfrac{V}{Z} = \dfrac{50\ \text{V}}{250\ \Omega} = \boxed{0.2\ \text{A}}$

$$\phi = \tan^{-1}\left(\frac{X_L - X_R}{R}\right) = \boxed{36.8°},\ V \text{ leads } I.$$

(b) $V_R = IR = 40\ \text{V at } \phi = 0°$

(c) $V_C = \dfrac{I}{\omega C} = 20\ \text{V at } \phi = -90° \quad \text{(I leads V)}$

(d) $V_L = I\omega L = 50\ \text{V at } \phi = +90° \quad \text{(V leads I)}$

***33.78** $L = 2\ \text{H},\ C = 10^{-5}\ \text{F},\ R = 10\ \Omega,\ V = (100 \sin \omega t)$

(a) The resonant frequency ω_0 produces the maximum current and thus the maximum power dissipation in the resistor.

$$\omega_0 = \frac{1}{\sqrt{LC}} = \frac{1}{\sqrt{(2)(10^{-5})}} = \boxed{224\ \frac{\text{rad}}{\text{s}}}$$

(b) $P = \dfrac{V^2}{2R} = \dfrac{(100)^2}{2(10)} = \boxed{500\ \text{W}}$

(c) $I = \dfrac{V}{Z} = \dfrac{V}{\sqrt{R^2 + \left(wL - \dfrac{1}{wC}\right)^2}}$ and $I_{\text{max}} = \dfrac{V}{R}$

$$I^2R = \frac{1}{2}I_{\text{max}}^2 R \text{ or } \frac{V^2}{Z^2}R = \frac{1}{2}\frac{V^2}{R^2}R$$

This occurs where $Z^2 = 2R^2$,

$$R^2 + \left(\omega L - \frac{1}{\omega C}\right)^2 = 2R^2,$$

$$\omega^4 L^2 C^2 - 2L\omega^2 C - R^2\omega^2 C^2 + 1 = 0$$

$$L^2C^2\omega^4 - (2LC + R^2C^2)\omega^2 + 1 = 0$$

$$[2^2(10 \times 10^{-6})^2]\omega^4 - [2(2)(10 \times 10^{-6}) + 10^2(10 \times 10^{-6})^2]\omega^2 + 1 = 0$$

$$\omega^2 = 51\ 130,\ 48\ 894$$

$$\omega_1 = \sqrt{48,894} = \boxed{221\ \frac{\text{rad}}{\text{s}}} \qquad \omega_2 = \sqrt{51,130} = \boxed{226\ \frac{\text{rad}}{\text{s}}}$$

33.79 (a) From Equation 33.48 $\frac{N_1}{N_2} = \frac{V_1}{V_2}$

Let the output impedance $Z_1 = \frac{V_1}{I_1}$ and the input impedance

$Z_2 = \frac{V_2}{I_2}$ so that $\frac{N_1}{N_2} = \frac{Z_1 I_1}{Z_2 I_2}$

But from Eq. 33.49 $\frac{I_1}{I_2} = \frac{V_2}{V_1} = \frac{N_2}{N_1}$

so combining with the previous result we have

$$\frac{N_1}{N_2} = \sqrt{\frac{Z_1}{Z_2}}$$

(b) $\frac{N_1}{N_2} = \sqrt{\frac{Z_1}{Z_2}} = \sqrt{\frac{8000}{8}} = \boxed{31.6}$

***33.80** (a) For maximum power transfer, the effective resistance of the 8 – Ω load (as viewed from the primary side) should be 3200 Ω. From Equation 33.50,

$$R_{\text{eff}} = \left(\frac{N_1}{N_2}\right)^2 R_2$$

Thus: $\frac{N_1}{N_2} = \left(\frac{R_{\text{eff}}}{R_2}\right)^{1/2} = \left(\frac{3200\ \Omega}{8\ \Omega}\right)^{1/2} = \boxed{20}$

The primary should have twenty times as many turns as the secondary.

(b) Using Equation 33.48 and substituting rms numerical values, we obtain

$$V_2 = V_1\left(\frac{N_2}{N_1}\right) = (80\text{ V rms})\frac{1}{20} = \boxed{4.00\text{ V (rms)}}$$

(c) The load current is $I_2 = \left(\frac{V_2}{R_2}\right) = \frac{4\text{ V rms}}{8} = \boxed{0.500\text{ A (rms)}}$

(d) Since the load is a pure resistance, the power is

$$P_2 = (I_{\text{rms}})^2 R_2 = (0.500\text{ A})^2(8\ \Omega) = \boxed{2.00\text{ W}}$$

(If the impedance-matching transformer were omitted and the load resistor connected directly to the AC source, the power in the load would be only 7.77×10^{-5} W).

(e) The rms current in the primary is $I_1 = \frac{V_1}{R_1} = \frac{80\text{ V rms}}{3200} = \underline{25\text{ mA (rms)}}$

So the current ratio is $\frac{I_1}{I_2} = \frac{25 \times 10^{-3}\text{ A rms}}{0.500\text{ A rms}} = \boxed{\frac{1}{20}}$

which is the inverse of the turns ratio.

33.81 $I_R = \dfrac{V_{\text{rms}}}{R}$; $I_L = \dfrac{V_{\text{rms}}}{\omega_L}$; $I_C = \dfrac{V_{\text{rms}}}{(\omega C)^{-1}}$

(a) $I = \sqrt{I_R^2 + (I_C - I_L)^2} = V_{\text{rms}}\sqrt{(\dfrac{1}{R^2}) + (\omega C - \dfrac{1}{\omega L})^2}$

(b) $\tan\phi = \dfrac{I_C - I_L}{I_R} = V_{\text{rms}}[\dfrac{1}{X_C} - \dfrac{1}{X_L}]\left(\dfrac{1}{V_{\text{rms}}/R}\right)$

$\tan\phi = R[\dfrac{1}{X_C} - \dfrac{1}{X_L}]$

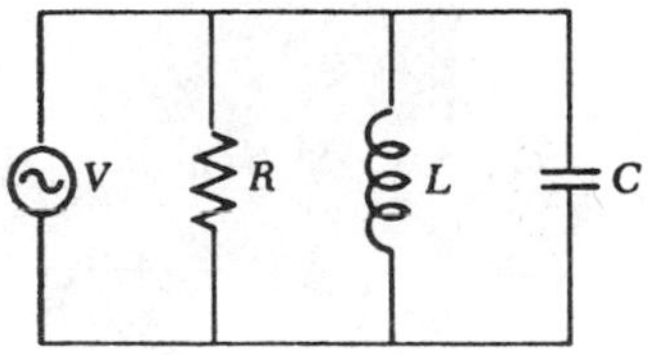

a

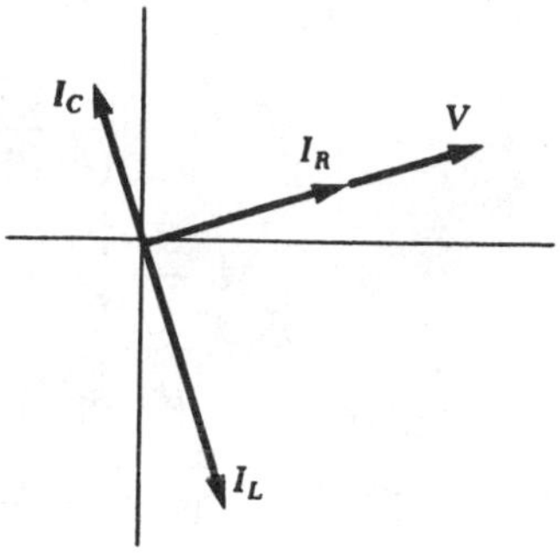

b

33.81

33.82 (a) $I = V_{\text{rms}}\sqrt{\dfrac{1}{R^2} + (\omega C - \dfrac{1}{\omega L})^2}$

$V_{\text{rms}} \longrightarrow V_{\text{rms(max)}}$ when $\omega C = \dfrac{1}{\omega L}$

$f = \dfrac{1}{2\pi\sqrt{LC}} = \dfrac{1}{2\pi\sqrt{(200\times10^{-3}\text{ H})(0.15\times10^{-6}\text{ F})}} = \boxed{919 \text{ Hz}}$

(b) $I_R = \dfrac{V_{\text{rms}}}{R} = \dfrac{120 \text{ V}}{80\ \Omega} = \boxed{1.50 \text{ A}}$

$I_L = \dfrac{V_{\text{rms}}}{\omega L} = \dfrac{120 \text{ V}}{(374 \text{ s}^{-1})(0.2 \text{ H})} = \boxed{1.60 \text{ A}}$

$I_C = V_{\text{rms}}(\omega C) = (120 \text{ V})(374 \text{ s}^{-1})(0.15\times10^{-6}\text{ F}) = \boxed{6.73 \text{ mA}}$

(c) $I_{\text{rms}} = \sqrt{I_R^2 + (I_C - I_L)^2} = \sqrt{(1.5)^2 + (0.0067 - 1.6)^2} = \boxed{2.19 \text{ A}}$

(d) $\phi = \tan^{-1}[\dfrac{I_C - I_L}{I_R}] = \tan^{-1}[\dfrac{0.0067 - 1.6}{1.5}] = \boxed{-46.7°}$

The current is lagging the voltage.

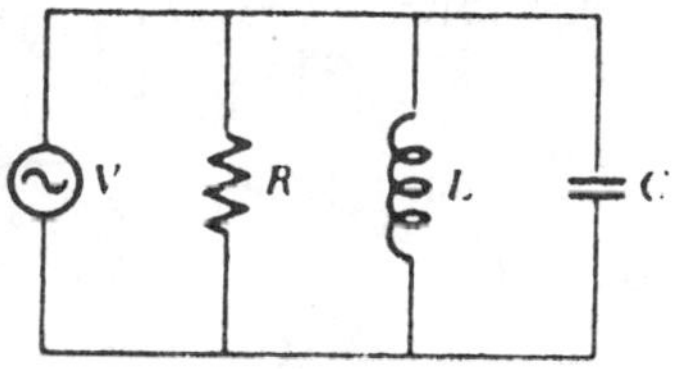

a

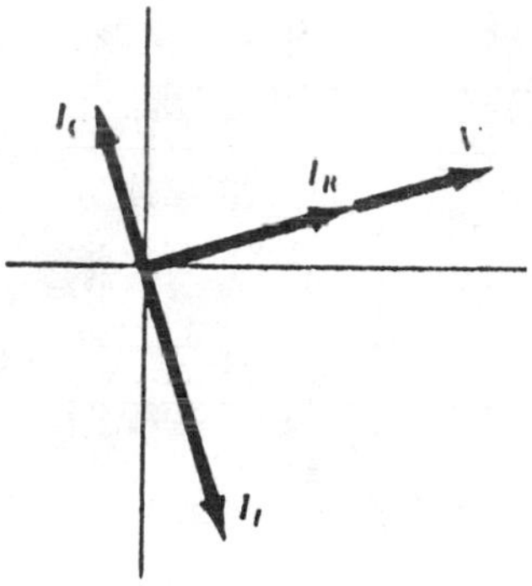
b

33.82

***33.83** From Equation (33.31),

(a) $\tan 30° = \dfrac{100\ \Omega}{R}$

$R = \boxed{173\ \Omega}$

(b) $(10 \text{ V})\cos 30° = \boxed{8.66 \text{ V}}$

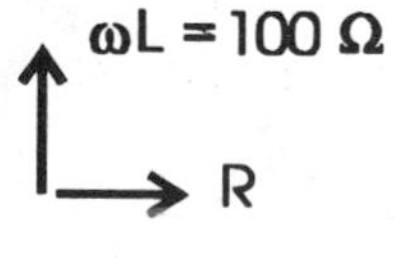

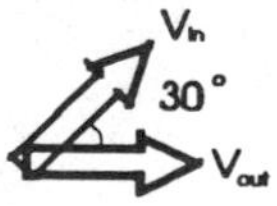

33.83

33.84 When $\omega = 4000\pi\ \text{s}^{-1}$,

$$X_L = \omega L = X_C = \frac{1}{\omega C} = 1884\ \Omega$$

$$\therefore L = \frac{1884}{4000\pi} = 0.15\ \text{H},\ \ R = 40\ \Omega$$

$$\therefore C = \frac{1}{(4000\pi)(1884)} = 42.2\ \mu\text{F}$$

(a)

$f(Hz)$	X_L	X_C	$Z(\Omega)$
300	282	12571	12288
600	565	6286	5720
800	754	4714	3960
1000	942	3769	2827
1500	1414	2514	1101
2000	1884	1884	40
3000	2828	1257	1572
4000	3768	942	2826
6000	5656	629	5027
10000	9420	377	9043

$Z = \sqrt{R^2 + (\omega L - \frac{1}{\omega C})^2}$

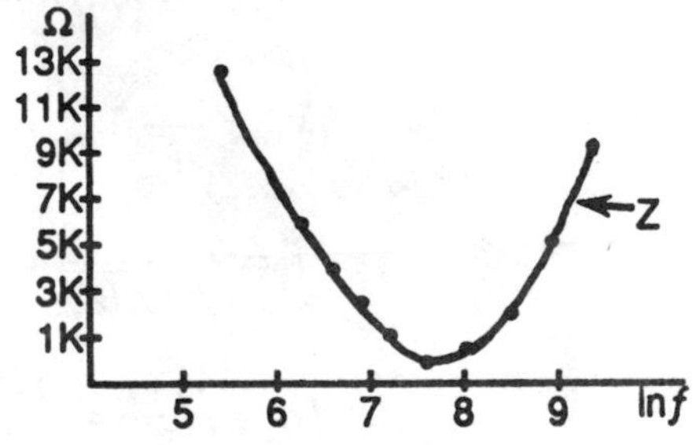

(b)

33.84

33.85 High-Pass Filter

$$\frac{V_{out}}{V_{in}} = \frac{R}{\sqrt{R^2 + (\frac{1}{\omega C})^2}}$$

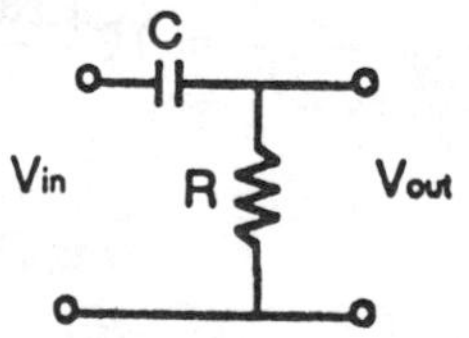

a

(a) $\frac{V_{out}}{V_{in}} = \frac{1}{2}$ when $\frac{1}{\omega C} = \sqrt{3}R$

$$\therefore \omega = \frac{1}{\sqrt{3}RC} = 1.15 \times 10^4 \text{ s}^{-1}$$

$$\text{or } f = \frac{\omega}{2\pi} = \boxed{1838 \text{ Hz}}$$

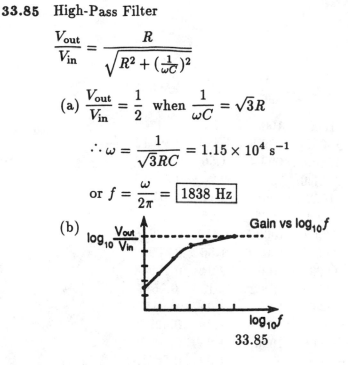

(b)

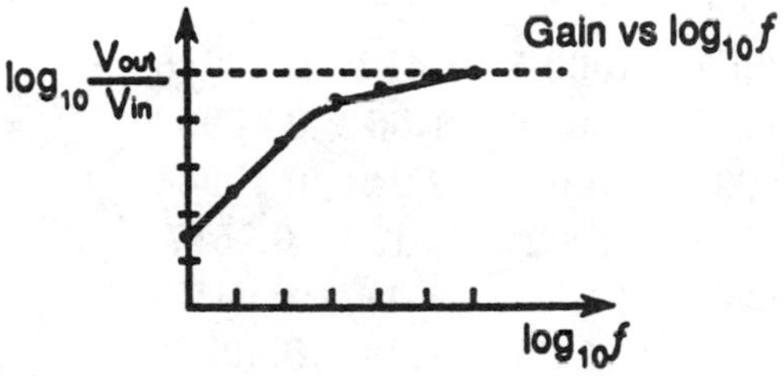

33.85

33.86 Low-Pass Filter

$$\frac{V_{out}}{V_{in}} = \frac{1/\omega C}{\sqrt{R^2 + (\frac{1}{\omega C})^2}}$$

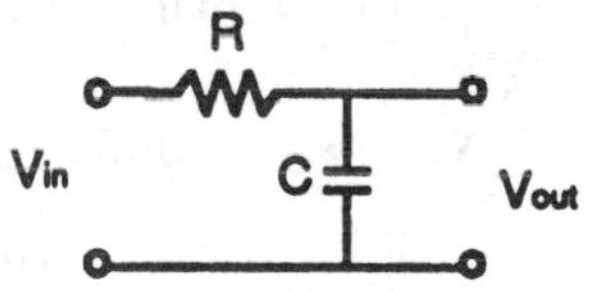

a

(a) $\frac{V_{out}}{V_{in}} = \frac{1}{2}$ when $\frac{1}{\sqrt{\omega^2 C^2 R^2 + 1}} = \frac{1}{2}$

or when $\omega^2 C^2 R^2 = 3$

$$\omega = \frac{\sqrt{3}}{RC} = 3.46 \times 10^4 \text{ s}^{-1}$$

$$\text{or } f = \frac{\omega}{2\pi} = 5513 \text{ Hz}$$

(b)

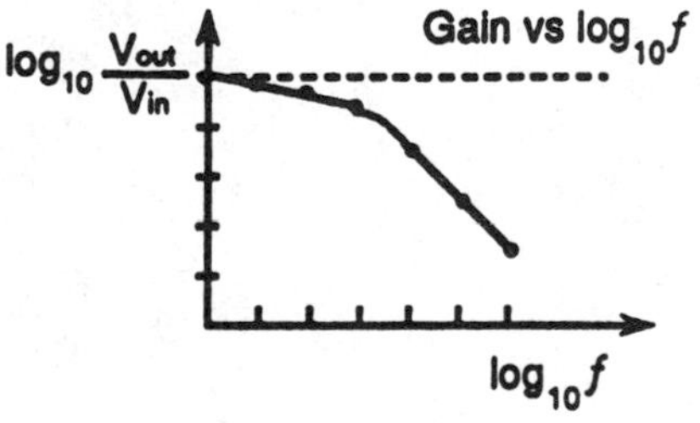

33.86

***33.87** $\omega_0 = \dfrac{1}{\sqrt{LC}} = 10^6\ \dfrac{\text{rad}}{\text{s}}$

$\omega_1\left(\dfrac{10^6}{\text{s}}\right)$	ωL	$\dfrac{1}{\omega C}$	Z	I^2R	
1	1000	1000	1	1	
1.0005	1000.5	999.5	1.414	0.50012	←
1.0006	1000.6	999.4	1.56	0.40998	
1.0010	1001.0	999	2.24	0.20016	
1.002	1002	998	4.12	0.0589	
1.004	1004	996	8.05	0.0154	
0.9995	999.5	1000.5	1.414	0.49988	←
0.9994	999.4	1000.6	1.56	0.40969	
0.9990	999	1001	2.24	0.19984	
0.9980	998	1002	4.13	0.0587	
0.9960	996		8.08	0.0153	
1.0004	1000.4	999.6	1.28	0.60985	
0.9996	999.6	1000.4	1.28	0.60966	
1.0001	1000.1	999.9	1.02	0.96154	

The full width at half maximum is

$$\Delta\omega = (1.000\text{ s} - 0.999\text{ s})\frac{10^6}{\text{s}}$$

$$= \frac{10^3}{\text{s}} = \frac{10\ \Omega}{1\text{ mH}}$$

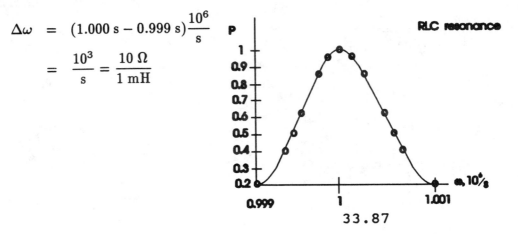

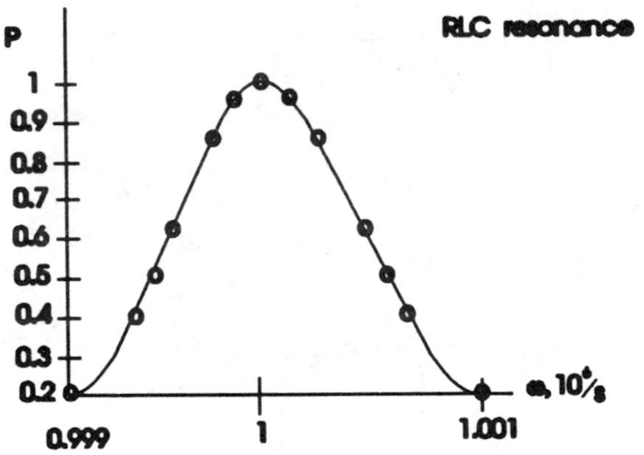

33.87

CHAPTER 34

34.1 $$c = \frac{1}{\sqrt{\mu_0\epsilon_0}} = \frac{1}{\sqrt{(4\pi \times 10^{-7}\ \mathrm{N/A^2})(8.854 \times 10^{-12}\ \mathrm{C^2/N \cdot m^2})}}$$

$$= (2.9979 \times 10^8)\sqrt{\frac{\mathrm{A^2 N \cdot m^2}}{\mathrm{N \cdot C^2}}} = 29979 \times 10^8\ \mathrm{m/s} = c$$

34.2 $$\frac{E}{B} = c$$

$$\frac{220}{B} = 3 \times 10^8$$

$$\boxed{B = 7.33 \times 10^{-7}\ \mathrm{T}}$$

34.3 (a) $$\frac{E}{H} = \frac{\mu_0 E}{B} = \mu_0 c = \frac{\mu_0}{\sqrt{\mu_0\epsilon_0}} = \sqrt{\frac{\mu_0}{\epsilon_0}}$$

(b) $$\sqrt{\frac{\mu_0}{\epsilon_0}} = \sqrt{\frac{4\pi \times 10^{-7}\ \mathrm{N/A^2}}{8.854 \times 10^{-12}\ \mathrm{C^2/N \cdot m^2}}} = 377(\frac{\mathrm{J}}{\mathrm{C^2/s}})(\frac{\Omega}{\mathrm{J \cdot s/C^2}}) = \boxed{377\ \Omega}$$

34.4 $$\frac{E}{B} = c$$

$$\frac{5.3 \times 10^{-3}}{B} = 3 \times 10^8$$

$$\boxed{B = 1.77 \times 10^{-11}\ \mathrm{T}}$$

34.5 (a) $$\frac{E}{B} = c$$

$$\frac{E}{5.4 \times 10^{-7}} = 3 \times 10^8$$

$$\boxed{E = 162\ \mathrm{V/m}}$$

(b) $$\frac{E}{5.4 \times 10^{-7}} = 0.8(3 \times 10^8)$$

$$\boxed{E = 130\ \mathrm{V/m}}$$

34.6 $v = \dfrac{1}{\sqrt{\kappa\mu_0\epsilon_0}} = \dfrac{1}{\sqrt{1.78}}c = 0.750c = \boxed{2.25 \times 10^8 \text{ m/s}}$

34.7 $E = \dfrac{1}{\sqrt{\epsilon_0\mu_0}} A e^{a(x-ct)}$

$$\frac{\partial E}{\partial x} = \frac{a(x-ct)}{\sqrt{\epsilon_0\mu_0}} A e^{a(x-ct)}$$

$$\frac{\partial E}{\partial t} = \frac{-ac(x-ct)Ae^{(x-ct)}}{\sqrt{\epsilon_0\mu_0}} = \frac{-ac(x-ct)}{\sqrt{\epsilon_0\mu_0}} A e^{a(x-ct)}$$

$B = Ae^{a(x-ct)}$;

$$\frac{\partial B}{\partial x} = a(x-ct)Ae^{(x-ct)}$$

$$\frac{\partial B}{\partial t} = -ac(x-ct)Ae^{(x-ct)}$$

From these we see that $\dfrac{\partial E}{\partial x} = -\dfrac{\partial B}{\partial t}$ since

$c = \dfrac{1}{\sqrt{\mu_0\epsilon_0}}$ and that $\dfrac{\partial B}{\partial x} = -\mu_0\epsilon_0 \dfrac{\partial E}{\partial t}$

***34.8** $\omega = 2\pi f = 6\pi \times 10^9 \text{ s}^{-1} = 1.88 \times 10^{10}/\text{s}$

$$k = \frac{2\pi}{\lambda} = \frac{\omega}{c} = \frac{6\pi \times 10^9}{3 \times 10^8} = 20\pi = 62.8 \text{ m}^{-1}$$

$$B_{\text{max}} = \frac{\text{E}}{c} = \frac{300 \text{ V/m}}{3 \times 10^8 \text{ m/s}} = 1\ \mu\text{T}$$

$$E = \left(300\ \frac{\text{V}}{\text{m}}\right) \cos(62.8\,x - 1.88 \times 10^{10} t)$$

$$B = (1.0\ \mu\text{T}) \cos(62.8\,x - 1.88 \times 10^{10} t)$$

34.9 (a) $f\lambda = c$

$f(50) = 3 \times 10^8$

$$\boxed{f = 6 \times 10^6 \text{ Hz} = 6.00 \text{ MHz}}$$

(b) $\dfrac{E}{B} = c$

$\dfrac{22}{B_0} = 3 \times 10^8$

$$\boxed{\boldsymbol{B}_0 = (73.3 \text{ nT})(-\boldsymbol{k})}$$

(c) $B = B_0(kx - \omega t)$

$k = \dfrac{2\pi}{\lambda} = \dfrac{2\pi}{50} = 0.126 \text{ m}^{-1}$

$\omega = 2\pi f = 2\pi(6 \times 10^6) = 3.77 \times 10^6 \text{ rad/s}$

$$\boxed{\boldsymbol{B} = (73.3 \text{ nT}) \cos(0.126x - 3.77 \times 10^7 t)(-\boldsymbol{k})}$$

34.10 $E = E_m \cos(kx - \omega t)$

$$\frac{\partial E}{\partial x} = -E_m \sin(kx - \omega t)(k)$$

$$\frac{\partial^2 E}{\partial x^2} = -E_m \cos(kx - \omega t)(k^2)$$

$$\frac{\partial E}{\partial t} = -E_m \sin(kx - \omega t)(-\omega)$$

$$\frac{\partial^2 E}{\partial t^2} = E_m \cos(kx - \omega t)(-\omega)^2$$

Show: $\dfrac{\partial^2 E}{\partial x^2} = -\mu_0 \epsilon_0 \dfrac{\partial^2 E}{\partial t^2}$

$$-(k^2) E_m \cos(kx - \omega t) = -\mu_0 \epsilon_0 (-\omega^2) E_m \cos(kx - \omega t)$$

$$\frac{k^2}{\omega^2} = \left(\frac{1}{f\lambda}\right)^2 = \frac{1}{c^2} = \mu_0 \epsilon_0$$

***34.11** (a) $B = \dfrac{E}{c} = \dfrac{100 \text{ V/m}}{3 \times 10^8 \text{ m/s}} = \boxed{3.33 \times 10^{-7} \text{ T}}$

(b) $\lambda = \dfrac{2\pi}{k} = \dfrac{2\pi}{10^7 \text{ m}^{-1}} = \boxed{6.28 \times 10^{-7} \text{ m}}$

(c) $f = \dfrac{c}{\lambda} = \dfrac{3 \times 10^8 \text{ m/s}}{6.28 \times 10^{-7} \text{ m}} = \boxed{4.78 \times 10^{14} \text{ Hz}}$

***34.12** $S = I = \dfrac{U}{At} = \dfrac{Uc}{V} = uc$

$$\frac{\text{Energy}}{\text{Unit Volume}} = u = \frac{I}{c} = \frac{1000\ \text{W/m}^2}{3\times10^8\ \text{m/s}} = \boxed{3.33\ \mu\text{J/m}^3}$$

34.13 Power $= SA = \dfrac{E_m^2}{2\mu_0 c}(4\pi r^2)$; solving for r we obtain

$$r = \sqrt{\frac{P\mu_0 c}{E_m^2 2\pi}} = \sqrt{\frac{(100\ \text{W})\mu_0 c}{2\pi(15\ \text{V/m})^2}} = \boxed{5.16\ \text{m}}$$

***34.14** (a) $I = \dfrac{(10\times10^{-3})\ \text{W}}{\pi(0.8\times10^{-3}\ \text{m})^2} = \boxed{4.97\times10^3\ \text{W/m}^2}$

(b) $u = \dfrac{I}{c} = \dfrac{4.97\times10^3\ \text{J/m}^2\cdot\text{s}}{3\times10^8\ \text{m/s}} = \boxed{16.6\ \mu\text{J/m}^3}$

34.15 $r = (5\ \text{mi})\left(\dfrac{1609\ \text{m}}{\text{mi}}\right) = 8045\ \text{m}$

$$S = \frac{P}{4\pi r^2} = \frac{250\times10^3\ \text{W}}{4\pi(8045\ \text{m})^2} = \boxed{3.07\times10^{-4}\ \text{W/m}^2}$$

34.16 (a) $S = \dfrac{P}{4\pi r^2} \longrightarrow r = \sqrt{\dfrac{P}{4\pi S}} = \sqrt{\dfrac{3.85\times10^{26}\ \text{W}}{4\pi(1000\ \text{W/m}^2)}} = \boxed{1.75\times10^{11}\ \text{m}}$

(17% larger than the Earth-Sun distance.)

(b) $u = \dfrac{S}{c} = \dfrac{1000\ \text{W/m}^2}{3\times10^8\ \text{m/s}} = \boxed{3.34\times10^{-6}\ \text{J/m}^3}$

***34.17** Using Equation 34.26,

$$I = \frac{E_{\rm m}^2}{2\mu_0 c} = \frac{P}{4\pi r^2}$$

$$P = \frac{E_{\rm m}^2}{2\mu_0 c} 4\pi r^2 = \frac{(0.2)^2(4\pi)(10^4)^2}{2(4\pi \times 10^{-7})(3 \times 10^8)}$$

$$P = \boxed{66.7\ \text{kW}}$$

34.18 $S_{\rm av} = \frac{c}{2\mu_0} B_m^2 = \boxed{0.201\ \text{W/m}^2}$

34.19 (a) $P = I^2 R = 150\ \text{W}; \quad A = 2\pi r L = 2\pi(0.9 \times 10^{-3}\ \text{m})(0.08\ \text{m}) = 4.52 \times 10^{-4}\ \text{m}^2$

$$S = \frac{P}{A} = \boxed{3.32 \times 10^5\ \text{W/m}^2} \text{ (points radially outward).}$$

(b) $B = \mu_0 \frac{I}{2\pi r} = \frac{\mu_0(1)}{2\pi(0.9 \times 10^{-3})} = \boxed{2.22 \times 10^{-4}\ \text{T}}$

$$E = \frac{\Delta V}{\Delta x} = \frac{IR}{\ell} = \frac{150\ \text{V}}{0.08\ \text{m}} = \boxed{1880\ \text{V/m}}$$

Note: $S = \frac{EB}{\mu_0} = 3.32 \times 10^5\ \text{W/m}^2$

***34.20** $I = \frac{100\ \text{W}}{4\pi(1\ \text{m})^2} = 7.96\ \text{W/m}^2$

$$u = \frac{I}{c} = 2.65 \times 10^{-8}\ \text{J/m}^3$$

(a) $u_{\rm E} = \frac{1}{2} u = \boxed{13.3 \times 10^{-9}\ \text{J/m}^3}$

(b) $u_{\rm B} = \frac{1}{2} u = \boxed{13.3 \times 10^{-9}\ \text{J/m}^3}$

(c) $I = \boxed{7.96\ \text{W/m}^2}$

34.21 (a) $S_{av} = \frac{P}{A} = \frac{5 \times 10^{-3}\ \text{W}}{4 \times 10^{-6}\ \text{m}^2} = 1.25 \times 10^3\ \text{W/m}^2$

$$S_{av} = \frac{E_m^2}{2\mu_0 c}$$

$$1.25 \times 10^3 = \frac{E_m^2}{2(4\pi \times 10^{-7})(3 \times 10^8)}$$

$$\boxed{E_m = 971\ \text{V/m}}$$

(b) $t = \frac{d}{v} = \frac{1}{3 \times 10^8} = 3.33 \times 10^{-9}\ \text{s}$

$$U = Pt = (5 \times 10^{-3})(3.33 \times 10^{-9}) = \boxed{1.67 \times 10^{-11}\ \text{J}}$$

or

$$U = u_{av}V = \frac{1}{2}\epsilon_0 E_m^2 (A\ell)$$

$$U = \frac{1}{2}(8.85 \times 10^{-12})(971)^2(4\ \text{mm}^2)(\frac{\text{m}}{1000\ \text{mm}})^2(1\ \text{m}) = 1.67 \times 10^{-11}\ \text{J}$$

34.22 (a) $B = \frac{E}{c} = \boxed{8.01 \times 10^{-7}\ \text{T}}$

(b) $S = \frac{EB}{\mu_0} = \boxed{153\ \text{W/m}^2}$

(c) $u_E = \frac{1}{2}\epsilon_0 E^2 = \boxed{2.55 \times 10^{-7}\ \text{J/m}^3}$

(d) $u_B = \frac{1}{2}\frac{B^2}{\mu_0} = \boxed{2.55 \times 10^{-7}\ \text{J/m}^3}$

34.23 (a) $E = cB = (3 \times 10^8\ \text{m/s})(1.8 \times 10^6\ \text{T}) = \boxed{540\ \text{V/m}}$

(b) $u_{av} = \frac{B^2}{\mu_0} = \frac{(1.8 \times 10^{-6})^2}{4\pi \times 10^{-7}} = \boxed{2.58 \times 10^{-6}\ \text{J/m}^3}$

(c) $S_{av} = cu_{av} = (3 \times 10^8)(2.58 \times 10^{-6}) = \boxed{774\ \text{W/m}^2}$

(d) The solar flux in Example 34.3 is 1000 W/m^2 which is greater then the value we calculated in part (c).

34.24 $S = I^2 \dfrac{R}{A}$; $I = \sqrt{\dfrac{SA}{R}} = \sqrt{\dfrac{(2.68 \times 10^3 \text{ W/m}^2)(2\pi)(1 \times 10^3 \text{ m})}{(2\ \Omega/\text{m})}} = \boxed{2.90 \text{ A}}$

34.25 $p = \dfrac{S}{c}$ complete absorption

$$p = \frac{25}{3 \times 10^8} = \boxed{8.33 \times 10^{-8} \text{ N/m}^2}$$

***34.26** The pressure p upon the mirror is $p = \dfrac{2S_{\text{av}}}{c}$ where

$S_{\text{av}} = \dfrac{P}{A}$ with A = cross-sectional area of the beam.

$$F = pA = \frac{2}{c}\left(\frac{P}{A}\right) A = \frac{2P}{c} = \frac{2(100 \times 10^{-3})}{(3 \times 10^8)} = \boxed{6.67 \times 10^{-10} \text{ N}}$$

***34.27** $I = \dfrac{P}{\pi r^2} = \dfrac{E_{\text{m}}^2}{2\mu_0 c}$

(a) $E_{\text{m}} = \sqrt{\dfrac{P \cdot 2\mu_0 c}{\pi r^2}} = \boxed{1.90 \times 10^3 \text{ N/C}}$

(b) $\dfrac{15 \times 10^{-3} \text{ J/s}}{3 \times 10^8 \text{ m/s}} = \boxed{5 \times 10^{-11} \text{ J/m}}$

(c) $P = \dfrac{U}{c} = \dfrac{5 \times 10^{-11}}{3 \times 10^8} = \boxed{1.67 \times 10^{-19} \text{ kg} \cdot \text{m/s}}$

***34.28** (a) $P = (S_{\text{av}})(\text{area}) = \left(6 \dfrac{\text{W}}{\text{m}^2}\right)(40 \times 10^{-4} \text{ m}^2) = 2.40 \times 10^{-2} \dfrac{\text{J}}{\text{s}}$

In one second, the total energy U impinging on the mirror is therefore 2.40×10^{-8} J. From Equation 39.33, the momentum p transferred each second for total reflection is

$$p = \frac{2U}{c} = \frac{2(2.40 \times 10^{-8} \text{ J})}{(3 \times 10^8 \text{ m/s})} = \boxed{1.60 \times 10^{-10} \frac{\text{kg} \cdot \text{m}}{\text{s}}} \quad \text{(each second)}$$

(b) $F = \dfrac{dp}{dt} = \dfrac{1.60 \times 10^{-10} \text{ kg} \cdot \text{m/s}}{1 \text{ s}} = \boxed{1.60 \times 10^{-10} \text{ N}}$

34.29 (a) $U = \frac{1}{2}SAt = \frac{1}{2}(750\ \text{W/m}^2)(0.5\ \text{m} \times 1\ \text{m})(60\ \text{s}) = \boxed{1.13 \times 10^4\ \text{J}}$

(b) $p = \frac{U}{c}$ for complete absorption; $p = \frac{2U}{c}$ for complete reflection. In our case 50% was reflected, so

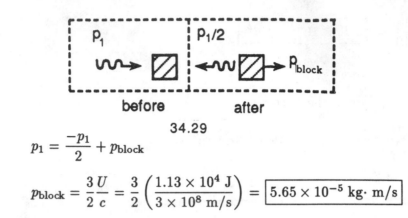

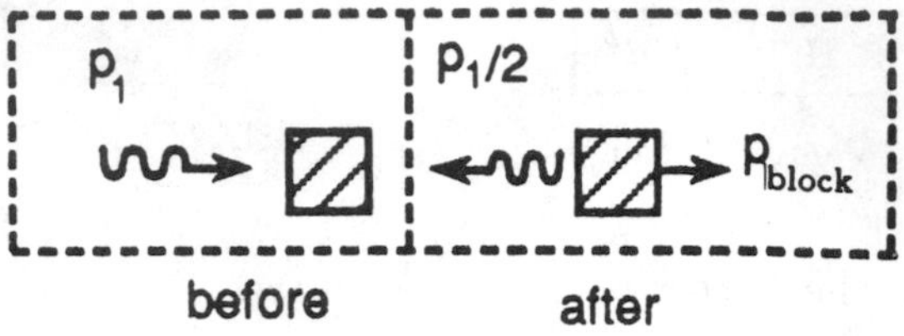

34.29

$$p_1 = \frac{-p_1}{2} + p_{\text{block}}$$

$$p_{\text{block}} = \frac{3}{2}\frac{U}{c} = \frac{3}{2}\left(\frac{1.13 \times 10^4\ \text{J}}{3 \times 10^8\ \text{m/s}}\right) = \boxed{5.65 \times 10^{-5}\ \text{kg} \cdot \text{m/s}}$$

***34.30** Assume $I = 1340\ \text{W/m}^2$

$$p = \frac{S}{c} = \frac{F}{A}$$

(a) $F = \frac{IA}{c} = \frac{(1340)\pi(6.4 \times 10^6)}{3 \times 10^8} = \boxed{5.7 \times 10^8\ \text{N}}$

(b) $F_{\text{grav}} = \frac{M_s G M_e}{r^2} = \frac{(2 \times 10^{30})(6.67 \times 10^{-11})(6 \times 10^{24})}{(1.5 \times 10^{11})}\ \text{N}$

$F_{\text{grav}} = \boxed{3.53 \times 10^{22}\ \text{N}}$

some 10^{14} times larger

34.31 (a) $P = S_{\text{av}}A = \left(\frac{\mu_0 J_0^2 c}{8}\right) A$

$$P = \left(\frac{4\pi \times 10^{-7}(10)^2(3 \times 10^8)}{8}\right)(1.2 \times 0.4) = \boxed{2.26 \times 10^3\ \text{W}}$$

(b) $S_{\text{av}} = \frac{\mu_0 J_0^2 c}{8} = \frac{(4\pi \times 10^{-7})(10)^2\ (3 \times 10^8)}{8} = \boxed{4.71 \times 10^3\ \text{W/m}^2}$

34.32 $S_{av} = \frac{\mu_0 J_0^2 c}{8}$

$$570 = \frac{(4\pi \times 10^{-7}) J_0^2 (3 \times 10^8)}{8}$$

$$\boxed{J_0 = 3.48\ \text{A/m}^2}$$

34.33 $\lambda = \frac{c}{f} = \frac{2.998 \times 10^8\ \text{m/s}}{20 \times 10^6\ \text{Hz}} = 14.99\ \text{m} \longrightarrow L = \frac{\lambda}{2} = \boxed{7.50\ \text{m}}$

34.34 $S_{av} = \frac{P_{av}}{4\pi r^2} = \frac{4 \times 10^3\ \text{W}}{4\pi (4 \times 1609\ \text{m})^2} = 7.68\ \mu\text{W/m}^2$

$$E_m = \sqrt{2\mu_0 c S_{av}} = 0.076\ \text{V/m}$$

$$\Delta V = E_m \cdot \ell = (76.1\ \text{mV/m})(0.65\ \text{m}) = \boxed{49.5\ \text{mV (amplitude) or } 35.0\ \text{mV (rms)}}$$

34.35 (a) $\mathcal{E} = -\frac{d\Phi_B}{dt} = -\frac{d}{dt}(BA\cos\theta) = -A\frac{d}{dt}(B_m \cos\omega t \cos\theta) = AB_m\omega(\sin\omega t \cos\theta)$

$\mathcal{E}(t) = 2\pi f B_m A \sin 2\pi f t \cos\theta = 2\pi^2 r^2 f B_m$. Thus $\mathcal{E}_m = 2\pi^2 r^2 f B_m \cos\theta$

Where θ is the angle between the magnetic field and the normal to the loop.

(b) If **E** is vertical, then **B** is horizontal, so the plane of the loop should be vertical, and the plane should point toward the transmitter.

34.36 (a) $\lambda = \frac{c}{f} = 535\ \text{m} \longrightarrow h = \frac{\lambda}{4} = \boxed{134\ \text{m}}$

(b) $\lambda = \frac{c}{f} = 187\ \text{m} \longrightarrow h = \frac{\lambda}{4} = \boxed{46.9\ \text{m}}$

34.37 $P = \dfrac{V^2}{R}$: $P \propto V^2$

$\Delta V = (-)E_y \cdot \Delta y = E_y \cdot \ell \cos\theta$

$\Delta V \propto \cos\theta \quad \therefore P \propto \cos^2\theta$

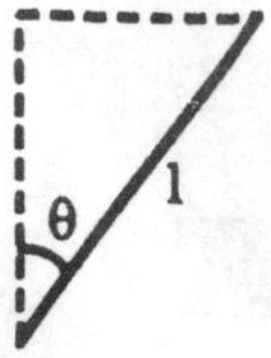

34.37

(a) $\theta = 15° \longrightarrow$ $\boxed{P = 0.933 P_{max}}$

(b) $\theta = 45° \longrightarrow$ $\boxed{P = 0.500 P_{max}}$

(c) $\theta = 90° \longrightarrow$ $\boxed{P = 0}$

34.38 (a) constructive interference occurs when $d\cos\theta = n\lambda$:

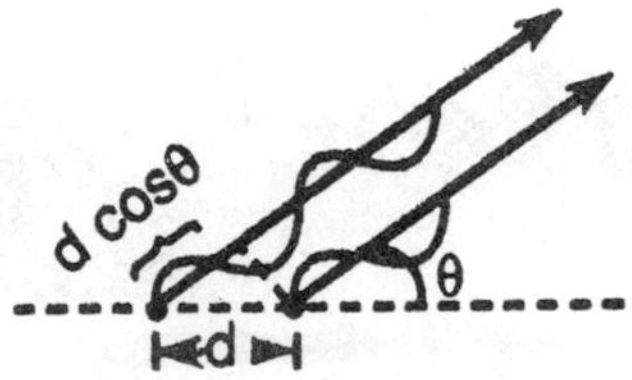

34.38

$$\cos\theta = n\frac{\lambda}{d} = n\left(\frac{\lambda}{\frac{1}{2}\lambda}\right) = 2n$$

$\therefore$ $\boxed{\text{strong signal @ } \theta = \cos^{-1} 0 = 90°, 270°}$

(b) destructive interference occurs when $d\cos\theta = \left(\dfrac{2n+1}{2}\right)\lambda$: $\cos\theta = 2n + 1$

$\therefore$ $\boxed{\text{weak signal @ } \theta \cos^{-1}(\pm 1) = 0°, 180°}$

34.39 (a) $f\lambda = c$

$(5 \times 10^{19}\ \text{Hz})\lambda = 3 \times 10^8$

$\boxed{\lambda = 6 \times 10^{-12}\ \text{m} = 0.006\ \text{Å}}$

(b) $f\lambda = c$

$(4 \times 10^9\ \text{Hz})\lambda = 3 \times 10^8\ \text{m/s}$

$\boxed{\lambda = 0.075\ \text{m}}$

34.40 $f = \dfrac{c}{\lambda} = \dfrac{3 \times 10^8\ \text{m/s}}{5.5 \times 10^{-7}\ \text{m}} = \boxed{5.45 \times 10^{14}\ \text{Hz}}$

34.41 (a) $f = \dfrac{c}{\lambda} = \boxed{3.00 \times 10^{10}\ \text{Hz}}$

(b) $f = \boxed{3.00 \times 10^{14}\ \text{Hz}}$

(c) $f = \boxed{5.17 \times 10^{14}\ \text{Hz}}$

(d) $f = \boxed{3.00 \times 10^{15}\ \text{Hz}}$

(e) $f = \boxed{3.00 \times 10^{20}\ \text{Hz}}$

34.42 (a) $\lambda_{\text{max}} = \dfrac{c}{f_{\text{min}}} = \dfrac{c}{540 \times 10^3} = \boxed{556\ \text{m}}$

$\lambda_{\text{min}} = \dfrac{c}{1600 \times 10^3} = \boxed{188\ \text{m}}$

(b) $\lambda_{\text{max}} = \dfrac{c}{88 \times 10^6} = \boxed{3.41\ \text{m}}$

$\lambda_{\text{min}} = \dfrac{c}{108 \times 10^6} = \boxed{2.78\ \text{m}}$

34.43 (a) CH_4 : $f_{\text{min}} = 66$ MHz $\lambda_{\text{max}} = \boxed{4.55\ \text{m}}$

$f_{\text{max}} = 72$ MHz $\lambda_{\text{min}} = \boxed{4.17\ \text{m}}$

(b) CH_6 : $f_{\text{min}} = 82$ MHz $\lambda_{\text{max}} = \boxed{3.66\ \text{m}}$

$f_{\text{max}} = 88$ MHz $\lambda_{\text{min}} = \boxed{3.41\ \text{m}}$

(c) CH_8 : $f_{\text{min}} = 180$ MHz $\lambda_{\text{max}} = \boxed{1.67\ \text{m}}$

$f_{\text{max}} = 186$ MHz $\lambda_{\text{min}} = \boxed{1.61\ \text{m}}$

34.44 (a) $P = SA = (1340\ \text{W/m}^2)4\pi(1.49 \times 10^{11}\ \text{m})^2 = \boxed{3.74 \times 10^{26}\ \text{W}}$

(b) $S = \dfrac{cB_{\text{m}}^2}{2\mu_0}$ so

$$B_m = \sqrt{\frac{2\mu_0 S}{c}}$$

$$B_m = \sqrt{\frac{2(4\pi \times 10^{-7}\ \text{N/A}^2(1340\ \text{W/m}^2)}{3 \times 10^8\ \text{m/s}}} = \boxed{3.35\ \mu\text{T}}$$

$$S = \frac{E_m^2}{2\mu_0 c}$$

$$E_m = \sqrt{2\mu_0 cS} = \sqrt{2(4\pi \times 10^{-7})(3 \times 10^8)(1340)} = \boxed{1.01 \times 10^3\ \text{V/m}}$$

34.45 $P = 0.3SA;$ $\quad A = \dfrac{P}{0.3S} = \dfrac{1 \times 10^6\ \text{W}}{(0.3)(1000\ \text{W/m}^2)} = \boxed{3330\ \text{m}^2}$

or the required area is approximately $(\frac{3}{4})$ of an acre.

34.46 (a) $\lambda = \dfrac{c}{f} = \boxed{1.50\ \text{cm}}$

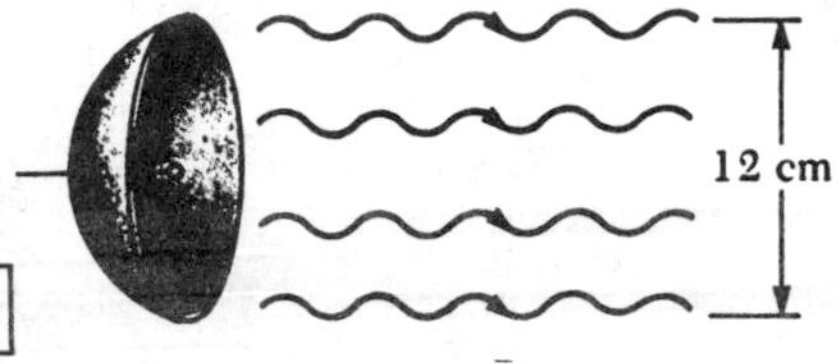

34.46

(b) $U = P \cdot \Delta t = (25 \times 10^3\ \text{W})(10^{-9}\ \text{s}) = \boxed{25.0 \times 10^{-6}\ \text{J}}$

(c) $u_{\text{av}} = \dfrac{U}{V} = \dfrac{25 \times 10^{-6}\ \text{J}}{\pi(0.06)^2(3 \times 10^8)(10^{-9})} = \boxed{7.37 \times 10^{-3}\ \text{J/m}^3}$

(d) $E_m = \sqrt{2U_{\text{av}}/\epsilon_0} = \boxed{4.08 \times 10^4\ \text{V/m}}$

$$B_m = \frac{E_m}{c} = \boxed{1.36 \times 10^{-4}\ \text{T}}$$

(e) $F = pA = \left(\dfrac{cu_{\text{av}}}{c}\right) A = \boxed{8.33 \times 10^{-5}\ \text{N}}$

34.47 (a) $B_m = \dfrac{E_m}{c} = \boxed{6.67 \times 10^{-16}\ \text{T}}$

(b) $S_{\text{av}} = \dfrac{E_m^2}{2\mu_0 c} = \boxed{5.31 \times 10^{-17}\ \text{W/m}^2}$

(c) $P_{\text{av}} = S_{\text{av}} A = \boxed{1.67 \times 10^{-14}\ \text{W}}$

(d) $F = p_{\text{av}} A = \left(\dfrac{S_{\text{av}}}{c}\right) A = \boxed{5.56 \times 10^{-23}\ \text{N}}$ ($\approx$ weight of 3000 H atoms!)

34.48 $S = \frac{EB}{\mu_0} = \frac{\frac{EB}{\mu_o} + \frac{EB}{\mu_0}}{2}$ where $E = Bc = \mu_0 cH$ and $B = \frac{E}{c}$

Therefore $S = \frac{(\frac{E}{\mu_0})(\frac{E}{c}) + (\frac{3\mu_0 H}{\mu_0})\mu_0 cH}{2} = [\epsilon_0 E^2 + \mu_0 H^2]\frac{c}{2}$

34.49 $P = \frac{S}{c} = \frac{\text{Power}}{Ac} = \frac{P}{2\pi r\ell c}$

$P = \frac{60}{2\pi(0.05)(1)(3\times 10^8\text{ m/s})} = \boxed{6.37\times 10^{-7}\text{ N/m}^2}$

34.50 $a = \frac{F}{m} = \frac{PA}{m} = \frac{2SA}{mc}$

$a = \frac{2(1340)(10^3\times 1500)}{(4000)(3\times 10^8)} = \boxed{3.35\times 10^{-3}\text{ m/s}^2}$

(Note that the pressure $= \frac{2S}{c}$ for *total reflection*)

***34.51** $u = \frac{1}{2}\epsilon_0 E_m^2$ (Equation 34.29)

$E_m = \sqrt{2u/\epsilon_0} = \boxed{95\text{ mV/m}}$

***34.52** $I_{surf} = (1350\text{ W/m}^2)(0.6) = 810\text{ W/m}^2$

$E_{abs} = \frac{1}{2}(810\text{ W/m}^2)(0.8\text{ m}^2)(60)(60)\text{ J}$

$E_{abs} = \boxed{1.2\text{ MJ}}$

34.53 $a = \frac{F}{m} = \frac{P_r A}{m} = \frac{SA}{mc} = \frac{P}{mc} = \frac{(100\text{ J})(0.2\text{ s}^{-1})}{(500\text{ kg})(3\times 10^8\text{ m/s})} = 1.33\times 10^{-11}\text{ m/s}^2$

Therefore $\Delta t = \frac{\Delta v}{a} = \frac{1\text{ m/s}}{1.33\times 10^{-11}\text{ m/s}^2} = \boxed{7.50\times 10^{10}\text{ s}}$

34.54 (a) $F_{\text{grav}} = \dfrac{GM_s m}{R^2} = (\dfrac{GM_s}{R^2})\rho(\dfrac{4}{3})\pi r^3$ where M_s = mass of sun,

r = radius of particle and R = distance from sun to particle.

Since $F_{\text{rad}} = \dfrac{S\pi r^2}{c}$ $\dfrac{F_{\text{rad}}}{F_{\text{grav}}} = (\dfrac{1}{r})(\dfrac{3SR^2}{4cGM_s\rho})$ or $\dfrac{F_{\text{rad}}}{F_{\text{grav}}} \propto \dfrac{1}{r}$

(b) From the result found in part (a), when $F_{\text{grav}} = F_{\text{rad}}$,

we have $r = \dfrac{3SR^2}{4cGM_s\rho}$

$$r = \frac{3(1.24\ \text{W/m}^2)(3.75\times 10^{11}/\text{m})^2}{4.(6.67\times 10^{-11}\ \text{N}\cdot\text{m}^2/\text{kg}^2)(1.99\times 10^{30}\ \text{kg})(1500\ \text{kg/m}^3)(2.997\times 10^8\ \text{m/s})}$$

$$= \boxed{3.78\times 10^{-7}\text{m}}$$

34.55 $F = P_r A = \dfrac{SA}{c} = \dfrac{PA}{Ac} = \dfrac{P}{c}$, $quad \tau = F(\dfrac{\ell}{2}) = \dfrac{P\ell}{2c}$, and $\tau = \kappa\theta$.

Therefore

$$\theta = \frac{P\ell}{2c\kappa} = \frac{(3\times 10^{-3})(0.06)}{2(3\times 10^8)(1\times 10^{-11})} = \boxed{3.00\times 10^{-2}\ \text{deg}}$$

34.56 (a) Let n = number of photons per unit volume

and Δx = thickness of the slab of material.

Then, $n = \dfrac{N}{\text{Volume}} = \dfrac{N}{A\Delta x} = (\dfrac{N}{A\Delta t})(\dfrac{\Delta x}{\Delta t})^{-1} = \dfrac{\Phi}{v}$ where the flux,

$\Phi \equiv \dfrac{N}{A\Delta t}$ and $v = \dfrac{\Delta x}{\Delta t}$

Therefore

$$n = \frac{10^{13}\ \text{photons/m}^2\text{/s}}{0.95(3\times 10^8\ \text{m/s})} = \boxed{3.51\times 10^4\ \text{photons/m}^3}$$

(b) $u = nU_{\text{photons}} = (3.51\times 10^4)(8.88\times 10^3)(1.6\times 10^{-19}) = \boxed{4.99\times 10^{-11}\ \text{J/m}^3}$

34.57 (a) $B_0 = \frac{E_0}{c} = \frac{175\text{ V/m}}{3\times10^8\text{ m/s}} = \boxed{5.83\times10^{-7}\text{ T}}$

$$k = \frac{2\pi}{\lambda} = \frac{2\pi}{(0.015\text{ m})} = \boxed{419\text{ m}^{-1}} \qquad \omega = kc = \boxed{1.26\times10^{11}\text{ rad/s}}$$

Since **S** is along x, and **E** is along y, **B** must be in the z direction. (That is $\mathbf{S}\propto\mathbf{E}\times\mathbf{B}$).

(b) $S_{\text{av}} = \frac{1}{2}S = \frac{E_0B_0}{2\mu_0} = \boxed{40.6\text{ W/m}^2}$

(c) $P_r = \frac{2S}{c} = \boxed{2.71\times10^{-7}\text{ N/m}^2}$

(d) $a = \frac{F}{m} = P_r\frac{A}{m} = (2.71\times10^{-7}\text{ W/m}^2)\frac{(0.75\text{ m}^2)}{(0.5\text{ kg})} = \boxed{4.07\times10^{-7}\text{ m/s}^2}$

34.58 (a) Treat the reflected wave as two separate processes: First, the motion of the car produces a "moving-observer" Doppler shift in the frequency of the waves striking the car:

$$f' = f(1+\frac{v}{c})$$

$$f' - f = \Delta f_1 = \frac{fv}{c}$$

Next, these Doppler-shifted waves are re-emitted by the moving source:

$$f'' = f'\left(\frac{1}{1-\frac{v}{c}}\right) \approx f'(1+\frac{v}{c}), \text{ using } (1+x)^n \approx 1+nx.$$

$f'' - f' = \Delta f_2 = f'\frac{v}{c}$ Together the two are shifted a total amount

$$\Delta f_1 + \Delta f_2 = (f+f')\frac{v}{c} \approx \boxed{\frac{2fv}{c}}$$

(b) At 35 mph, $\Delta f = \frac{2(10.525\times10^9\text{ Hz})(35\ \frac{\text{mi}}{\text{h}})(\frac{1\text{ h}}{3600\text{ s}})}{186{,}000\ \frac{\text{mi}}{\text{s}}} = \boxed{1.10\text{ kHz}}$

At 80 mph, $\Delta f = \frac{2(10.525\times10^9\text{ Hz})(80\ \frac{\text{mi}}{\text{h}})(\frac{1\text{ h}}{3600\text{ s}})}{186{,}000\ \frac{\text{mi}}{\text{s}}} = \boxed{2.51\text{ kHz}}$

***34.59** (a) $P = \frac{F}{A} = \frac{I}{c}$

$$F = \frac{IA}{c} = \frac{P}{c} = \frac{100\ \text{J}\cdot\text{s}}{\text{s}\ 3\times10^8\ \text{m}} = 3.33\times10^{-7}\ \text{N} = (110\ \text{kg})a$$

$$a = 3.03\times10^{-9}\ \text{m/s}^2$$

$$\text{x} = \frac{1}{2}a\text{t}^2 \quad \text{t} = \sqrt{\frac{2\text{x}}{a}} = 8.12\times10^4\ \text{s} = \boxed{22.6\ \text{h}}$$

(b)
$$0 = (107\ \text{kg})v - 3\ \text{kg}(12\ \text{m/s} - v)$$
$$= (107\ \text{kg})v - 36\ \text{k}\cdot\text{g m/s} + (3\ \text{kg})\ \text{v}$$
$$v = \frac{36}{110} = 0.327\ \text{m/s} \qquad \text{t} = \boxed{30.6\ \text{s}}$$

***34.60** $I = \frac{B_m^2 c}{2\mu_0} = \frac{P}{4\pi r^2}$

$$B_m = \sqrt{\frac{P}{4\pi r^2}\frac{2\mu_0}{c}} = \sqrt{\frac{10^4}{4\pi(5000)^2}\frac{2(4\pi\times10^{-7})}{3\times10^8}}$$

$$B_m = \boxed{5.16\times10^{-10}\ \text{T}}$$

Since the magnetic field of the earth is approximately 5×10^{-5} T, the earth's field is some 100,000 times stronger.

***34.61** (a) From Maxwell's first equation (34.1)

$$Q = \epsilon_0(E\cdot A)$$

$I = \frac{dQ}{dt} = \epsilon_0\frac{d}{dt}(E\cdot A)$ and since $Ed = V$,

$$I = \frac{\epsilon_0 A}{d}\frac{d}{dt}(E\cdot d) = \frac{\epsilon_0 A}{d}\frac{dV}{dt}$$

Noting that $\frac{\epsilon_0 A}{d}$ is the capacitance,

$$I_d = C\frac{dV}{dt}$$

(b) $\frac{dV}{dt} = \frac{I_d}{C} = \frac{IA}{10^{-6}\ \text{F}} = \boxed{10^6\ \text{V/s}}$

***34.62** We use the extended form of Ampère's law, Equation 34.6. Since no moving charges are present, $I = 0$ and we have

$$\oint \mathbf{B} \cdot d\boldsymbol{\ell} = \mu_0 \varepsilon_0 \frac{d\Phi_E}{dt}$$

In order to evaluate the integral, we make use of the symmetry of the situation. Symmetry requires that no particular direction from the center can be any different from any other direction. Therefore, there must be *circular symmetry* about the central axis. We know the magnetic field lines are circles about the axis. Therefore, as we travel around such a magnetic field circle, the magnetic field remains constant in magnitude. Setting aside until later the determination of the *direction* of **B**, we integrate $\oint \mathbf{B} \cdot d\boldsymbol{\ell}$ around the circle at $R = 0.15$ m to obtain $2\pi RB$. Differentiating the expression $\Phi_E = AE$, we have

$$\frac{d\Phi_E}{dt} = \left(\frac{\pi d^2}{4}\right) \frac{dE}{dt}$$

$$\text{Thus } \oint \mathbf{B} \cdot d\boldsymbol{\ell} = 2\pi RB = \mu_0 \varepsilon_0 \left(\frac{\pi d^2}{4}\right) \frac{dE}{dt}$$

$$\text{Solving for } B \text{ gives} B = \frac{\mu_0 \varepsilon_0}{2\pi R} \left(\frac{\pi d^2}{4}\right) \frac{dE}{dt}$$

Substituting the numerical values yields

$$B = \frac{(4\pi \times 10^{-7}\ \text{H/m})(8.85 \times 10^{-12}\ \text{F/m})(\pi)(0.10\ \text{m})^2(20\ \text{V/m} \cdot \text{s})}{(2\pi)(0.15\ \text{m})(4)}$$

$$= \boxed{1.85 \times 10^{-18}\ \text{T}}$$

In Figure 34.20, the direction of the *increase* of electric field is out of the plane of the paper. By the right-hand rule, this implies that the direction of **B** is *counterclockwise*. Thus the direction of **B** at P is upwards.

***34.63** $f = 90\text{ MHz},\ E_m = 2 \times 10^{-3}\text{ V/m}$

(a) $\lambda = \dfrac{c}{f} = \boxed{3.33\text{ m}}$

$$T = \frac{1}{f} = \boxed{1.11 \times 10^{-8}\text{ s}}$$

$$B_m = \frac{E_m}{c} = \boxed{6.67 \times 10^{-12}\text{ T}}$$

(b) $\mathbf{E} = (2 \times 10^{-3}\text{ V/m}) \cos 2\pi \left(\dfrac{x}{3.33\text{ m}} - \dfrac{t}{1.11\text{ ns}}\right) \mathbf{j}$

$$\mathbf{B} = (6.67 \times 10^{-12}\text{ T}) \cos 2\pi \left(\frac{x}{3.33\text{ m}} - \frac{t}{1.11\text{ ns}}\right) \mathbf{k}$$

(c) $I_{AV} = \dfrac{E_m^2}{2\mu_0 c} = \dfrac{(2 \times 10^{-3})^2}{2(4\pi \times 10^{-7})(3 \times 10^8)}$

$$I_{AV} = \boxed{5.31 \times 10^{-9}\text{ W/m}^2}$$

(d) $I_{av} = cu_{av} \quad u = \boxed{1.77 \times 10^{-17}\text{ J/m}^3}$

(e) $p = \dfrac{2I}{c} = \dfrac{(2)(5.3 \times 10^{-9})}{3 \times 10^8} = \boxed{3.54 \times 10^{-17}\text{ Pa}}$

CHAPTER 35

35.1
$$c = \sqrt{1/\mu_0\epsilon_0}$$
$$= \sqrt{1/(4\pi \times 10^{-7}\mathrm{N \cdot s^2/C^2})(8.854 \times 10^{-12}\ \mathrm{C^2/N \cdot m^2})}$$
$$= 2.998 \times 10^8\ \mathrm{m/s}$$

35.2
$$\Delta x = ct;\ c = \frac{\Delta x}{t} = \frac{2(1.5 \times 10^8\ \mathrm{km})(1000\ \mathrm{m/km})}{(2.2\ \mathrm{min})(60\ \mathrm{s/min})}$$
$$= \boxed{2.27 \times 10^8\ \mathrm{m/s}}$$

35.3 $c = \dfrac{\Delta d}{\Delta t}$; $\Delta d = c\Delta t$; To find the average distance between the earth and sun we want $\Delta d/2$.

$$\frac{\Delta d}{2} = \frac{ct}{2} = \frac{1}{2}(2.9979 \times 10^8\ \mathrm{m/s})(1320\ \mathrm{s})$$
$$= 1.98 \times 10^{11}\ \mathrm{m} = \boxed{1.98 \times 10^8\ \mathrm{km}}$$

35.4 For a *total* path length of $d = 2\ell$, the time traveled between faces on the rotating wheel is $t = 2\ell/c$. During this time the wheel rotates through an angle, $\theta = \omega t$. Therefore

$$\omega = \frac{c\theta}{d} = \frac{(3 \times 10^8\ \mathrm{m/s})(2\pi/32\ \mathrm{rad})}{(8\ \mathrm{mi})(1.61 \times 10^3\ \mathrm{m/mi})}$$
$$\omega = \boxed{4570\ \mathrm{rad/s}}$$

35.5 $t = \dfrac{2\ell}{c}$; $\theta = \omega t = \omega(\dfrac{2\ell}{c})$ so

$$\omega = \frac{c\theta}{2\ell} = \frac{(3 \times 10^8)[2\pi/(720)]}{2(11.45 \times 10^3)} = \boxed{114\ \mathrm{rad/s}}$$

35.6 For $d = 40$ m; $t = \frac{d}{v} = \frac{40 \text{ m}}{3 \times 10^8 \text{ m/s}} = 1.33 \times 10^{-7}$ s

For $\frac{1}{360}$ rev $\Longrightarrow$ $\omega = \frac{\theta}{t} = \frac{(1/360)}{1.33 \times 10^{-7} \text{ s}} = 2.09 \times 10^4$ rps.

The next speed yielding transmission is twice this or 4.18×10^4 rps.

For $d = 4000$ m; $t = \frac{d}{v} = \frac{4000 \text{ m}}{3 \times 10^8 \text{ m/s}} = 1.33 \times 10^{-5}$ s

For $\frac{1}{360}$ rev $\rightarrow \omega = \frac{\theta}{t} = \frac{(1/360)}{1.33 \times 10^{-5} \text{ s}} = 2.09 \times 10^2$ rps.

The next speed yielding transmission is twice this or 4.18×10^2 rps.

35.7 $t = \frac{2(9 \times 10^3 \text{ m})}{3 \times 10^8 \text{ m/s}} = 6 \times 10^{-5} \text{ s} = 60\ \mu\text{s}$

35.8 Because of refraction effects, the coin's apparent depth = $\boxed{75 \text{ cm}}$

35.9 (a) $f = \frac{c}{\lambda} = \frac{3 \times 10^8 \text{ m/s}}{6.328 \times 10^{-7} \text{ m}} = \boxed{4.74 \times 10^{14} \text{ Hz}}$

(b) $\lambda_{\text{glass}} = \frac{\lambda_{\text{air}}}{n} = \frac{632.8 \text{ nm}}{1.5} = \boxed{422 \text{ nm}}$

$c_{\text{glass}} = \frac{c_{\text{air}}}{n} = \frac{3 \times 10^8 \text{ m/s}}{1.5} = \boxed{2 \times 10^8 \text{ m/s}}$

35.10 For all practical purposes, the index of refraction of air is 1,

so $n_1 = 1$. Also $n_2(\text{ water}) = 1.333$. Then, using Snell's law (Eq. 35–8), we have

$1 \sin\theta_1 = 1.333 \sin\theta_2$

so that $\sin\theta_2 = \dfrac{1}{1.333}\sin 35^\circ$

from which $\theta_2 = 25.5^\circ$.

The average wavelength of sodium yellow light in vacuum (or air) is $\lambda_1 = 5893$ Å.

Therefore, using Eq. 35–5, we find the wavelength in water to be

$$\lambda_2 = \frac{n_1}{n_2}\lambda_1 = \frac{1}{1.333}(5893\ \text{Å}) = \boxed{4421\ \text{Å}}$$

35.11 $n_1 \sin\theta_1 = n_2 \sin\theta_2$

$\sin\theta_1 = 1.33 \sin 45^\circ$

$\sin\theta_1 = (1.33)(0.707) = 0.940$

$\theta_1 = \boxed{70.5^\circ} \longrightarrow 19.5^\circ$ above the horizon.

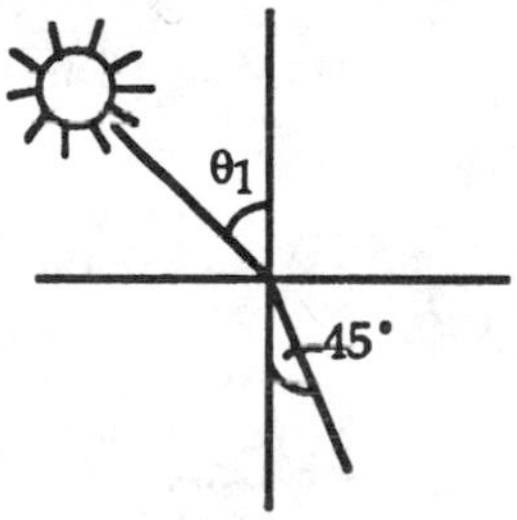

35.11

35.12 $n_1 \sin\theta_1 = n_2 \sin\theta_2$; $1 \sin 30^\circ = 1.333 \sin\theta_2$

$\boxed{\theta_2 = 22.0^\circ}$

35.13 $n_1 \sin\theta_1 = n_2 \sin\theta_2 \Longrightarrow \theta_1 = \sin^{-1}[(n_2/n_1)\sin\theta_2]$

$\theta_1 = \sin^{-1}[(1.458/1)\sin(37^\circ)] = \boxed{61.3^\circ}$

35.14 $n_1 \sin\theta_1 = n_2 \sin\theta_2$; $1.333 \sin 37^\circ = n_2 \sin 25^\circ$

$n_2 = 1.898 = \dfrac{c}{v}$; $\quad v = \dfrac{c}{1.898} = \boxed{1.58 \times 10^8\ \text{m/s}}$

35.15 $n_1 \sin\theta_1 = n_2 \sin\theta_2; \quad \theta_2 = \sin^{-1}(\frac{n_1 \sin\theta_1}{n_2})$

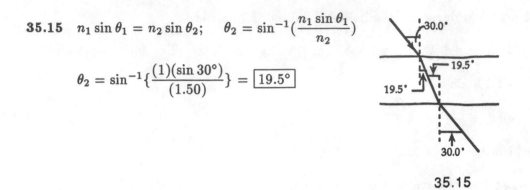

$$\theta_2 = \sin^{-1}\{\frac{(1)(\sin 30°)}{(1.50)}\} = \boxed{19.5°}$$

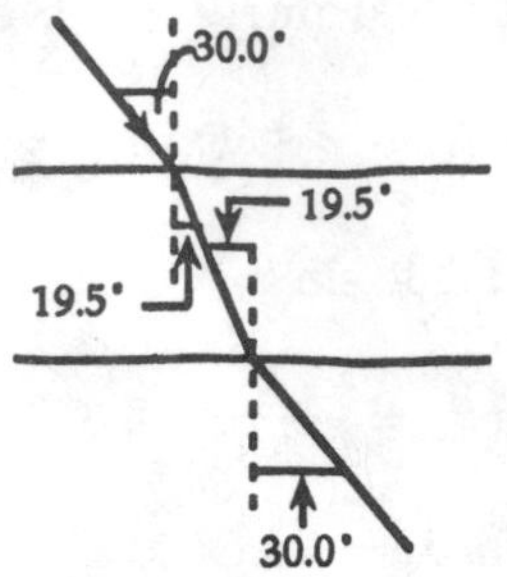

35.15

***35.16** (a) Flint Glass $v = \frac{c}{n} = \frac{3 \times 10^8 \text{ m/s}}{1.66} = \boxed{1.81 \times 10^8 \text{ m/s}}$

(b) Water $v = \frac{c}{n} = \frac{3 \times 10^8 \text{ m/s}}{1.333} = \boxed{2.25 \times 10^8 \text{ m/s}}$

(c) Zircon $v = \frac{c}{n} = \frac{3 \times 10^8 \text{ m/s}}{1.923} = \boxed{1.56 \times 10^8 \text{ m/s}}$

***35.17** (a) Water $\lambda = \frac{\lambda_0}{n} = \frac{436 \text{ nm}}{1.333} = \boxed{327 \text{ nm}}$

(b) Glass $\lambda = \frac{\lambda_0}{n} = \frac{436 \text{ nm}}{1.52} = \boxed{287 \text{ nm}}$

35.18 Let α equal the angle between the reflected ray and the refracted ray.

Therefore $\alpha = 180° - (\theta_1 + \theta_2)$; (see Figure 35.10a). From Snell's

law $\theta_2 = \sin^{-1}[(\frac{n_1}{n_2}) \sin\theta_1] = \sin^{-1}[(\frac{1}{1.49}) \sin 53°] = 32.4°$

Therefore $\alpha = 180° - (53° + 32.4°) = \boxed{94.6°}$

35.19 $\lambda_0 = n_w \lambda_w = n_b \lambda_b \Longrightarrow \frac{n_w}{n_b} = \frac{\lambda_b}{\lambda_w} = \frac{390 \text{ nm}}{438 \text{ nm}} = \boxed{0.890}$

35.20 $\sin\theta_1 = n_w \sin\theta_2$

$$\sin\theta_2 = \frac{1}{1.333} \sin\theta_1 = \frac{1}{1.333} \sin(90° - 28°) = 0.66$$

$$\theta_2 = \sin^{-1} 0.66 = 41.5°$$

$$h = \frac{d}{\tan\theta_2} = \frac{3 \text{ m}}{\tan 41.5°} = \boxed{3.4 \text{ m}}$$

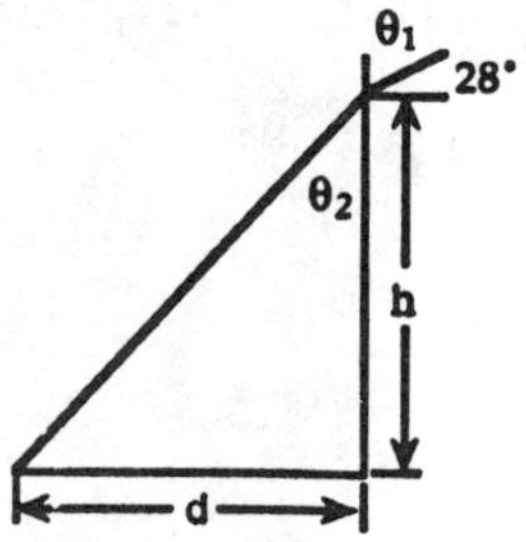

35.20

35.21 $n_1 \sin\theta_1 = n_2 \sin\theta_2; \quad \theta_2 = \sin^{-1}(\frac{n_1 \sin\theta_1}{n_2});$

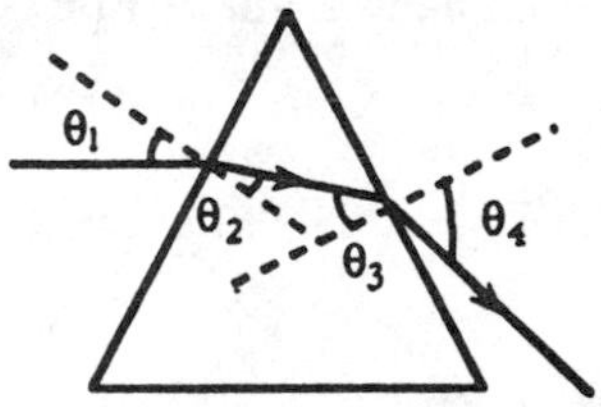

35.21

$$\theta_2 = \sin^{-1}\{\frac{(1)(\sin 30°)}{1.50}\} = 19.5°$$

$$\theta_3 = \{[(90° - 19.5°) + 60°] - 180°\} + 90° = 40.5°$$

$$n_3 \sin\theta_3 = n_4 \sin\theta_4; \quad \theta_4 = \sin^{-1}(\frac{n_3 \sin\theta_3}{n_4});$$

$$\theta_4 = \sin^{-1}\{\frac{(1.50)(\sin 40.5°)}{1}\} = 77°$$

35.22 $n = \frac{\sin(\phi + \delta_m)/2}{\sin(\phi/2)} = \frac{\sin(60° + 37°)/2}{\sin(60°/2)} = \boxed{1.50}$

35.23 From Eq. 35.9 $n = \frac{\sin[(\phi + \delta_m)/2]}{\sin(\phi/2)}$. Therefore

$$\delta_m = 2[\sin^{-1}(\frac{n \sin\phi}{2}) - \phi/2] = 2[\sin^{-1}(1.52 \sin\pi/24) - \pi/24]$$

$$\delta_m = 0.138 \text{ rad} = \boxed{7.89°}$$

35.24 $n_1 \sin\theta_1 = n_2 \sin\theta_2;\ \theta_2 = \sin^{-1}(\frac{n_1 \sin\theta_1}{n_2})$

$$\theta_{Blue} = \sin^{-1}\{\frac{(1)(\sin 30°)}{1.6500}\} = 17.640°$$

$$\theta_{Red} = \sin^{-1}\{\frac{(1)(\sin 30°)}{1.6150}] = 18.035°$$

$$\Delta\theta = \theta_{Red} - \theta_{Blue} = 18.035° - 17.640° = \boxed{0.395°}$$

35.25 $n = \frac{\sin[(\Phi + \delta_m)/2]}{\sin(\Phi/2)}$

for small Φ, $\delta_m \approx \Phi$

$$n \approx \frac{(\Phi + \delta_m)/2}{\Phi/2}$$

so $\delta_m = (n - 1)\Phi$, where Φ is in radians

35.26 (a) $1.62 = \frac{\sin[(30° + \delta_m)/2]}{\sin(30°/2)}$; *quad* $\delta_m = 19.6°$

$$\delta_m \approx (1.62 - 1)(30)(\pi/80) = 0.32 \text{ rad} = \boxed{18.6°}$$

(b) $1.62 = \frac{\sin[(10° + \delta_m)/2]}{\sin(10°/2)}$; $\quad \delta_m = 6.23°$

$$\delta_m \approx (1.62 - 1)(10)(\pi/180) = 0.108 \text{ rad} = \boxed{6.20°}$$

35.27 Expect a small apex angle, therefore use the small angle approximation. (Problem 25)

$$\delta_m = (n-1)\phi \text{ or } \phi = \frac{\delta_m}{(n-1)} = \frac{10°}{(1.544-1)} = \boxed{18.4°}$$

35.28 $n(700 \text{ nm}) = 1.455; \quad n \sin\theta = n' \sin\theta'$

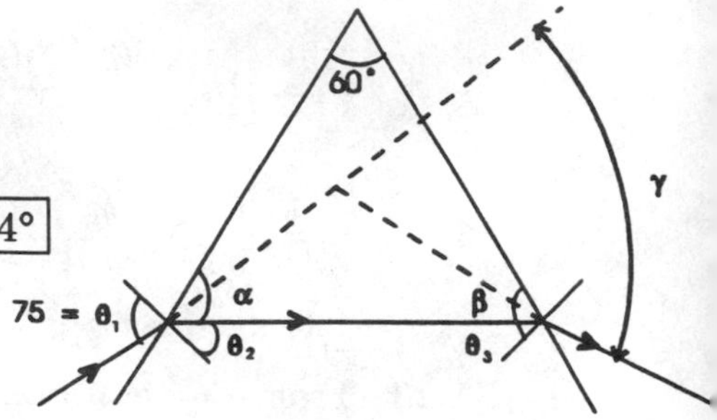

35.28

(a) $1 \sin 75° = 1.455 \sin\theta_2; \quad \theta_2 = \boxed{41.6°}$

(b) $\theta_3 + \beta = 90°;\ \theta_2 + \alpha = 90°;\ \alpha + \beta + 60° = 180°$

$$\Longrightarrow 60° - \theta_2 - \theta_3 = 0 \Longrightarrow 60° - 41.6° = \theta_3 = \boxed{18.4°}$$

(c) $1.455 \sin 18.4° = 1 \sin\theta_4 = 1 \sin\theta_4; \quad \theta_4 = \boxed{27.3°}$

(d) $\gamma = (\theta_1 - \theta_2) + [\beta - (90° - \theta_4)]$

$$= 75° - 41.6° + (90° - 18.4°) - (90° - 27.3°) = \boxed{42.3°}$$

35.29 From Eq. 35.9

$$n = \sin(\frac{\Phi + \delta_m}{2}) / \sin(\Phi/2)$$

Solving for δ_m,

$$\delta_m = 2\sin^{-1}(n \sin\frac{\Phi}{2}) - \Phi$$

$$\delta_m = 2\sin^{-1}(2.2 \sin 25°) - 50°$$

$$\delta_m = \boxed{86.8°}$$

35.30 (a) At the first refraction,

$$\sin\theta_2 = \frac{\sin\theta_1}{n}$$

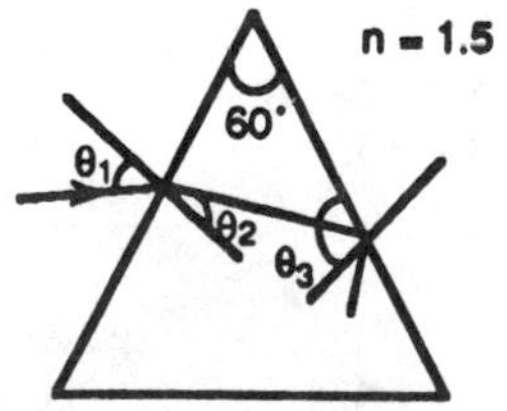

35.30

Total internal reflection occurs for

$1.5 \sin\theta_2' = 1 \qquad$ (Eq. 35.10)

$$\theta_2' = \sin^{-1}(\frac{1}{1.5}) = \sin^{-1}(0.667) = 41.8°$$

$$\theta_2 = 60° - \theta_2' = 18.26°$$

Since $\sin\theta_1 = n \sin\theta_2$,

$$\theta_1 = \sin^{-1}(n \sin\theta_2) = \boxed{27.9°}$$

(b) At minimum deviation, the angles of incidence and departure are the same. Use (Eq. 35.9)

$$\theta_1 = \frac{\Phi + \delta_m}{2} = \sin^{-1}[n \sin\frac{\Phi}{2}]$$

$$\therefore \theta_1 = \sin^{-1}[0.750] = \boxed{48.6°}$$

***35.31** For the incoming ray,

$$\sin\theta_2 = \frac{\sin\theta_1}{n}$$

Using Figure 35.19,

$$(\theta_2)_{\text{Violet}} = \sin^{-1}\left(\frac{\sin 50°}{1.66}\right) = 27.48°$$

$$(\theta_2)_{\text{Red}} = \sin^{-1}\left(\frac{\sin 50°}{1.62}\right) = 28.22°$$

For the outgoing ray, $\theta_2' = 60° - \theta_2$, and

$$\sin\theta_3 = n\sin\theta_2'$$

$$(\theta_3)_{\text{Violet}} = \sin^{-1}[1.66\sin 32.52°] = 63.17°$$

$$(\theta_3)_{\text{Red}} = \sin^{-1}[1.62\sin 31.78°] = 58.56°$$

The dispersion is $\Delta\theta_3 = 63.17° - 58.56° = \boxed{4.61°}$

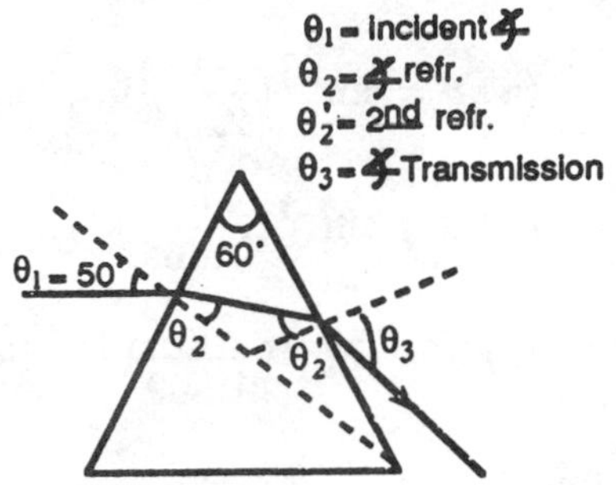

35.31

***35.32** From Snell's Law

$$n_1\sin\theta_1 = n_2\sin\theta_2$$

At the extreme angle of viewing, $\theta_2 = 90°$.

$$(1.59)(\sin\theta_1) = 1\cdot\sin 90°$$
$$\theta_1 = 38.97°$$

Therefore, the depth of the air bubble is

$$\frac{r_d}{\tan\theta_1} < d < \frac{r_p}{\tan\theta_1}$$

1.08 cm < d < 1.17 cm

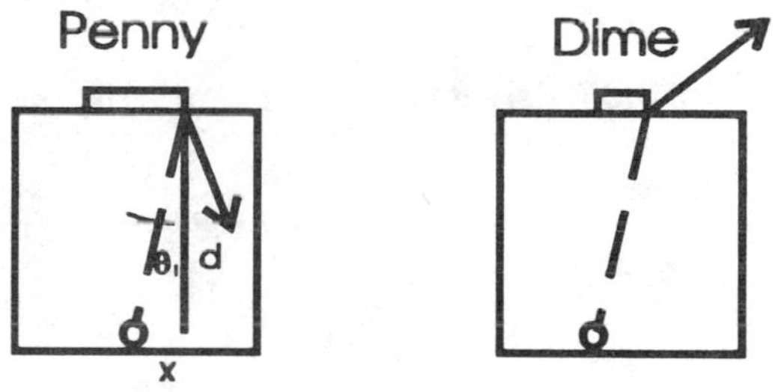

35.32

***35.33** For total internal reflection,

$$n_1\sin\theta_1 = n_2\sin 90°$$
$$(1.50)\sin\theta_1 = (1.33)\cdot 1$$
$$\theta_1 = \boxed{62.45°}$$

35.34 For water, $\theta_c = \sin^{-1}\left(\frac{1}{1.33}\right)$

$\theta_c = 48.7°$

$\alpha = 41.3°$

$h = 15\tan\alpha = \boxed{13.2\text{ m}}$

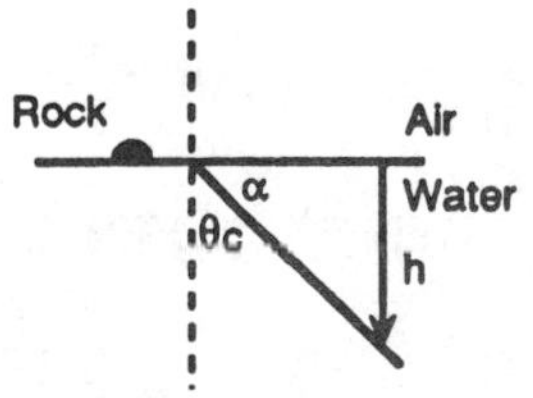

35.34

35.35 $1.0 \sin 90° = n \sin \theta = 1;$

(a) $\theta = \sin^{-1}(\frac{1}{2.419}) = \boxed{24.4°}$

(b) $\theta = \sin^{-1}(\frac{1}{1.66}) = \boxed{37.0°}$

(c) $\theta = \sin^{-1}(\frac{1}{1.309}) = \boxed{49.8°}$

35.36 $\sin \theta_c = \frac{n_2}{n_1}; \quad \theta_c = \sin^{-1}(\frac{n_2}{n_1})$

(a) Diamond: $\theta_c = \sin^{-1}(\frac{1.333}{2.419}) = 33.4°$

(b) Flintglass: $\theta_c = \sin^{-1}(\frac{1.333}{1.66}) = 53.4°$

(c) Ice: since $n_2 > n_1$ there is no critical angle.

35.37 $\sin \theta_c = \frac{n_2}{n_1}$ (Eq. 35.10)

$n_2 = (n_1)(\sin 88.8°) = (1.0003)(0.9998)$

$n_2 = \boxed{1.0001}$

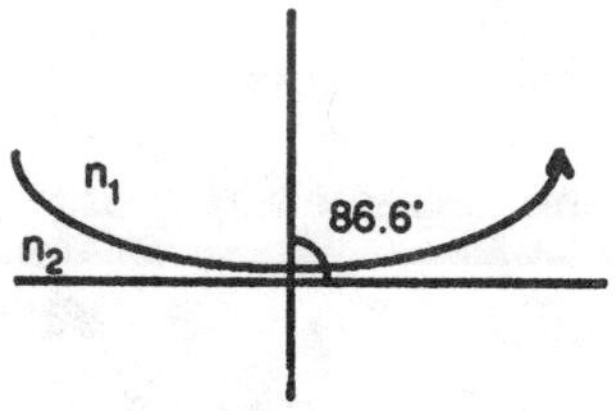

35.37

35.38 $\theta_1 = \sin^{-1}\frac{1}{n} = \sin^{-1}(\frac{1}{2.417}) = \boxed{24.4°}$

35.39 $\sin \theta_c = \frac{n_2}{n_1} = \frac{1}{1.5} = 0.667$

$\theta_c = 41.8°$

and the light will remain within the fiber for angles

$\alpha \leq \boxed{48.2°}$

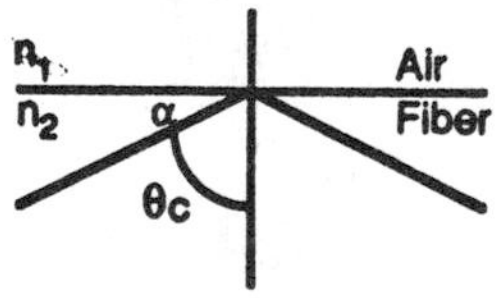

35.39

35.40 $\theta_2 = \frac{\theta_1}{2}$ or $\theta_1 = 2\theta_2; \quad n_1 \sin \theta_1 = n_2 \sin \theta_2$

$(1) \sin 2\theta_2 = (1.56) \sin \theta_2 \quad \Longrightarrow 2 \sin \theta_2 \cos \theta_2 = 1.56 \sin \theta_2$

$\cos \theta_2 = \frac{1.56}{2} \quad \Longrightarrow \theta_2 = \cos^{-1}(\frac{1.56}{2}) = 38.74°$

$\theta_1 = 2\theta_2 = 2(38.74°) = \boxed{77.5°}$

35.41 Eq. 35.9 gives the index of refraction in terms of the angle of minimum deviation and the apex angle of the prism:

$n = \dfrac{\sin[(\phi + \delta_m)/2]}{\sin(\phi/2)}$. This gives

$$\begin{aligned} \delta_m &= 2\{\sin^{-1}[n \sin(\phi/2)] - \phi/2\} \\ &= 2\{\sin^{-1}(1.61 \sin \pi/6) - \pi/6\} = 0.824 \text{ rad.} \end{aligned}$$

It can be shown from the geometry of the arrangement (see Ex. 35.7 of the text) that

$$\theta = \frac{1}{2}(\phi + \delta_m) \text{ or } \phi = \frac{1}{2}(\pi/3 + 0.824) \text{ rad} = 0.674 \text{ rad} = \boxed{53.6^\circ}$$

35.42 $n_1 \sin\theta_1 = n_2 \sin\theta_2$; $\theta_2 = \sin^{-1}(\dfrac{n_1 \sin\theta_1}{n_2})$

where $\theta_1 = 90^\circ$ and $\theta_2 = \theta_{2_{max}}$

$$\theta_2 = \sin^{-1}\{\frac{(1)(\sin 90^\circ)}{1.333}\} = \boxed{48.6^\circ}$$

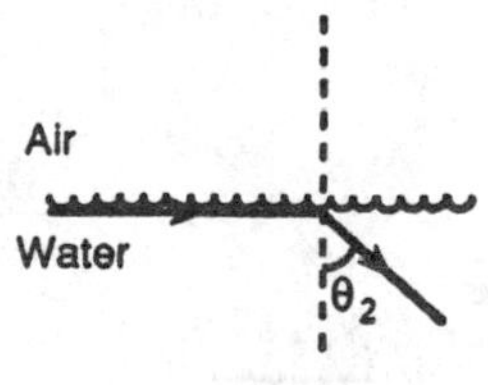

35.42

35.43 For water,

$$\sin\theta_c = \frac{1}{4/3} = \frac{3}{4}$$

$$\theta_c = \sin^{-1}(0.750) = 48.6^\circ$$

$$d = 2 \tan\alpha = 2 \tan 48.6^\circ = \boxed{2.27 \text{ m}}$$

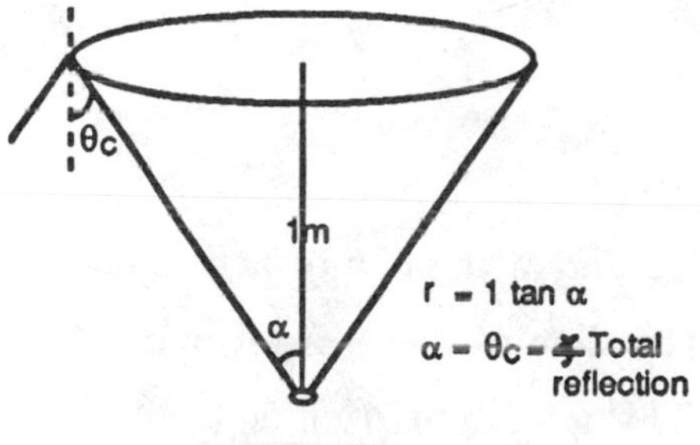

35.43

35.44 (a) $dx = h d\theta$

$$\begin{aligned} v_{\text{floor}} &= \frac{dx}{dt} = h\frac{d\theta}{dt} \\ &= (10^3 \text{ cm})\frac{2\pi \text{ rad}}{(24 \text{ h})(60 \text{ min/h})} = \boxed{4.36 \text{ cm/min}} \end{aligned}$$

(b) $v_{\text{ceiling}} = 2\dfrac{dx}{dt} = \boxed{8.72 \text{ cm/min}}$

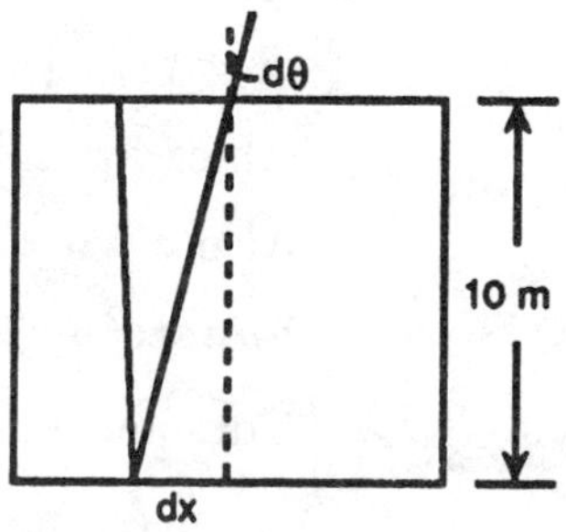

35.44

35.45 $\tan\theta_1 = 4/h \Longrightarrow \tan\theta_1 = 2\tan\theta_2;$

$\tan\theta_2 = 2/h \Longrightarrow \tan^2\theta_2 = 4\tan^2\theta_2;$

$\Longrightarrow \sin^2\theta_1/(1-\sin^2\theta_1) = 4[\sin^2\theta_2/(1-\sin^2\theta_2)],$ (1).

$n_1\sin^2\theta_1 = n_2\sin\theta_2 \Rightarrow \sin\theta_1 = 1.333\sin\theta_2$ squaring both sides $\Longrightarrow \sin^2\theta_1 = 1.778\sin^2\theta_2,$

Substitute this value into (1) which yields

$1.778\sin^2\theta_2/(1-1.778\sin^2\theta_2) = 4(\sin^2\theta_2)/(1-\sin^2\theta_2).$

Let $\sin^2\theta_2 = x \quad \Longrightarrow 0.444/(1-1.778x) = 1/(1-x)$

$0.444 - 0.444x = 1 - 1.778x \quad \Longrightarrow 1.333x = 1 - 0.444 = 0.556$

so $x = 0.417 = \sin^2\theta_2$

$\theta_2 = \sin^{-1}(0.417)^{1/2} = 40.2°$

$$h = \frac{2\text{ cm}}{\tan\theta_2} = \frac{2\text{ cm}}{\tan(40.2°)} = 2.37\text{ cm}$$

35.46 $$t = t_1 + t_2 = \frac{h_1}{c\cdot\cos\theta_1} + \frac{h_2}{(c/n)\cos\theta_2}$$

$$t = \frac{h_1\sec\theta_1}{c} + \frac{h_2 n\sec\theta_2}{c}$$

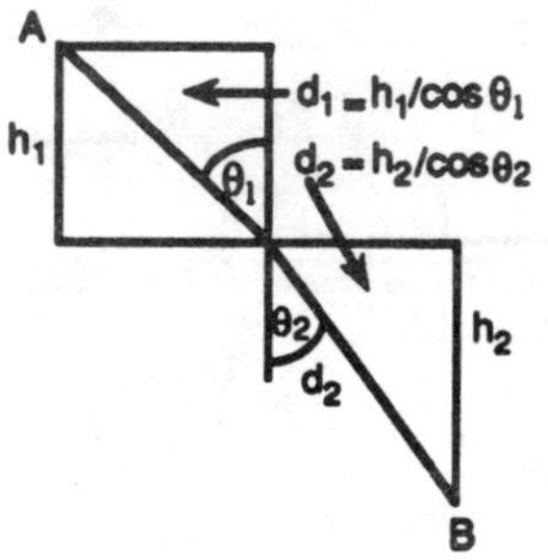

35.46

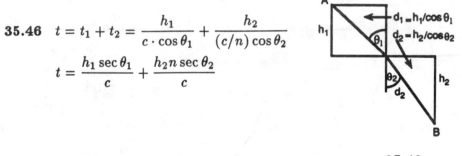

35.47 To derive the law of *reflection*, locate point 0 so that the time of travel from point A to point B will be minimum. The *total* light path is

$+\ell = a\sec\theta_1 + b\sec\theta_2$. The time of travel is

$t = (1/v)(a\sec\theta_1 + b\sec\theta_2)$. If point 0 is displaced by dx, then

$dt = (1/v)(a\sec\theta_1\tan\theta_1 d\theta_1 + b\sec\theta_2\tan\theta_2 d\theta_2) = 0 \quad (1)$

(since for minimum time $dt = 0$.)

Also $c + d = a\tan\theta_1 + b\tan\theta_2 =$ constant

so $a\sec^2\theta_1 d\theta_1 + b\sec^2\theta_2 d\theta_2 = 0 \qquad (2)$.

Combine equations (1) and (2) to find: $\boxed{\theta_1 = \theta_2}$

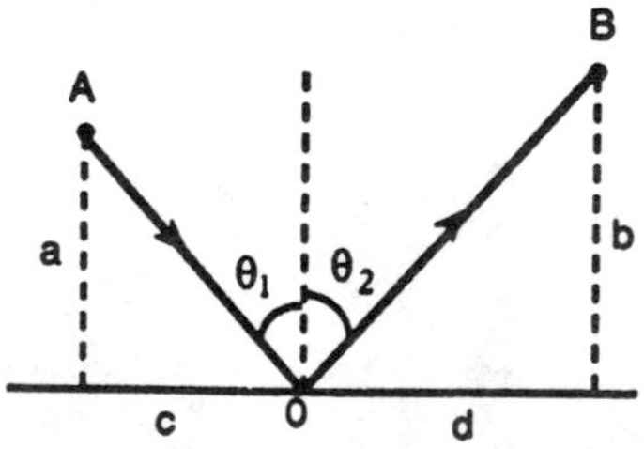

35.47

***35.48**

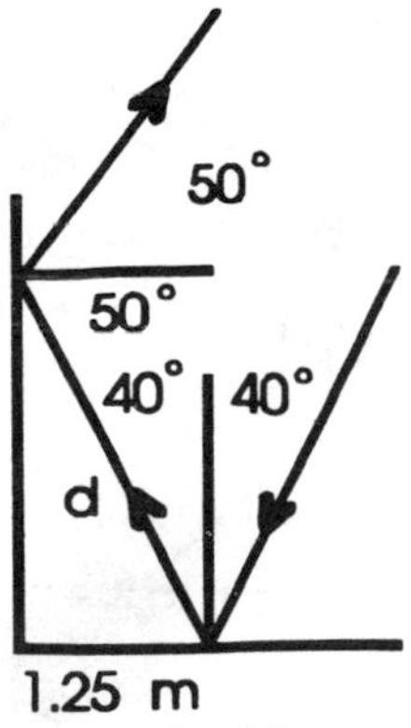

35.48

(a) $\sin 40° = \dfrac{1.25\text{ m}}{d}$ $\quad d = \boxed{1.94\text{ m}}$

(b) At 50° above the horizontal to the right, antiparallel to its original direction.

35.49 (a) For polystyrene *surrounded by air* internal reflection requires

$\theta_3 = \sin^{-1}(\frac{1}{1.49}) = 42.2°$ and then from the geometry

$\theta_2 = 90 - \theta_3 = 47.8°$. From Snell's law, this would require

that $\theta_1 \geq 90°$. Therefore, total internal reflection

is not possible in this case.

(b) For polystyrene surrounded *by water*, we have

$\theta_3 = \sin^{-1}(\frac{1.33}{1.49}) = 63.2°$ and $\theta_2 = 26.8°$

and from Snell's law $\theta_1 = \boxed{30.3°}$

(c) *Not possible* since the beam is initially travelling in a

medium of lower index of refraction.

***35.50** From geometry,

$$A = \alpha + \beta$$

$$B = \alpha + \beta + A = 2A$$

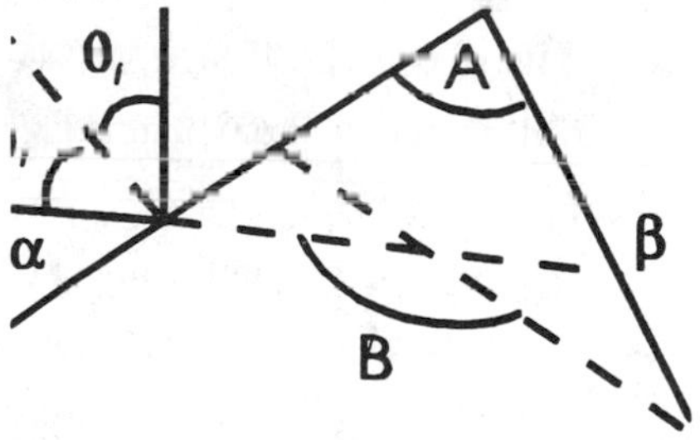

35.50

35.51 $r = d\sin\gamma$

$$\cos\phi = \frac{h}{r} = \frac{h}{d\sin\gamma} = \frac{2}{8\sin 42^\circ} = 0.373$$

$\phi = 68.1^\circ$

$\theta = 360^\circ - (2\times 68.1^\circ) = 223.8^\circ$

$$\frac{223.8^\circ}{360^\circ} = 62.2\%$$

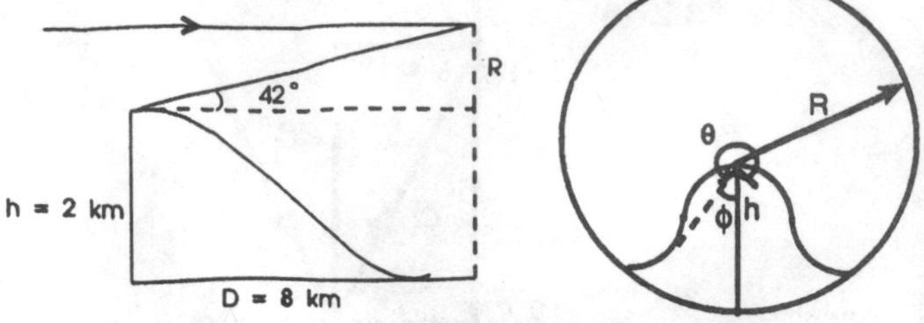

35.51

***35.52** From Snell's Law, $1\sin\theta_1 = \frac{4}{3}\sin\theta_2$

$z = r\cos\theta_1 \quad x = r\sin\theta_1 \quad \frac{r}{R} = \frac{\sin\theta_2}{\sin\theta_1} = \frac{3}{4}$

$d = R\cos\theta_2 \quad x = R\sin\theta_2$

$$\frac{z}{d} = \frac{r\cos\theta_1}{R\cos\theta_2} = \frac{3}{4}\frac{\cos\theta_1}{\sqrt{1-\sin^2\theta_2}} = \frac{3}{4}\frac{\cos\theta_1}{\sqrt{1-\frac{9}{16}\sin^2\theta_1}}$$

Since $\sin^2\theta_1 = 1-\cos^2\theta_1$,

$$\frac{z}{d} = \frac{3\cos\theta_1}{\sqrt{7+9\cos^2\theta_1}}$$

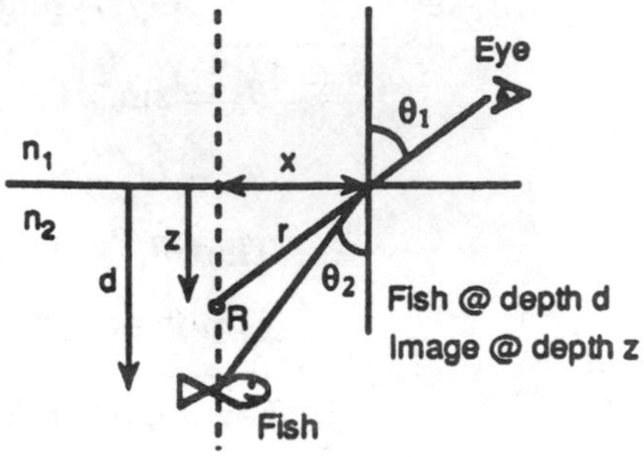

35.52

35.53 Refer to the figure at the right.
We see that $\theta_2 + \alpha = 90^\circ$
and
$\theta_2 + \beta = 90^\circ$,
so $\theta_2 + \theta_3 + \alpha + \beta = 180^\circ$.
Also from the figure we see
$\alpha + \beta + \phi = 180^\circ$; therefore
$\phi = \theta_2 + \theta_3$.
By applying Snell's law at the first and second refracting surfaces, we find
$\theta_2 = \sin^{-1}[(\sin\theta_1)/n]$ and
$\theta_3 = \sin^{-1}[(\sin\theta_4)/n]$.
Substituting these values into the expression for ϕ
$\phi = \sin^{-1}[(\sin\theta_1)/n] + \sin^{-1}[(\sin\theta_4)/n]$.
The limiting condition for internal reflection at the second surface is $\theta_4 \longrightarrow 90^\circ$. Under these conditions we have
$\sin\theta_1 = n\sin[\phi - \sin^{-1}(1/n)]$ or
$\theta_1 = \sin^{-1}[(n^2-1)^{1/2}\sin\phi - \cos\phi]$.

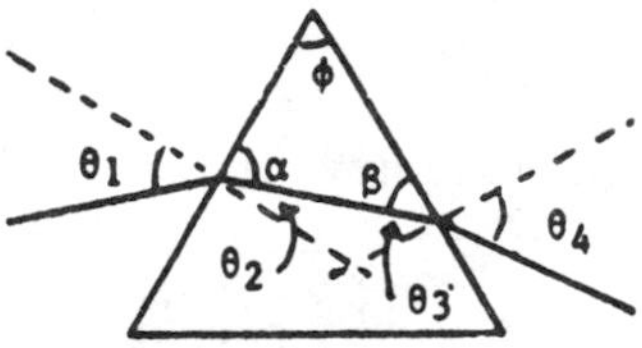

35.53

***35.54** $n = 1.55$, $\theta_1 = 20°$,

$$1 \cdot \sin 20° = 1.55 \sin \theta_2$$
$$\theta_2 = 12.75°$$

From the internal triangle,

$$12.75° + \theta_3 = 40°$$
$$\theta_3 = 27.25°$$

On exit, $1.55 \sin 27.25° = 1 \cdot \sin \theta$

$\boxed{\theta = 45.2°}$

***35.55** Confined laser beam

On entrance, $\sin 50° = 1.48 \sin \theta_2$

$$\theta_2 = 31.17°$$

The beam strikes the top face at $x_1 = \dfrac{1.55 \text{ mm}}{\tan 31.17°} = 2.562 \text{ mm}$

Therefore, the beam strikes a face every $2\Delta x_1 = 5.124$ mm.

Since the slab is 420 mm long, the beam makes $\dfrac{420 - 2.562}{5.124} = 81$ more reflections, for a total of $\boxed{\text{82 reflections}}$.

***35.56**

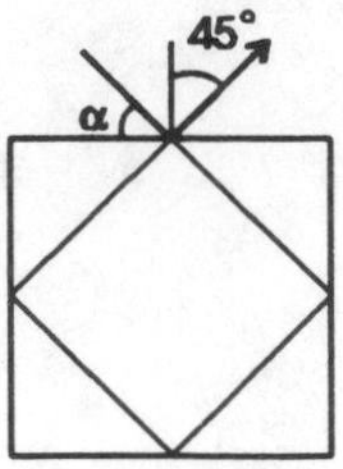

a

35.56

<u>45.0°</u>

<u>yes</u>

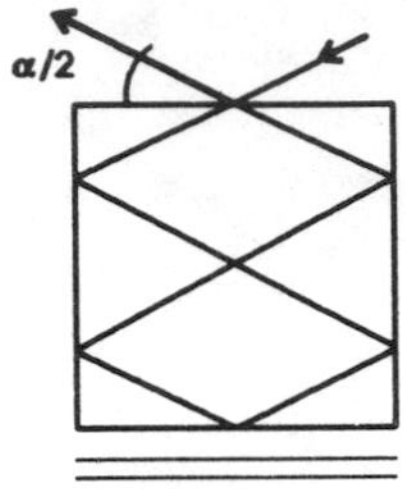

b

35.56

If entrance angle is halved, the number of reflections from the side faces is doubled.

***35.57**

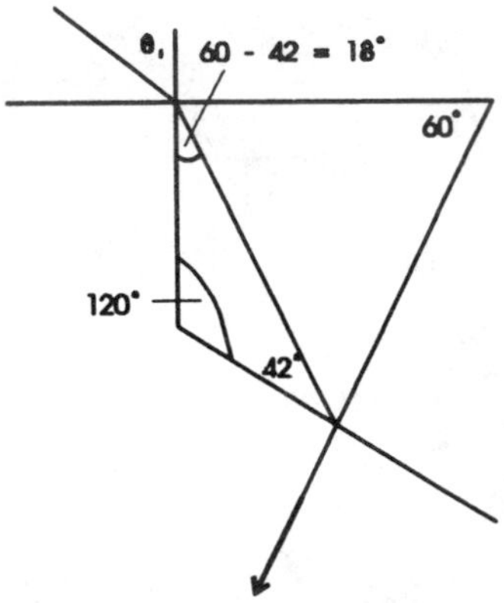

35.57

$$n \sin 42° = \sin 90°$$

$$n = \frac{1}{\sin 42°} = 1.5557$$

$$\sin \theta_1 = n \sin 18°$$

$$\sin \theta_1 = \frac{\sin 18°}{\sin 42°}$$

$$\theta_1 = \boxed{28.7°}$$

***35.58**

$\sin \theta_1$	$\sin \theta_2$	$\sin \theta_1 / \sin \theta_2$
0.174	0.131	1.3304
0.342	0.261	1.3129
0.500	0.379	1.3177
0.643	0.480	1.3385
0.766	0.576	1.3289
0.866	0.647	1.3390
0.940	0.711	1.3220
0.984	0.740	1.3314

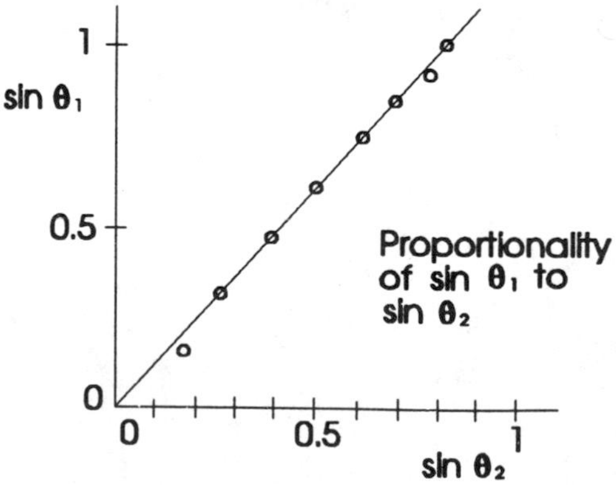

35.58

The slope of the line is $\overline{n} = 1.3276 \pm 0.011$

and $n = \boxed{1.328 \pm 0.8\%}$

CHAPTER 36

36.1

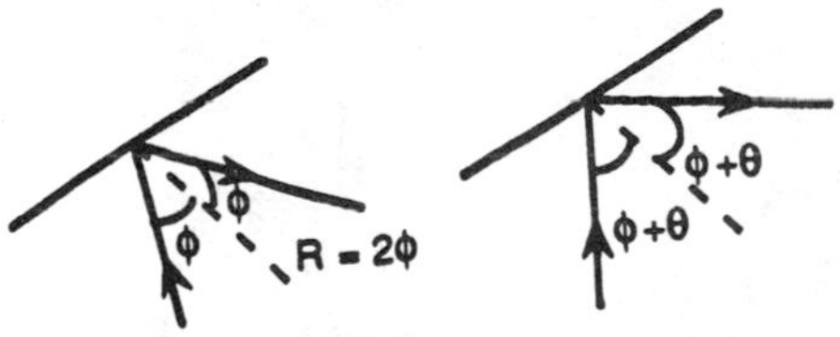

36.1

$R = 2\phi + 2\theta$

36.2

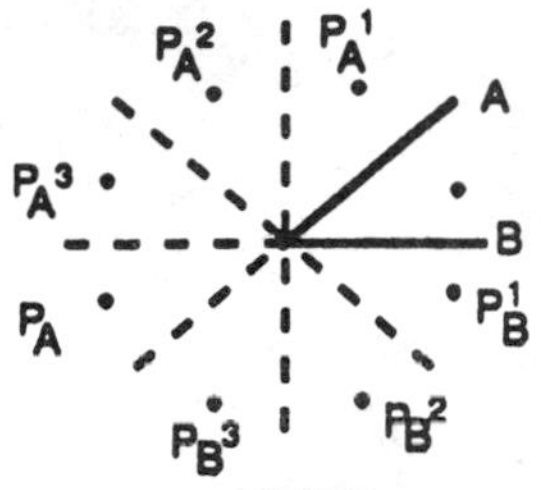

36.2

Seven images are observed

36.3 $h = h' = L = 5'10'' = 70''$; $h' = h/2 = 70''/2 = 35'' = 2'11''$

36.3

***36.4** A graphical construction produces 5 images, with images I_1 and I_2 directly into the mirrors from I_0 the object and (I_0, I_3, I_4) and (I_1, I_2, I_5) forming the vertices of equilateral triangles.

36.5 $\frac{1}{s'} + \frac{1}{s} = \frac{1}{f}$ and when $M = -\frac{s'}{s} = 4$ we have

$$\frac{1}{(-4s)} + \frac{1}{s} = \frac{1}{f} \quad \text{or} \quad s = \frac{3}{4}f = \frac{3}{4}(40 \text{ cm}) = \boxed{30 \text{ cm}}$$

36.6 $\frac{1}{s} + \frac{1}{s'} = \frac{1}{f} = \frac{1}{(20 \text{ cm})}$; $\quad M = -\frac{s'}{s} = \frac{1}{2} \quad \Longrightarrow s' = -\frac{s}{2}$;

$$\frac{1}{s} - \frac{2}{s} = \frac{1}{(20 \text{ cm})} \quad \Longrightarrow -\frac{1}{s} = -\frac{1}{(20 \text{ cm})} \quad s = 20 \text{ cm} = \boxed{0.20 \text{ m}}$$

36.7 (a) $\frac{1}{s}+\frac{1}{s'}=\frac{2}{R} \quad \Longrightarrow \frac{1}{90\text{ cm}}+\frac{1}{s'}=\frac{2}{(60\text{ cm})}$

$$\frac{1}{s'}=\frac{2}{(60\text{ cm})}-\frac{1}{(90\text{ cm})}=0.022\text{ cm}^{-1}$$

$s'=45$ cm;

$$M=-\frac{s'}{s}=-\frac{(45\text{ cm})}{(90\text{ cm})}=-\frac{1}{2}$$

(b) $\frac{1}{s}+\frac{1}{s'}=\frac{2}{R} \quad \Longrightarrow \frac{1}{(20\text{ cm})}+\frac{1}{s'}=\frac{2}{(60\text{ cm})}$

$$\frac{1}{s'}=\frac{2}{(60\text{ cm})}-\frac{1}{(20\text{ cm})}=-0.0167\text{ cm}^{-1}$$

$s'=-60$ cm;

$$M=-\frac{s'}{s}=-\frac{(-60\text{ cm})}{(20\text{ cm})}=3$$

(c) Diagrams are similar to Figures 36.6 and 36.9b in Physics for Scientists and Engineers.

36.8 $M=-\frac{s'}{s}$. For a real image $s>0$ and in this case $M=-4$.
Therefore $s'=-sM=120$ cm
and from Eq. 36.4

$$R=\frac{2ss'}{(s'+s)}=\frac{2(30\text{ cm})(120\text{ cm})}{(150\text{ cm})}=\boxed{48\text{ cm}}$$

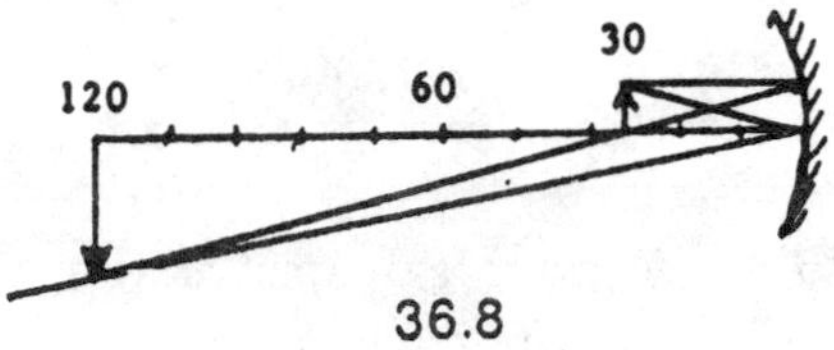

36.8

36.9 (a) $\frac{1}{s}+\frac{1}{s'}=\frac{1}{f} \quad \Longrightarrow \frac{1}{(20\text{ cm})}+\frac{1}{s'}=\frac{1}{(40\text{ cm})}$;

$\frac{1}{s'}=-0.075\text{ cm}^{-1} \quad \Longrightarrow s'=-13.3$ cm;

$$M=-\frac{s'}{s}=-\frac{(-13.3\text{ cm})}{(20\text{ cm})}=0.667$$

(b) $\frac{1}{s}+\frac{1}{s'}=\frac{1}{f} \quad \Longrightarrow \frac{1}{(60\text{ cm})}+\frac{1}{s'}=-\frac{1}{(40\text{ cm})}$;

$\frac{1}{s'}=-0.0417\text{ cm}^{-1} \quad \Longrightarrow s'=-24$ cm;

$$M=-\frac{s'}{s}=-\frac{(-24\text{ cm})}{(60\text{ cm})}=0.4$$

(c) See the figure at the right

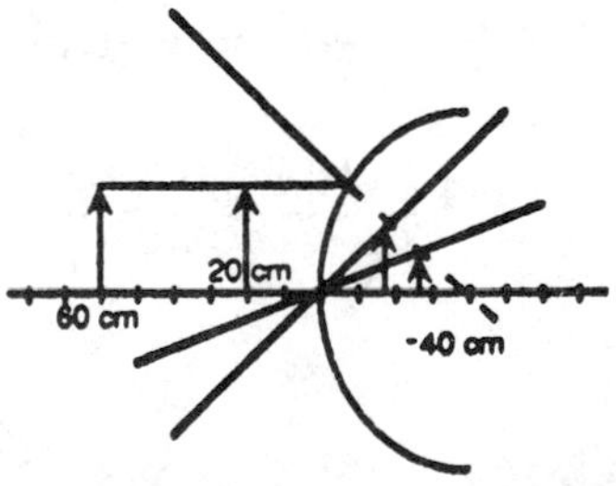

36.9

36.10 $\frac{1}{0.49} + \frac{1}{s'} = -\frac{1}{0.35}$ (Convex mirror)

(a) $s' = \boxed{-\ 0.204\ \text{m}}$

(b) $M = -\frac{s'}{s} = +\frac{0.204}{0.49} = \boxed{0.417,\ \text{Erect}}$

36.11 (Use Table 36.1)

$M = -\frac{s'}{s} = +2 \longrightarrow$ Concave, virtual image.

$$\frac{1}{0.1} - \frac{1}{0.2} = \frac{1}{f}$$

$f = 0.2$ m

$\therefore\ \boxed{r = 40\ \text{cm}}$

36.12

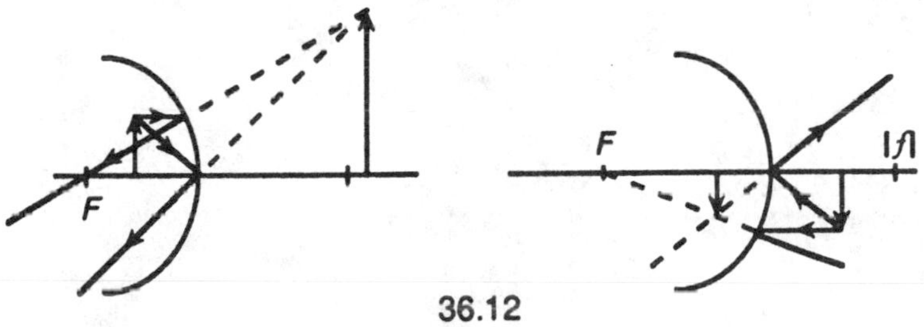

36.12

36.13 (a) $s' = (s + 5\ \text{m})$ and since the image must be real $M = -\frac{s'}{s} = -5$
or $s' = 5s$. Therefore $s + 5 = 5s$ or $s = 1.25$ m and $s' = 6.25$ m.
From Eq. 36.4,

$$R = \frac{2ss'}{(s' + s)} = \frac{2(1.25)(6.25)}{(6.25 + 1.25)} = \boxed{2.08\ \text{m (concave)}}$$

(b) From part (a) $s = 1.25$ m; The mirror should be $\boxed{1.25\ \text{m}}$ in front of the object.

36.14 The real image formed by the concave mirror serves as a real object for the convex mirror with $s = 50$ cm and $s' = -10$ cm.
Therefore from Eq. 36.6

$$f = \frac{s's}{s + s'} = \frac{(-10\ \text{cm})(50\ \text{cm})}{50\ \text{cm} + (-10\ \text{cm})} = -12.5\ \text{cm}$$

$R = 2f = \boxed{-25\ \text{cm}}$

36.15 (a) $\frac{1}{s}+\frac{1}{s'}=\frac{2}{R} \implies \frac{1}{(30\text{ cm})}+\frac{1}{s'}=\frac{2}{(-40\text{ cm})}$

$$\frac{1}{s'}=-\frac{2}{(40\text{ cm})}-\frac{1}{(30\text{ cm})}=-0.0833\text{ cm}^{-1}$$

$s'=-12$ cm;

$$M=-\frac{s'}{s}=-\frac{(-12\text{ cm})}{(30\text{ cm})}=0.4$$

(b) $\frac{1}{s}+\frac{1}{s'}=\frac{2}{R} \implies \frac{1}{(60\text{ cm})}+\frac{1}{s'}=-\frac{2}{(40\text{ cm})}$

$$\frac{1}{s'}=-\frac{2}{(40\text{ cm})}-\frac{1}{(60\text{ cm})}=-0.0666\text{ cm}^{-1}; \quad s'=-15\text{ cm};$$

$$M=-\frac{s'}{s}=-\frac{(-15\text{ cm})}{(60\text{ cm})}=0.25$$

(c) Since $M>0$, the images are erect.

36.16 $\frac{1}{s}+\frac{1}{s'}=\frac{1}{f} \qquad f=\frac{R}{2}=1.5$ cm

$$\frac{1}{s}+\frac{1}{s'}=-\frac{10}{15}$$

(a) $s'=-\frac{15}{11}$ cm (Behind mirror)

(b) $M=-\frac{s'}{s}=\boxed{\frac{1}{11}}$

36.17 $\frac{n_1}{s}+\frac{n_2}{s'}=(n_2-n_1)R=0$; since $R\implies\infty$; $\frac{n_1}{s}=-\frac{n_2}{s'}$ or $\frac{1.309}{(50\text{ cm})}=-\frac{1}{s'}$

$$s'=-\frac{(50\text{ cm})}{1.309}$$

$$=-38.20\text{ cm or }\boxed{11.8\text{ cm above the floor}}$$

36.18 $\frac{n_1}{s} + \frac{n_2}{s'} = \frac{(n_2 - n_1)}{R}$; $\frac{1}{s} + \frac{1.5}{s'} = \frac{0.5}{(6 \text{ cm})} = \frac{1}{(12 \text{ cm})}$;

(a) $\frac{1}{(20 \text{ cm})} + \frac{1.5}{s'} = \frac{1}{(12 \text{ cm})}$

$$s' = (1.5)(1/12 \text{ cm} - 1/20 \text{ cm})^{-1} = \boxed{45 \text{ cm}}$$

(b) $\frac{1}{(10 \text{ cm})} + \frac{1.5}{s'} = \frac{1}{(12 \text{ cm})}$

$$s' = (1.5)(1/12 \text{ cm} - 1/10 \text{ cm})^{-1} = \boxed{-90 \text{ cm}}$$

(c) $\frac{1}{(3 \text{ cm})} + \frac{1.5}{s'} = \frac{1}{(12 \text{ cm})}$

$$s' = (1.5)(1/12 \text{ cm} - 1/3 \text{ cm})^{-1} = \boxed{-6 \text{ cm}}$$

36.19 When Eq. 36.8 is solved for s' we find

$$s' = \frac{n_2 R s}{s(n_2 - n_1) - n_1 R}$$

In this problem, $n_1 = 1, n_2 = 1.5,$ and $R = -8$ cm.

(a) For $s = 20$ cm;

$$s' = \frac{(1.5)(-8 \text{ cm})(20 \text{ cm})}{(20 \text{ cm})(1.5 - 1) - (1)(-8 \text{ cm})} = \boxed{-13.33 \text{ cm}}$$

(b) For $s = 10$ cm;

$$s' = \frac{(1.5)(-8 \text{ cm})(10 \text{ cm})}{(10 \text{ cm})(1.5 - 1) - (1)(-8 \text{ cm})} = \boxed{-9.23 \text{ cm}}$$

(c) For $s = 3$ cm;

$$s' = \frac{(1.5)(-8\text{cm})(3 \text{ cm})}{(3 \text{ cm})(1.5 - 1) - (1)(-8 \text{ cm})} = \boxed{-3.79 \text{ cm}}$$

***36.20** Utilizing Equation 36.11, both above and below the surface,

$$\frac{1}{f} = (n - 1)\left(\frac{1}{R_1} - \frac{1}{R_2}\right) \quad \text{(air)}$$

$$\frac{1}{f'} = (n - n_1)\left(\frac{1}{R_1} - \frac{1}{R_2}\right) \quad \text{(water)}$$

$$\frac{1}{f\,(n - 1)} = \frac{1}{f'(n - n_1)}$$

$$\underline{f' = \frac{n - 1}{n - n_1} f}$$

36.21 From Eq. 36.8 $\frac{n_1}{s} + \frac{n_2}{s'} = \frac{(n_2 - n_1)}{R}$

Solve for s' to find $s' = \frac{n_2 R s}{s(n_2 - n_1) - n_1 R}$

In this case $n_1 = 1.5$, $n_2 = 1$, $R = -15$ cm, and $s = 10$ cm so,

$$s' = \frac{(1)(-15\text{ cm})(10\text{ cm})}{(10\text{ cm})(1 - 1.5)(-15\text{ cm})} = -8.57\text{ cm}$$

Therefore the $\boxed{\text{apparent depth is 8.57 cm}}$

36.22 When $R \longrightarrow \infty$, Eq. 36.8 for a plane surface becomes $s' = -(n_2/n_1)s$
First find the location of the image of the *bottom* of the glass plate as formed by the glass.
$s_1' = -(1.33/1.66)(-0.08\text{ m}) = 0.0641$ m below the top of the glass or 0.184 m below the top of the water. Next use the image found above as an object and locate the image formed by the water layer.
$s_2' = (1/1.33)(-0.1841\text{ m}) = 0.1384$ m below the surface of water. Now find image of the *top* surface of the glass formed by the water
$s_3' = -(1/1.33)(-0.12\text{ m}) = 0.090$ m. Therefore the apparent thickness of the glass is
$\Delta t = 0.1384\text{ m} - 0.090\text{ m} = \boxed{0.048\text{ m}}$

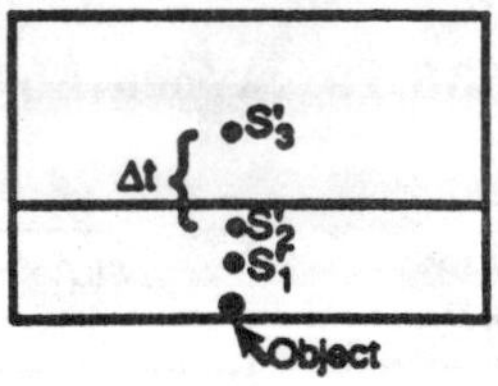

36.22

36.23 From Eq. 36.8

$$s' = \frac{n_2 R s}{s(n_2 - n_1) - n_1 R}$$

$$s' = \frac{(1)(-4\text{ cm})(4\text{ cm})}{(4\text{ cm})(1 - 1.55) - (1.55)(-4\ ;\text{cm})} = -4\text{ cm}$$

Magnification $M = -\frac{n_1 s'}{n_2 s} = -\frac{(1.55)(-4\text{ cm})}{(1)(4\text{cm})} = 1.55$

and the image height, $h' = Mh = 1.55(2.5\text{ mm}) = \boxed{3.88\text{ mm}}$

36.24 $\frac{n_1}{s} + \frac{n_2}{s'} = \frac{n_2 - n_1}{R}$ $n_1 = 1.33$

$n_2 = 1$

$s = 0.1$

$R = -0.15$

$s' = \boxed{-9 \text{ cm inside the bowl}}$

36.25 $s = \infty$

$s' = +2R$

$\frac{1}{s} + \frac{n'}{s'} = \frac{n' - 1}{R}$

$0 + \frac{n'}{2R} = \frac{n' - 1}{R}$

$n' = 2$

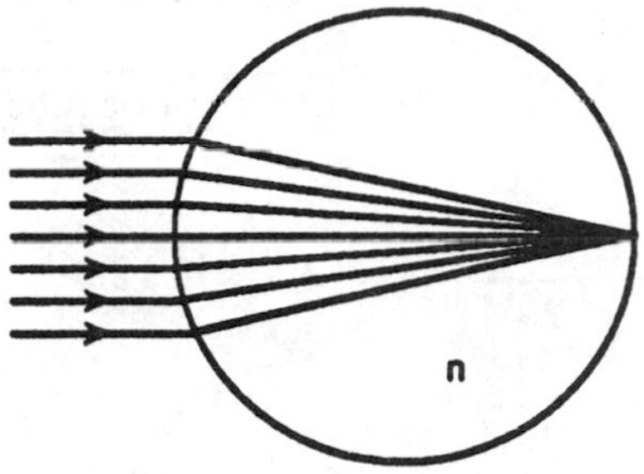

36.25

36.26 (a) $\frac{1}{s} + \frac{1}{s'} = \frac{1}{f} \implies \frac{1}{(32 \text{ cm})} + \frac{1}{(8 \text{ cm})} = \frac{1}{f}$

$\boxed{f = 6.40 \text{ cm}}$

(b) $M = -\frac{s'}{s} = \frac{(8 \text{ cm})}{(32 \text{ cm})} = \boxed{-0.25}$

(c) Since $f > 0$, the lens is converging.

36.27 (a) $\frac{1}{f} = (n-1)[\frac{1}{R_1} - \frac{1}{R_2}] = (1.44 - 1)[\frac{1}{(12 \text{ cm})} - \frac{1}{(-18 \text{ cm})}]$

and $f = \boxed{16.4 \text{ cm}}$

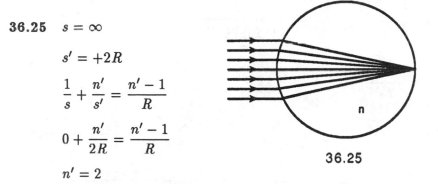

(b) $\frac{1}{f} = (0.44)[\frac{1}{(18 \text{ cm})} - \frac{1}{(-12 \text{ cm})}]$ and $f = \boxed{16.4 \text{ cm}}$

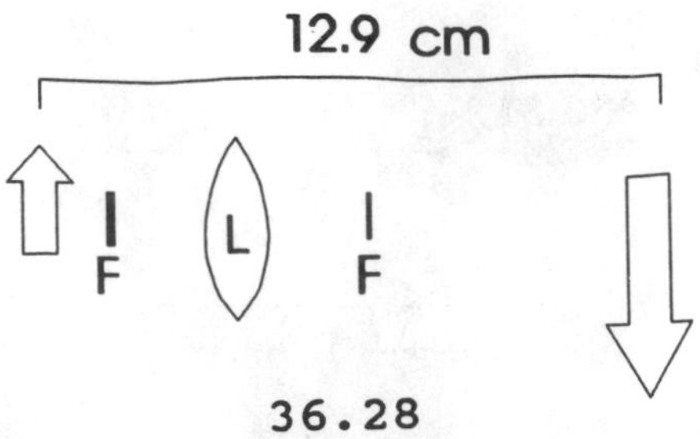

36.28

***36.28** (a) $\frac{1}{s}+\frac{1}{s'}=\frac{1}{2.44}$ $\quad s+s' = 12.9$

$$\frac{1}{s}+\frac{1}{12.9-s} = \frac{1}{2.44}$$
$$12.9 = \frac{1}{2.44}(12.9\,s-s^2)$$
$$s^2-12.9s+31.476 = 0$$
$$s = \frac{12.9\pm\sqrt{12.9^2-4\times 31.476}}{2}=\frac{12.9\pm 6.36}{2}$$
$$s = \boxed{3.27\text{ cm or }9.63\text{ cm}}$$

(b) $\frac{1}{s}+\frac{1}{s'} = \frac{1}{2.44}$ $\quad s'=-s-12.9$

$$\frac{1}{s}-\frac{1}{s+12.9} = \frac{1}{2.44}$$
$$2.44(12.9) = s^2+12.9s$$
$$0 = s^2+12.9s-31.476$$
$$s = \frac{-12.9\pm\sqrt{12.9^2+4\times 31.476}}{2}$$
$$s = \boxed{2.10\text{ cm}}$$

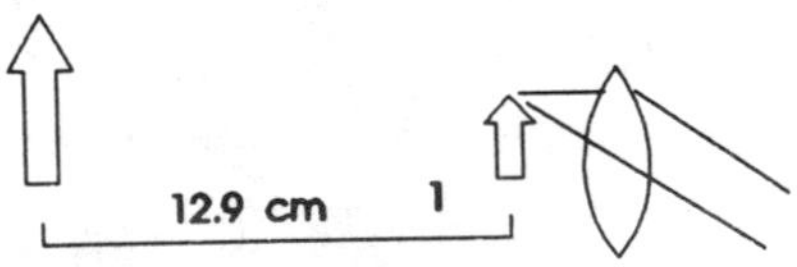

36.28b

36.29 $\frac{1}{s}+\frac{1}{s'}=\frac{1}{f}$ $\quad s = 1\text{ m}$

$$f = 0.2\text{ m}$$

$s'=+\frac{1}{4}$ m.

$$M=-\frac{s'}{s}=\boxed{-\frac{1}{4}}$$

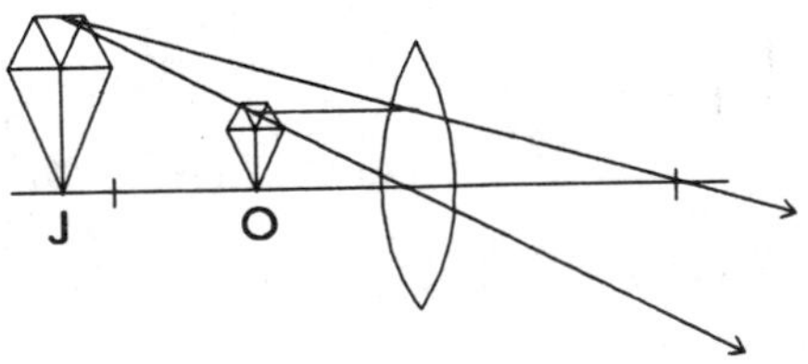

36.30

***36.30**

$$\frac{1}{s}+\frac{1}{s'} = \frac{1}{f}$$
$$\frac{1}{s}+\frac{1}{-30} = \frac{1}{12.5}$$
$$s = 8.8235\text{ cm}$$
$$M = -\frac{s'}{s}=-\frac{-30}{8.82}=\boxed{3.40,\text{ upright}}$$

***36.31**

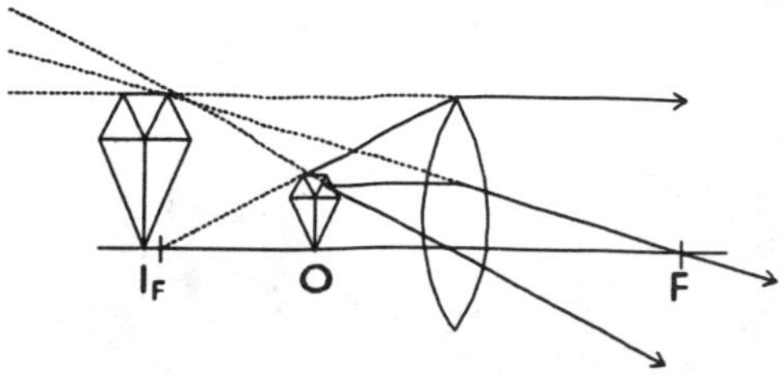

36.31

36.32 $\frac{1}{s} + \frac{1}{s'} = \frac{1}{f}$ and $M = -\frac{s'}{s}$

$M = \frac{f}{(f - s)}$ and $h' = -Mh$

(a) $M = \frac{40}{(40 - 50)} = -4$, so $h' = -(-4)(4\text{ cm}) = \boxed{16\text{ cm}}$

(b) $M = \frac{40}{(40 - 60)} = -2$, so $h' = -(-2)(4\text{ cm}) = \boxed{8\text{ cm}}$

(c) $M = \frac{40}{(40 - 80)} = -1$, so $h' = -(-1)(4\text{ cm}) = \boxed{4\text{ cm}}$

(d) $M = \frac{40}{(40 - 100)} = -\frac{2}{3}$, so $h' = -(-\frac{2}{3})(4\text{ cm}) = \boxed{2.67\text{ cm}}$

(e) $M = \frac{40}{(40 - 200)} = -\frac{1}{4}$, so $h' = -(-\frac{1}{4})(4\text{ cm}) = \boxed{1\text{ cm}}$

(f) $M = \frac{40}{(40 - \infty)} = 0$, so h' will be a point image. $h' = \boxed{0}$

36.33 (a) $\frac{1}{s} + \frac{1}{s'} = \frac{1}{f}$; $\quad \frac{1}{(20\text{ cm})} + \frac{1}{s'} = \frac{1}{(-32\text{ cm})}$

so $s' = -(\frac{1}{20} + \frac{1}{32})^{-1} = \boxed{-12.3\text{ cm}}$

(to the left of the lens)

(b) $M = -\frac{s'}{s} = \frac{(12.3\text{ cm})}{(20\text{ cm})} = \boxed{0.615}$

36.34

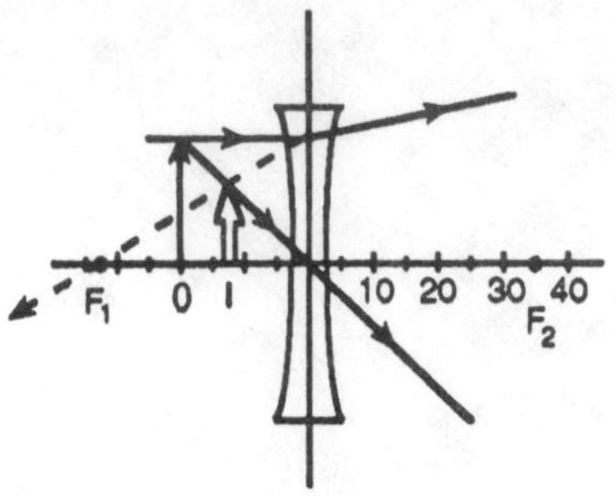

36.34

36.35 Following through the development of the thin lens formula, it can be shown that for a lens of index of refraction n imposed in a medium of index n', the lens maker's equation (36.11) is written

$$\frac{1}{f} = (\frac{n}{n'} - 1)(\frac{1}{R_1} + \frac{1}{R_2})$$

$$\therefore f = [(\frac{1}{1.33} - 1)(\frac{1}{0.2} + \frac{1}{0.3})]^{-1}$$

$$\boxed{f = -0.484 \text{ m}}$$

36.36 (a) $\frac{1}{s} + \frac{1}{s'} = \frac{1}{f}; \quad f = (\frac{1}{s} + \frac{1}{s'})^{-1}$

$$= [\frac{1}{(80 \text{ cm})} - \frac{1}{(40 \text{ cm})}]^{-1} = \boxed{-80 \text{ cm}}$$

(b) $\frac{1}{f} = (n-1)(\frac{1}{R_1} - \frac{1}{R_2})$

$$n = \frac{1}{f}(\frac{1}{R_1} - \frac{1}{R_2})^{-1} + 1$$

$$n = (\frac{1}{80})(\frac{1}{40} + \frac{1}{50})^{-1} + 1 = \boxed{1.278}$$

***36.37** $M = 2 = \frac{s'}{s} = \frac{2.84 \text{ cm}}{s}$

$s = 1.42$ cm

$$\frac{1}{1.42 \text{ cm}} + \frac{1}{-2.84 \text{ cm}} = \frac{1}{f}$$

$$f = \boxed{2.84 \text{ cm}}$$

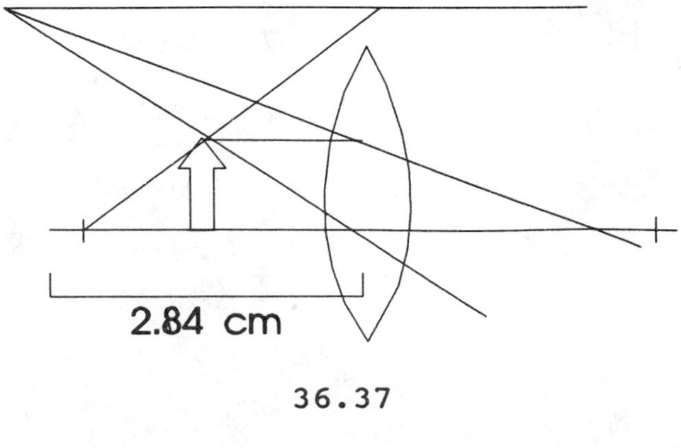

36.37

36.38 $\frac{t_1}{f_1^2} = \frac{t_2}{f_2^2} \quad \Longrightarrow t_1 = t_2\frac{f_1^2}{f_2^2} = [(1/32)\ \text{s}]\frac{(f/16)^2}{(f/8)^2} = \boxed{7.81\ \text{ms}}$

36.39 The film exposure is proportional to the product $(1t)$ and by Eq. 36.15,

$$I \sim \frac{1}{(f = \text{number})^2}$$

Therefore to maintain the correct exposure we require

$$I_1t_1 = I_2t_2 \quad \text{or} \quad \frac{t_1}{(f = \text{number}_1)^2} = [\frac{t_2}{(f = \text{number}_2)^2}$$

or $(f\text{-number})_2 = (f\text{-number})\ _1[\frac{t_2}{t_1}]^{1/2} = (f/4)[\frac{1/128}{1/16}]^{1/2}$

or the new setting should be $\boxed{f/1.4}$

36.40 Since $s' \approx f \quad (s >> f,$ see text)

$$M = -\frac{s'}{s} \cong -\frac{f}{s} = -\frac{0.05}{5} = \boxed{-0.01}$$

$$h' = hM = (1.7)(-0.01) = \boxed{-1.7\ \text{cm}}$$

36.41 $P = \frac{1}{f} = \frac{1}{s} + \frac{1}{s'} = \frac{1}{\subset nfty} - \frac{1}{0.25} = -4$

$P = \boxed{-\ 4\ \text{diopters}}$, a diverging lens.

36.42 $\frac{1}{f} = +1.5 \quad \Longrightarrow f = 0.667\ \text{m} = 66.7\ \text{cm};$

$$\frac{1}{s} + \frac{1}{s'} = \frac{1}{f} \quad \Longrightarrow s' = (\frac{1}{f} - \frac{1}{s})^{-1} = [\frac{1}{(66.7\ \text{cm})} - \frac{1}{(25\ \text{cm})}]^{-1} = \boxed{-40\ \text{cm}}$$

Therefore, the near point for the unaided eye is found at 40 cm.

36.43 $\frac{n_1}{s} + \frac{n_2}{s'} = \frac{(n_2 - n_1)}{R}; \quad n_1 = 1,\ n_2 = 1.34,$

$s = \infty$ and $s' = 2.2$ cm;

$$R = (n_2 - n_1)(\frac{n_1}{s} + \frac{n_2}{s'})^{-1} = (1.34 - 1)(\frac{1}{\infty} + \frac{1.34}{2.2})^{-1} = \boxed{0.558\ \text{cm}}$$

36.44 $\frac{1}{s}+\frac{1}{s'}=\frac{1}{f} \implies \frac{1}{\infty}+\frac{1}{s'}=\frac{1}{f} \implies \frac{1}{s'}=\frac{1}{f} \implies s'=f=6.5\text{ cm}$

Assuming the lens moves toward the object,

$s = 200\text{ cm} - \text{x}$ and $s' = 6.5 + x$

$$\frac{1}{(200-x)}+\frac{1}{(6.5+x)}=\frac{1}{6.5}$$

Solving the quadratic equation gives $x = 0.218$ cm;

If one assumes $x << 200$ such that $200 - x \approx 200$, then

$$\frac{1}{200}+\frac{1}{(6.5+x)}=\frac{1}{6.5}$$

$$x = (\frac{1}{6.5}-\frac{1}{200})^{-1} - 6.5 = \boxed{0.218\text{ cm}}$$

36.45 Power $P = \frac{1}{f} = \frac{1}{s'}+\frac{1}{s} = \frac{1}{(-0.90)}+\frac{1}{0.25} = \boxed{+2.89\text{ diopters}}$

36.46 $P = \frac{1}{f} = \frac{1}{s}+\frac{1}{s'};\quad s=\infty,\ s' = -200\text{ cm} = -2\text{ cm};$

$$P = \frac{1}{\infty} - \frac{1}{(2\text{ m})} = \boxed{-0.5\text{ diopters}}$$

36.47 $m = \frac{25}{25f/(f+25)} = \frac{25}{25(10)/(10+25)} = \boxed{3.5}$

36.48 $\frac{1}{s}+\frac{1}{-25\text{ cm}}=\frac{1}{f}$

$f = 5$ cm (a 20 diopter lens)

(a) $s = \boxed{-4.16\text{ cm}}$

(b) $M = 1 + \frac{25\text{ cm}}{f} = \boxed{6}$

36.49 $f_O = 20$ m $\qquad f_E = 0.025$ m

$$M = \frac{f_O}{f_E} = 800\times$$

The image is inverted (See Fig. 36.30)

36.50 $m = \frac{f_0}{f_E} = \frac{80}{0.025} = \boxed{3200\times}$

36.51 $m = -\frac{f_0}{f_e} = -\frac{(75\text{ cm})}{(4\text{ cm})} = \boxed{-18.8}$

36.52 Using Eq. 36.20

$$M = -(\frac{L}{f_0})(\frac{25\text{ cm}}{f_e}) = -(\frac{23\text{ cm}}{0.4\text{ cm}})(\frac{25\text{ cm}}{2.5\text{ cm}}) = \boxed{-576}$$

36.53 $M = M_1 m_e = \frac{M_1(25\text{ cm})}{f_e}$

$$\Longrightarrow f_e = (\frac{M_1}{M})(25\text{ cm}) = (\frac{-12}{-140})(25\text{ cm}) = 2.14\text{ cm}$$

36.54 From $\frac{1}{s} + \frac{1}{s'} = \frac{1}{f}$, we find

$$f = \frac{s's}{(s+s')} = \frac{(8\text{ cm})(10\text{ cm})}{(10\text{ cm} + 8\text{ cm})} = \boxed{4.44\text{ cm}}$$

and $s' = \frac{fs}{(s-f)} = \frac{(4.44\text{ cm})(20\text{ cm})}{(20\text{ cm} - 4.44\text{ cm})} = \boxed{5.71\text{ cm}}$

Real object since $s' > 0$.

36.55 (a) $s_1 = s_2'$, $s_2 = s_1'$

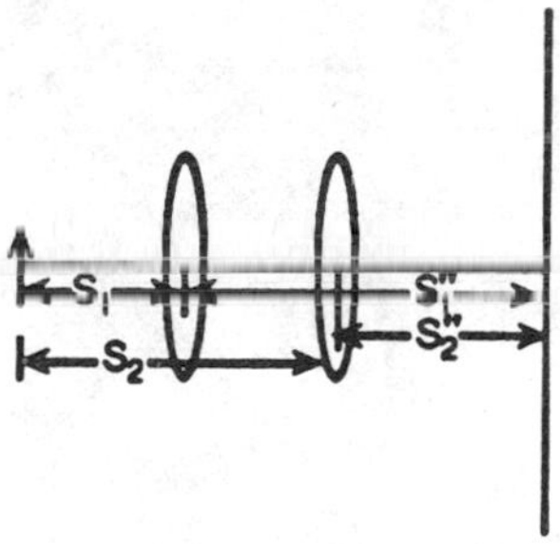

36.55

$$\frac{M_1}{M_2} = \frac{3}{2} = \frac{s_1'/s_1}{s_2'/s_2}$$

$$\therefore s_2 = \sqrt{\frac{3}{2}}s_1$$

$$s_1 = s_2 - 10\text{ cm} = \sqrt{\frac{3}{2}}s_1 - 10\text{ cm}$$

$$s_1 = \frac{10\text{ cm}}{\sqrt{\frac{3}{2}} - 1} = 44.5\text{ cm}$$

$$s_1' = s_2 = s_1 + 10\text{ cm} = 54.5\text{ cm}$$

$$\frac{1}{f} = \frac{1}{s} + \frac{1}{s'} = \frac{1}{44.5\text{ cm}} + \frac{1}{54.5\text{ cm}}$$

$$f = 24.5\text{ cm}$$

(b) $s + s' = 44.5\text{ cm} + 54.5\text{ cm} = 99.0\text{ cm}$

36.56 $m = \frac{-s'}{s} = \frac{-1}{s}(\frac{1}{f} - \frac{1}{s})^{-1}$

For $s = 2f$,

$$m = \frac{-1}{2f}(\frac{1}{f} - \frac{1}{2f})^{-1} = \frac{-1}{2f}(\frac{1}{2f})^{-1} = -1$$

For $m = +1$,

$$-\frac{1}{s} = \frac{1}{f} - \frac{1}{s}$$

This occurs when $f \rightarrow \infty$

36.57

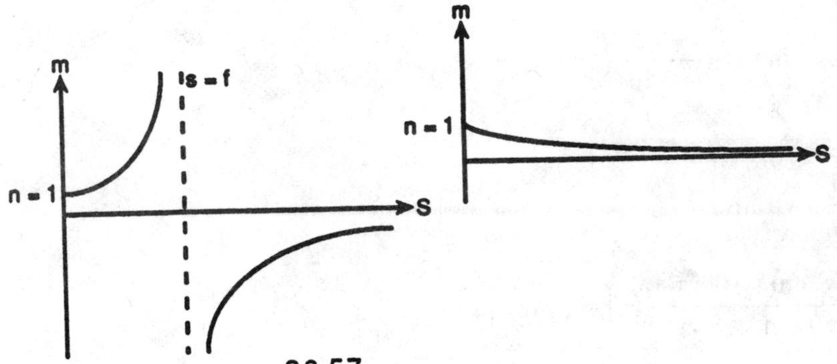

36.57

***36.58** Because these two lenses are *not* in contact, we cannot use the lens-combination formula. Instead, we investigate the focusing properties of each individual lens by itself. The first step is to locate the image formed by the first lens, pretending that the second lens is absent. Applying the lens equation, we obtain

$$\frac{1}{s}+\frac{1}{s'}=\frac{1}{f_1} \qquad \Rightarrow \qquad \frac{1}{15\text{ cm}}+\frac{1}{s'}=\frac{1}{10\text{ cm}}$$

Solving for s' yields $\underline{s' = +30.0\text{ cm}}$

Thus the image would fall 30 cm to the right of the first lens if the second lens were absent. Because the second lens is 15 cm to the right of the first lens, the rays are still convergent when they strike the second lens (constituting a "virtual object" for the second lens), so the object distance s_2 for the second lens is -15 cm. Thus:

$$\frac{1}{s_2}+\frac{1}{s_2'}=\frac{1}{f_2} \qquad \Rightarrow \qquad \frac{1}{-15\text{ cm}}+\frac{1}{s_2'}=\frac{1}{-20\text{ cm}}$$

Solving for s_2' gives $s_2' = \boxed{60.0\text{ cm}}$

The final image is 60 cm to the right of the second lens. The image is inverted because the first lens produced a real, inverted image, and the second lens, being divergent, cannot itself produce a further inversion. Though the lens is divergent, its strength is not sufficient to change the incident converging rays to diverging rays; the *positive* value of s_2' signifies *converging* rays, forming a final real image.

The overall magnification for the two-lens system is the product

$$M = M_1M_2 = \left(\frac{s_1'}{s_1}\right)\left(\frac{s_2'}{s_2}\right) - \left(-\frac{30\text{ cm}}{15\text{ cm}}\right)\left(-\frac{60\text{ cm}}{-15\text{ cm}}\right) = -8.00$$

As a check, we note that the negative sign signifies an inverted final image. The final image is real, inverted, and is magnified 8 times.

36.59 From Eq. 36–8,

$$\frac{n}{s}+\frac{n'}{s'}=\frac{n'-n}{R}$$

$$\therefore \frac{1}{s'}=\frac{1-1.56}{-0.06\text{ m}}$$

$$s' = \boxed{0.107\text{ m}}$$

36.60 $\dfrac{n'}{s_1} + \dfrac{n}{s_1'} = \dfrac{n - n'}{R_1}$ (1)

At the second interface,

$$\frac{n}{s_2} + \frac{n'}{s_2'} = \frac{n' - n}{R_2} \qquad (2)$$

Since, for a thin lens, $s_2 = s_1'$,

$$\frac{-n}{s_1'} + \frac{n'}{s_2'} = \frac{n' - n}{R_2} \qquad (3)$$

Adding (3) to (1) and dropping the subscripts on s and s' ,

$$\frac{n}{s} + \frac{n'}{s'} = (n - n')(\frac{1}{R_1} - \frac{1}{R_2})$$

To find the focal length, let $s = \infty$.

$$\frac{n'}{s'} = (n - n')(\frac{1}{R_1} - \frac{1}{R_2})$$

$$\frac{1}{s'} = \frac{1}{f} = (\frac{n}{n'} - 1)(\frac{1}{R_1} - \frac{1}{R_2})$$

36.61 $\dfrac{1}{s} + \dfrac{1}{s'} = \dfrac{1}{f} = \dfrac{1}{0.2} = 5$

$$\frac{1}{s'} + \frac{1}{s''} = \frac{1}{f} = \frac{1}{0.2} = 5$$

$$\therefore \quad \frac{1}{s} + \frac{1}{s'} = \frac{1}{s'} + \frac{1}{s''}$$

and $s'' = s = \boxed{20 \text{ cm}}$

***36.62** (a) 60.0°

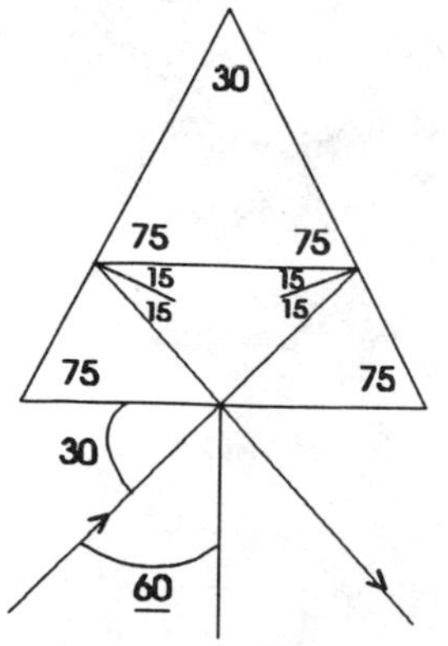

36.62a

(b) 75.0°

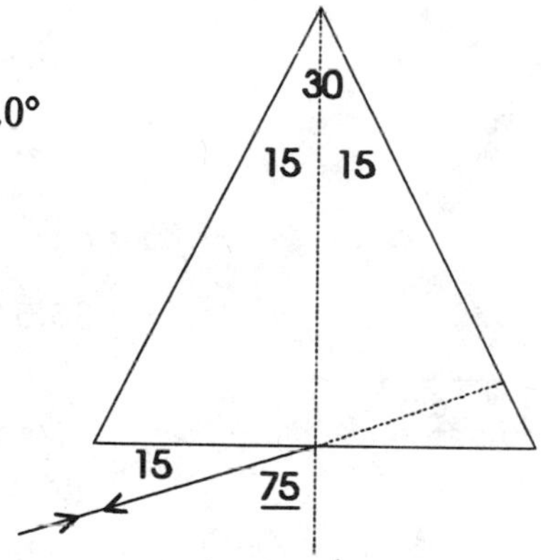

36.62b

(c) 45.0° yes

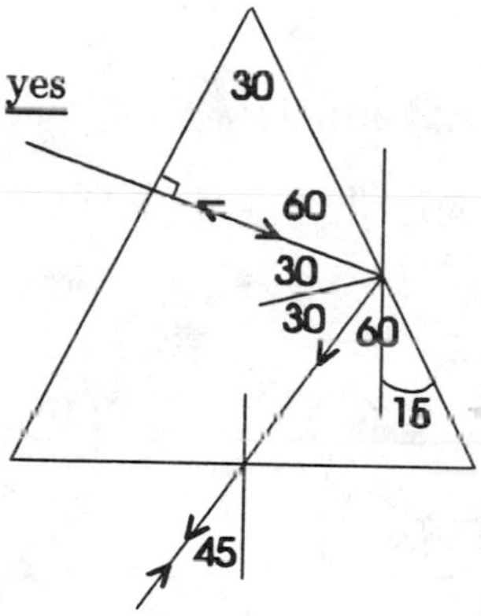

36.62c

(d) 30.0°

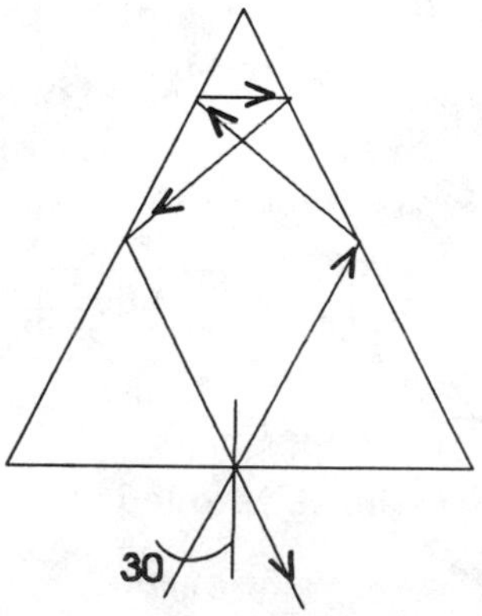

36.62d

36.63 (a) $P = \frac{1}{f} = \frac{1}{s} + \frac{1}{s'} = \frac{1}{(0.0224\text{ m})} + \frac{1}{\infty} = 44.6$ diopters

(b) $P = \frac{1}{f} = \frac{1}{s} + \frac{1}{s'} = \frac{1}{(0.33\text{ m})} + \frac{1}{\infty} = 3.03$ diopters

36.64 (a) $\frac{1}{s} + \frac{1}{s'} = \frac{2}{R}$; and when $R = 40$ cm, $s' = \frac{20s}{(s-20)}$

where s and s' are in cm.

(b) $s'(5) = \boxed{-6.67\text{ cm}}$

$s'(10) = \boxed{-20\text{ cm}}$

$s'(40) = \boxed{40\text{ cm}}$

$s'(60) = \boxed{30\text{ cm}}$

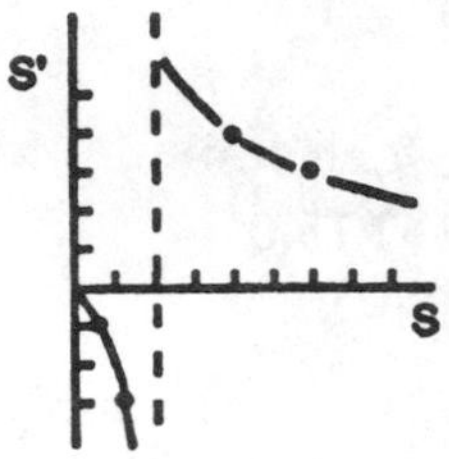

36.64

(c) Each unit on the graph is equal to $\boxed{10\text{ cm}}$

36.65 From Eq. 36.12

$$s_1' = \frac{f_1 s_1}{(s_1 - f_1)} = \frac{(-6\text{ cm})(12\text{ cm})}{12\text{ cm} - (-6\text{ cm})} = -4\text{ cm}$$

When we require that $s_2' \longrightarrow \infty$, Eq. 36.12 becomes $s_2 = f_2$ and in this case, $s_2 = d - (-4\text{ cm})$. Therefore $d + 4\text{ cm} = f_2 = 12$ cm and $\boxed{d = 8\text{ cm}}$

36.66 We must solve for s' in Eq. 36.12 in each case

(a) $s' = \frac{fs}{(s-f)} = \frac{(20\text{ cm})(50\text{ cm})}{(50\text{ cm} - 20\text{ cm})} = \boxed{33.3\text{ cm}}$

(b) $s' = \frac{(20\text{ cm})(30\text{ cm})}{(30\text{ cm} - 20\text{ cm})} = \boxed{60\text{ cm}}$

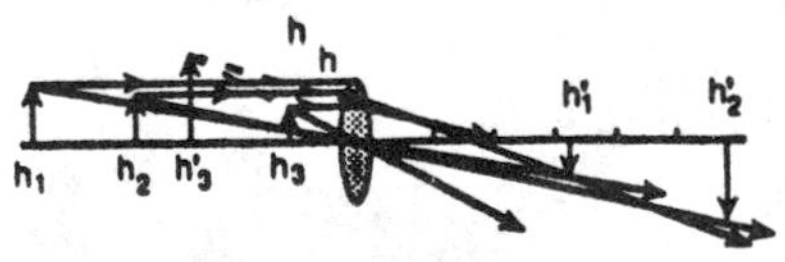

36.66

(c) $s' = \frac{(20\text{ cm})(10\text{ cm})}{(10\text{ cm} - 20\text{ cm})} = \boxed{-20\text{ cm}}$

(d) In each case $M = -\frac{s'}{s}$. Therefore $M_1 = \frac{33.3}{50} = \boxed{-0.667}$

$M_2 = -\frac{60}{30} = \boxed{-2}$ and $M_3 = -(-\frac{20}{10}) = \boxed{2}$

The first two images are inverted and the third one is erect.

***36.67** In each case $s = \dfrac{fs'}{(s' - f)}$ and $M = -\dfrac{s'}{s}$

(a) For $s' = 4f$, $s = \dfrac{f(4f)}{(4f - f)} = \boxed{\dfrac{4}{3}f}$

(b) For $s' = -3f$, $s = \dfrac{f(-3f)}{(-3f - f)} = \boxed{\dfrac{3}{4}f}$

(c) For case (a), $M = -\dfrac{4f}{(4/3)f} = \boxed{-3}$

For case (b), $M = -\dfrac{(-3f)}{(3/4)f} = \boxed{4}$

***36.68**

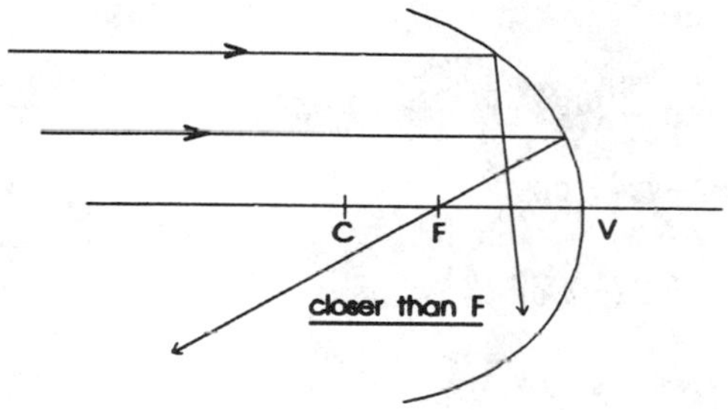

36.68

36.69 (a) $\frac{n_1}{s} + \frac{n_2}{s'} = \frac{(n_2 - n_1)}{R}$ and when $R = \infty$, $s = -s'(n_1/n_2)$

Therefore $s = -(-35\text{ cm})(\frac{1.5}{1}) = \boxed{52.5\text{ cm}}$
(Refer to sign conventions in Table 36.2)

(b) $M = -\frac{n_1 s'}{n_2 s} = \frac{h'}{h}$ or $h' = -h(\frac{n_1 s'}{n_2 s})$

$$h' = \frac{(-1.5\text{ cm})(1.5)(-35\text{ cm})}{(1)(52.5\text{ cm})} = \boxed{1.5\text{ cm}}$$

36.70 From Eq. 36.12 we find $s' = \frac{fs}{(s-f)}$. For the converging lens

this becomes $s_1' = \frac{(8\text{ cm})(4\text{ cm})}{(4-8)\text{ cm}} = -8\text{ cm}.$

Therefore for the diverging lens $s_2 = 6\text{ cm} - (-8\text{ cm}) = 14\text{ cm}$ and

$$s_2' = \frac{f_2 s_2}{(s_2 - f_2)} = \frac{(-16\text{ cm})(14\text{ cm})}{14\text{ ; cm} - (-16\text{ cm})} = -7.47\text{ cm}.$$

The final image is located $\boxed{7.47\text{ cm}}$ *to the left of the diverging lens and is virtual since* $s_2' < 0$.

The image size is $h' = hM_1M_2 = h(-\frac{s_1'}{s_1})(-\frac{s_2'}{s_2})$

$$h' = (1\text{ cm})[-(-\frac{8\text{ cm}}{4\text{ cm}})][-(-\frac{7.47\text{ cm}}{14\text{ cm}})] = \boxed{1.067\text{ cm}}$$

The final image is *erect* since $M_1M_2 > 0$.

36.71 $\frac{1}{s} + \frac{1}{s'} = \frac{1}{f}$ $(f = 1.5\text{ m})$

$$\frac{1}{\infty} + \frac{1}{s'} = \frac{1}{f}$$

$s' = 1.5$ m, from the mirror.

$$h' = (\Delta\theta)(1.5) = (0.5)(\frac{\pi}{180})1.5 = \boxed{1.3\text{ cm}}$$

36.72 Size of moon with unaided eye at near point

$$\frac{x(\text{cm})}{25(\text{cm})} = \frac{3.5 \times 10^3}{3.84 \times 10^5} \qquad x = 0.225\text{ cm}$$

With $20\times$ magnification, $d_{25} = \boxed{4.5\text{ cm}}$

36.73 (a) $f = \frac{R}{2} = \boxed{-0.40 \text{ cm}}$

(b) $\frac{1}{s} + \frac{1}{s'} = \frac{1}{f}$

$s = 25$ cm

$f = -0.40$ cm

$s' = -3.9$ mm (behind the cornea)

$M = -\frac{s'}{s} = 0.016$

$d' = (0.016)(3.4) = \boxed{0.54 \text{ mm}}$

***36.74** $\frac{1}{s} + \frac{1}{-19} = \frac{1}{20}$

$s = 9.74359$ cm

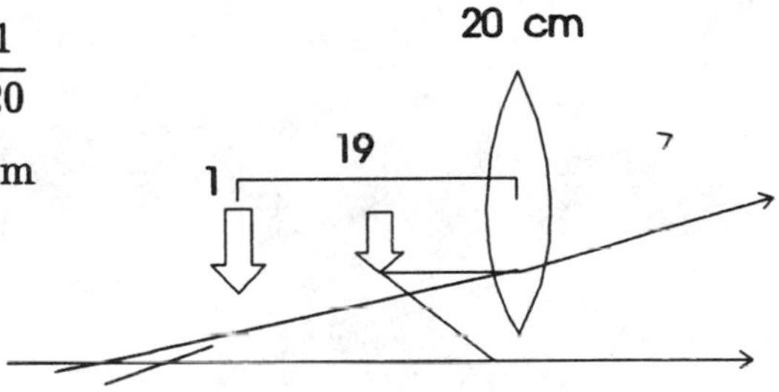

36.74a

(a) $\frac{1}{s} + \frac{1}{40.25641} = \frac{1}{10}$

$s = \boxed{13.3 \text{ cm}}$

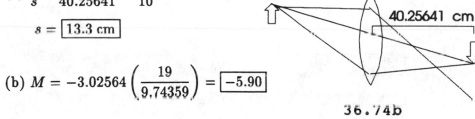

(b) $M = -3.02564\left(\frac{19}{9.74359}\right) = \boxed{-5.90}$

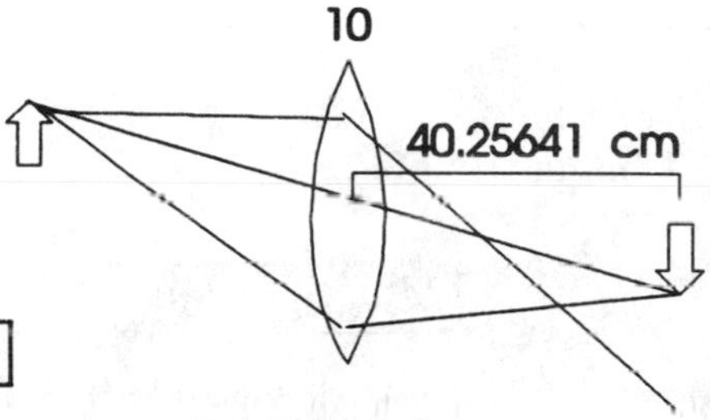

36.74b

(c) The final image is inverted.

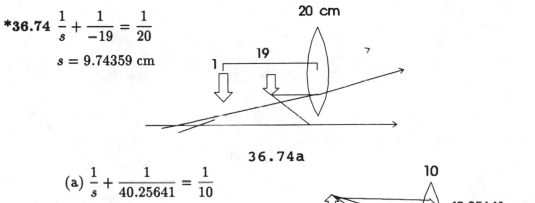

36.75 (a) 30 cm and 1.2 m

(b) 24 cm

(c) Real, inverted, diminished in size.

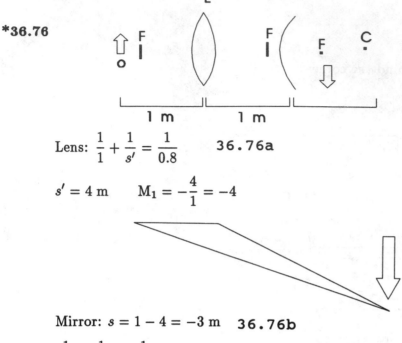

***36.76**

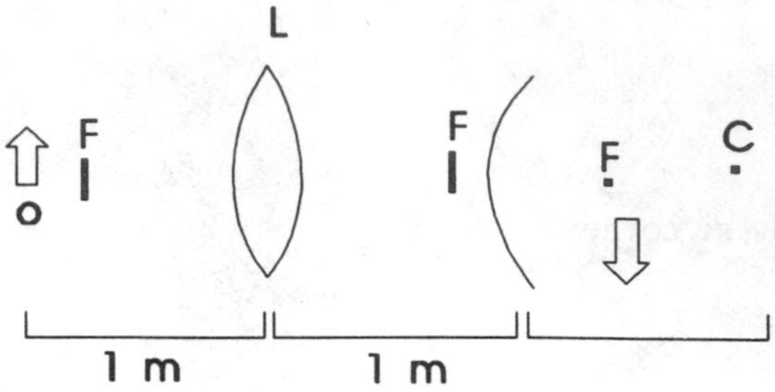

Lens: $\frac{1}{1} + \frac{1}{s'} = \frac{1}{0.8}$ **36.76a**

$s' = 4$ m $\quad M_1 = -\frac{4}{1} = -4$

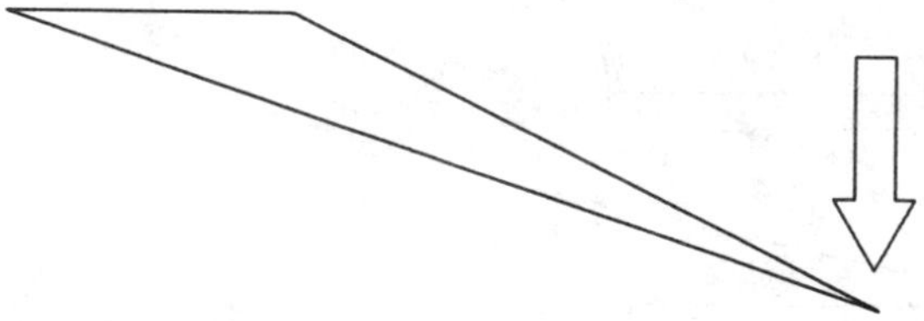

Mirror: $s = 1 - 4 = -3$ m **36.76b**

$$\frac{1}{-3} + \frac{1}{s'} = \frac{1}{-0.5}$$

$s' = -0.6$ m $\quad M_2 = -\frac{-0.6}{-3} = -\,0.2$

$$\boxed{M_{overall} = +0.8}$$

60.0 cm right of mirror virtual, $M = 0.8$, erect, diminished

***36.77** The upper mirror makes an image at infinity. Lower mirror makes image at its focal point, at hole in upper mirror. Thus, the image is real, inverted, and actual-size.

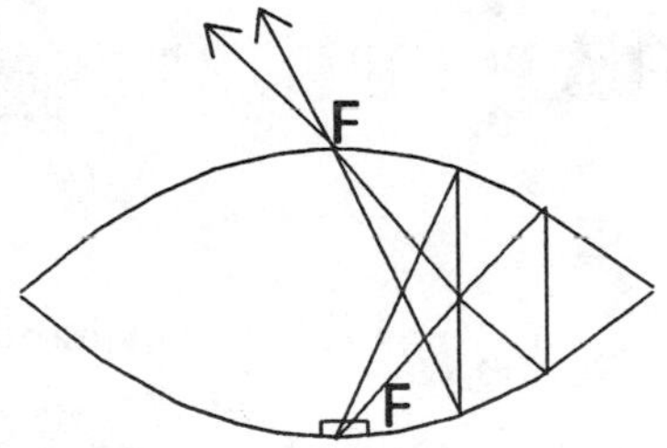

36.77a

$$\frac{1}{s}+\frac{1}{s'}=\frac{1}{f}$$

$$\frac{1}{7.5}+\frac{1}{s'}=\frac{1}{7.5} \qquad s'=\infty$$

$$\frac{1}{\infty}+\frac{1}{s'}=\frac{1}{7.5} \qquad s'=7.5$$

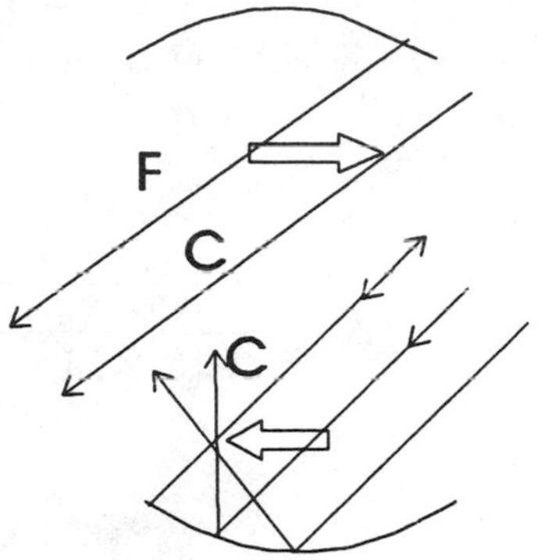

36.77b

Light directed into the hole in the upper mirror reflects as shown, to behave as if it were reflecting from the hole.

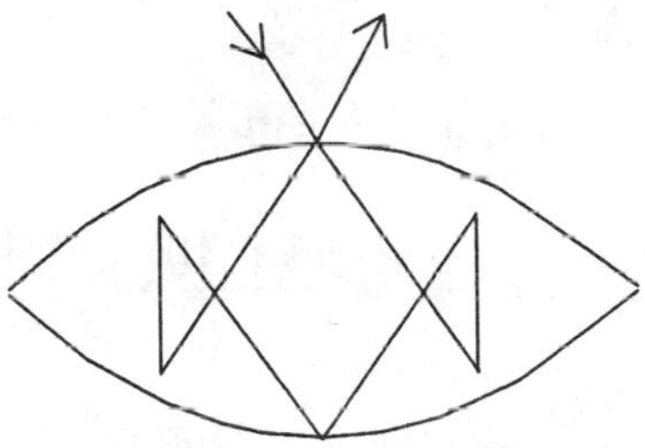

36.77c

CHAPTER 37

37.1 (a) For the bright band $y_{\text{bright}} = \dfrac{\lambda L m}{d}$ where $m = 1$, so

$$y = \frac{(5.46 \times 10^{-7}\text{m})(1.2\text{ m})}{(2.5 \times 10^{-4}\text{ m})} = \boxed{2.62 \times 10^{-3}\text{ m}}$$

(b) For the dark band $y_{\text{dark}} = \dfrac{\lambda L}{d}(m + \dfrac{1}{2});$ $m = 0, 1, 2, 3, \cdots$

$$y_2 - y_1 = \frac{\lambda L}{d}[(1 + \frac{1}{2}) - (0 + \frac{1}{2})]$$

$$\Delta y = \frac{(5.461 \times 10^{-7}\text{ m})(1.2\text{ m})}{(2.54 \times 10^{-4}\text{ m})} = \boxed{2.62 \times 10^{-3}\text{ m}}$$

37.2 $\Delta y_{\text{bright}} = \dfrac{\lambda L}{d} = \dfrac{(632.8 \times 10^{-9})(5)}{2 \times 10^{-4}}\text{ m} = \boxed{1.58\text{ cm}}$

37.3 $y_{\text{bright}} = \dfrac{\lambda L}{d} m$ For $m = 1$

$$\lambda = \frac{yd}{L} = \frac{(5 \times 10^{-4})(3.4 \times 10^{-3})}{3.3}\text{ m} = \boxed{515\text{ nm}}$$

***37.4** Taking $m = 0$ and $y = 0.2$ mm in Equation 37.6 gives

$$L \approx \frac{2dy}{\lambda}$$

$$= \frac{2(0.4 \times 10^{-3}\text{ m})(0.2 \times 10^{-3}\text{ m})}{442 \times 10^{-9}\text{ m}} = 0.36\text{ m}$$

$$L = \boxed{36\text{ cm}}$$

Geometric optics incorrectly predicts bright regions opposite the slits and darkness in between. But as this example shows, interference can produce just the opposite.

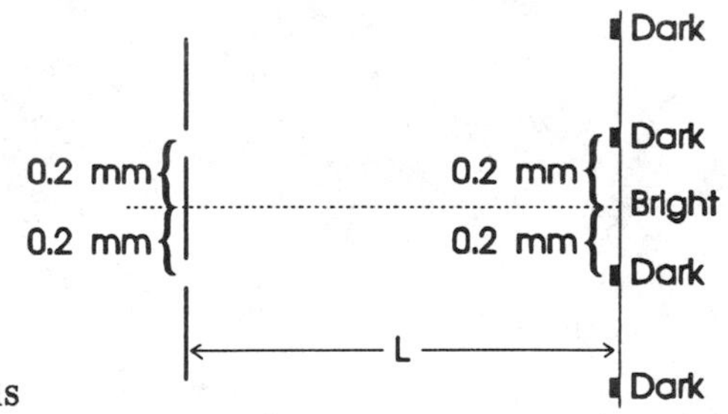

37.4

37.5 For the bright band $y_{\text{bright}} = \dfrac{\lambda L m}{d} \implies L = \dfrac{y_{\text{bright}} d}{m\lambda}$

For $m = 2$ and $y_{\text{bright}} = 10d = 2 \times 10^{-3}$ m

$$L = \frac{(2 \times 10^{-3}\text{ m})(2 \times 10^{-4}\text{ m})}{(2)(5.8 \times 10^{-7}\text{ m})} = \boxed{0.340\text{ m}}$$

***37.6** $d = 8.3 \times 10^{-5}$ m, L = 2.5 m

(a) $\lambda = 570 \times 10^{-9}$ m (Yellow light)

From Equation 37.5,

$$\Delta y_{\text{max}} = \frac{\lambda L}{d} = \boxed{1.72 \text{ cm}}$$

(b) $\lambda = 410 \times 10^{-9}$ m (Blue light)

From equation 37.5,

$$2\Delta y_{\text{max}} = \frac{2\lambda L}{d} = \boxed{2.47 \text{ cm}}$$

(c) The separation between the minima is the same as the separation between the maxima.

37.7 For the dark band: $y_{\text{dark}} = \frac{\lambda L}{d}(m + \frac{1}{2}) \implies d = \frac{\lambda L}{y_{\text{dark}}}(m + \frac{1}{2})$

For the third dark band $m = 2$

$$d = \frac{(6 \times 10^{-7} \text{ m})(0.8 \text{ m})(2.5)}{1.2 \times 10^{-2} \text{ m}} = 1 \times 10^{-4} \text{ m}$$

For the bright band: $y_{\text{bright}} = \frac{\lambda L m}{d}$ For the first bright band $m = 1$

$$y_{\text{bright}} = \frac{(6 \times 10^{-7} \text{ m})(0.8 \text{ m})(1)}{1 \times 10^{-4} \text{ m}} = \boxed{4.80 \times 10^{-3} \text{ m}}$$

***37.8** (a) $y_{2\text{max}} = \frac{2\lambda L}{d}$

$$\lambda = \frac{(d)y_{2\text{max}}}{2L} = \frac{(3 \times 10^{-4} \text{ m})(4 \times 10^{-3})}{2(1)} = \boxed{600 \text{ nm}}$$

(b) $y_{3\text{max}} = \frac{3\lambda L}{d} = \frac{3}{2}y_{2\text{max}} = \boxed{6 \text{ mm}}$

(c) $y_{\text{dark}} = \frac{\lambda L}{2d} = 1$ mm

$$\theta \cong \frac{\Delta y}{L} = \boxed{10^{-3} \text{ radians}}$$

37.9 $y = \frac{\lambda L}{d}(m + \frac{1}{2}) = \frac{(656.3 \times 10^{-9} \text{ m})(0.4 \text{ m})}{(5 \times 10^{-4} \text{ m})}(8 + \frac{1}{2}) = 4.4628 \times 10^{-3}$ m

$$\% \text{ error} = \frac{(4.4630 - 4.4628)}{4.463} \times 100\ \% = \boxed{4.48 \times 10^{-3}\ \%}$$

***37.10** (a) The distance of the car from the two antennas is

$$d_1 = \sqrt{(1000)^2 + (250)^2} = 1030.776 \text{ m}$$
$$d_2 = \sqrt{(1000)^2 + (550)^2} = 1141.271 \text{ m}$$
$$\Delta = d_2 - d_1 = 2\lambda \quad \lambda = \boxed{55.25 \text{ m}}$$

(b)
$$2.5\lambda = \sqrt{(1000)^2 + (400 + y + 150)^2} - \sqrt{(1000)^2 + (400 + y - 150)^2}$$
$$139.119 = \sqrt{(1000)^2 + (550 + y)^2} - \sqrt{(1000)^2 + (250 + y)^2}$$

One can solve iteratively using a small computer or square both side, factor, and square again to find $\boxed{y = 123.2 \text{ m}}$

37.11 $d \sin\theta = (m + \frac{1}{2})\lambda$; For $m = 1$,

$$d = (1 + \frac{1}{2})\frac{\lambda}{\sin\theta} = (1.5)\frac{(546 \times 10^{-9} \text{ m})}{\sin(18/60)} = \boxed{1.56 \times 10^{-4} \text{ m}}$$

37.12 (a) The path difference $\delta = d \sin\theta$ and when $L >> y$

$$\delta \approx \frac{yd}{L} = \frac{(1.8 \times 10^{-2} \text{ m})(1.50 \times 10^{-4} \text{ m})}{140 \text{ m}} = \boxed{1.93 \times 10^{-6} \text{ m}}$$

(b) $\frac{\delta}{\lambda} = \frac{1.93 \times 10^{-6} \text{ m}}{6.43 \times 10^{-7} \text{ m}} = 3$ or $\boxed{\delta = 3\lambda}$

(c) Point P will be a *maximum* since the path difference is

an integer multiple of the wavelength.

37.13 $I_{av} = I_0 \cos^2(\frac{\pi d \sin\theta}{\lambda})$; for small θ

$\sin\theta = \frac{y}{L}$, and $I_{av} = 0.75 I_0$;

$$y = \frac{\lambda L}{\pi d}\cos^{-1}(\frac{I_{av}}{I_0})^{1/2}$$
$$= \frac{(6.0 \times 10^{-7})(1.2 \text{ m})}{\pi(2.5 \times 10^{-3} \text{ m})}\cos^{-1}(\frac{0.75 I_0}{I_0})/ = \boxed{4.80 \times 10^{-5} \text{ m}}$$

37.14 $I = I_0 \cos^2(\frac{\pi y d}{\lambda L})$

$$\frac{I}{I_0} = \cos^2[\frac{\pi(1.8 \times 10^{-4} \text{ m})(6 \times 10^{-3} \text{ m})}{(6.563 \times 10^{-7} \text{ m})(0.8 \text{ m})}] = \boxed{0.968}$$

37.15 $I = I_0 \cos^2(\frac{\pi y d}{\lambda L})$

$$\lambda = (\frac{\pi y d}{L})[\cos^{-1}(\frac{I}{I_0})^{1/2}]^{-1}$$

$$\lambda = \frac{\pi(1 \times 10^{-3}\ \text{m})(2 \times 10^{-4}\ \text{m})}{1.6\ \text{m}}[\cos^{-1}(0.36)^{1/2}]^{-1} = \boxed{423.5\ \text{nm}}$$

37.16 $I = I_0 \cos^2(\frac{\pi y d}{\lambda L})$ and when $\frac{I}{I_0} = 0.6$ we have

$$\frac{d}{\lambda} = (\frac{L}{\pi y})\cos^{-1}(0.6)^{1/2} = \frac{(1.4\ \text{m})}{(8\pi \times 10^{-3}\ \text{m})}\cos^{-1}(0.775) = \boxed{38.1}$$

(Note that $\cos^{-1}(0.775)$ must be expressed in radians)

37.17 $\frac{I}{I_0} = \cos^2(\frac{\pi d \sin\theta}{\lambda}) = \cos^2[\frac{\pi(2.5 \times 10^{-4}\ \text{m})\sin\theta}{5.46 \times 10^{-7}\ \text{m}}] = \cos^2[1439 \sin\theta]$

$\theta(deg)$	I/I_0
0.0	1.0
0.05	0.0965
0.1	0.651
0.125	1.0
0.15	0.659
0.2	0.091
0.25	0.091
0.3	0.1

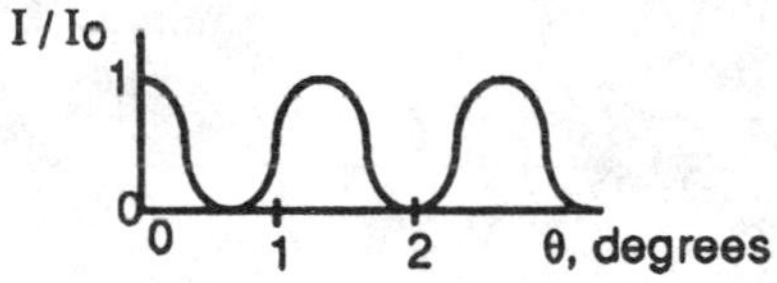

37.17

37.18 $\phi = \frac{2\pi}{\lambda} d \sin\theta \approx \frac{2\pi}{\lambda} d(\frac{y}{L})$

(a) $\phi = \frac{2\pi}{(5 \times 10^{-7}\ \text{m})}(1.2 \times 10^{-4}\ \text{m})\sin(\frac{1}{2}) = \boxed{13.2\ \text{rad}}$

(b) $\phi = \frac{2\pi}{(5 \times 10^{-7}\ \text{m})}(1.2 \times 10^{-4}\ \text{m})(\frac{5 \times 10^{-3}}{1.2}) = \boxed{6.28\ \text{rad}}$

37.19 (a) $\phi = 0.333 = \dfrac{2\pi d \sin\theta}{\lambda}$

$$\theta = \sin^{-1}\left(\frac{\lambda\phi}{2\pi d}\right) = \sin^{-1}\left[\frac{(5\times 10^{-7}\text{ m})(0.333)}{2\pi(1.2\times 10^{-4}\text{ m})}\right] = \boxed{1.27\times 10^{-2}\text{ deg}}$$

(b)
$$d\sin\theta = \frac{\lambda}{4}$$
$$\theta = \sin^{-1}\left(\frac{\lambda}{4d}\right)$$
$$= \sin^{-1}\left[\frac{5\times 10^{-7}\text{m}}{4(1.2\times 10^{-4}\text{ m})}\right] = \boxed{5.97\times 10^{-2}\text{ deg}}$$

37.20 (a) $\dfrac{I}{I_0} = \cos^2\left(\dfrac{\phi}{2}\right)$ (Eq. 37.11)

Therefore $\phi = 2\cos^{-1}\left(\dfrac{I}{I_0}\right)^{1/2} = 2\cos^{-1}(0.64)^{1/2} = \boxed{1.29\text{ rad}}$

(b) $\delta = \dfrac{\phi\lambda}{2\pi} = \dfrac{(1.29\text{ rad})(4.86\times 10^{-7}\text{ m})}{2\pi} = \boxed{9.98\times 10^{-8}\text{ m}}$

37.21 (a) $\dfrac{I}{I_0} = 0.064 = \cos^2\left(\dfrac{\phi}{2}\right)$

$$\phi = 2\cos^{-1}\left(\frac{I}{I_0}\right)^{1/2} = 2\cos^{-1}(0.064)^{1/2} = \boxed{2.63\text{ rad}}$$

(b) $\delta = \dfrac{\lambda\phi}{2\pi} = \dfrac{(587.5\times 10^{-9}\text{ m})(2.63)}{2\pi} = \boxed{246\text{ nm}}$

37.22 $y_{\text{bright}} = \dfrac{\lambda L}{d} = \dfrac{(632.8\times 10^{-9})(2)}{2\times 10^{-4}} = 6.328\times 10^{-3}\text{ m}$

$y_{\text{bright}} = \boxed{\pm 6.33\text{ mm}}$ For small θ, equal intensity at center of each maximum